QL
666
O6
W7
v. 2

V

D1462613

HANDBOOKS OF AMERICAN NATURAL HISTORY

ALBERT HAZEN WRIGHT, ADVISORY EDITOR

Handbook of Snakes

BY ALBERT HAZEN WRIGHT

AND ANNA ALLEN WRIGHT

HANDBOOK OF

SNAKES

OF THE UNITED STATES AND CANADA

BY ALBERT HAZEN WRIGHT

PROFESSOR OF ZOOLOGY, EMERITUS, CORNELL UNIVERSITY

AND ANNA ALLEN WRIGHT

VOLUME II

Comstock Publishing Associates

A DIVISION OF CORNELL UNIVERSITY PRESS

ITHACA, NEW YORK, 1957

ⓒ 1957 BY CORNELL UNIVERSITY

All rights reserved. This book, or parts thereof, must not be reproduced in any form without permission in writing from the publisher, except by a reviewer who wishes to quote brief passages in a review of the book.

First published 1957

PRINTED IN THE UNITED STATES OF AMERICA BY THE

VAIL-BALLOU PRESS, INC., BINGHAMTON, NEW YORK

Contents

VOLUME II

	Page Number of		
	Account	Fig.	Map
Oxybelis: Pike-headed Tree Snakes	565	75	
Oxybelis aeneus auratus	565	563	566
Phyllorhynchus: Leaf-nosed Snakes	569	69	
Phyllorhynchus browni browni	571	577	569
Phyllorhynchus browni lucidus	574		569
Phyllorhynchus decurtatus nubilus	576	577	569
Phyllorhynchus decurtatus perkinsi	580	584	569
Pituophis: Bull Snakes, Pine Snakes, Gopher Snakes	585	69	
Pituophis catenifer catenifer	588	584	589
Pituophis catenifer affinis	593	597	589
Pituophis catenifer annectens	596	597	589
Pituophis catenifer deserticola	600	605	589
Pituophis catenifer pumilus	604		589
Pituophis catenifer sayi	604	605	589
Pituophis melanoleucus melanoleucus	609	614	589
Pituophis melanoleucus lodingi	613	614	589
Pituophis melanoleucus mugitus	616	621	589
Pituophis melanoleucus ruthveni	620	621	589
Pituophis catenifer heermanni	626		
Pituophis catenifer stejnegeri	626	625	
Rhadinaea: Yellow-lipped Snakes	627	79	
Rhadinaea flavilata	627	631	628
Rhinocheilus: Long-nosed Snakes	630	69	
Rhinocheilus lecontei lecontei	633	631	634
Rhinocheilus lecontei clarus	638	641	634
Rhinocheilus lecontei tessellatus	642	641	634
Salvadora: Patch-nosed Snakes	644	75	
Salvadora grahamiae grahamiae	646	647	646
Salvadora grahamiae lineata	649	652	646
Salvadora hexalepis hexalepis	651	652	646
Salvadora hexalepis deserticola	654	657	646

v

LIBRARY
ASHEVILLE BILTMORE COLLEGE
ASHEVILLE, NORTH CAROLINA

	Page Number of		
	Account	Fig.	Map
Salvadora hexalepis mojavensis	658	657	646
Salvadora hexalepis virgultea	660	662	646
Seminatrix: Red-bellied Mud Snakes	663	79	
Seminatrix pygaea pygaea	664	662	667
Seminatrix pygaea cyclas	666	663	667
Seminatrix pygaea paludis	667	663	667
Sonora: Ground Snakes	669	73	
Sonora episcopa episcopa	672	675	668
Sonora episcopa taylori	676	675	668
Sonora semiannulata semiannulata	678	680	668
Sonora semiannulata blanchardi	679	680	668
Sonora semiannulata gloydi	683	685	668
Sonora semiannulata isozona	686	685	668
Sonora semiannulata linearis	688	689	668
Stilosoma: Short-tailed Snakes	692	69	
Stilosoma extenuatum	693	698	693
Storeria: Brown Snakes	696	79	
Storeria dekayi dekayi	697	698	708
Storeria dekayi temporalineata	703	705	708
Storeria dekayi texana	704	705	708
Storeria dekayi victa	707	711	708
Storeria dekayi wrightorum	712	711	708
Storeria occipitomaculata occipitomaculata	714	720	715
Storeria occipitomaculata obscura	721	720	715
Tantilla: Black-headed Snakes	722	79	
Tantilla atriceps	725	729	722
Tantilla coronata coronata	728	729	733
Tantilla coronata mitrifer	732		
Tantilla coronata wagneri	733	736	733
Tantilla eiseni eiseni	737	736	722
Tantilla eiseni transmontana	738		722
Tantilla gracilis gracilis	740		733
Tantilla gracilis hallowelli	742	745	733
Tantilla nigriceps nigriceps	746	745	722
Tantilla nigriceps fumiceps	748	754	733
Tantilla utahensis	750		722
Tantilla wilcoxi wilcoxi	752		722
Thamnophis: Garter Snakes, Ribbon Snakes	755	71	
Thamnophis angustirostris	762	754	763
Thamnophis cyrtopsis cyrtopsis	766	771	767
Thamnophis cyrtopsis ocellata	772		767

LIBRARY
ASHEVILLE BILTMORE COLLEGE
ASHEVILLE, NORTH CAROLINA

Page Number of

	Account	Fig.	Map
Thamnophis elegans elegans	772	771	756
Thamnophis elegans aquaticus	774		756
Thamnophis elegans atratus	775	779	756
Thamnophis elegans biscutatus	778	779	756
Thamnophis elegans couchi	782	785	763
Thamnophis elegans gigas	784	785	763
Thamnophis elegans hammondi	788	791	763
Thamnophis elegans hydrophila	790	791	763
Thamnophis elegans terrestris	794	796	767
Thamnophis elegans vagrans	795	796	756
Thamnophis eques megalops	799	802	756
Thamnophis marcianus marcianus	803	802	763
Thamnophis marcianus nigrolateris	804	807	763
Thamnophis ordinoides ordinoides	806	807	756
Thamnophis radix radix	810	813	763
Thamnophis radix brachystoma	814	813	763
Thamnophis radix butleri	816	819	763
Thamnophis radix haydeni	820	819	763
Thamnophis sauritus sauritus	824	827	767
Thamnophis sauritus proximus	828	827	767
Thamnophis sauritus sackeni	832	831	767
Thamnophis sirtalis sirtalis	834	843	834
Thamnophis sirtalis concinnus	844	843	834
Thamnophis sirtalis fitchi	846	850	767
Thamnophis sirtalis infernalis	851	850	834
Thamonophis sirtalis parietalis	854	857	834
Thamnophis sirtalis pickeringi	858	857	834
Thamnophis sirtalis tetrataenia	861	867	767
Thamnophis elegans nigrescens	864		
Thamnophis sirtalis trilineata	865		
Trimorphodon: Lyre Snakes	866	81	
Trimorphodon lambda	869	867	869
Trimorphodon vandenburghi	872	877	869
Trimorphodon vilkinsoni	876	877	869
Tropidoclonion: Lined Snakes	879	71	
Tropidoclonion lineatum lineatum	879	881	880
Elapidae: Coral Snakes	885	33	
Micruroides: Arizona Coral Snakes	885	886	
Micruroides euryxanthus	886	887	891
Micrurus: Coral Snakes	890	886	
Micrurus fulvius fulvius	890	895	891

	Page Number of		
	Account	Fig.	Map
Micrurus fulvius barbouri	894	895	891
Micrurus fulvius tenere	897	900	891
Crotalidae: Pit vipers	901		
Ancistrodon: Copperheads, Moccasins	901	902	
Ancistrodon contortrix contortrix	903	900	904
Ancistrodon contortrix laticinctus	907	909	904
Ancistrodon contortrix mokeson	910	909	904
Ancistrodon contortrix pictigaster	915	917	904
Ancistrodon piscivorus piscivorus	916	917	921
Ancistrodon piscivorus leucostoma	921	922	921
Crotalus: Rattlesnakes	925	926	
Crotalus adamanteus	936	937	943
Crotalus atrox	941	947	943
Crotalus cerastes cerastes	948	947	951
Crotalus cerastes laterorepens	950	952	951
Crotalus cerastes cercobombus	955	952	951
Crotalus horridus horridus	956	963	951
Crotalus horridus atricaudatus	962	963	951
Crotalus lepidus lepidus	966	969	971
Crotalus lepidus klauberi	970	969	971
Crotalus mitchelli pyrrhus	974	976	971
Crotalus mitchelli stephensi	977	976	971
Crotalus molossus molossus	980	984	986
Crotalus pricei pricei	985	984	986
Crotalus ruber ruber	989	992	943
Crotalus scutulatus scutulatus	994	992	943
Crotalus tigris	998	999	971
Crotalus viridis viridis	1001	1007	951
Crotalus viridis abyssus	1008	1007	951
Crotalus viridis cerberus	1010	1010	951
Crotalus viridis decolor	1012	1015	951
Crotalus viridis helleri	1014	1015	951
Crotalus viridis lutosus	1018	1023	951
Crotalus viridis nuntius	1024	1023	951
Crotalus viridis oreganus	1029	1030	951
Crotalus willardi willardi	1034	1035	951
Sistrurus: Ground Rattlesnakes, Pigmy Rattlesnakes, Massasaugas	1040	902	
Sistrurus catenatus catenatus	1042	1047	1042
Sistrurus catenatus tergeminus	1048	1051	1042
Sistrurus catenatus edwardsi	1050		1042

CONTENTS

	Page Number of		
	Account	*Fig.*	*Map*
Sistrurus miliarius miliarius	1052	1051	1042
Sistrurus miliarius barbouri	1055	1057	1042
Sistrurus miliarius streckeri	1058	1057	1042

GLOSSARY 1063
IMPORTANT NORTH AMERICAN REFERENCES 1070
INDEX 1075

COLUBRIDAE (*continued*)

PIKE-HEADED TREE SNAKES

Genus *OXYBELIS* Wagler (Fig. 22)

Size large, 49–60 inches; form long, slender with tail ⅔ as long as body; body compressed, in one 53-inch snake, vertical diameter was 14 mm. and horizontal diameter 10 mm.; ventrals rounded extending up the side; snout long and sharp, head elongate, distinct from neck, just back of eye 1½–2 times as deep as neck; neck slender as a lead pencil and several inches in length; head often held like that of a crane; usually no loreal; anal divided; in U.S. forms, caudals paired; scales smooth or faintly keeled, 17 rows to 13 rows near vent, with apical pits, may appear barklike as tips of scale surfaces turn up, and many individual scales and plates readily shed. Canthus rostralis distinct; ½ or more of frontal ahead of anterior interocular line; internasals almost exactly as long as prefrontals; anterior chin shields shorter than posterior with 3–4 rows of gulars between tips and ventrals (U.S. form); 2 deeply grooved posterior fangs in the 18–27 maxillary teeth. Scale rows oblique, but not equally so cephalad and caudad. Synonyms: *Coluber, Dryinus.*

Tropical vine snake, Pike-headed tree snake

Oxybelis aeneus auratus (Bell) 1825. Fig. 167; Map 44

Other common names: Arizona long-headed snake; Arizona vine snake; pike-headed snake.

Range: From desert mountains of Arizona near the international boundary s. to Yucatan.—U.S.A.: Ariz. Mex. *Elevation*—2,000 to 4,000 feet.

Size: Adults from 49 to 60 inches have been taken in the United States.

Distinctive characteristics: A large medium, smooth, 17-rowed long-snouted, elongate, arboreal snake, quaker drab or mouse gray above, and venter cartridge buff becoming cinnamon posteriorly. Taylor (Gen., 1951) says it is "variable in color: green, bronzy, grayish or reddish above, uniform or flecked with brown." Ventrals 187–200; caudals 178–184. Scales in oblique arrangement, transverse rows curved. "A large *Oxybelis,* similar in habit and coloration to *O. acuminatus* but differing from that species in having a much

565

smaller eye and a much longer and differently shaped snout" (Barbour and Amaral).

Color: A snake from Tucson, Ariz., received from Vorhies and described June 15, 1936; from Pajaritos Mt. section of Arizona west of Nogales. The neck is astonishingly slender, the head pointed, long-snouted, and often held up like that of a crane and vibrating as if in delicate balance. The dorsal color of the body proper to the tip of the tail, for about 8 scales transversely is pallid quaker drab, pale mouse gray, or pale ecru-drab. For the first 5 inches the dorsal color is a mixture of buffy brown, sayal brown, or chamois

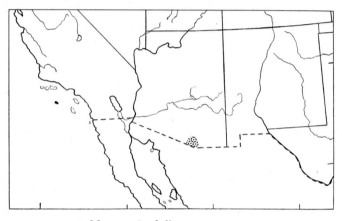

Map 44. *Oxybelis aeneus auratus.*

with the pale mouse gray of the dorsal band, and showing little touches of marguerite yellow or seafoam yellow. The top of the head and neck are buffy brown, becoming on the neck almost sayal brown. The scales of the dorsal band are not specked with black or are only occasionally so, while on the sides, under the lens, the first 4½ scale rows are seen to be heavily flecked with black on the dorsal band color, thus appearing to the unaided eye mouse gray or hair brown with flecks of dorsal color.

A snake taken at Pena Blanca Spring, Ariz., and sent us by G. W. Harvey, Nogales, Ariz., Oct. 14, 1937. The middorsal color of the body proper for about 8 scales transversely is drab-gray or smoke gray, with conspicuous interscale color of marguerite yellow or seafoam yellow for ⅓ of its length. In the cephalic half the dorsum is heavily flecked with longitudinal dashes of black. Both the yellow interscale color and the black dashes are particularly prominent in the cephalic 6 inches. The sides of the body are hair brown. The top of the head is drab. There is a clear-cut black line from the eye to the nostril along the upper edge of the upper labials, a prominent black caudal margin to the preocular, and in addition a black cephalic margin to the postoculars. The upper and lower labials are lemon yellow. The iris is black in front and rear with pale drab-gray in the lower portion and above. The pupil rim is pale drab-gray. The underside of the head and the neck for 2 inches are pale lemon yellow. From about 3 inches back of the head, the pale lemon yellow of the neck extends as a thin median line down the belly, flanked on either side with cinnamon or pinkish cinnamon. It extends thus for 8 to 10 inches, becoming thereafter a very narrow line of cinnamon or pinkish cinnamon. Very soon, this cinnamon border to the yellow ceases to be a continuous band and becomes a border to the ventrals of mouse gray. The anal plate is cinnamon.

Habitat: "Two specimens of a snake species I had not previously seen were brought to me in 1925, which aroused interest because of their extreme slenderness and unusual appearance. The first of these was brought in preserved condition by Mr. S. H. Beattie of Tubae, Arizona, who reported that it was taken in April in Calabasas Canyon. This canyon extends from a point in the Santa Cruz Valley about 50 miles south of Tucson, in a southwesterly direction to and across the international boundary west of Nogales, in the Tumacacori Mountains. The snake was captured only 2 or 3 miles from the border, within the state of Arizona. It measures 1328 mm. in total length; tail, 541 mm., and about 14 mm. in diameter at the widest part.

"In June 1925, a living specimen was brought in by Mr. W. W. Akers of Tucson, who states that it was captured in the edge of this city. . . . The living specimen, on our learning its identity, was at once placed in quarters sufficiently commodious so that limbs of palo verde could be provided for it, and on these branches this slender creature spends its days. Although rated as mildly poisonous, it has been freely handled and shows little disposition to bite human caretakers. It feeds on some of the common small lizards when these are provided for it, kills by gripping them tightly well back in the mouth until the poison has done its work, and then swallows the prey as described by Ditmars. This specimen is about 1315 mm. in total length; tail 438 mm., but it is evident that a portion of the latter is missing. By comparison of proportions, using the other specimen as a standard, this one should have a tail length of about 601 mm., and a total length of about 1478 mm. It is about 14 mm. in vertical diameter, and 10 mm. in horizontal diameter. It can pass readily between two pins standing but 10 mm. apart without noticeable constriction of the body" (Vorhies).

"According to the residents, these snakes are not uncommonly seen in the Pena Blanca area. Our specimen was brought to us by a rancher who found it on the top of a ridge. As he rode up on horseback, the snake became alarmed and climbed an adjacent oak tree with astonishing rapidity. It is a female with 4 eggs in the oviduct, the largest measuring 5.5 cm. in length. On the right side of the head the 8th and 9th upper labials are fused, otherwise the scutellation is normal; the ventrals number 201, the subcaudals 166" (Campbell).

Breeding: Oviparous. We know next to nothing of this topic. We believe all known are adults, measurements being such as 1,226, 1,315, 1,350, 1,478 mm. C. W. Hall (Gen., 1951) has a male 1,220 mm. and a female 1,235 mm.

Field notes: June, 1934, Tucson: Went out to call on S. H. Beattie, the gentleman who brought Vorhies the original specimen of *Oxybelis microphthalmus* from near the Mexican line. L. P. Wehrle took us to his home. The first snake he secured in Calabasas Canyon. It was a large specimen. He was with someone else, and the other man put his hand on the snake and the snake moved. He grabbed it. The third one was much smaller and was secured at Pena Blanca Springs resting along the wire fence and he felt he had to use gloves on it. The first one was very gentle, but wild. It attempted to escape, going into his shirt. This one escaped in the house, and he wondered where it was. He found the snake stretched along 4 nails. The small one fed on lizards, seized them crosswise. Mr. Beattie said Berry Campbell found one *Oxybelis* dead. He was at Pena Blanca when Campbell took *R. tarahumara* and remembers how Campbell rejoiced. Beattie said to see Uhl Kuhn, Plant Quarantine man at Nogales, Arizona, and to see his partner, G. W. Harvey. If Harvey is not home, go ¼ mile further to a Spanish war veteran, Kimmel.

June 20, 1934, Pena Blanca Springs: In the evening Mr. Kimmel, who lives above Harvey, came to the spring for water. He said two weeks before in a vine over his door, a little child discovered a bush snake. He saw those Mr. Beattie caught. He said in general these snakes were gentle and leisurely, but once in a while would bite quite vigorously. When they get started, they travel fast through vines, bushes, and trees. Doesn't believe there are many snakes around here because javelinas eat them and there are lots of javelinas.

June 21, 1934: With G. W. Harvey after *Rana tarahumarae*. He always speaks of this snake as the "pike-headed tree snake."

Authorities: [1]

Barbour, T., and A. do Amaral (Ariz., 1926)
Bogert, C. M., and J. A. Oliver (Ariz., 1945)
Campbell, B. (Ariz., 1934)
Clark, P. J., and R. F. Inger (Gen., 1942a)
Vorhies, C. T. (Ariz., 1926)

1925–1950, A. H. and A. A. Wright: We saw the first live specimen of Vorhies in 1925 in Tucson when he was away on a vacation. Later he sent us specimens. We have delighted in introducing live new forms to their herpetologic describers who have had nothing but preserved material for

---

[1] 1955, R. G. Zweifel and K. S. Norris (*Amer. Midl. Naturalist,* **54**:245) in Sonora: "At Guirocoba this was the third most abundantly obtained snake being exceeded only by *Leptophis* and *Drymarchon*. One individual was encountered crawling rapidly along the ground with its head well elevated above the surface. The lack of sharp distinction between the dorsal and ventral coloration may be related to the semiarboreal habits of the animal. The grayish ground color of *Oxybelis* is strikingly similar to the color of certain climbing vines abundant at Guirocoba."

the original description. Never did a describer more enthusiastically beam than Barbour when I placed in his hands a beautiful live *Oxybelis microphthalmus,* his creation.

1945: C. M. Bogert and J. A. Oliver are probably correct in calling *Oxybelis microphthalmus* a part of *Oxybelis aeneus auratus.* They discuss this *Oxybelis* complex through 10½ pages, which see. In none of the live southern Arizonan specimens we have seen was there a "reddish" coloration.

LEAF-NOSED SNAKES

Genus *PHYLLORHYNCHUS* Stejneger (Fig. 19)

Size small, 6–20 inches; chunky; tail short (per cent 8 ♀–16.4 ♂); head slightly broader than neck; snout truncate, shovellike, rostral enlarged with free lateral edges separating internasals; anal entire; scales smooth or keeled in rows 21-19-17; subocular ring of scales; 1 pair chin shields (posterior if present like gulars); 2 nasals; loreal present; upper labials 6 (5–9), lower 9 (7–11); maxillary teeth with a diastema, 6, 7, 8 or 9 + 3 or 4 (*perkinsi*); sulcus of hemipenis bifurcated on extreme distal end; pupil of eye vertically elliptical. Synonyms: *Lytorhynchus, Phimothyra.*

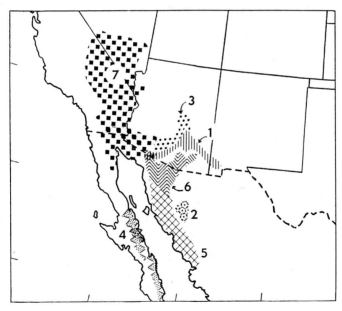

Map 45. *Phyllorhynchus*—1, *b. browni;* 2, *b. fortitus;* 3, *b. lucidus;* 4, *d. decurtatus;* 5, *d. norrisi;* 6, *d. nubilus;* 7, *d. perkinsi.*

KEY TO THE GENUS *PHYLLORHYNCHUS*
(After Klauber with *P. b. fortitus* of Bogert added)

a. Dorsal body blotches (not including tail spots) less than 17.

   b. Blotches equal to or less than 2x(1.23–1.56) interspaces, brown, extending to scale row 3 (2).

      c. Males with 166 or fewer ventrals and 36 or fewer subcaudals; females with 179 or fewer ventrals and 26 or fewer subcaudals, Body-blotches considerably longer than the interspaces.

                                              P. browni browni

      (S.e. Pinal County and e. Pima County, w. to Organ Pipe Cactus National Monument, Pima Co., Ariz.)

      cc. Males with 167 or more ventrals and 37 or more subcaudals; females with 180 or more ventrals and 27 or more subcaudals. Body blotches little, if any, longer than the interspaces.   *P. b. lucidus*
(Northeastern Maricopa Co., Ariz., along the mountain bases, from near Cave Creek to Indian Wells.)

   bb. Blotches longer and closer together than *P. b. browni,* 4–5 x width of interspaces, slaty gray, extending to scale row 1 or 2, rostral exceptionally large and more strongly raised above surrounding scales of snout and blunter at upper end where it reaches prefrontals than in any other member of genus.   *P. b. fortitus*
(Type from Alamos, Son., in Rio Fuerte drainage area.)

aa. Dorsal body blotches (not including tail spots) 17 or more, brown.

   b. Males with 168 or more ventrals; females with 179 or more. Body blotches usually distinctly narrower (along the body) than the interspaces.   *P. d. perkinsi*
(Southern California, on the e. or desert side of the mountains, from the Death Valley region s. to n.e. Baja California; also cent. Clark Co., Nev., s.e. through Mojave, w. Maricopa and Yuma Cos., Ariz., to extreme n.w. Sonora, Mexico. Intergrades with *P. d. nubilus* in the area from s.w. Yavapai Co. to w. Pinal Co., Ariz.)

   bb. Males with 167 or fewer ventrals; females with 178 or less. Body blotches usually equal to or wider (along the body) than the interspaces.

      c. Dorsal body blotches (not including tail spots) 34 or less; males without conspicuous keels on the dorsal scales.

                                      P. decurtatus decurtatus
(Cent. and s. Baja California. Probably intergrades with *P. d. perkinsi* in n. cent. Baja California. Smith and Langebartel [Ariz., 1951] make the s. Sonora and n. Sinaloa specimens a new form with keeled dorsals and fewer ventrals and caudals.)

      cc. Dorsal body blotches (not including tail spots) 35 or more; males with conspicuous keels on the dorsal scales.   *P. d. nubilus*

(Vicinity of Tucson, Pima Co., Ariz.; w. cent. and n.w. Sonora, Mex.)

Brown's leaf-nosed snake (4—Van Denburgh 1922), Pima leaf-nosed snake (3)

Phyllorhynchus browni browni Stejneger 1890. Fig. 168; Map 45

Other common names: Brown's flat-nosed snake (2—Ditmars 1907); leaf-nosed snake.

Range: From s.w. New Mexico to s.e. Pinal Co., Ariz., and s.w. across Pima Co. to Organ Pipe National Monument, Ariz.—Ariz.; N.M. *Elevation* —1,000 to 3,000 feet.

Size: Adults, 6.6–15.4 inches. Before 1935 the sizes recorded ranged from 325–345 mm. Klauber's specimens ranged from 166–396 mm. Klauber's (1943b) measurements for 25 males and 13 females were: mean over-all length 290.08 mm. males, 296.33 mm. females; maxima, 1,027 (244) mm. males, 892 (200) mm. females.

Distinctive characteristics: A small, delicate, beautiful, 19-rowed snake, glistening white below and vinaceous-buff or pinkish above with dark-bordered, dark olive-buff dorsal saddles 17 (9–15) or less on body, and much longer than interspaces. Subralabials 6 (7–8); infralabials 8 or 9 (10–11); loreals 2 or 3 (1–4); oculars 2 (3); temporals 2 (3) + 3 (4).

Color: A snake from Sabino Canyon, Tucson, Ariz., received from C. T. Vorhies, July 1, 1935. There are 12 dorsal spots on the body and 2 on the tail. Two and one-half scale rows back of the parietals is a uniform dark neck saddle of sepia, bister, mummy brown, or brownish olive. This saddle, concave on its sides, is 20 scales transversely in front, 16 in the rear, and 14 in the middle After an interspace of 6 scales, a series of dorsal saddles begins. The first 2 or 3 are hourglasslike, or concave on the sides. Thereafter, some are thus and others are rounded. The dark color of the neck saddle borders these spots, covering 3 scales in front and rear and 1 scale on the sides. Sometimes this dark lateral border is very narrow. The centers of these dorsal saddles are lighter, being isabella color, tawny-olive, or dark olive-buff, heavily dotted with sepia, bister, brownish olive, or mummy brown. The top of the rear of the head and the 13 interspaces of the back are pale flesh color, pinkish buff, pale vinaceous-pink, or even shrimp pink. For 5 or 6 scale rows down to the lateral edge of the dorsal saddles, the center of each scale is sprinkled with sepia, bister, brownish olive, or mummy brown. Below the dorsal saddles the first 2½ scale rows are glistening white. From the margins of the 6th, 5th and 4th upper labials, a band of color like that of the neck saddles extends to the eye and across the front of the supraoculars, frontal, and rear of prefrontals. The other upper labials, face, and top of head forward except the rostral are glistening white. The rostral is white heavily clouded with deep olive or deep grayish olive, which almost makes a border on either side of the rostral. The internasals, prenasals, and postnasals are white with brownish olive dots. In the eye, the pupil is vertical, the iris is buffy brown, cinnamon, or vinaceous-pink near the pupil and especially above it; and the rest colored like the saddle spots. The eye has a milky wash of pale flesh color, pinkish buff, or pale vinaceous-pink. The ventral surfaces are a beautiful glistening white.

Habitat: Previous to 1926 all we knew was that the specimens came from north or south of Tucson or from near San Xavier Mission. Of the little on this topic, we give two notes from works seldom quoted: *"Phyllorhynchus browni* Stejneger. One specimen of this rare little snake was taken about 9 o'clock one evening in the mesquite association near the mouth of one of the canyons" (Ortenburgers).

"Earlier in the same season that the first *C. cinctus* was received, a specimen of the rare *Phyllorhynchus browni* Stejneger was secured. This was brought to Tucson by a Papago Indian from near San Xavier Mission, a few miles southwest of the city. Only 4 specimens of this species have been previously recorded, all from near Tucson, and 2 of them from San Xavier Mission. On June 15, 1925, Mr. W. M. Burhans of Tucson captured another specimen of *P. browni*. This one came into the engine room of a local ice plant at 2 A.M. Its length is 345 mm.; tail 45 mm. It is thus slightly larger than the single record given by Van Denburgh" (Vorhies).

Finally in 1940 Klauber gave us a much clearer picture of its habitat: *"Browni,* as it is found in the vicinity of Tucson, seems to prefer brushy areas, especially mesquite, and, to a somewhat lesser extent, salt bush. While occasionally found under stones, or dug out in the course of excavations, it can best be collected by the method of driving along the road at night, as has been discussed elsewhere. Specimens have been collected in this way in June and July, at air temperatures of from 74 to 92 deg. Fahr. It has been taken at 8:10, 8:13, 8:30, 8:45, 9:00, 9:20, 9:30, 10:30, 10:50, 11:00, 11:10, and 11:57 P.M. There are indications that its season of greatest activity is somewhat later than that of *P. d. perkinsi* in southern California, the best collecting following the advent of the summer rains experienced in the part of Arizona where it occurs. It prefers somewhat humid nights. It seems to be a more plentiful snake than *nubilus.* Charles E. Shaw and Cyrus S. Perkins collected 9 specimens of *browni* (3 alive and 6 run over) in two evening drives around Tucson in mid-July, but only one *nubilus* was found."

Breeding: Oviparous. Males to 362, females to 396 mm. Probably the 166-mm. males and 180-mm. females were juveniles.

Field notes: June 13, 1942: On return from Oracle Junction we picked up our first *Phyllorhynchus b. browni.* It was on the hill.

June 14, Sunday: Where we got *P. b. browni* last night was 5½ miles n. of our camp or 8 miles from central Tucson. It is on the bench where Mr. Reed has his place directly opposite citrus grove with an oleander row beside the road. It is a mesquite cholla, Opuntia bench and easily falls in the same area, foothills of Santa Catalinas, as Sabino Canyon area where Herbert Brown found them.

June 14, Tucson region—9:25 P.M. start, 90°F.: One-half mile w. of Ajo Junction Anna spied a *P. b. browni* at the edge of the road. It was very still. The instant I sought to catch it, it vigorously tried to go away—so much so that she thought I was going to lose it. 11:15 P.M., temp. 81°: we had found nothing previously on San Xavier Mission Road. We rode down the Mission Road again as far as the Indian Reservation, but found nothing after we caught *P. browni browni* w. of Ajo Junction.

June 16, Tuesday: Rode down Nogales Road about 15 miles. About 12 miles out found a live *Phyllorhynchus browni* and on return found a dead one in much the same locality. Both were in the middle of the road.

Authorities:

Bogert, C. M., and J. A. Oliver (Ariz., 1945)
Boulenger, G. A. (Gen., 1893–96)
Brown, A. E. (Gen., 1901)
Cope, E. D. (Gen., 1900)
Hensley, M. M. (Ariz., 1950)
Klauber, L. M. (Gen., 1935, 1943b)

Linsdale, J. M. (Ariz., 1933)
Ortenburger, A. I. and R. D. (Ariz., 1927)
Stejneger, L. (Ariz., 1890)
Van Denburgh, J. (Gen., 1922)
Vorhies, C. T. (Ariz., 1926)

1922, J. Van Denburgh: "Habits—unknown. The first 2 specimens were collected by Mr. Herbert Brown. Mr. Karl P. Schmidt writes me that 2 others were taken together at night July 16, 1916, at the San Xavier Mission, near Tucson, Arizona."

1933, J. M. Linsdale: (What is his *Phyllorhynchus* from Caborca, Son., Mex., which Bogert and Oliver do not include in their accounts?)

1935, L. M. Klauber: "Such confusion as has existed in the past concerning the status of the two forms of the genus resulted from lack of material and the peculiarities of the ranges. Of course a question may be raised as to the propriety of separating two forms morphologically so similar, upon a basis of pattern, especially as their ranges overlap. In the present instance, the numerical hiatus in the blotch count is so great that there appears little chance that intermediates will be found. In fact specimens of *decurtatus* [now *d. nubilus*—A.H.W.] from *browni* territory tend to have a high number of blotches; *decurtatus* has the fewest spots in the Cape Region of Lower California and in southern Sonora, and there *browni* does not occur."

1940, L. M. Klauber (Gen.): More material, more forms. Restrictive ranges. Arizona-Sonora territorial gaps. "At the time I last surveyed the genus *Phyllorhynchus* only 8 specimens of *browni* were available. All were males, and one of these has been transferred to the new subspecies *lucidus*. It will be useful therefore, to present the statistics of all the specimens of *browni browni* now available, numbering 19 males and 16 females."

1945: C. M. Bogert and J. A. Oliver in their description of a new form, *P. b. fortitus,* from Sonora make many comparisons with *browni, lucidus,* and *decurtatus* and contribute a scholarly addition to our meager knowledge of the structure, taxonomy, and relationships.

1950, M. M. Hensley, Ajo National Monument: "This series of 11 male specimens represents the common form of *Phyllorhynchus* collected. . . . Ventral scale counts, with 2 exceptions, fall well within the range of typical *browni,* varying from 154 to 161 and averaging 157. The caudals range from 19 to 35 with a mean of 29.3. The two unusual variants in ventrals Nos. 5568 and 5571 with 170 each, also interestingly had the lowest caudals with 23 and 19, respectively. . . . So far as is known, this marks the first definite record of *P. b. browni* in Mexico and the second appearance of the species in that country [26.5 miles s. of Ajo, Ariz., 8.6 miles s. of Sonoyta, Mex.]."

1950: This shows quite a change from our imperfect knowledge of 25 years ago, thanks to an avocational herpetologist.

Maricopa leaf-nosed snake (4—Klauber 1940c)

Phyllorhynchus browni lucidus Klauber 1940. Map 45

Range: Phoenix-Superior region, n.e. Maricopa Co., Ariz. *Elevation*—1,000 to 2,000 feet, possibly higher.

Size: The type is 187 mm. (7.5 inches) long.

Distinctive characteristics: Klauber's (Gen., 1940c) diagnosis is based on: "*Type.*—No. 28,819 in the collection of LMK, collected in Enchanto Valley, 7 mi. w. of Cave Creek, Maricopa County, Arizona. Received from V. Housholder, May 21, 1938. Paratype, a specimen in the collection of Earl Sanders from 11 mi. east and 1 mi. north of Mesa, Maricopa County, Arizona, in the vicinity of Indian Wells. *Diagnosis.*—A subspecies of *Phyllorhynchus browni* characterized by high ventral and subcaudal scale counts, and some modifications in pattern, as compared with the typical form." (See Key.)

Color: We have never seen one alive. We use Klauber's (Gen., 1940c) description of the type: "The head is marked with chocolate brown on a cream background. There is a wide dark band across the anterior half of the frontal; this passes backward across the eyes to the angle of the mouth; from here it widens into 2 parallel bands on the neck, which join again dorsally about 1 head length behind the head. There is also a large dark blotch on the parietals; this blotch is not present in *P. b. browni* and is only rudimentary in the paratype of the new subspecies. There are dark punctations on the face and edges of the rostral, the nasals, and internasals, with a few scattered on the prefrontals and loreals. On the body there is a series of 13 subcircular chocolate blotches. Longitudinally these cover slightly more space than the interspaces; on the sides they extend down as far as the 2nd row of scales above the ventrals. The centers of the blotches are somewhat lighter than the edges, and, as the lighter color is restricted to scale centers, the blotches appear hatched with dark longitudinal lines. Laterally between the blotches, there is a secondary series of small spots, longer than wide, engaging the first 2 lateral rows. Surrounding these there are a few dark punctations, reminiscent of the patches of punctations which characterize the lateral areas between blotches in *P. b. browni*. The ground color in the body is creamy-white as is also the ventral surface. There are 3 dorsal spots on the tail.

Habitat: So little is known of its habitat and range, conjecture is futile. In 1940 Klauber held that it "will probably be found all along the bases of the mountains to the north and east of Phoenix," but if the Ajo material is truly *lucidus,* its range is considerably extended.

Breeding: Oviparous. Probably the 247-mm. male and 187-mm. female are juveniles.

Authorities:

Bogert, C. M., and J. A. Oliver (Ariz., 1945)
Gloyd, H. K. (Ariz., 1940)
Hensley, M. M. (Ariz., 1950)
Klauber, L. M. (Gen., 1935b, 1940)

1935(b), L. M. Klauber: "This specimen, taken by Earl Sanders not far from Mesa, Arizona, has 172 ventrals and 40 caudals, compared with a maximum of 160 and 33 in the Tucson group (all males). The blotches are smaller and darker in color than those from around Tucson, but in number and shape of blotches this specimen is just as distinctive as the others."

1940, L. M. Klauber: "The body blotches in *P. b. browni* are usually indented laterally, and often approach a dumb-bell shape. In *lucidus* there are indentations on the middorsal line, so that the paired lobes are transverse, rather than longitudinal as in *browni.*"

1940, H. K. Gloyd: "During the latter part of May and early June we worked the roads of the desert west of Superior almost every night. . . . The desert leaf-nosed snake (*Phyllorhynchus decurtatus*) was fairly common, but we found only two specimens of the Maricopa leaf-nosed snake (*Phyllorhynchus browni lucidus*), a little known form quite recently described . . . and hence a special prize."

1950, A. H. and A. A. Wright: It is not always the case that there are so many photographs of a form as rare as this subspecies. Klauber's description is of two specimens, and he furnishes a photograph. Gloyd secures two and presents a photograph. In the same year, 1949, two diverse Cornellians, unknown to each other, one an engineer, Walter F. Flood, Jr., the other an ornithologist and herpetologist, Max Hensley, independently showed us photos of this form from the Ajo region. Four photos in all from 5, possibly 6, specimens of a very rare snake. Of course the Ajo material may be intermediate.

1950, M. M. Hensley: "2.2 miles S. of Ajo (5572); 12.6 miles S. Ajo (5578); 20 miles S. Ajo (5648); 22 miles S. Ajo (5577). As in the case of *P. decurtatus,* the area investigated proved to include a zone of intergradation also for the subspecies of *P. browni.* The 4 northernmost specimens taken resembled *lucidus* in having the narrow body blotches that tend to be indented along the middorsal line and in having parietal spots (except in No. 5648 where they are entirely lacking). Only one specimen (5578) shows a tendency of the frontal band to unite laterally with the secondary series of lateral spots. . . . Scalation counts suggest intergradation with *b. browni.* . . . The occurrence of this form southwest of the type locality extends the range considerably (175 miles) in the direction opposite to that suggested by Klauber (1940), who expected it north and east of Phoenix."

Cloudy leaf-nosed snake (Klauber 1940)

Phyllorhynchus decurtatus nubilus Klauber 1940. Fig. 169; Map 45

Range: From Tucson, Ariz., s.w. to n.w. and w. cent. Sonora, Mex.—U.S.A.: Ariz. Mex.: Sonora. *Elevation*—2,000 to 3,000 feet.

Size: In his original description Klauber (Gen., 1940) had specimens 173–408 mm. or 7–16.3 inches. Our material falls within these extremes. Klauber's (Gen., 1943b) measurements of 8 males and 4 females are: mean over-all 288.50 mm. males, 272.50 mm. females; maxima 343 (50) mm. males, 408 (33) mm. females.

Distinctive characteristics: "A subspecies of *P. decurtatus* distinguished from the typical subspecies by a high number of dorsal blotches and generally maculate appearance. Also, *nubilus* males have strongly keeled dorsal scales, while *P. d. decurtatus* males are keeled only faintly, if at all. From *P. d. perkinsi,* the new subspecies is differentiated by the relative sizes of the dorsal blotches and interspaces, the blotches being wider longitudinally than the interspaces in the new form. There are also differences in scalation, the new subspecies having fewer ventrals and subcaudals than perkinsi" (Klauber, Gen., 1940).

A small, 19-rowed, very spotted snake with 59–72 dorsal spots on body and 8–13 on tail. Three more lateral rows—in other words, a pattern clouded. The spots are brown with pinkish cinnamon centers. Ventrals 157–176; caudals 20–33. Venter white.

Color: Two snakes secured 11 miles south of Tucson, Ariz., June 26, 1942. We went to see H. E. Weisner at 6:30 P.M. He had two little brown snakes in sand in a square can. They are *P. d. nubilus.* One snake is very spotted on back and sides. The ground color on parietals and neck is pale cinnamon-pink extending to the first black spots which make a bar across the neck. Caudad of this the background is pale pinkish cinnamon becoming pale

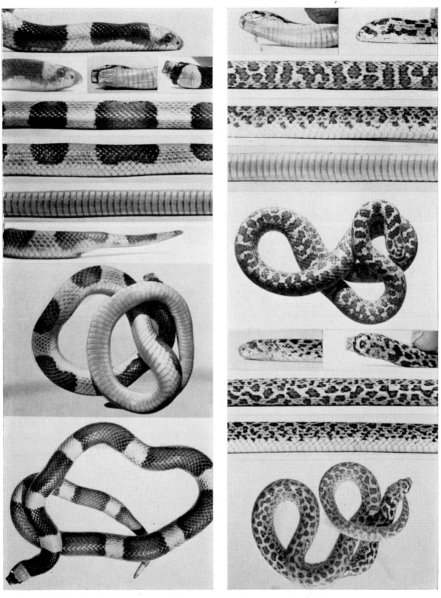

Fig. 168. *Phyllorhynchus browni browni,* Sabino Canyon, Tucson, Ariz., C. T. Vorhies.

Fig. 169. *Phyllorhynchus decurtatus nubilus,* H. E. Weisner ranch, 11 miles south of Tucson, Ariz.

pinkish buff. The back is marked with brown spots which are in fact pinkish cinnamon in their centers with edges black. There are 72 dorsal spots on body plus 13 on the tail. There are about 3 rows of larger light-centered spots, and on 3rd to 7th rows are 3 irregular rows of black spots. Here also is a wash of pinkish cinnamon. There is an occasional brown spot on the 2nd scale row. A dark band starts in the middle of the last upper labial, crosses the suture of the lowest 2nd-row temporal, the suture of 7th and 6th upper labials, crosses the lowest 1st-row temporal, the 2 lower postoculars, eye, front of supraocular, edge of upper preocular, crosses the rear half of prefrontals and edge of frontal. The frontal bears a light-centered triangle, its base forward and the other 2 sides following suture line of parietals. The parietal has a similar black band from its outer edge half way to interparietal suture. The rostral is pale olive-buff. The iris is dotted with buff-pink and vinaceous-cinnamon, the pupil vertical. The side of face and under part of head are white. The ventrals are white, as are the first 2 scale rows.

Second snake looks to be a female. The band on the head is much more prominent than in the first snake, and there are 8 large dorsal bands across the neck and forward body, as would be expected in *P. d. decurtatus*. There are 65 dorsal spots on the body plus 8 on the tail. These spots are more regular than in the first snake, more nearly transverse, sometimes completely crossing dorsum, or broken into 2 parts or spots to form Y's. Below these saddle spots on the 3rd to 6th or 7th rows are 3 irregular rows of small spots irregular in shape. The pinkish cinnamon centers are more prominent in this snake; hence it has a more general tan appearance.

Pattern phases of same species? This form comes in the area of the *piceus-frenatus* problem. Is it like it or *Rhinocheilus l. clarus* and *lecontei?* Klauber (Gen., 1940), its describer, poses the question thus: "There remains the question whether *nubilus* and *browni* are only pattern phases of the same species, as has been found to be the case with the king snakes of the San Diegan area in southern California. This is possible, for, with the limited material now available, no scale count differences can be demonstrated statistically. However, the absence of intermediates, such as characterize the king snakes, together with differences in blotch colors and head pattern, not evident in the king-snake complex, would indicate that such a relationship probably does not exist. The finding of females of *browni,* since the issuance of the previous paper, at least proves that the *browni* pattern is not an ex-emplification of sexual dimorphism. Upon the evidence so far available *decurtatus* and *browni* are to be considered separate species. A subspecific relationship is impossible, since *decurtatus nubilus* and *browni* occupy the same territory. After all, the only evidence suggesting that *nubilus* and *browni* are pattern phases of a single subspecies lies in the similarity of their lepidosis in the Tucson area, and the tendency, which both have, toward higher ventral and subcaudal scale counts in specimens from the northwest toward Wickenburg."

Habitat: Most of our knowledge of the ecology of this desert form we owe to Lee Arnold, who collected for Klauber and who introduced us to H. E. Weisner. Klauber (Gen., 1940) gives us about all we know concerning this species: "Like other species and subspecies of *Phyllorhynchus, nubilus* hisses and strikes when annoyed, and flattens the neck like a dewlap. The tongue is pink in life, almost colorless at the tip. The pupil is vertically elliptical, the iris flecked with green and gold. Specimens have been collected along the road at 9:40 P.M. (93°F.), 10:18 P.M. (84°F.), 11:20 P.M. and 2:25 A.M. This is probably a fairly common snake around Tucson, although somewhat rarer than *browni,* and considerably less common than the subspecies *decurtatus perkinsi* in some areas of the Colorado Desert in southern California. It seems to prefer brushy areas, particularly mesquite, and to a less extent, salt bush and creosote bush. It is easiest collected by driving at night along paved roads, when the snakes will be disclosed by the headlights of the car as they cross the pavement. Lee Arnold, from whom most of the ecological notes on this subspecies were obtained, secured 5 specimens, 2 alive and 3 run over, in the course of 495 miles (31 hours) of driving in June and July of 1939."

Breeding: Oviparous. Males 300 (approx.)—343 mm., females 300 (approx.)—408 mm.

Field notes: June 26, 1942: Went to see Mr. Weisner. Imagine our surprise when he said he had 2 spotted snakes from his pit and when we saw them—unbelievably—they were *Phyllorhynchus d. nubilus.* What a pit! *C. cinctus* June 24, *Phyllorhynchus d. nubilus,* 2 of them, June 26. Did anyone ever produce the goods in better style than Mr. Weisner? A fine mesquite thicket, immense apiary, birds protected, area ungrazed—an ideal nature sanctuary made by a real nature lover and keen observer. Here many a naturalist has worked.

Authorities:

Bogert, C. M., and J. A. Oliver (Ariz., 1945)

Hensley, M. M. (Ariz., 1950)

Klauber, L. M. (Gen., 1935b, 1940)

Linsdale, J. M. (Ariz., 1933)

Schmidt, K. P. (Baja Calif., 1922)

1922, K. P. Schmidt: "A specimen (AMNH No. 20590) collected by Dr. F. E. Lutz and J. A. G. Rehn near Tucson agrees with *browni* in every scale character, but has the dorsal coloration of *decurtatus* while a second specimen from the same locality is a typical *browni.*"

1933, J. M. Linsdale: "On June 1, 1926, a specimen of *Phyllorhynchus* was found by Charles L. Camp at Alamo Muerto, 30 miles west of Caborca, Sonora, Mexico." Of four specimens from Sonora, L. M. Klauber (Gen.,

1940) remarks, "These are intermediate between *decurtatus nubilus* and *decurtatus decurtatus* in number of body blotches and tail spots; they more nearly resemble *nubilus* in the character of the blotches and in possessing dorsal keels."

1940, L. M. Klauber: *"Nubilus* seems to intergrade with both *perkinsi* and *decurtatus decurtatus,* but via different routes—with the former by way of Central Arizona, and the latter through Sonora. . . . Through central Arizona, from Congress Junction, Yavapai County, to the vicinity of Casa Grande and Coolidge, Pinal County, a series comprising 24 *perkinsi* differ from *nubilus* in having higher ventral and subcaudal counts, fewer and more widely separated dorsal blotches, head marks less evident, lateral blotches smaller and less prominent and lateral interspaces less clouded. In all these characteristics the central Arizona specimens are intermediate, which is entirely consistent and to be expected from a geographical standpoint. While recognizing these specimens as intergrades, for purposes of segregation in collections I would suggest their allocation to *perkinsi,* since most of them tend in that direction when classified by pattern."

1945: C. M. Bogert and J. A. Oliver in their description of *P. b. fortitus* discuss *P. d. decurtatus* and *P. d. nubilus,* of which they examined 14 specimens: "Thus, dentitional characters seem to confirm Klauber's conclusions concerning the relationships of the subspecies of *decurtatus,* but they offer no additional proof concerning the validity of two genetically distinct but morphologically similar species, *decurtatus* and *browni,* which inhabit the same region in Arizona."

1950, M. M. Hensley: "28.5 miles S. Ajo (5582); . . . 15 miles S. Sonoyta, Sonora, Mexico (5646). . . . The present specimens, likewise, are in part considered intergrades; at least the northern specimens appear to be intermediate. Other specimens from farther south in Sonora (Alamo Muerto and Guaymas) are regarded as intergrades between *P. d. decurtatus* and *P. d. nubilus* by Klauber."

Desert leaf-nosed snake (5—Klauber 1934),
Leaf-nosed snake

Phyllorhynchus decurtatus perkinsi Klauber 1935. Fig. 170; Map 45

Range: Southern Nevada through Mojave and Colorado deserts of California and Yuma desert of Arizona into adjacent Sonora, Mex., and n.e. Baja California, Mex.—U.S.A.: Ariz.; Calif.; Nev. Mex.: Baja Calif.; Sonora. *Elevation*—Sea level to 2,000 or more feet. Below 1,000 feet (Nevada); deserts and desert foothills from Colorado River to about 2,500 feet (Klauber, Calif., 1931a).

Size: Klauber (Gen.) in his description of 1935b had material 165 mm. (6.6 inches)—485 mm. (19.4 inches). His 1940c paper (Gen.) has a male

495 mm. (20 inches). His (Gen., 1943b) measurements of two series (I—214 males and 148 females, II—34 males and 16 females) are: mean over all, I—340.34 mm. males and 329.91 mm. females, II—356.79 males, 292 mm. females; maxima I—495 (tail 75) mm. males, 486 (tail 44) mm. females, II—510 (tail 82) mm. males, 435 (tail 50) mm. females.

Distinctive characteristics: "A subspecies of *Phyllorhynchus decurtatus* characterized by a high ventral scale count and small, widely separated body blotches" (Klauber, Gen., 1935). A small, mainly smooth, 19 rowed, buffy pink or pinkish snake with 24–48 pecan brown dorsal saddles on the body. It has a square nose. Venter glistening white. Ventrals 168–196; caudals 24–41.

Color: A snake from 10 miles east of Blythe, Riverside Co., Calif., collected by L. H. Cook, and received from L. M. Klauber, May 30, 1930. The background of the back is buff-pink on the rear half, becoming onion-skin pink on the forward half; the tip of the tail is vinaceous-pink. On the body to the vent are 31 saddle spots of pecan brown with black borders; several of the spots are broken into 2 spots. Along the sides are 2 or 3 rows of smaller spots, some of which are merged into larger ones. These lateral spots appear darker than the dorsal ones, because the dark borders are proportionally greater. The top of the head is buff-pink with a dark spot on each parietal. Across the head and through the eyes is a band of pecan brown. Below the eyes, this band is bordered with black. The large scale on the tip of the snout is white with a light olive-gray center. The iris is vinaceous-tawny, the pupil black. The ventral plates are white with iridescent reflections of pale vinaceous-pink.

A snake from Edom, Riverside Co., Calif., 10 miles from Indio, received May, 1940, from Kern. The background of the back is vinaceous-pink with a middorsal row of tawny-olive spots faintly outlined with saccardo's umber, 36 on the body, 6 on the tail. Lateral spots are saccardo's umber. The tail is shell pink.

Habitat: Only 30 years ago when we traveled near Kane Springs, Calif. (see Medden) we picked up the 4th known specimen of *Phyllorhynchus d. perkinsi*, the 3rd being Klauber's San Felipe one of 1924. How we did appreciate Miss Atsatt's excellent photograph! Miss Atsatt kept her specimen from Mar. 25 to July 20, 1921. She discovered it in Tahquitz Creek under a rock in a depression in the sand. "Rare" then; most common now, thanks to the San Diego group who have helped so much in the understanding of our desert species.

The specimen that Klauber found in 1924 was his first and, as we said above, the third recorded. Seven years later he was cautious and wrote (Calif., 1931a), "Even *P. decurtatus,* long believed to be one of the rarest species in California, is *moderately* [our italics] common in the sandy areas of the desert, but this does not mean that it is easy to collect." (This article uses such words as *tedious, uncertain, occasional, difficult.*) But another seven years later (Gen., 1939), see the éclat and zing in his "How good does this collecting ever get? Sometimes it is astonishing. Here are the results of 35 minutes (8 miles of travel) from 10:25 to 11:00 o'clock on the night of June 25, 1938, in the vicinity of the Narrows, San Diego County, temperature about 88°F.: [5 *Phyllorhynchus d. perkinsi,* 2 *Arizona e. occidentalis,* and 1 *Crotalus cerastes*]. All of these snakes were found crossing the road. This was at the rate of one live snake per mile or one in each 4½ minutes."

In one table he shows these snakes to be nocturnally active from 7 P.M. to 12:29 A.M., most between 8 and 9; in another table of temperatures this species is out from 66°–94.5°F., most at 88°. He finds it a snake of non-irrigated districts. As to ecological conditions, he has 21 in rocky desert, 112 in brushy desert, 10 in sandy desert, and 66 in barren desert. It is distinctly then a desert species extending into the desert foothills.

"Three specimens of the Desert Leaf-nosed Snake were taken on Route 86 near Sells and on the road between Ajo and Organ Pipe National Monument. Times of capture ranged from 8:30 until 12 midnight, while temperatures were 70–80 degrees. These snakes measured 17¼, 14½, 16 inches. Two more specimens were seen DOR. We watched with special interest the ridiculous antics of the Desert Leaf-nosed snakes. As you probably know, when disturbed they assume an exaggerated version of the angered pose of the rattlesnake. This behavior, mentioned as common to all the Leaf-nosed snakes by Schmidt and Davis, was observed only in *P. decurtatus perkinsi; P. browni lucidus* and, for the few days we had it alive, *P. browni browni* would never assume this stance. Tiny *perkinsi* will rear up with a sharp crook in his neck and weave from side to side. This may be followed by a comic opera lunge made with the mouth closed and, at least in our specimens, without any hiss whatever. When picked up and handled, *Phyllorhynchus,* like many burrowing snakes, seeks to bury its head in the folds of skin between one's fingers" (Flood's journal).

For extended notes on habitat, see Klauber (Gen., 1935), pp. 24–25.

Period of activity: Klauber's "Sixteen Year Census" has *P. d. perkinsi,* Mar., 5 snakes; Apr., 23; May, 106; June, 91; July, 31; Aug., 15; Sept., 17; Oct., 1; Total, 289. Rank 13, per cent 2.23 (Gen., 1939). *Hibernation*—"Two small adult individuals were collected within a few inches of each other, approximately 30 inches below the surface of a small sand dune. No temperatures were available for this depth, but at 40 inches the temperature was 19.5°C." (Cowles).

Concerning temperatures, Cowles and Bogert (Gen., 1944) found that this species displays "acute discomfort at 36.5°C. The critical maximum is reached for subadults at 38°C. . . . but continuous exposure to a body temperature of 36°C. for a period of 2 hours eventually brought death to all 6." One evening at 83–86°F., Klauber found 9 specimens. Three days later at 93–95°F. at night (115°F. in daytime) they were scarcer.

Breeding: Oviparous. Males 441–510 mm., females 300 (approx.)–486 mm. *Eggs*—Number,-2–4. *"Phyllorhynchus* usually lays from 2 to 4 eggs (7 individuals noted with 4 eggs, 2 with 3, 1 with 2). The eggs of 2 specimens were measured; the first, 428 mm., over all, contained 3 eggs about 10x35 mm.; the second, 327 mm. long, contained 2 eggs, 8x37 mm. The eggs seem very large proportionate to the size of the adult" (Klauber, Gen., 1935). "Most of the females with eggs contain 3 or 4" (Klauber, Gen., 1940).

Young—"Nothing seems to be known of its breeding habits except that the young are hatched from eggs" (Perkins). Klauber's (Gen., 1943b) minima are 173 (19) mm. and 168 (16) mm. for males and 171 (16) mm. and 190 (19) mm. for females.

Food: "The Leaf-nosed Snake feeds upon insect larvae, small lizards and their eggs. Small specimens jerk off and eat gecko tails. . . . When annoyed it puffs out its throat vertically apparently with the intention of looking formidable, but with such a little snake the valiant gesture is merely ridiculous" (Perkins).

"Little is known concerning the food habits of the leaf-nosed snakes. Presumably they eat insects and lizards; but in the spring they seem to feed largely on lizard eggs, especially those of *Coleonyx variegatus.* Thus of 11 specimens in one lot, collected in late May, 5 contained lizard eggs. One contained 11 such eggs in all stages of digestion from the full egg to the folded empty sheath about to be excreted. A young adult specimen of *perkinsi,* when placed in a bag with several *Coleonyx variegatus* ate the tails off of two. The tails had not previously been dropped, thus indicating that the snake must have seized them with the usual result. The lizards were too large to have been eaten entirely, although a large leaf-nosed snake could easily eat a small gecko and has been observed to do so in captivity. Out of 21 geckos caught one night 5 had recently lost their tails, no doubt partly the result of leaf-nosed snakes' attacks. In captivity the leaf-nosed snake drinks water readily, although it can rarely have access to water in the wild. . . . *Phyllorhynchus* defends itself by assuming a striking coil with retracted neck and head. It lunges forward with a slight hiss and sometimes opens the mouth when striking. Probably its worst enemy, since they are active at the same time and inhabit the same localities, is *Arizona elegans occidentalis,* which is known to feed upon it, as well as on other snakes, lizards, and mammals" (Klauber, Gen., 1935).

Authorities:

Atsatt, S. R. (Calif., 1921, 1923)
Bogert, C. M., and J. A. Oliver (Ariz., 1945)
Brattstrom, B. H. (Gen., 1953a)
Brown, A. E. (Gen., 1901)
Cowles, R. B. (Gen., 1941a)
Cowles, R. B., and C. M. Bogert (Gen., 1944; Nev., 1936)

Hensley, M. M. (Ariz., 1950)
Klauber, L. M. (Gen., 1935b, 1939a, 1940c, 1943b; Calif., 1924a, 1931a, 1932, 1934a)
Medden, R. V. (Calif., 1927)
Perkins, C. B. (Calif., 1949)
Slevin, J. R. (Ariz., 1931)
Van Denburgh, J. (Gen., 1922)

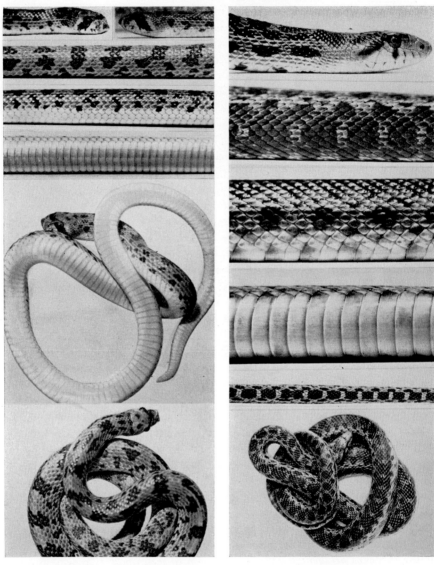

Fig. 170. *Phyllorhynchus d. perkinsi,* 10 miles east of Blythe, Calif., L. H. Cook through L. M. Klauber.

Fig. 171. *Pituophis catenifer catenifer,* Corvallis, Ore., K. Gordon.

1940: L. M. Klauber has over 350 specimens available. "The outstanding fact developed is the commonness of this snake, once considered rare. For example out of 279 live snakes encountered on the roads of San Diego County while driving 2,985 mi. at night on the desert, 110 or almost 40 per cent were leaf-nosed snakes."

1945: C. M. Bogert and J. A. Oliver mainly compare their new *P. b. fortitus* with *P. b. browni*. In *P. d. perkinsi* they found that the maxilla had a diastema followed by 4 enlarged teeth instead of 3 as in the other *Phyllorhynchus* forms.

1950, M. M. Hensley: "A total of 16 specimens of *P. decurtatus,* all males, were taken along Arizona highway 85 south of Ajo, Arizona, to a point some 15 miles south of Sonoyta, Sonora, Mexico."

BULL SNAKES, PINE SNAKES, GOPHER SNAKES

Genus *PITUOPHIS* Holbrook (Fig. 19)

Size, large to very large, 36–100 inches; form robust; tail relatively short; head slightly distinct from neck; vertical laminform epiglottis; eye large; anal entire; caudals in 2 series; scales keeled except for several lower rows, with apical pits, in 27–37 rows, mostly 29, 31, or 33; rostral penetrates between internasals; supraoculars and parietals paired; prefrontals 2–4, rarely 5 or 6 (4 in most U.S. forms); nasal divided; preoculars 1 or 2 (3); postoculars normally 3 or 4; may have azygous (anterior frontal) plate; loreal, usually present, is longer than high, not infrequently divided into 2 or 3 small scales; upper labials 8 or 9, sometimes 7 or 10; one usually contacting orbit in U.S. forms; lower labials 10–15, mostly 12 or 13 (commonly 14 in *mugitus* and *ruthveni*); anterior chin shields longer and wider than posterior and in close contact; posterior ones usually separated by a few scales; 2–3 rows of gulars between tips of chin shields and ventrals; in U.S. forms dorsal pattern of saddles or spots vary in number 22–94 on body, 6–36 on tail, except in *lodingi* which is black; maxillary teeth 14–18, solid, without a diastema, decreasing slightly posteriorly; mandibular teeth 16–22 decreasing slightly posteriorly; hemipenes: slightly bilobed, sulcus spermaticus simple and diagonal to tip of one lobe; basal ⅔ of surface smooth except for irregular grooves and minute spinules, the rest covered with irregular rows of calyces each bearing a terminal spine. The unique vertical laminiform epiglottis magnifying its "hiss or growl" is illustrated in Fig. 19. (See also White and Cope under "Authorities" in the account of *P. c. sayi.*) Synonyms: *Arizona, Churchilla, Coluber, Elaphis, Epiglottophis, Pityophis, Rhinechis, Spilotes.*

KEY TO THE GENUS *PITUOPHIS*

a. Prefrontals normally 2; eye over 2 upper labials; lower labials commonly 11. (Mexico.)   *P. deppei deppei*

aa. Prefrontals normally 4 (occ. 2, 3, 5); eye contacts 1 upper labial (4 or 5).

  b. Rear angle of rostral acute; rostral much higher than wide, sometimes height 2 x breadth, narrowed above and penetrating far between internasals; dorsal spots in part forming transverse bands with dorsal intervals merging into lateral intervals; spots may be obscure anteriorly or back uniformly black; dorsal spots normally less than 41; total spots 32–45; body spots 25–39 (25–41); tail spots normally 7–9 (5–10); number (range) of ventrals less dorsal spots 168–196; series of dark elongate spots 2–3 plates long on ends of ventrals and widely spaced (intervals of 3–5 plates).

    c. Dorsum uniformly glistening black with most of belly black or slate; lower labials 14; young and sometimes adults indistinctly spotted (31–39) like *P. m. mugitus;* scale rows 29 (29–31).

                                                  P. m. lodingi

    cc. Dorsum spotted, never uniform black.

      d. Anterior spots mahogany red to chestnut, clouded and indistinct on cephalic 2/3; general color drab or brown, the intervals 4–5 scales longitudinally; lower labials 12–15; total spots 31–39; body 26–29; tail 8–9 (5–10); scale rows 33 (29–35).

                                                  P. m. mugitus

    dd. Spots and saddles full length.

      e. Saddles distinct, bone brown to black on buff to white background (black and white in alcohol); venter clear except for terminal spots at 4–5 plate intervals; lower labials 12 (10–13); total saddles 32–35 (30–39); body 24–27 (22–3); tail 6–7 (5–10); scale rows 29 (27–31).

                                P. melanoleucus melanoleucus

      ee. Saddles in cephalic region with *catenifer-sayi*-like-intervals of 1 1/2–2 1/2 scales longitudinally, bone brown to russet on cream or colonial buff ground; venter quite spotted; lower labials 13–14; total saddles 40–45; body 31–36; tail 9; scale rows 29 on neck, 28 on mid-body, 20 at tail (to 33 mid-body).   *P. m. ruthveni*

  bb. Rear angle of rostral obtuse except in *c. sayi*, rostral as broad as high or height never more than 1 1/2 x breadth and usually penetrating less than 1/2 along internasal suture (except *c. sayi*); dorsal spots normally more than 50; total 55–85 (48–100); body 48–65 (41–83);

tail 12–21 (10–24); the series of dark terminal ventral spots (except *P. c. vertebralis*) on one ventral, if present, not elongate, and with intervals of 2–3 plates.

c. Snout sharp, rear angle of rostral acute or right angle (more like *m. melanoleucus*), rostral narrow, considerably higher than wide and *bulging* above adjacent plates, penetrating at least 1/2 along internasal suture; labial sutures all conspicuously dark; cephalic interspaces narrow, 2 scales wide; spots quadrangular (6–10 scales wide), seldom uniting with lateral spots; spots and interspaces in less contrast, browns darker and less diverse, less red in posterior spots, the light interspaces yellow to buff (compare *c. affinis*); body blotches 36–66; tail spots 9–19.   *P. c. sayi*

cc. Snout blunt; rear angle of rostral from above obtuse; rostral broad but little higher than broad, not bulging above adjacent scales, penetrating less than 1/2 on internasal suture; some labial sutures without dark margins (except *c. affinis*).

d. "Ground color of lateral areas between blotches not suffused with gray, being cream or buff, although there are often black or brown streaks on the keels of scales in these interspaces; ratio of tail length to length over-all usually less than .15 in adult males and .14 in adult females" (Klauber). Number of mean ventrals less mean body spots 158–191 (range 145–200); body spots 34–64 (except *c. deserticola* 40–75); tail spots 8–19 (like *sayi* group).

e. Anterior blotches usually red, red-brown, or brown; mid-body interspaces 3–3 1/2 scales.

f. "Anterior dorsal blotches usually brown, separated from each other and from adjacent lateral series; . . . posterior dorsal blotches brown or dark-brown (at base of tail); no dark subcaudal stripe usually present" (Klauber); series of dark labial sutures complete but narrower than in *c. sayi;* spots on ends of ventrals involving single plate or lacking.   *P. c. affinis*

ff. "Anterior dorsal blotches red and confluent laterally; posterior dorsal blotches black (at base of tail); a dark subcaudal stripe usually present" (Klauber); black labial sutures obscure or absent; dark terminal ventral spots elongate, involving at least 2 plates.   *P. c. vertebralis* (Baja Calif.)

ee. Anterior dorsal blotches black, often confluent, 1–4 often making a dorsal neckband; anterior light dorsal interspaces containing many scales with black or brown keels; interspaces in mid-body 2–3 scales wide; labial suture markings back of eye usually lacking, on suture 4th–5th labial marked like most *catenifer* subspecies.

P. c. deserticola

[Baja Calif. insular forms in this group at end of key are *c. insulanus* and *c. bimaris.*]

dd. "Ground color of lateral areas between blotches suffused with gray especially posteriorly, this color covering entire scales and not being restricted to their keels; ratio of tail length to length over-all usually exceeding .15 in adult males and .14 in adult females" (Klauber); number mean ventrals less mean body spots 117–147, range 108–163; body spots normally 52–90 (except *c. catenifer* 41–99); and tail spots 14–33.

    e. "Anterior dorsal blotches brown or if black then separated from each other and from adjacent lateral series" (Klauber).

P. catenifer catenifer

    ee. "Anterior dorsal blotches black, irregularly confluent with each other and with the adjacent lateral series" (Klauber). *P. c. annectens*

[Insular forms in this group are *c. coronalis, c. fuliginatus* in Baja Calif., *c. pumilus* in U.S.]

Data from Klauber in *c. affinis* group:

"d² Anterior light dorsal interspaces without dark streaks on keels of scales.

    Body blotches more than 50.   *P. c. insulanus*
    Body blotches less than 50.   *P. c. bimaris*

"dd² in Pacific *catenifer* group

    Supralabials usually not in contact with eye.   *P. c. coronalis*
    One or more supralabials contact eye.

        2 parallel dark stripes on underside of tail; scales rows 31–35, mid-body.   *P. c. fuliginatus*
        no paired dark stripes on underside of tail; scale rows 29 or fewer, mid-body.   *P. c. pumilus*"

Coast gopher snake (9—Van Denburgh 1897)
Pacific gopher snake (5)

Pituophis catenifer catenifer (Blainville) 1835. Fig. 171; Map 46

Other common names: Adder; (Bellona) bull snake; Churchill's bull snake; gopher snake; Oregon bull snake; Pacific bull snake (5); Pacific pine snake; western bull snake; western gopher snake (7—Van Denburgh 1897); western pine snake; yellow gopher snake.

Range: Oregon, w. of Cascades s. into California, w. of Sierras to n. Santa Barbara County and Tehachapi Mts.—U.S.A.: Calif.; Ore. Can.: B.C. *Elevation*—Seacoast to 6,000 or 7,000 feet. Most records below 2,000 feet. 6,200 feet (Grinnell, Calif., 1908); 4,900, 5,500–6,300 feet (Atsatt, Calif., 1913); 260–3,200 feet (Grinnell, Dixon, Linsdale); 8,000 feet (Stejneger, Calif., 1893).

Size: Adults, 36–84 inches.

Longevity: 11 years (Perkins, Gen., 1951, 1954).

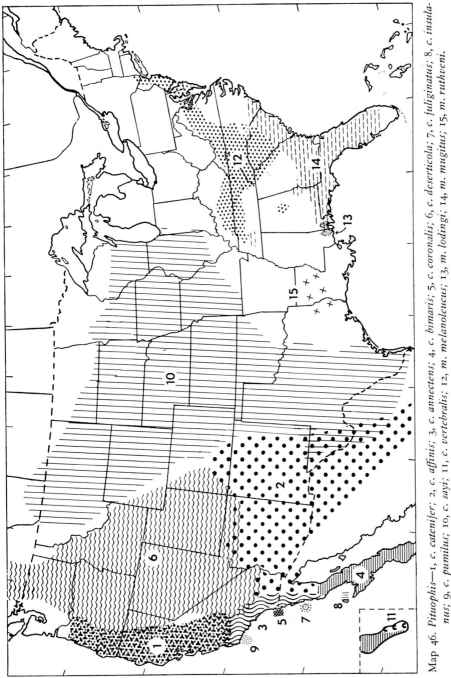

Map 46. *Pituophis*—1, *c. catenifer*; 2, *c. affinis*; 3, *c. annectens*; 4, *c. bimaris*; 5, *c. coronalis*; 6, *c. deserticola*; 7, *c. fuliginatus*; 8, *c. insulanus*; 9, *c. pumilus*; 10, *c. sayi*; 11, *c. vertebralis*; 12, *m. melanoleucus*; 13, *m. lodingi*; 14, *m. mugitus*; 15, *m. ruthveni*.

Distinctive characteristics: "A subspecies, having a proportionately longer tail than any other except *annectens,* and its island derivatives. It has more blotches than the subspecies further inland, and has a characteristic suffusion of grayish punctations on the sides and under the tail, which *deserticola* and *affinis* lack. From *annectens* it differs in having fewer ventral scales, on the average, and more regularly formed and better-separated anterior blotches. In most areas it has fewer blotches than *annectens,* and these are more often brown anteriorly, as compared to black in *annectens.* It usually lacks the twin subcaudal stripes of *fuliginatus,* the complete ring of ocular scales of *coronalis* and averages more scale rows than *pumilus*" (Klauber, Gen., 1947).

Color: A snake from Arroyo Mocho, 7 miles s.e. of Livermore, Alameda Co., Calif., collected by W. W. Dalquest, March 14, 1943. The back is marked with 54 bister dorsal spots on the body and 17 on the tail. The large saddle spots are 7 to 9 scales transversely and about 4 scales long, concave in front and rear, somewhat pointed on the sides, and sometimes uniting with lateral spots. Alternating with them is a series of bister spots about 3 scales transversely and 2½ longitudinally, but appearing longer than high. On the 4th to 6th rows of scales is a prominent series of vertical bister bars 1 to 1½ scales longitudinally. Between these bars and the upper series are some irregular bister spots. The background for 15 to 21 middorsal rows is colonial buff or deep colonial buff. The adjoining 5 rows are ecru-olive or dark olive-buff. The first 3 rows are marguerite yellow with a distinct wash of vinaceous-fawn at the base of scales and along the keel. There is a bister band across top of head involving front of supraoculars, front of frontal, and rear of prefrontals. This band is resumed back of the eye extending obliquely to just back of the angle of the mouth. The top of the head ahead of the bister band is deep olive-buff. On the neck are 2 nuchal longitudinal spots of bister and a median one which extends forward to the parietals, where it is constricted and then expanded to a broad spot with an emarginate front border. The frontal has 2 small spots of bister on its rear. The iris is ferruginous except for the forward lower quarter, which is black like the vertical bar below the eye. The pupil rim is marguerite yellow. Below the eye the suture line between 4th and 5th upper labials is the prominent vertical black bar which extends also along the suture between the 7th and 8th lower labials. The ground color of labials is white, as is the underside of the head. The ventrals are marguerite yellow with a spot of black or bister on either end of every 3rd plate near the outer edge.

Abnormal coloration—Storer had a partial albino with black lacking. Fitch (Calif., 1935) recorded a 7-striped individual and Fisher (Calif., 1935) a 9-striped specimen with cream and brown stripes alternating.

Habitat: This timid, very tame, terrestrial pet rarely goes into the water or up into the trees. One author held that it lived in "valleys, slopes, meadows," i.e., almost any habitat. Another said it occurred throughout his area below the Canadian zone. Many have called it most common in cultivated areas such as pasture lands on the coast, or in grasslands along irrigation ditches. Often along road margins and in the road they may be found DOR. Other recorded habitats are: on the banks of streams in sandy and gravelly spots, on black adobe soil, in leaf litter of blue oaks, in dense Douglas fir forest. Rarely is it under cover and seldom aquatic, although one was seen floating passively down stream.

Fitch in 1949 (Calif.) gave us the best study of this species. In the area of the Experimental Range he recorded 256 gopher snakes and 932 rattlesnakes, a ratio of 1 to 3.7. "The gopher snake is more likely to choose situations having a thick cover of vegetation, while the rattlesnake prefers barren and rocky places." In 1951 Hawken (Calif., 1951) showed that the water system of San Francisco served as an automatic trap. In San Mateo County 3 lakes 6 miles long serve as water supply. Snakes get into the flume and are carried into the concrete tower where brush accumulates. In 27 trips between Apr. 17 and June 20, 1949, 582 specimens were secured, 165 of which were *Pituophis c. catenifer*.

Period of activity: *First appearance*—Mar. 13, 1893 (Stanford No. 4026); Mar. 22 (Fitch, Calif., 1947); Apr. 6, May 9 (Grinnell, Dixon, and Linsdale); Apr. 7 (Fitch, Calif., 1935); Apr. 11 (Fisher, Calif., 1925); Apr. 13, 1913 (CAS No. 36121); May 15 (Fisher, Calif., 1935). MVZ dates are from Feb. 22 to Dec. 16. "It emerges from hibernation at about the same time in March or April depending upon the weather, and is diurnal until hot weather sets in" (Fitch, Calif., 1949). *Fall disappearance*—Early Nov. (Storer); Nov., Dec. 4 (Fitch, 1949). *Hibernation*—"During the winter, gopher snakes are practically never seen abroad. They spend this part of the year underground, coming out if at all only on the warmest days. At Snelling, on January 6, 1915, while Mr. Camp was excavating the burrow of a kangaroo rat, he found a snake of this species in one of the rodent's tunnels. The snake was quite lively, showing none of the torpidity ordinarily to be expected of a hibernating animal" (Grinnell and Storer).

Breeding: Oviparous. Males 760–1,360 mm., females 750–1,270 mm. *Mating and egg deposition*—We excerpt Fisher's (Calif., 1925) detailed account: "The male had been caught the early part of March the same year and the female on April 11. . . . On April 21 they were placed together in a cage with several other snakes. Copulation was first noted on the night of April 21. . . . On April 28 another female gopher snake was put in the cage, and the following day copulation with the original male took place. . . . On August 7, 5 eggs were found in the cage in the corner with the female, and the next day 5 more were laid. These eggs were not uniform in size. Their average might be roughly said to be 1 by 2 inches. They were elliptical, rather truncate ended, in shape, and were covered with a heavy, tough membrane. They were not in any way connected with one another, and were found scattered about the corner of the cage occupied by the female."

In his Rogue River study Fitch (Ore., 1936) stated: "In preparing to mate the male grasped the body of the female in his jaws. Possibly males recognize the female by scent. A male seeing another gopher snake crawling a few feet away would pursue it, but after catching up and nosing the other, would quickly lose interest if the second snake happened to be another male."

Eggs—Number, 10–20. In the excerpt from Fisher the laying of 10 eggs was mentioned. Klauber noted a specimen with 10 eggs, Van Denburgh recorded the laying of 19 eggs on July 13 and 14, 1897. Schmidt and Davis (Gen., 1941) recorded 10–19 eggs, but did not specify whether they were *annectens, deserticola,* or *catenifer.* Gordon said that the eggs are laid in the summer and usually number a score or less. Time of deposition, mid-July or early summer. Size, not recorded.

"The eggs when first laid are covered with a loose soft sticky, parchment-like white membrane. This quickly dries and hardens, shrinking upon the substance of the egg until quite tense, and cementing each egg to the others upon which it is laid. After the membranous shell has become dry it ceases to shrink, and if the substance of the egg be reduced as by evaporation, wrinkles appear upon its surface. However, the softness of the shell and its power to shrink upon its contents are restored by the application of water. The eggs as laid formed a great cluster surrounded by the coiled body of the snake. The latter hissed fiercely when the eggs were removed, although she had not shown the slightest resentment when handled on previous days" (Van Denburgh, Calif., 1898).

Young—Klauber (Gen., 1947) stated: "*Catenifer* and *deserticola* are about 370 mm. over-all at birth." Of the 129 specimens that Miss Stull sexed, 59 measured 31–54 cm. Besides these there were 12 which she merely called young and whose sizes ran from 20 to 45 cm. Of her 59, 44 were from 31 to 45 cm. We suspect the young at hatching vary from 31 to 35 cm. The Santa Cruz Island specimen (CAS 36121) 272 mm. long puzzles us. Fitch (Calif., 1947), who has no figures available on the number of eggs produced in his experimental area, says: "Newly hatched gopher snakes taken in late September (3), October (24), and November (1) averaged around 400 mm. in length; 23 are between 350 and 450, while 5 were less than 350 mm. . . . Mortality rate is highest in the young during their first few weeks of life, between time of hatching and retirement into hibernation. Elimination of more than 80 per cent of the young that emerge from their first hibernation, during the subsequent year, is indicated by the relatively small number surviving in the 600 to 900 mm. group." The smallest specimens we have seen are: CAS No. 27333, Apr. 21, 1911, 396 mm. long. CAS

No. 43521, Apr. 7, 1917, 368 mm. long. SU No. 5633, fall, 1897, 358 mm. long.

Food: Rodents, lizards. Gordon, Grinnell and Storer, Fitch (Ore., 1936; Calif., 1947), Howard (Calif., 1949).

Authorities:

Bradt, G. McC. (Gen., 1950)
Cooper, J. G. (Gen., 1860)
Cronise, T. F. (Gen., 1868)
Fisher, E. M. (Calif., 1925, 1935)
Fitch, H. S. (Calif., 1935, 1949; Ore., 1936)
Gordon, K. (Ore., 1939)
Grinnell, J., and T. Storer (Calif., 1924)

Grinnell, J., J. Dixon, and J. M. Linsdale (Calif., 1930)
Hallowell, E. (N.M., 1854)
Storer, T. (Calif., 1916)
Stull, O. G. (Gen., 1940)
Van Denburgh, J. (Gen., 1922; Calif., 1898, 1920)

Sonora gopher snake, Arizona gopher snake
(11—Van Denburgh 1922)

Pituophis catenifer affinis Hallowell 1852. Fig. 172; Map 46

Other common names: Adder (Coues 1875); Arizona bull snake (5); bull snake (12—Coues 1875); blow snake; eastern bull snake; gopher snake; prairie bull snake; western bull snake.

Range: Desert areas of s.e. California and n.e. Baja California, Mex., and Grand Canyon region in Arizona; thence e. into cent. New Mexico and s. across w. tip of Texas to Coahuila, Mex., and thence westward to Baja California.—U.S.A.: Ariz.; Calif.; Colo.; N.M.; Tex. Mex.: Baja Calif., Chihuahua; Coahuila; San Luis Potosí; Sonora. *Elevation*—Mainly 500 to 7,500 feet, some at sea level and some to 9,000 feet. Sea level to 5,300 feet (Van Denburgh, Gen., 1922); 3,500-6,000 feet (Little, Ariz., 1940); 5,300 feet (Stejneger, Ariz., 1903); 4,000–8,000 feet (Bailey, N.M., 1913); to 6,000 feet or higher (Ruthven); to 6,000 feet (Gloyd); over 9,000 feet (Mosauer, N.M., 1932); 7,000 feet (Taylor, Gen., 1952).

Size: Adults, 36–90 inches. Few over 7 feet. Klauber's (Gen., 1943b) measurements of 31 males and 23 females are: mean over all, males 783.06 mm., and females 815.26 mm.; maxima, 1,495 mm. (tail 189) males, 1,566 mm. (tail 197) females.

Longevity: 10 years 8 months (Perkins, Gen., 1951); 12 years; 4 years 1 month (Kauffeld, Gen., 1951); 13 years 4 months (Perkins, Gen., 1954).

Distinctive characteristics: "A subspecies which can be distinguished from *catenifer, annectens, fuliginatus, coronalis* and *pumilus* by its proportionately shorter tail and fewer body blotches. It can be segregated from *deserticola, bimaris* and *insulanus* by its brown anterior blotches compared with black in the others. It may be separated from *vertebralis* since it lacks the black subcaudal stripe which characterizes the latter; also, *vertebralis* has black dorsal blotches at the base of the tail, while those of *affinis* are brown or dark brown. *Affinis* has a rostral which is relatively wider and not so prominently raised above the surrounding scales as in *sayi;* also, when the rostral is viewed from above, the anterior curve is flatter in *affinis* than in *sayi"* (Klauber, Gen., 1947).

Color: A snake from San Vicente, Tex., found by T. J. Miller, May 15, 1934. The back of the body is crossed by 42 saddles, with 11 additional ones on the tail. Beginning on the neck, and for some distance down the back, they are buckthorn brown and cover about 10 scales transversely. On the rear half of the body and on the tail, these saddles become russet. In the same way, on the forward half, the interspaces between the saddles are antimony yellow, becoming on the rear ochraceous-buff, and on the tail light cadmium. The first few saddles have narrow partial black margins. In the last ¾ of the snake's length, these are little apparent. Alternating with the dorsal saddles is a row of smaller dark spots on the 7th to 13th rows of scales. And alternating with these is a less distinct series on the 4th to 7th rows of scales. Many of the scales below the saddles bear russet median lines just back of the apex. The top of the head, and the nape, are deep colonial buff. Across the supraoculars, frontal, and rear edges of the prefrontals is a buckthorn brown band. From the rear of the eye to the rear edge of next to the last upper labial is a postocular band of the same color. The top of the supraocular, frontal, and parietals is spotted with 1 to 3 mummy brown dots. The labials, face, and forward part of the top of the head are light buff or even pale ochraceous-salmon. Below the eye is a prominent vertical black band, and each labial suture is indicated with the same. The front and lower part of the iris are mummy brown or black like the vertical band below the eye; the upper part is buckthorn brown; the rear is deep colonial buff. The lower side of the head and neck are light buff, the forward half of the belly an almost clear warm buff. The rear of the venter and the underside of the tail are light cadmium. Beginning on the forward part of the venter, there is on either end of every 3rd or 4th ventral plate, a cinnamon-brown or prout's brown spot. Soon these spots become less distinct and are tawny or russet.

Habitat: In 1907 Ruthven held that "the wide range of habitat of the species in this locality, is in harmony with its extensive geographic range." He recorded it in the greasewood plains, in the mesquite association on the plains, in the creosote bush association on alluvial slopes, in the Piñon-cedar zone on the mountain slopes at 6,000 feet and even in pine-spruce forest of the higher elevations. Other habitats noted are sandy tracts, underside of boards, canyon near the river, desert plains, mountain canyons, beneath soap bushes in sandy desert, chaparral-woodland, lowland plains, sides of highways, and irrigated fields. Klauber's (Calif., 1931a; Gen., 1939a) summations are: "orchard or vineyard 7, cultivated field 104, grass 42, rocky desert 17, brushy desert 54, sandy desert 6, barren desert 4. Total 234."

Lewis (N.M., 1950) found this snake on the eastern slope of the Organ Mts. between 4,300–4,000 foot contours. "These slopes are stream built and show Yucca-mesquite-ephydra-grassland associations."

Period of activity: *First appearance*—Mar. 17, Apr. 9 (Van Denburgh, Slevin); Apr. 17 (Cooper, Calif., 1869); May 10 (CAS No. 17547). *Fall disappearance*—July 20 (Van Denburgh and Slevin); Sept. 23 (MacCoy, Ariz., 1932). "They were evidently quite common, for Mr. Price preserved more specimens of this species than any other snake. All were secured in May and June" (Van Denburgh, Ariz., 1897). MVZ dates are Mar. 27 to Dec. 25. The "Sixteen-Year Census" reports Apr., 1 snake; May, 5; June, 1; July, 2; Sept., 3; Oct., 1, total 13 (Klauber, Gen., 1939a).

Breeding: Oviparous. Males 750 (approx.)–2,033 mm., females 750 (approx.)—1,880 mm. We discover little evidence on this topic before 1947. The two smallest specimens we have seen are: CAS 17547, Cave Creek, Ariz., J. S. Carlson, May 10, 1910, total length 494 mm. (tail 60), and Stanford University No. 1131, Lowell, Ariz., W. W. Price and Wilbur, 1893, total length 377 mm. (tail 48). Klauber's (Gen., 1943b) minima are: 415 mm. (tail 60) males, 439 mm. (tail 57) females.

In 1935 Cowles (Calif.) published an extended account of how a San Diegan gopher snake attempted to mate with a desert gopher snake. Did it? Later (Aug. 8, 1933) the female laid an egg. Still later it laid 3 perfect and 3 imperfect eggs. Two eggs hatched Nov. 7, the young being 348 and 320 mm. in length, one patterned like the female and the other like a San Diegan gopher snake.

In 1947 Klauber (Gen.) called the forms of the Colorado desert in Riverside, Imperial, and San Diego Counties *affinis* not *deserticola*. Klauber recorded that "a captive *affinis* laid eggs June 29 and they began to hatch September 12, with a 77-day period of incubation," and that "one *affinis* laid 12 eggs; two others contained 8 and 9 eggs."

A detailed account of mating is recounted by Gloyd (Gen., 1947). Near Superior, Ariz., he had 3 in a bag, a female and 2 males. He sensed a commotion in the bag and dumped the 3 on a porch at 1 P.M. The large male began biting the female and small male's neck and body. The small male pulled away. The biting lasted about 10 minutes. Then the male without entwining the female's body inserted the hemipenis and this lasted 20 minutes. Later that day about 7 P.M. there was another copulation. The female on July 7 laid 22 infertile eggs (averaging 35x51 mm.).

Food: Small mammals, birds, lizards. Ruthven, Little and Keller (N.M., 1937), Dodge, Gloyd, Klauber (Gen., 1947).

Authorities:

Dodge, N. N. (Ariz., 1938)
Gloyd, H. K. (Ariz., 1937a)
Hallowell, E. (N.M., 1854)

Johnson, J. (Calif., 1936)
Klauber, L. M. (Gen., 1939a, 1941, 1947)

McKee, E. D., and C. M. Bogert (Ariz., 1934)
Ortenburger, A. I. and R. D. (Ariz., 1927)
Ruthven, A. G. (Ariz., 1907)
Schmidt, K. P. (Baja Calif., 1922)
Stull, O. G. (Gen., 1940)
Van Denburgh, J. (Gen., 1920; N.M., 1924b)
Van Denburgh, J., and J. R. Slevin (Ariz., 1913)

1940, O. G. Stull: "The name *P. catenifer rutilus* was proposed by Van Denburgh in 1920 for the Arizona gopher snakes. Since Arizona and New Mexico specimens are identical, *rutilus* becomes a synonym of *affinis.*"

1941, L. M. Klauber: "Lastly, there is the relationship of *affinis* and *deserticola.* Miss Stull concludes that they are separate species, overlapping in the lower basin of the Colorado River in southeastern California and northeastern Lower California. . . . With some 85 specimens now available from this area, I do not find the presence of two species readily apparent."

1947, L. M. Klauber: "*Affinis* intergrades with *sayi* along a zone as yet ill-defined." (The *deserticola-affinis* contacts are difficult. Klauber assigns Salton Basin forms to *affinis.*)

San Diegan gopher snake (14—Van Denburgh 1922), Pacific bull snake (4—Ruthling 1915)

Pituophis catenifer annectens Baird and Girard 1853. Fig. 173; Map 46

Other common names: Coastal gopher snake; gopher snake; Pacific gopher snake.

Range: From coast to desert slopes from San Gabriel and San Bernardino Mts. s. into n.w. Baja California to Rosario River.—U.S.A.: Calif. Mex.: Baja Calif. *Elevation*—Sea level to 6,300 feet. Coast to the lower reaches of the desert foothills (Klauber, Gen., 1939a); ocean to desert's edge (Bogert); ocean to desert foothills (Perkins, Calif., 1938); 5,200 feet (Linsdale); to 6,000 feet (Bogert); 4,900, 5,500–6,300 feet (Atsatt, Calif., 1913).

Size: Adults, 36–75 inches. Klauber's (Gen., 1943b) measurements of 155 males and 144 females are: mean over all 789.66 mm. males, 642.21 mm. females; maxima 1,844 mm. (tail 284) males, 1,504 (tail 210) mm. females.

Longevity: 14 years, 4 months (Perkins, Gen., 1951); 15 years 2 months (Perkins, Gen., 1954).

Distinctive characteristics: "A subspecies particularly notable for its high blotch counts and relatively long tail, and for the grayish suffusion in the ground color laterally and caudally, which characters will adequately separate it from all except *catenifer* and the related island forms. It has more blotches and ventral scales, on the average, than *catenifer,* and its anterior blotches are more often irregular and confluent; also, they are more frequently black" (Klauber, Gen., 1947).

Fig. 172. *Pituophis c. affinis,* San Vicente, Tex.

Fig. 173. *Pituophis c. annectens:* 1,5,6, San Juan Capistrano, Calif., L. M. Klauber; 2-4, Monrovia, Calif., C. W. Kern.

Color: A snake from L. M. Klauber, described June 9, 1928. The scales of the general background of the back are light brownish olive or isabella color, most of them edged with deep colonial buff or reed yellow. Toward the tail, the interspaces between the dorsal spots are buffy brown. There is a middorsal row of square brownish olive or olive spots 6–7 scales wide, slightly united at the corners with the smaller spots, 3 scales wide, of an alternating row. Below this row are 2 more rows of spots, each alternating with the ones above and below. The last row is on the 5th and 6th rows of scales. The scales below this last row are ecru-olive with reed yellow edges. The 3 rows of dorsal spots of brownish olive are more or less distinct on the neck. Back of the parietals the head is a uniform dark olive-buff. Most of the dorsal head plates are buffy olive, those ahead of the eyes being ecru-olive like those of the side of the head. There is a small brownish olive vertical bar below the eye, and an indefinite oblique area of the same back of the eye. One or 2 of the labials below the subocular bar are dark-edged. The iris is orange-cinnamon or mars orange with an area of brownish olive in the front. There is a narrow pupil rim of pale pinkish buff or "yellowish." The under parts are empire yellow or apricot yellow toward the head and buff-yellow or maize yellow toward the vent. The underside of the tail is water green. On each alternate ventral or on every 2nd or 3rd plate is a deep slate-blue spot.

Abnormal coloration—Albinism. Klauber (Gen., 1924a, 1931a) reported two albinos and Walker (*Natural History,* **55**: 382–383) gave another albino.

Habitat: Klauber (Gen., 1924a), Perkins (1938, 1949), Bogert, and Von Bloeker all call this beautiful snake common in all areas from the ocean, over the mountains, to the desert's edge. In Baja California, Linsdale found it crawling among pine needles, under willows near camp, and crawling through grass in a creek bottom and in an orchard among weeds and grasses.

Klauber (Gen., 1939) in his "Sixteen Year Census" gave coast 1,083 snakes; inland valleys 692; foothills 673; mountains 71; desert foothills 55; undetermined 15. Total 2,591.

Period of activity: *First appearance*—Apr. 12 (CAS No. 43589); May 3 (Van Denburgh); May 4 (Linsdale). "Sixteen Year Census"—Jan., 21 snakes; Feb., 50; Mar., 194; Apr., 484; May, 764; June, 602; July, 160; Aug., 63; Sept., 89; Oct., 103; Nov., 38; Dec., 23. Total 2,591 (Klauber, Gen., 1939). *Fall disappearance*—Oct. 1, 25, Oct. 21, Dec. 22 (Linsdale). MVZ dates are Mar. 2 to Dec. 22.

Breeding: Oviparous. Males 750 (approx.)–1,880 (possibly 2,033) mm., females 750 (approx.)–1,862 mm. *Eggs*—Number, 3–18. "The number of eggs in 13 *annectens* clutches deposited in captivity varied from 3 to 12, with an average of 6–8. A very large specimen . . . contained 18 eggs; 2 others contained 8 and 9 eggs. . . . The eggs are, proportionate to those of other snakes, quite large measuring up to 30x90 mm." (Klauber, Gen., 1947). Time of deposition, mid-June to Sept. 1. Klauber records May 27, June 29, July 7, 17, 21, Aug. 16–29 for egg deposition. Size, 30x90 mm. (Klauber).

Young—Time of hatching, Aug. 8–Oct. 1. "The earliest to hatch was Sept. 15, the latest Oct. 21, the mean date Sept. 29. The period of incubation has been quite constant; minimum elapsed days 64, maximum 71, mean 66½. . . . Five captive bred *annectens* had incubation periods of 65, 67, 73, 75, and 76 days. . . . Freshly hatched snakes are most prevalent along the roadside between Sept. 20 and Oct. 10" (Klauber, Gen., 1947). Size, 14–17 inches (350 mm.–425 mm.). Klauber gives 380 mm. as the over-all size at birth for *annectens*. The smallest we have seen was 350 mm. Miss Stull had 13 specimens 350 mm. to 440 mm. in length—1, 35 cm.; 2, 36 cm.; 1, 37 cm.; 1, 41 cm.; 3, 42 cm.; 1, 42.5 cm.; 3, 43 cm.; 2, 44 cm. The smallest wild material Klauber gives is 350 mm., but he credits Perkins with two 322 mm. each. Klauber's (Gen., 1943b) measurements are: 322 mm. (tail 56) male, 322 mm. (tail 48) female.

Food: Mice, rats, rodents, bats, lizards, birds' eggs. Perkins (1949), Meek (Calif., 1905), Stephens (Calif., 1921a), Ruthling (Calif., 1916b), Cochran (Gen., 1928), Von Bloeker, Klauber (Gen., 1947), Grinnell (Calif., 1908).

Authorities:

Bogert, C. M. (Calif., 1930)
Grinnell, J. and H. W. (Calif., 1907)
Klauber, L. M. (Gen. 1939a, 1947; Calif., 1924a, 1931a, 1932)
Linsdale, J. M. (Baja Calif., 1932)

Perkins, C. B. (Calif., 1938, 1949)
Stull, O. G. (Gen., 1940)
Van Denburgh, J. (Gen., 1922)
Von Bloeker, J. C., Jr. (Calif., 1942)

1907, J. and H. W. Grinnell. The Grinnells make this appeal: "This is most often met with of all our snakes, and taken on the whole, has the most favorable reputation with the ordinary run of people. Most ranchers and country people have learned to recognize in the gopher snake an efficient destroyer of these pests of the farm, gophers and squirrels, and accordingly seldom offer injury willfully.

"But with city people who now and then drive into the country it is different. The gopher snake has an unfortunate habit of crawling out into the open roads, especially on warm spring days, evidently with the purpose of basking in the grateful sunshine. Along comes the city man with his instinctive but unreasonable fear and hatred for snakes in general and he attacks the harmless and slow-moving gopher snake to the usual destruction of the latter. So often one sees the mangled remains along roadsides. It is evident that snakes are far less common than they used to be 20 years ago, at the same time gophers and ground squirrels are in many districts more of a pest than ever before; and the reason is obvious. In commendable contradistinction to the deplorable thoughtlessness of the average person is the good sense of the occasional farmer who actually invites the gopher snakes to make their home on his land. We know of a few such who bring to their ranches every snake they can readily capture. And we have been repeatedly assured by many people that many an old gopher who had proved too wise for traps and apparently immune to poison, had finally met his waterloo in the long gullet of a gopher snake.

"The snake is introduced into the burrow of the rodent and disappears. In a few hours he reappears, languidly crawling into the sunshine, while a huge bulge about two-thirds the way along his mottled body gives proof of what has happened down in the dark underground galleries. The school teachers and pupils of the county can do a good turn by advertising the good services of snakes in general, recommending their protection on grounds of economic value. This appeals to many people who would never admit the inhumanity of killing a snake."

1949, C. B. Perkins: "This is . . . the most beneficial snake in killing mice, rats and other rodents that are so destructive of crops. . . . In June, 1940, we received from Corona a giant Gopher Snake, six feet two and a half inches long, but four and a half feet is usually considered a large specimen. . . . There is a sounding-board flap of skin in the mouth of the Gopher Snake which makes possible a very loud hiss when the snake expels its breath." (See Fig. 19, 6 q, p. 69.)

Desert gopher snake (32—Van Denburgh 1897), Desert bull snake

Pituophis catenifer deserticola Stejneger 1893. Fig. 174; Map 46

Other common names: Arizona bull snake; bull snake (3—C. H. Merriam 1892); desert bull snake; gopher snake (34); (Great Basin) blow snake; (Great Basin) gopher snake (5); sage brush gopher snake; southern bull snake; Utah blow snake; Utah gopher snake; western bull snake.

Range: The *Artemisia* region—from Mojave desert northward e. of the Sierra Nevada in California, and e. of the Cascades in Oregon and Washington into cent. British Columbia and s. through Palouse prairie and Great Basin to s.w. Wyoming, w. Colorado, and n.w. New Mexico to n. Arizona.— U.S.A.: Ariz.; Calif.; Colo.; Ida.; Nev.; N.M.; Ore.; Ut.; Wash.; Wyo. Can.: B.C. *Elevation*—300 to 8,000 feet. 300–2,500 feet (Stull, 1940); 3,500–7,000 feet (Linsdale); 4,000–5,000 feet (Johnson, Bryant, Miller); 4,000–8,000 feet (Bailey, N.M., 1913); 5,300 feet (Stejneger, Ariz., 1903); 5,400, 6,000 feet (Taylor, Nev., 1912); 5,300 feet (Mittleman); 5,800–7,000 feet (Eaton, Ariz., 1935b); 6,500 feet (Ruthven); 7,000 feet (Linsdale, Nev., 1938); 500–6,500 feet (Ruthven).

Size: Adults, 36–72 inches. The specimens Van Denburgh called *stejnegeri* were 33.7–53.3 inches long. Klauber's (Gen., 1943b) measurements of 23 males and 13 females (Mojave Desert) are: mean over all, 910.48 mm. males,

826.20 mm. females; maxima, 1,364 mm. (tail 187) males, 1,194 mm. (tail 165) females.

Distinctive characteristics: "A subspecies having a shorter tail than *catenifer, annectens,* or their island offshoots—*pumilus, coronalis,* and *fuliginatus;* also it has fewer body blotches on the average. It generally has black anterior blotches, whereas *vertebralis* has red and *affinis* and inland *catenifer* have brown. *Deserticola* has more blotches than *bimaris,* and usually has clearly defined frontal, postocular, and subocular dark marks, which are generally absent in *insulanus. Deserticola* may be segregated from *sayi* by its blunter snout and wider rostral" (Klauber, Gen., 1947).

Color: A snake from L. T. Murray of Billings, Mont., caught in Twin Falls Co., Ida., 22 miles south of Rogerson on highway 93, very near the Idaho-Nevada line, and sent Oct. 10, 1948. Preoculars one. On each side the 5th supralabial sends a narrow blunt point to the eye. Color in general is darker than that of more southern snakes. The interblotch streaking is heavy on the sides, dark keel spots are prominent in the dorsal light spots. The cephalic light dorsal spots are warm buff; the rear ones have a tendency toward apricot buff to light ochraceous-salmon. There are 58 dorsal blotches on the body, 15 on the tail. The lateral line of spots continues on the tail for 6 spots before bars are formed. On the sides in mid-body there are 2 rows of lateral spots between the ones touching the dorsal spots and the spots on ends of ventrals. In this last respect this snake is more like the ones from Kayenta, Ariz., and Delta, Ut., than the one from Deep Springs, Calif., in which the lower row of spots is almost entirely lacking. The lateral neck stripe is ¾ inch long before there is a break. It is soon broken in the snake from Pullman, Wash., and in the ones from Delta, Ut., and Kayenta, Ariz. The lateral neck stripe is long in the one from Deep Springs, Calif. The top of head and the face are wood brown to buffy brown, and the head stripes are brown. The transverse frontal band is much more prominent than in our Delta and Kayenta specimens, but not more so than in the Deep Springs snake. In the same way, the postocular band is not as pronounced as in the Deep Springs one, but stronger than in the Kayenta and Delta ones in which there is practically no postocular band. The subocular bar is more prominent in this than in the Deep Spring snake while it is almost absent in the Kayenta and Delta ones. The postparietal, temporal, and posttemporal regions are much more spotted than our Kayenta or Deep Springs specimens. In this respect it is more like the Pullman, Wash., snake, although not as heavily marked as that one. The upper labial and lower labial dark margins are prominent, and there is 1 dark upper labial margin back of the eye, as in the Pullman one. None of the others have any back of eye. These dark margins are much more prominent than in the Deep Springs and Kayenta snakes, where they are almost lacking. These margins are stronger than in the Delta snake. (See *P. c. stejnegeri.*)

Habitat: Early authors held that the ecological distribution of this species embraced all land habitats, mountains and basins at about all altitudes; that it was wide ranging and widely tolerant. Some have assigned these snakes to the drier regions as dry sage brush and desert regions. They have been found in open deserts or those with light, heavy, or rocky brush and in the dunes. Many have remarked them in cultivated lands, in alfalfa, hay, and grain fields. Only one author remarked their presence in the *Chrysothamnus* zone along streams, in sage brush on the hills and flats of the basin floor, on the slopes and rock slides, and in the canyons of the mountains. Not infrequently they have been taken near a swamp, in a cattail marsh, near a spring, or along creeks and rivers. One remarked that they occurred around the fields and farms of small towns, but not the large ones where they would be indiscriminately destroyed.

Period of activity: *Early appearances*—Apr. 23, 26, May 7, 11, 12, June 4 (Stejneger); May 14, 16 (Blanchard); May 11 (Taylor, Nev., 1912); Apr. 27 (Evenden, Ida., 1946); May 2, 20 (Hardy). *Fall disappearance*—Oct. 5 (Taylor); Sept. 23 (Slevin, CAS 36285); Oct. 16 (Everman, CAS 39553); September, Oct. 24 (Hardy). MVZ has dates March 24 to Sept. 19. *Hibernation*—Woodbury and Smart (Ut., 1950) record this form as one of the 7 species of snakes in the *Crotalus v. lutosus* den.

Breeding: Oviparous. Males 750 (approx.)–1,440 mm., females 750 (approx.)–1,750 mm. *Mating*—Woodbury (Ut., 1941) described a combat between 2 males observed by a party on an island of Great Salt Lake: "The posterior parts of the bodies were closely entwined like the strands of a rope, as if for copulation, but the anterior parts were free. During the quarter or half hour of watching, the larger of the 2 males, about 5½ feet long, appeared to be gradually constricting and crowding the smaller male out from his entwined position. The reaction of the smaller male to this crowding was to strike at the other's head which recoiled when hit and immediately returned a return strike. The female was entirely passive, evincing no interest or choice between the combatants, which occasionally rested between struggles. . . . [The larger male was captured.] First, it indicates that gopher snakes are promiscuous. . . . Second, it indicates that copulation takes place after the snakes have left their winter dens (April in this locality), and that breeding activities play no part in den life."

Later, Hansen (Ut., 1950) reported a 40-inch male holding a 35-inch male with his mouth. Thrice the smaller escaped, and thrice was captured. At first the smaller was thought to be a female, because of its aggressive actions. Do the males at times make mistakes in sex recognition?

Eggs—In 1915 Richardson found that a Carson City specimen contained large eggs on July 9. Cowles reported eggs from Aug. 8 onwards from an apparent mating of a San Diegan gopher snake with a desert gopher snake

—7 eggs in all (4 perfect, 3 imperfect). Was the desert gopher snake *deserticola* or rather *affinis?* Two hatched Nov. 7. In 1938 Dodge held that "the eggs laid in July are deposited in sand frequently in layers, with several inches of sand covering them." In 1931 Woodbury gave the most data on this topic: "Its eggs are sometimes found buried in the loose soil at the depth of several inches. The eggs are usually oval or elliptical and measure 4 to 5 cm. by 2½ to 3 cm. A pair kept in the laboratory copulated on May 22. Grant Rasmussen, a student caring for the snakes, reports that the eggs were laid on July 10, a gestation period of 49 days. He reports the female irritable and vicious prior to egg-laying. In depositing the eggs she coiled in a circle and dropped 4 eggs side by side into a hole a few inches deep that she had previously scooped out of the sand. A second layer of 4 eggs was deposited on top of the first and was covered by a gelatinous substance which firmly cemented the eggs together upon drying." In 1940 Linsdale commented, "A large female found on July 30 contained large eggs." Klauber in 1947 observed that "specimens of *deserticola* have been noted with 4, 10, and 11 eggs," and Hardy had a captive laying "6 eggs in a cage June 18, 1937." The evidence then seems to show that 4–11 eggs are laid in June, July, and August.

Young—We have very little on the young of this species. Beginning with Cowles' record of 320 and 348 mm., which are probably not for this subspecies, we have a starting point. If one canvasses Stull's (1940) large table of over 300 specimens, he will find one young 33 cm.; one, 34 cm.; 2, 35 cm.; 1, 35.5 cm.; 1, 36 cm.; 1, 36.5 cm.; 1, 37 cm.; 1, 38 cm.; 3, 39 cm. or a total of 12 shorter than 40 cm., and at least 10 more shorter than 45 cm. We believe these young which hatch in September and October are from 330–390 mm. in size at birth. The smallest we have seen is 406 mm. from St. George, Ut.

Food: Rodents, young birds, and their eggs. Richardson; Ruthven and Gaige; Grinnell, Dixon, and Linsdale; Johnson, Bryant, and Miller; Dodge; Woodbury (Ut., 1931); Pack (Ut., 1930).

Authorities:

Blanchard, F. N. (Wash., 1921)
Dodge, N. N. (Ariz., 1938)
Gordon, K. (Ore., 1939)
Grinnell, J., J. Dixon, and J. M. Linsdale (Calif., 1930)
Hardy, R. (Ut., 1938)
Johnson, D. H., M. D. Bryant, and A. H. Miller (Calif., 1948)
Klauber, L. M. (Gen., 1947)
Linsdale, J. M. (Nev., 1940)
Logier, E. B. S. (B.C., 1932)
Lord, J. K. (B.C., 1866)
Mittleman, M. B. (Ariz., 1942)
Pack, H. J. (Ut., 1919, 1930)
Richardson, C. H. (Nev., 1915)
Ruthven, A. G. (Ut., 1932)
Ruthven, A. G., and H. T. Gaige (Nev., 1915)
Stejneger, L. (Calif., 1893)
Stull, O. G. (Gen., 1932, 1940)
Van Denburgh, J. (Gen., 1920)
Woodbury, A. M. (Ut., 1931, 1941)

1920: J. Van Denburgh proposed a northern race or subspecies for a northern group of the desert gopher snake. He called it *P. c. stejnegeri* because the scale rows were 31 or 33, preoculars usually 2, ventrals over 230, and subcaudals 59 to 64. Stull (1932), Tanner (Ut., 1939), and Klauber do not recognize it, though the last-named writer still holds it an open question.

1947, L. M. Klauber: On the basis of color pattern rather than scales, Klauber revised his ideas about the gopher snakes of eastern Riverside County, Imperial County, and the eastern rim of San Diego County and southward and called them *affinis*. He used the blotches on the neck, etc., as his criteria. Like us, he never enjoyed Van Denburgh's key or Stull's key, yet they had material difficult to analyze.

Santa Cruz Island gopher snake

Pituophis catenifer pumilus Klauber 1946. Map 46

Range: Santa Cruz Island, Calif.

Size: Adults, 25.4–31.5 inches (646–788 mm.). The smallest specimen recorded is 228 mm.

Distinctive characteristics: "A subspecies most closely resembling *P. c. catenifer* and *P. c. annectens* of the mainland and differing in tail length and pattern from all other mainland species. It most nearly resembles *annectens* in pattern, including color and blotch counts, but is nearer *catenifer* in the number of ventral and subcaudal scales. It differs from both in having fewer scale rows—although with some overlapping and in being stunted in size. In comparison with other island forms, *pumilus* has more blotches and proportionately longer tail than *insulanus*, lacks the parallel dark subcaudal stripes and extensive dark head blotches of *fuliginatus*, and is without the subocular scales of *coronalis*" (Klauber).

Authorities:

Klauber, L. M. (Calif., 1946)   Van Denburgh, J., and J. R. Slevin
Van Denburgh, J. (Gen., 1922)   (Calif., 1914)

Bull snake (69—Brons 1882), **Prairie bull snake** (2)

Pituophis catenifer sayi (Schlegel) 1837. Fig. 175; Map 46

Other common names: Common bull snake (2); Great Basin bull snake; Mexican bull snake; North American bull snake; pilot snake; pine snake; plain bull snake; Say's bull snake; Say's pine snake (Coues and Yarrow 1878); speckled (chain) adder; spotted bull snake; spotted gopher snake; western bull snake (10—Taylor 1892); western gopher snake; western pine snake (Jordan 1876); yellow (bull) snake; yellow gopher snake.

Range: Prairie and grassland from Chicago, Ill., n.w. to w. Montana, s.w. Saskatchewan, and s.e. Alberta, Can.; s.e. across Wyoming, e. Colo-

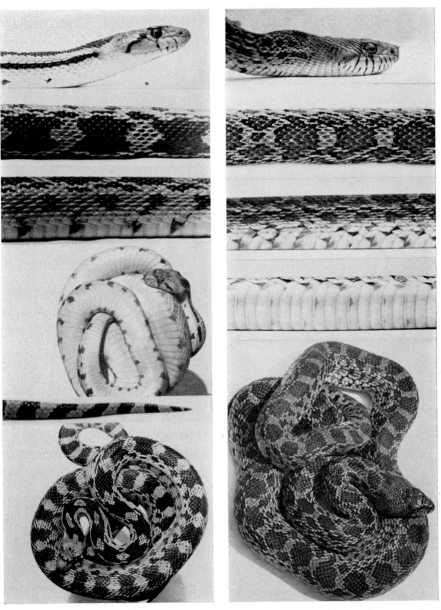

Fig. 174. *Pituophis c. deserticola,* Deep Spring, Calif., W. Rundle.

Fig. 175. *Pituophis c. sayi,* Brownsville, Tex.: 1–4, H. C. Blanchard; 5, "Snake King."

rado, New Mexico, and Texas to Mexico (n.w. Chihuahua, Coahuila, Nuevo León, Tamaulipas); thence n. through cent. Texas, Oklahoma, s. Missouri, and s. Illinois to e. Indiana.—U.S.A.: Ark.; Colo.; Ia.; Ill.; Ind.; Kan.; Minn.; Mo.; Mont.; Neb.; N.M.; N.D.; Okla.; S.D.; Tex.; Wis.; Wyo. Can.: Alta.; Sask. Mex.: Chihuahua; Coahuila; Nuevo León; Tamaulipas. *Elevation*—Sea level to 2,000 feet. Many records to 5,000, possibly to 6,000 feet; 9,000 feet (Mosauer); 5,300 feet (Stejneger, Ariz., 1903); 9,000 feet (Ellis and Henderson).

Size: Adults, 36–100 inches. Some estimates of the early days gave 9, 10, 11, or 12 feet. There are quite a few real measurements such as Brown's (in 1903) 8.3 feet in length with a circumference of 8.4 inches.

Longevity: More than 4 years; more than 2 years (Kauffeld, Gen., 1951).

Distinctive characteristics: "Rostral less than twice as long as broad; dorsum always with more than 40 distinct dark spots . . . frequently more than 1 preocular; azygous often present between frontal and prefrontals; sum of ventrals and caudals added to number of dorsal spots on body and tail rarely exceeding 360. Rostral nearly twice as long as broad; posterior spots not reddish; spots quadrangular or bar-shaped" (Stull). "Snout sharper; rostral narrow, considerably higher than wide, raised conspicuously above the adjacent scales and (when viewed from above) with a sharp curve of small radius at the front" (Klauber).

Color: A snake from Texas, found Apr. 24, 1925. The back is marked with dark-edged square blotches which are cinnamon-brown in the forward portion and prout's brown in the caudal portion of the body. There is a row of alternating spots of the same color on the 10th to 13th rows of scales. The color between the large dorsal blotches is ochraceous-buff, becoming on the interspaces of the tail light ochraceous-buff. There is a row of cinnamon-brown spots covering 1 to 3 scales on the 5th and 6th scale rows, and also on the 3rd row of scales. Thus, the sides are speckled with cinnamon-brown, black, and cartridge buff or ivory yellow. The top of the head and the muzzle are sayal brown or tawny-olive. There is a cinnamon-brown bar from the front of one eye across the top of the head to the front of the other eye. There is also a band of old gold extending obliquely from the eye to the angle of the mouth. The lower labials are white with rear edges of warm blackish brown. The upper labials are in part pale vinaceous-pink with rear edges like those of the lower labials. In the eye, the pupil rim is a thin line of light buff. The iris is warm buff and ochraceous-orange with a black spot in the front. The underside of the head is white, the neck and first ventral plates cartridge buff. After the first 10 or 15 ventrals, there is a black spot on either end of the plates, at first spaced every 3 plates, but soon occurring on each ventral. Then appear 2 rows of spots down mid-belly which are black cephalad, and which become russet or tawny and quite prominent caudad.

A snake from Palo Pinto, Tex., received from Philip Harter, Nov. 16,

1938. Snake is 7(?) feet long, tending toward *P. c. deppei;* 33 scales around middle of snake; 2 prefrontals, one of which shows a tendency toward partial division; 9 supralabials, the 5th entering the eye; the 6th has small extra scale above, one of the postoculars thus interfering. The back bears 47 quadrate saddle spots on the body and 12 plus a tip spot on the tail.

Habitat: A canvass of most of the authors showed that prairies are named first (11 authors). For example, Higley in 1889 wrote: "It is not likely that any of such size [as 9 feet] have been found since the prairie regions have become more thickly settled." We could write a paper on the observations of early travelers on the depletion of animals and plants in the prairies. The next area of preference is cultivated areas or agricultural districts (8), then fields (6), also farmlands (2), grasslands (2), meadows (2), and (1 each) alfalfa fields, grain fields, clover fields, cornfields. In their search for food around houses they ascend trees and banks and crawl into nesting boxes, about granaries, sheds, and vacant farm buildings, in gardens, and over golf courses. Roads are given as a habitat 6 times. Four short references to the toll of the roads are: Burt (Kan., 1927), Strecker and Williams (Tex., 1927), Ortenburger and Freeman (Okla., 1930), and Burt (Kan., 1931). Other habitats given by authors are bluffs, river valleys, springs, bars of rivers, slopes of hills, prairie pools, ponds, rocky hillsides, streams, burrows, sand-hills, and many other places affording niches.

Jameson and Flury (Tex., 1949) have given us a definite statement for a restricted area: "Bull snakes are found most commonly in the Plains belt, but a few were found in the Roughland belt. Four specimens were collected from the following associations of the Plains belt: catclaw-tobosa, two; creosote bush-catclaw-black-brush, one; tobosa-grama, one. One specimen from the Roughland Belt was taken from the lechuguilla-beargrass association. A specimen was taken by Blair in the catclaw-grama association in April, 1948." Milstead, Mecham, and McClintock recorded their 6 specimens from the hackberry, mesquite-creosote, cedar-savannah, and cedar-oak associations.

Period of activity: *Early appearances*—Mar. 29, Apr. 3 (Burt., Gen., 1935); Mar. 30, Apr. 15, 18, 23, May 4, 14 (A.H.W.); Apr. 25 (Burt, Kan., 1933); Apr. 29, May 3, 9 (Gloyd); Apr. 29, May 4, 10, 15, 16, 20, 22, 26, 29 (Marr, Gen., 1944); May 1 (Gloyd, Kan., 1932); May 1, 10, 14, 22 (Ellis and Henderson); May 12, 13, 14, 15 (Burt and Hoyle, 1935). *Fall disappearance*—Aug. 5, 6, 7, 29, Sept. 1 (A.H.W.); Aug. 17, 27, Sept. 7 (Burt and Hoyle, Gen., 1935); Aug. 28 (Burt, Gen., 1935); Aug. 28, Sept. 19, 24, Oct. 14, 16 (Burt, Kans., 1927); Sept. 1 (Allen, Mont., 1874); Oct. 12 (Marr); late in November (Ellis and Henderson). MVZ dates are from Mar. 20 to Sept. 19.

Hibernation—"I buried 5 young Bull Snakes and 1 adult December 5. I placed them in a box partially filled with earth and rubbish and buried them about 2½ feet deep. I took them up again March 10. They were all in good condition, but were not very active until April 10" (Branson). "In a few instances Bull Snakes have been known to kill Rattlesnakes. . . . Furthermore, during . . . October, many of us have frequently seen both species coiled up together sunning themselves around the entrance to their winter den or place of hibernation"(Over). Schroder (Ill., 1950) wrote about blue racers and bull snakes hibernating in an abandoned burrow of a mammal—2 chambers 36 inches below ground, temperature of air and animals 44°. The snakes were in 2 entwined masses—5 blue racers and 2 bull snakes in one, 2 racers and 3 bull snakes in the other.

Breeding: Oviparous. Males 755–1805 mm., females 809–2250 mm. *Mating*—"During the rutting season they seem to follow each other by the scent, as I noticed upon one occasion that having captured a fine living specimen and placed it with others in a barrel near my tent, a very large snake of the same species was found a very short time after but a short distance from my reptile prison, being on its way in a direct line from the locality whence the other had just been brought" (Suckley in Cooper, Gen., 1860). "Two were encountered in courtship 6 miles southeast of Corning [Iowa] on May 26, 1943. The male had grasped the female just behind the head" (Loomis, Ia., 1948).

Eggs—Number, 5–22. 5 (1 author), 9 (1), 10 (3), 12 (4), 13 (1), 16 (1), 18 (1), 19 (1), 22 (1). Time of deposition, July–Aug. 15. Size, 1.66 to 2.7 inches x 1.1 to 1.7 inches. The largest record is 57x39 mm. or 56x42 mm., the shortest 41.6x27.6 mm. The eggs are elliptical, rough, tough, leathery, adherent. Branson's eggs were 2.8 inches.

Young—Time of hatching, last of August to Oct. 1. Authors give time from deposition to hatching as 2 months, 71–75 days, 8 weeks, 81 to 85 days. Size, 15–17 inches. Branson gives 15–15.5 inches as the size of hatchlings. Another record is Gloyd's concerning 13 hatchlings: 5 males average 424 mm. long, 8 females 412.5 mm., average for 13, 416 mm. Minton (Ind., 1944) wrote that eggs are laid in early summer and hatch in late August; on Sept. 22 he found a young 22.5 inches long. Of Stull's young specimens 440 mm. or shorter, we note 16 examples 330–440 mm. in length with an average of 407 mm. Recently, Mehrtens (Kan., 1952) had hatchlings 10¼–11¾ inches in length.

Food: Rodents, birds, insects. Over, Gloyd, Guthrie (Ia., 1926).

Authorities:

Branson, E. B. (Kan., 1904)
Burt, C. E. (Gen., 1935; Kan., 1931)
Cope, E. D. (Gen., 1883, 1891)
Ellis, M. M., and J. Henderson (Colo., 1913)
Gloyd, H. K. (Kan., 1928)
Hisaw, F. L., and H. K. Gloyd (Kan., 1926)
Hudson, G. E. (Neb., 1942)

Hurter, J. (Mo., 1911)
Klauber, L. M. (Gen., 1947)
Milstead, S. W., J. S. Mecham, and H. McClintock (Tex., 1950)
Morse, A. P. (Neb., 1927)
Mosauer, W. (N.M., 1932)
Over, W. H. (S.D., 1923)
Stull, O. G. (Gen., 1940)
White, C. A. (Gen., 1884)

1928, H. K. Gloyd: "This large prairie-frequenting species common throughout most of the state, is one of the few snakes which many farmers are beginning to recognize as an ally in the struggle against injurious rodents. Although captive specimens fed occasionally upon birds and eggs, a decided preference in favor of pocket gophers, rats, mice, rabbits and ground squirrels seemed to be indicated."

Pine snake (54—Bartram 1791), Common pine snake

Pituophis melanoleucus melanoleucus (Daudin) 1803. Fig. 176; Map 46

Other common names: Bull snake (26—Bartram 1791); black and white snake; carpet snake; chicken snake; common bull snake; eastern bull snake; eastern pine snake; horn(ed) snake; New Jersey pine snake; North American pine snake; northern pine snake; pilot snake; white gopher snake.

Range: Extreme s.e. New York across New Jersey, and e. Maryland; through w. Virginia, w. North Carolina, w. South Carolina to n.e. Georgia; thence n.w. through e. Tennessee to s. Kentucky.—Ga.; Ky.; Md.; N.C.; N.J.; N.Y.; S.C.; Tenn.; Va. *Elevation*—Mainly below 500 feet, but possibly some to 1,000 or 2,000 feet. 1,000 feet (Dunn, N.C., 1917; Va., 1917).

Size: Adults, 36–100 inches.

Longevity: 4 years 6 months (Flower, Gen., 1925); 8 years 1 month (Conant and Hudson, Gen., 1949); 10 years 5 months (Perkins, Gen., 1951); more than 5 years 4 months; more than 5 years 3 months; more than 2 years 11 months (Kauffeld, Gen., 1951); 13 years 5 months (Perkins, Gen., 1954).

Distinctive characteristics: "While *mugitus* is pied rusty brown or red and white, *lodingi* is uniformly black above and slate-gray below, and *ruthveni* is brown with darker brown spots, *melanoleucus* is distinctly black and white" (Stull, Gen., 1943).

Color: A snake from Lakewood, N.J., received from W. H. Caulwell, May 26, 1930. The back is marked with dark saddle spots of bone brown or clove brown. The light interspaces between these saddle spots are vinaceous-buff in mid-body and pale olive-buff on the caudal third of the body and on the tail. The saddle spots are not distinct on the forward fourth of the body as the whole dorsum there becomes more or less bone brown or clove brown with touches of pale olive-buff to tilleul buff. In the middle third of the body, on the 4th to 10th rows of scales, is a series of dark spots alternating with the dorsal saddles. The interspace color of this lateral series is intermediate between vinaceous-buff or pale olive-buff and the glistening white of the belly. The caudal third of the body has the dark saddles and the alternating dark spots very clear, with no light centers and with the interspaces distinctly defined. The saddle spots of the tail are lighter, have russet centers, and extend to the subcaudals, there being no alternating lateral series on the tail. The plates on top of the head are tilleul buff or pale pinkish buff with the sutures more or less margined with bone brown. The labial plates are white, the upper ones edged with dark. The caudal half of the iris ring is white, while the rest of the eye is washed with natal brown with an indefinite outer rim of black. The underside of the head is white. Along the 1st row of scales and on the ends of 2 to 3 ventrals are clearly outlined spots of black. On the forward part of the body, these may be 4 or 5 plates apart with the mid-belly clear glistening white. In the caudal half of the body, besides these lateral spots, there may be 2 other irregular rows, which may or may not have a touch of russet. On the tail the sutures of the subcaudals are russet, as are the 1st and 2nd rows of scales.

Two snakes hatched in captivity Sept. 18, 1951, from eggs laid June 28. The female was caught by Mr. and Mrs. John New in Warren Grove, N.J., June 6. Neither young snake had shed, but both appeared close to doing so. They were 39 and 35 cm. at birth. The spotting on one is very distinct. There are 23 black saddles on the body, counting the neck bar, and 7 on the tail. Interspaces are wood brown to avellaneous with the lower 3 rows, interspaces, and ends of ventrals vinaceous-fawn to light congo pink. On tail and rear of body, 19 dorsal saddles unite with lateral spots to make bands completely across dorsum; whereas forward, the large lateral spots alternate with dorsal saddles. There is also another series of lateral spots on rows 2 and 3 which extend onto the ends of 2 or 3 ventrals. The top of head is olive-brown spotted with black. A black bar extends between eyes across rear of prefrontals and front of supraoculars, passing through eye and down almost to labial border on upper labial sutures 5–6. This is bordered fore and aft with wood brown. The face is avellaneous, becoming on upper labials vinaceous-buff. The lower labials and chin shields are white. The venter is light vinaceous-fawn to buff with the center clear.

The other snake has 26 saddles on the body and 7 on the tail. The dorsal interspaces are avellaneous, with the first 3 scale rows light vinaceous-fawn. A few lateral spots are centered indistinctly with natal brown. For the cephalic 6 inches, the upper lateral spots are elongate and the first 5 are linear, 1 scale wide, 5–7 scales long. The venter is vinaceous-fawn to light vinaceous-fawn toward the neck. The dorsal black bands on the tail, unlike those of No. 1, almost completely encircle the tail. Otherwise the center of the belly is clear.

Habitat: Bartram's name, "pine snake," is appropriate. Holbrook thought so too. Subsequent authors have either called pine forests or pine barrens its characteristic habitat. Variations are "dry pine woods," "wooded sandy regions," "dry sandy areas," "pine woods," "open sandy spots," "open sandy cultivated fields," "loose sand," "sandy soil," "long leafed pine section." Early, Holbrook wrote: "The *Pituophis melanoleucus* inhabits the pine forests along the sea coast but I believe is not found far in the interior of the Atlantic states, though I have heard of its existence west of the Alleghanies."

Occasionally it occurs in other than sandy coastal areas, e.g., "also reported from swampy parts" (Trapido) and in western Virginia on a road "bordered on each side by a rather steep slope covered with laurel and rhododendron" (Dunn). Funkhouser's record for it in eastern Kentucky, once unjustly questioned, is now verified. In 1947 besides the Blount and Murphy record we have Wood (Tenn., 1947) recording it at Abrams Creek Ranger Station near the Great Smokies National Park. In 1948 Savage (Ky., 1948) referred to Hibbard's specimen from Edmonson County, Ky., and added Trigg County, Ky. In 1949 Chenoweth (Ky., 1949a) gave two more Kentucky counties, Barren and Hart. The region of its occurrence, however, is mainly that known by such diverse appellations as upper coastal and piedmont plain, coast pine belt, southeastern coniferous forest, Atlantic and Gulf coastal region pine barrens and strand vegetation.

Period of activity: *First appearance*—"The adults breed in May on emergence from hibernation" (Trapido); Apr. 21, May 24, 29 (Brimley, N.C., 1922); May 21 (Wood, Tenn., 1947). *Fall disappearance*—Aug. 14, 30 (Neill, Ga., 1941); Aug. 19 (Dunn).

Breeding: Oviparous. Males 1,260–1,850 mm., females 1,250–1,760 mm.

Eggs—Number, 7–24. Following Lockwood's 7–12 eggs in 1875–80, W. H. Smith gave 7–12 in 1882, Moore 10 in 1893, Jennison 7–9 in 1910, Funkhouser 15–20 in 1925, Conant and Bailey 9 in 1936, Ditmars 15–24 in 1936, Trapido a "dozen or so" in 1937, Conant and Bridges 7–24 in 1939, Conant and Downs 7–9 in 1940, Schmidt and Davis 7–12 in 1941, Perkins 6 in 1940 and 6 in 1941, J. G. New 10 in 1951. Time of deposition, May–July. In 1951 New (N.J.) collected 10 eggs, June 28; Perkins observed that oviposition came April 28, 1940, and Feb. 5, 1941, the 1940 eggs hatching in 78 days, those of 1941 in 79 days.

Size, 1.8–2.64 inches in length x 1–1.8 inches in diameter. Records are: 22 lines x 16 lines (Lockwood); extremes 50–64x37–45; average 59x41 mm. (Moore); extremes 53.5–61x26.4–32.4 mm., average 56x31.3 mm. (Conant and Bailey); 2¼ inches x 1¼ inches (Trapido); two groups—(1) extremes 48–61 mm. x 32–35 mm., average 51.71x33.75; (2) extremes 57–66x31–34 mm., average 59.5x32.57. Average size 52.5x41.5 mm.—near hatching, Aug. 10; two hatched between 4:15 P.M. Sept. 18 and 8:45 A.M. Sept. 19 (New).

In 1875 Lockwood reported that the pine snake laid 2 adherent clusters of 7 and 5. Of these eggs he wrote: "They were in fact as large as the eggs of an ordinary bantam fowl. One of them weighed 543 grs., and the whole weighed about 15 ounces avoirdupois. They were of nearly the same form and size at each end, except that at the upper end, or the last end evicted, was a little cusp, or teat-like prominence, precisely such as characterizes the fossil coprolites, and due to the same cause, the nipping off, or closing up of the cloaca, as the egg in its soft condition passed out. The eggs at this precise moment must be quite soft, as they were agglutinated together side by side. An attempt to separate a pair succeeded in pulling off a portion of the shell which adhered to the other egg. In this regard the resemblance to insect eggs was striking. The shell had a fine and pretty marking, as of reticulation." In 1878 Lockwood (N.J., 1880) found a nest in an open sandy spot in the pines about 3 inches below the surface. The deposit contained 41 eggs. Moore's female chose a loose area in a squash-and-cucumber field and excavated a tunnel 6–8 inches below the surface, where the eggs were in a single coherent mass. "When fresh, the egg shell was flexible and elastic, and of a very tough parchment-like character; and was very tensely and firmly stretched over its contents; but after a few days' exposure to evaporation, it became somewhat loose and wrinkled." Trapido wrote: "A dozen or so are laid in burrows in the sand 6 to 8 inches below the surface in early summer, hatching about 2 months later. Burrows may be used from year to year and by more than one snake."

Young—Time of hatching, August and September. Moore studied their development in detail, but not embryos before they were 6½ inches in length. Size, small pine snakes 14 to 16 inches have been found. The record of Conant and Bridges (Gen., 1939) is of young 14¾–17¾ inches in length; Perkins (Gen., 1943) found them 20 inches. Jennison allowed some adult pine snakes to enter the conservatory in June and on Oct. 18 was surprised to see a pine snake 13 inches long. In the next few days, 7 or 8 were collected among the steam pipes. On the subsequent March 7, he found one measuring "16½ inches, a growth of 3½ inches in about 4 months." New's hatchlings (see "Color") were 35 and 39 cm. at birth.

Food: Rats, mice, small mammals, moles, birds' eggs. Holbrook, Boulenger (Gen., 1915), Davis.

Authorities:

Bateman, G. C. (Gen., 1897)
Conant, R., and R. M. Bailey (N.J., 1936)
Davis, W. T. (N.J., 1909)
Dunn, E. R. (Va., 1917)
Holbrook, J. E. (Gen., 1836–42)
Horton, B. J. (Gen., 1903)
Jennison, G. (Gen., 1910)
Lockwood, S. (N.J., 1875, 1880)
McLees, F. (Gen., 1928)
Moore, J. P. (N.J., 1893)
Neill, W. T., Jr. (Ga., 1941, 1948a)
Trapido, H. (N.J., 1937)
Wied, M. zu (Gen., 1865)

1842, J. E. Holbrook: "A good deal of doubt has arisen as to the propriety of continuing the specific name *melanoleucus* of Daudin, as his description is copied from Bartram."

1875, S. Lockwood: Read the whole delightful article.

1893, J. Moore: His article, "The eggs of *Pituophis*," is still one of our very best discussions of the egg-shell, its interior, and its development.

1917, E. R. Dunn: "Records for the Pine Snake, *Pituophis melanoleucas*

(Daudin), outside of Florida and New Jersey are few and far between. In fact the only ones I have been able to find are the one in Brimley's North Carolina list from Swain Co., N.C., and a specimen in the National Museum from Blount Co., Tenn. Both of these localities are in the Big Smoky Mountains. It is of interest then that a dead specimen about 3′ 6″ long was found on August 19, on the road across the "Spur" between Nimrod Hall and Milboro Springs, in Bath Co., Va."

1935, H. R. Sass (Gen., 1935): There is much merit in his argument that the "great horned serpent" is *Pituophis* or *Ophisaurus* instead of *Farancia* or *Abastor*.

Black pine snake (4—Ditmars 1936), Black bull snake (2—Löding 1922)

Pituophis melanoleucus lodingi Blanchard 1924. Fig. 177; Map 46

Other common names: Black Pituophis; bull snake; (Loding's) pine snake.

Range: From Mobile Bay, Ala., into adjacent territory of Mississippi.—Ala.; Miss. *Elevation*—Most records below 100 feet; possibly to 500 feet.

Size: The few adults taken measured 48–72 inches.

Distinctive characteristics: "Similar to *Pituophis melanoleucus* (Daudin), but almost entirely black above and below" (Blanchard, 1925b). "Uniformly black above and slate-gray below" (Stull).

Color: A snake from Mobile, Ala., received from H. P. Löding, June 12, 1929. The back is a glistening black, with the first 4 or 5 scale rows fuscous or olive. The upper and lower labials, like the underside of the head, are marked with considerable buffy brown or olive-brown. The eye is black. The centers of many of the ventrals are russian blue or dutch blue, while their edges and ends are black. The underside of the tail is drab, avellaneous, or buffy brown.

Habitat: The Gulf coastal plain pine barrens and strand vegetation of Harshberger represent the area in which this form occurs. Formerly this form was in somewhat dry sandy land that once grew pine forests, later Satsuma peaches, both of which have largely vanished. Will the form vanish? We fear that no one will thoroughly work out its life history or that of Ruthven's pine snake before they are gone.

Breeding: Oviparous. Males 1,010–1,800 mm., females 1,600–1,800 mm.

Field notes: Apr. 6, 1934: Went out to Theodore, Ala., to see old camping place of 1917 (not on No. 90). Collected on old Pascagoula road. . . . We saw 2 snakes cross the road. Each black. Now we wonder if they were pine snakes or racers. Mr. Mackie says he has seen bull snakes back of his place.

Went out with Mr. Löding. He said the first *P. lodingi* he saw was a dead snake in the road between Irvington and Theodore, Ala. It was just beyond

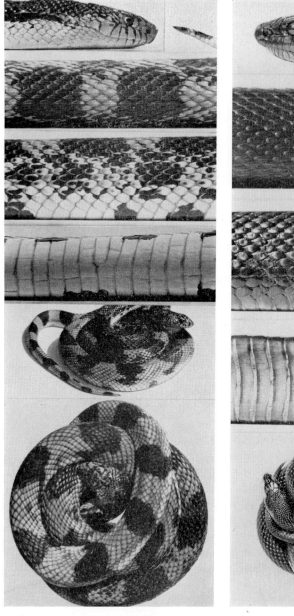

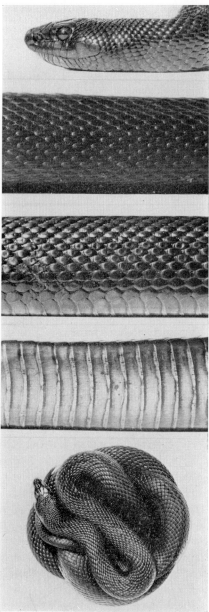

Fig. 176. *Pituophis melanoleucus melano-*
leucus, Lakewood, N.J., W. H. Caulwell.

Fig. 177. *Pituophis m. lodingi,* Mobile,
Ala., H. P. Loding.

Theodore near a bridge. Said he, "I passed it and thought it a gopher snake." Then he and his companion, T. S. Van Aller, thought more about it and thought maybe they had better go back and look at it. So they did. It was beginning to smell. Van Aller said he thought he could stand it. They brought it home, and after one of them had left the room several times, they had it well injected. Löding said he had a horrible dream later of pulling something putrid out of his mouth. This is the history of a type specimen. They sent it to Washington, and Blanchard was there and he made it *P. lodingi.*

The second *P. lodingi* he brought home in a paper sack. Left it in his den. When he looked for it the next morning it was gone. While he was looking around, his wife said, "What are you doing?" "I just lost something." "It isn't a snake?" she queried. "Yes, it is, but it is perfectly harmless." Then he found it later upstairs under a dresser, and it hissed vigorously at him.

Van Aller said he once found one with a young rabbit in it, and the snake was resting over two other young rabbits. He found it because the rabbits were squealing.

Apr. 7: Went out with Mr. Löding and Mr. Van Aller to Davie's Lake, a Sphagnaceae-bordered pond. Coming back, Löding and Van Aller said they had seen *P. lodingi* 5 feet 11 inches long. Van Aller said young *P. lodingi* are banded. Mrs. Davie said the bull snakes, black, get very large.

Apr. 8: Specimens in Löding's collection. Remark after time spent with Löding, "*P. lodingi* ranges from Theodore, Ala., to Irvington to Grand Bay and possibly into Mississippi."

Authorities:

Blanchard, F. N. (Ala., 1920, 1925b) Stull, O. G. (Gen., 1940)
Löding, H. P. (Ala., 1922)

1920, F. N. Blanchard: "A Black *Pituophis.* . . . This is apparently the first example of its genus to be reported from Alabama, and, so far as I know, there are no records for Georgia, Mississippi, and Louisiana. This specimen was found dead on the Hall's Mill Road, in the vicinity of high, sandy hills near Hall's Mill Road Creek, about 14 miles southwest of Mobile. A second specimen, which Dr. Löding informs me is like this one, was taken alive at Grand Bay, 26 miles southwest of Mobile, by Mr. E. D. King, Jr. The latter, a female, was kept in confinement for over a week, but refused to eat, so was preserved and deposited in the Charles Mohr Museum in Mobile."

1925, Blanchard: "On July 28, 1920, Mr. Löding took a third adult black bull-snake at Irvington, a location half-way between the former two. This has been deposited in the Alabama Natural History Museum at University, Alabama. On April 30, 1924, Mr. Löding secured a fourth adult black bull-snake in the same general region as the other three. The territory over which these 4 specimens have been taken, Mr. Löding writes, consists now mostly of Satsuma orange and pecan orchards, but was formerly fairly high and dry pine lands."

1944, A. H. and A. A. Wright: On June 12, 1917, at Le Roy, Ala., straight north of Mobile 50 or 60 miles in the adjoining county of Washington we wrote this journal note: "Took *Pituophis melanoleucus* black phase. Saw another today normally (spotted) colored."

This experience plus the fact that we did not collect the normal one has caused us to be very conservative about *lodingi* and *ruthveni* (2 specimens). We have seen nearly as many *lodingi* as anyone, have covered its range with my friend Löding, have seen it alive and in hand, but is it a good sub-species? Is it like the melanistic garter south and north of Lake Erie, or if it is banded when young are there actually within its range normal adult *melanoleucus?* There are Gulf naturalists who do not hold it a good form. Are they right? Only time will prove what we have. Our notes made at Mobile Apr. 6–8, 1934, are missing, and only field notes plus remarks on U.S. National Museum Nos. 62340 and 29503 (75292) remain.

1950, A. H. and A. A. Wright: This year we went through s.w. of Mobile (*P. m. lodingi* country) and into the Alexandria region (*P. m. ruthveni* country). These two colonies and the restricted distribution (very spotty) of *P. melanoleucus* and *P. m. mugitus* cause us to wonder about the status of the two, the Löding and Ruthven pine snakes, which may soon vanish from their restricted ranges.

Florida pine snake (8—Rea 1910), Pine snake
(4—Bartram 1791)

Pituophis melanoleucus mugitus Barbour 1921. Fig. 178; Map 46

Other common names: Bull snake (Bartram 1791); Florida bull snake; goose snake; southern pine snake.

Range: From Palm Beach Co., Fla., n. over Florida and w. to Mobile Bay; across extreme s. Alabama and northward e. of the fall line in Georgia, South Carolina, and s.e. North Carolina.—Ala.; Fla.; Ga.; N.C.; S.C.; Tenn. *Elevation*—Sea level to 500 feet.

Size: Adults, 36–90 inches.

Distinctive characteristics: "Similar to *P. m. melanoleucus,* but heavily washed and pied with rusty brown, not black. Ventrals and subcaudals of Florida examples average about 280, as against 267 for specimens from Carolina and New Jersey. The scale rows about the middle of the body are 31–33 (usually 33), on the neck 29–31, and anterior to the vent 22, 23, or 24. In the Northern specimens examined the mid-body rows are 27, neck 25, and anterior to vent 21 or 22" (Barbour, Fla., 1921).

From E. R. Allen, the person who more than anyone else has handled them alive, come two terse characterizations: "Large, attractive, powerful snake. Pale gray with brown blotches." "Attains a length of 7½ feet. It is dull white on the back becoming pure white on the sides. Along the back are a series of large dark blotches quite close together."

Color: A snake from Lake Alfred, Fla., received from L. E. Dills, Mar. 11, 1930. The background color of the forward part of the body is drab, while that of the caudal part is between deep olive-buff and avellaneous. The cephalic ⅔ of the back is marked with obscure spots of bay that have little suggestion of ventral extensions. The rear third of the body and the tail bear pronounced saddles, which may be burnt sienna or which may become bay on the dorsum or in part of their centers. Many of these saddles extend to terminal spots on the ventrals. The top of the head and the upper labials are vinaceous-buff. The same color extends along the 1st 2 or 3 rows of scales, becoming light vinaceous-fawn along the middle of the body. The eye in general is black with white or vinaceous-buff at the rear of the pupil and somewhat over the top of it. The underside of the body is white with a pale olive-buff or olive-buff cast. The ventral areas are almost free of spots except on the ends of each 5th to 7th ventral, where a clove brown spot may occur. On the caudal third of the body these spots are wood brown, and on the tail are entirely lacking.

A snake from Chesser Island, Okefinokee Swamp, Ga., June 25, 1922. The spots on the back are mahogany red, chestnut, hay's russet, or dragon's-blood red. The light intermediate areas are avellaneous or light drab, as is also the top of the head. There is much bone brown spread over the upper parts on the first cephalic foot of the snake. The iris is almost black, and the tongue is black. The under parts are white with a row of spots on either side. Each spot covers the ends of 3 ventrals with intervals of 4 or 5 plates. Cephalad, these spots are warm sepia, mars brown, or chestnut brown; caudad, they are like the dorsal saddles.

Two young snakes (preserved), from Fort Benning, Ga., kindness of Dr. W. J. Hamilton, Jr., and Capt. T. A. Pollock. We describe in detail the small one because it is so variant. Its body is 17¼ inches long + 2¾ inches of tail; the scale rows 30-29-22; ventrals 223 + caudals 54; lower labials 13. The background color of the sides is pale olive-buff, becoming in the intervals between dorsal spots deep olive-buff; the saddles on the forward half of the body are emarginate, but on the rear half, square; bone brown on the rear and natal brown forward; the body spots number 24 and are 8–10 scales wide with 4 longitudinal neck stripes 7–8 scales long; there are 6 tail spots which unite with the lateral spots to make broad bars; whereas on the body the dorsal spots are separated from the series of alternating spots on the 4th to 8th rows of scales; in the middle of the body, there is in this row a spot directly opposite the saddle, but a close examination of the saddle reveals 2 longitudinal spots of light brownish olive. If these should become bars, we would be confronted with 46 saddles, an approach toward *P. m. ruthveni*. An inch back of the head, the dorsal saddle sends forward 2 black-edged olive-brown bars; separated from these are 2 bars; on the 5th and the edge of the 6th rows of scales is a similar narrow stripe which continues in broken fashion for more than half the length of the body; this pattern on the body suggests *P. catenifer* of the west; the rear of the head back of the frontal is light brownish olive; across the front of the supraocular, frontal, and rear half of prefrontals is a prominent band of buffy olive or olive outlined by primrose yellow; this bar goes through the eye and reappears on the middle postocular and upper edges of the 6th and 7th upper labials; under parts are marguerite yellow, belly plates occasionally having a spot on one end.

The other snake from Fort Benning more closely approaches the typical coloration of *P. m. mugitus* descriptions. The scale rows are 31-31-23; the ventrals 237 + 51 caudals; the spots are 18 on body + 5 on tail, the rear 13 being quite distinct; the 5 anterior ones are almost lost, and for 6–7 inches of the forward length of the body, spots cannot be recognized; the lower labials are 14 on one side, 13 on the other.

Habitat: Before Neill's work of 1941 (Ga.), the notes on this topic were very few, viz., dry, sandy, pine woods, pine forest near a bayou, flatwoods, and oak ridges. Neill seemed to indicate that the coastal plain pine snakes were *P. m. mugitus* and that they resided in "arid dusty expanses of white sand, overgrown with broom-sedge, witch grass, prickly pear and dog-fennel, and with occasional patches of scrubby oaks and a scattering of long-leaf and loblolly pines"—a territory of pocket gophers, *Peromyscus,* eastern ground doves, race runners, and *Heterodon simus.*

Very surprising and noteworthy is Sinclair's record of *P. m. mugitus* in Natchez Trace State Park, Henderson Co., Tenn., contrasted with *P. m. melanoleucus* in e. Tennessee. If it is at Fort Benning, Ga., maybe it is in the intervening country to w. Tennessee. But again we feel that eastern *Pituophis* are very spotty in distribution.

Period of activity: *Early appearances*—Mar. 28 and Apr. 1, 1951, at Fort Benning, Ga. (Capt. T. A. Pollock).

Breeding: Oviparous. Males to 1,770 mm., females to 1,800 mm. *Eggs*—Number, 4–8. Neill (Gen., 1951) gives us our best evidence from observations on 3 females. One deposited 4 eggs June 21, 1948, 92–109 mm. long and 44–52 mm. wide. Another laid 8 cream-colored eggs July 21, 1950, 71–87 mm. by 33–38 mm. in width. The third deposited 5 pure-white eggs 72–85 mm. long by 33–36 mm. wide. *Young*—Neill records a juvenile (with umbilical scar) 555 mm. and another Dec. 5, 1948, 580 mm. long.

Food: Rodents, live birds. Loennberg, Carr

Authorities:

Barbour, T. (Fla., 1921, 1940)

Bartram, W. (Fla., 1791)

Carr, A. F., Jr. (Fla., 1940a)

Loennberg, E. (Fla., 1895)

Neill, W. T. (Ga., 1941, 1947a)

Rea, P. M. (S.C., 1910)

Sinclair, R. M. (Tenn., 1950)

Stull, O. G. (Gen., 1940)

1894, E. Loennberg: "The common form of this snake in South Florida has large, reddish saddle blotches on the back, becoming anteriorly more and more obsolete and finally showing only a slight mottling on the yellowish gray ground color."

1901, A. E. Brown (Gen.): "Of nearly 100 Florida specimens which I have seen, all were uniformly tinged with rusty brown over the whole upper surface."

1921: T. Barbour describes the Florida pine snake as a new species *P. melanoleucus mugitus.*

1940, T. Barbour: "Pine Snakes, Black and Brown—I have just been reading Dr. Francis Harper's masterly paper upon the work of Bartram and others, in the *American Midland Naturalist* (23 [3] July [May], 1940: 718)." Dr. Barbour held that "Bartram erred."

1950, R. M. Sinclair: "The Tennessee locality is so distinct from others recorded for the species that the possibility of human transportation must be considered. I regard the possibility remote since the Florida Pine Snake is fairly common at Natchez Trace State Park [Henderson Co., Tenn.], where the natives call it a bull snake."

1951, A. H. and A. A. Wright: In the light of our confusing experiences with *lodingi, ruthveni,* and *mugitus* in the field, we are startled by 2 juvenile snakes Hamilton shows us from Fort Benning, Ga. These were taken by Captain Pollock. The recent Henderson Co., Tenn., record in western Tennessee was a surprising capture, yet if we follow Neill's interpretation for the pine snake of Georgia and South Carolina, the fall line (almost cretaceous line) ought, if projected westward, to hit Fort Benning, Ga., and in the northward extension therefrom of the Mississippi embayment line we find Henderson County on it in the same Eutaw and Ripley formations. With *P. m. melanoleucus* invading eastern Kentucky and Tennessee we must confess we know little of these 4 subspecies on their meeting borders. Spotty distribution is often due to spotty locations of collectors and institutions, but the spotty distribution of the pine snake seems to be due to the isolated nature of suitable habitats. Still when we know western and central Georgia, most of Alabama and Mississippi and central and eastern Tennessee much better, we may have to revise this opinion.

To return to the two Fort Benning, Ga., specimens. The longer one, 31¼ inches, one readily would call *P. m. mugitus,* but the smaller one, 20 inches long, on first sight reminded us more of *P. catenifer* patterns. We need more studies of the young of these 4 races before their status can be firmly established.

Louisiana pine snake, Ruthven's pine snake (3—Ditmars 1936)

Pituophis melanoleucus ruthveni Stull 1929. Fig. 179; Map 46

Other common names: Bull snake (Viosca trade list 1930); Louisiana bull snake; spotted bull snake.

Range: From Jackson, Natchitoches, Rapides and Vernon Parishes of w. cent. Louisiana, to Polk County in e. Texas.—La., Tex. *Elevation*—100 to 500 feet.

Size: Adults to 60 inches. Until Fitch's collection of 3 specimens, only 2 specimens were known. His specimens have not been measured. In 1951 Conant (by letter) told us of about 12 records.

Distinctive characteristics: "[*Pituophis*] *m. ruthveni* has the dorsum pale brown with 50 chocolate-brown spots on the body and tail. . . . Anterior spots more or less distinct; posterior spots often red (Long Leaf, La.)" (Stull, Gen., 1940).

The scalation of snake from Long Leaf, Rapides Parish, La., loaned us by Percy Viosca, was as follows: scale rows—31-31-22; ventrals 218; caudals 60; upper labials 8, lower labials 14; oculars 3; tail 0.131 of total length.

Structure and scalation of a snake from Polk Co., Tex., described August, 1951. Total length $59\frac{1}{2}$ inches, of which tail is $7\frac{5}{8}$ inches. The eye is about equal to the labial on which it rests. Rostral height $1\frac{1}{2}$ x breadth and extends $\frac{2}{3}$ distance between internasals. Scales keeled except 7 lower rows; scale rows 29 on neck, 28 mid-body, 20 at anus; 213 ventrals counting anal + 60 on tail; lower labials 13 on right, 14 on left; upper labials 7 right, 8 left; tendency on right showing indication of subdivision, 5th upper labial separated from eye by lowest postocular, 4th enters eye on both sides; preocular 1; postoculars 3; loreal small, over suture 2 + 3; nasals 2; prefrontals 4; supraocular as broad as frontal; parietal as broad as long or broader than long with 2 prominent postparietals; temporals left 2 + 3 + 4, right 2 + 4 + 5.

Color: A snake from Livingston, Polk Co., Tex., received from J. P. Kennedy Aug. 21, 1951. There are 36 dorsal spots on the body and 9 on the tail, the saddles in the rear being mahogany red, about 7–8 scales transversely and 4–$4\frac{1}{2}$ longitudinally, the scales having a tendency toward dark edges on the rear; the dorsal spots are progressively darker forward, passing through bay and chestnut to bone brown or black, and in the cephalic third showing a tendency for the outlines of the spots and bars to be obscured, and with this a tendency also for the dorsal spots to be somewhat divided by groups of light scales of isabella color on either side of the meson within the saddles, thus appearing to partially divide each saddle into 2 somewhat irregular parts, a casual glance at cephalic region suggesting *P. c. sayi*. On the tail are lateral spots covering 1 or 2 scales of brazil red within the ivory yellow interspace color located on the 2d and 3d, sometimes on the 1st, scale rows;

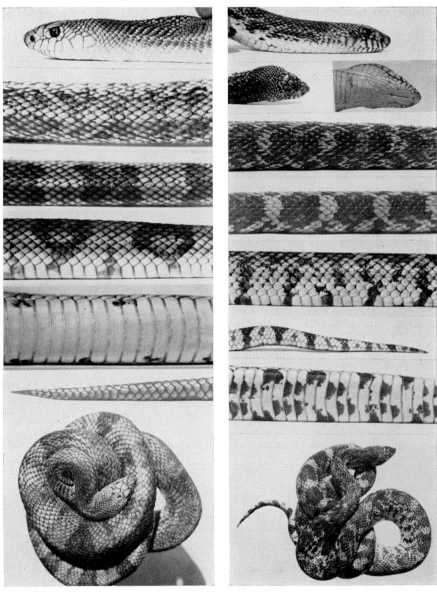

Fig. 178. *Pituophis m. mugitus:* 1–5, Lake Alfred, Fla., L. E. Dills; 6,7, Ocala, Fla., E. R. Allen.

Fig. 179. *Pituophis m. ruthveni,* Liberty, Tex., J. P. Kennedy.

on posterior part of body are mahogany red bars alternating with the dorsal
saddles occurring on 1st to 8th or 9th rows and extending onto the ends of
1 or 1½ ventral plates; there is also a series of narrow vertical bars of the
same color, extensions of the dorsal spots and on the 7th to 3d rows of
scales; in the forward 1½ feet, these bars become mummy brown and much
less prominent; in the cephalic portion these bars and lateral extensions of
saddles become spots instead of vertical bars, in the first cephalic foot the
arrangement becoming a series of black spots on ends of 1 or 2 ventral
plates sometimes extending to 3d scale row, sometimes stopping at the first.
Above this on the 3d to 6th rows is a series of spots alternating with the
dorsal saddles, the whole pattern in the cephalic region being somewhat
obscured because the interval scales have dark basal and often tip margins.
Intervals on rear ⅔ are colonial buff about 2 or 1 + ⅔ scales longitudinally
and 5–6 transversely, the intervals then beginning to have bone brown or
black touches and on the neck being narrow bars. The plates of top of head
from internasals to parietals are heavily spotted with russet or kaiser brown,
with the rear tips of temporal scales for an inch or more of the same color,
the background there and on the head being chamois. There are no head
stripes. The labials and face are cartridge buff, the first 6–7 sutures of upper
and lower labials pronounced mummy brown, with a slight tendency toward
a spot of russet above the 6th–7th upper labial suture. The eye is black. The
venter of the head is clear massicot yellow, of the neck straw yellow, the
belly plates on forward part of body sulphur yellow to naphthalene yellow,
each plate with at least 2 rectangular or triangular spots of mummy brown
to black; in the rear half the spots being cinnamon brown and grouped in
3s and 4s, making little bands on either side of the mid-venter, being usually
on the plates lying between the lateral bars, the mid-venter in this region
being pale ecru-drab. (See note on young *P. m. mugitus* from Fort Benning,
Ga.)

Habitat: Little is known about the exact locus of either of the 2 specimens
first recorded. The third specimen came from 5 miles s.e. of Zavalla, An-
gelina Co., Tex. (USNM 83672). Not until Fitch's note in w. Louisiana
were additional specimens recorded. He wrote: "Louisiana Bull Snake
Pituophis melanoleucus ruthveni 3; these and several others seen or reported were all in dry sandy long leaf pine woods." He described the
region at length and some of the changes coming with the cutting of pine,
training of soldiers, and invasions of animals. *P. m. ruthveni* has a very
slender hold.

It is a snake of the long-leaf pine area of Louisiana and Texas. Rapides
and Vernon Parishes comprise the greater part of the Louisiana area. This
pineland has now been cut until little of the original forest remains, and few
of these fine snakes are seen. Rapides Parish has an area of almost 1,500
square miles, 900 of which were long-leaf pine uplands, on soil usually

sandy and infertile cut by many streams and bayous with their fertile alluvial soil, the Red River plain running diagonally across the parish from
northwest to southeast with an average width of 12 miles. Our journal note
about our ride on May 13, 1950, tells how we found the country: "Leesville,
La.: After the hot and humid but rainless weather of Florida and the Gulf
Coast, the rain and cool nights we've had here are very welcome. As we
crawled over the roads from Oakville through Glenmora to Forest Hill,
across to Leesville, up to Alexandria and back to Leesville through Flatwoods, we hoped for a glimpse of a bull snake. We agree they are very
rare. With so many long-leaf pines cut, leaving great areas bare, we have to
picture the country from the small samples that are left. Where would these
snakes now find shelter and where find their customary food? We fear they
are among the 'Vanishing Americans.' Yesterday's trip was in part a beautiful ride through the long-leaf pine areas with many small areas still wooded.
All the lowlands and small creeks were in flood from the heavy rain of the
morning. The stand of pine around Flatwoods is fine, not being turpentined,
near the road at least, but there was no underbrush; it looked to us as if it
must have been burnt over."

J. W. Harshberger (Ecol., 1911) has described this long-leaf pine island
west of the Mississippi as follows: "West of the Mississippi River, the long-
leaf pine is limited to the sands and gravels of the latest Tertiary formations. . . . In the center of this region the pine ridges alternate with tracts
of white oak and hickory. Tending toward the Red River the pure forest
of *Pinus palustris* is unbroken. In Texas this forest formation extends from
Sabine River west to the Trinity River and from the grassy savannas of the
coast region north and are unrivalled elsewhere except perhaps in Louisiana.
This forest area is unique in its isolation far to the southwest of the main
long-leaf pine belt east of the Mississippi." (See Map 1, No. 6.)

Letters from John C. Wottring and Werner H. Gottsch in 1951 brought
us news of the capture of *Pituophis melanoleucus* in eastern Texas. The
latter wrote: "I have another piece of news for you. . . . J. P. Kennedy on
June 2 of this year collected a *Pituophis* which looks to me like *P. melanoleucus* in the thickly wooded region in East Texas, in Polk County. The
area where he found the *Pituophis* is the northern part of the so-called Big
Thicket. . . . [It] should occur also in Tyler and Hardin counties, at least as
far south as there is a continuous growth of pines and sandy soil." This very
welcome find is within 100 miles (air line) of Fitch's collecting spots out of
Leesville, La. Part of Polk County lies within the pine flats of Fenneman's
diagram and within Sargent's area of Long Leaf Pine, both of which cross
Louisiana in the known range of *P. m. ruthveni*. Furthermore, Polk County
lies within the same three geologic structures as Vernon and Rapides Parishes
of Louisiana: Continental deposits, Alum bluff, and Catahoula sandstone.
"The specimen was collected on June 2, 1951, sunning itself at the side of a

small sandy road about 21 miles southeast of Livingston, Polk County, Texas. In my opinion this territory is ideal pine snake habitat. The soil is sandy; vegetation consists of long-leaf pine and various hardwoods" (letter from J. P. Kennedy).

Breeding: Oviparous. Males 1,520–1,550 mm., females 1,750 mm.

Food: Rodents.

Field notes: May 12, 1950: Came to Leesville because of Fitch's success in reporting 3 Ruthven's pine snakes from this area. At Forest Hills, the old abandoned huge Fort Claiborne camp. The country is cut-over pine lands with small oaks, occasionally a woods near a stream such as Spring Creek at Melder.

May 13, Leesville, La.: One report was that a man began to cut off these forests 40 years ago. Then later, with this section alive with troops and maneuvers, the snakes suffered badly. Armadillos came in fast and probably prey on snakes. A man near Slagle reports, "We used to see bull snakes when I was a boy, but they are scarce now." At Hinestown we discovered that some mistake the king snakes for bull snakes. One man asserted, "Armadillos came in 25 years ago. They bother snakes. I know bull snakes or king snakes. They are spotted."

The postmaster at Elmer, La., holds these snakes very rare. His wife said that "she knew bullsnakes, but her father knew them better. He might know some boys who could get some. Few snakes in pine woods anyway except where the water courses are."

On Apr. 24, 1947, we had written Mr. A. J. Barton, postmaster at Melder. He had answered, "We do not have a snake locally known as Pine snake. But we do have three species that live in the Pine Hills—the coach whip, the blue runner, and the bull snake, also the chicken snake." Today, May 13, we called on him. He said, "Bull snakes are now rare. That fellow (I had quoted Fitch) has it about right. When you wrote me, I tried to get someone to try for it, but was not successful. Back in the old days when there were sawmills all through this country and railroads to take lumber out, they were more numerous. The last time I recall seeing one was when I was walking along the railroad checking trees. I ran across a 5-foot bull snake. He hissed at me and was very 'boastful,' not afraid of me at all. I had no business with him and let him alone. The chances of getting one alive are very small. The best place to try would be the Forestry Service, which at certain seasons has many men working."

On May 4, 1947, Mr. J. Leonard Blevins, Glenmora, La., wrote us: "The snake you want is here but not too many.

Authorities:

Burt, C. E. (Tex., 1935b)
Fitch, H. S. (La., 1949)
Fugler, C. M. (La., 1955)

Smith, H. M., and J. P. Kennedy (Tex., 1951)
Stull, O. G. (La., 1922; Gen., 1940)

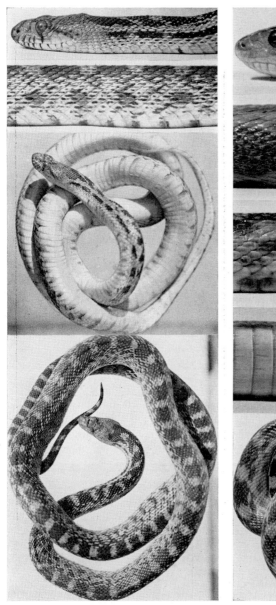

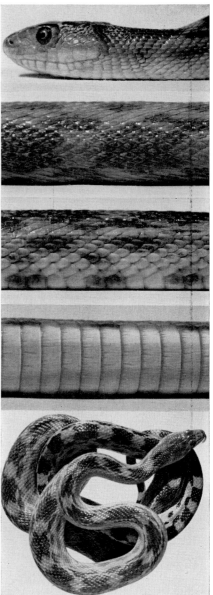

Fig. 180. *Pituophis c. stejnegeri,* Delta, Utah, L. M. Klauber.

Fig. 181. *Pituophis c. vertebralis,* San Diego Zoo, Calif.

1922: O. G. Stull described the form.

1935b: C. E. Burt discussed *Pituophis* of Texas.

1949: H. S. Fitch while at Leesville for 4 months picked up our best information on this form.

1951, J. P. Kennedy: (See letter under "Habitat.") As in 1950 the discovery of *Lampropeltis blairi* Flury by Axtell was the herpetologic event of the year in Texas, so in 1951 Kennedy's capture of a live 5-foot *Pituophis m. ruthveni* in the Big Thicket is the year's high point in Texan herpetology.

1955: C. M. Fugler adds Jackson Parish, La. (Clark, *Journ. Tenn. Acad. Sci.,* **24** [1949]) and also Dr. G. H. Lowery's capture at Bellewood, Natchitoches Parish, La. (*Herpetologica,* **11**:24). Because of the 250 miles between *lodingi* and *ruthveni,* he concludes it is a *P. catenifer* subspecies. This consideration would have less merit were it any other U.S. snake species. *P. m. melanoleucus* itself has very disjointed pockets from New Jersey southward.

PROBLEMATICAL FORMS

Pituophis catenifer heermanni Hallowell 1853

Van Denburgh photographed it and said it ranged in the Klamath region, Ore., Sacramento valley, n. portion of San Joaquin valley, n. and cent. slopes on the w. side of the Sierra Nevada. Everyone now follows Klauber's assignment of it to the synonymy of *P. c. catenifer.*

Pituophis catenifer stejnegeri Van Denburgh and Slevin 1920. Fig. 180 (Now considered *P. c. deserticola.*)

Miss Stull (Gen., 1940) considered this form of Utah, Idaho, and Washington to be *P. c. deserticola* and most herpetologists have followed her. In 1947 Klauber agreed but wrote that "while *stejnegeri* cannot be considered valid on scale characters, . . . it is by no means certain that *deserticola* should not be split into a northern and southern subspecies."

YELLOW-LIPPED SNAKES

Genus *RHADINAEA* Cope (Fig. 24)

Small to moderate, normally below 20 inches; proportionately long tail; normal head shields; head slightly distinct; anal divided; 17–21 scale rows without scale pits; 1 loreal; 2 internasals, 2 nasals; 7 or 8 upper labials; 1–3 pre- and usually 2 postoculars; pattern striped or almost unicolor; "small; usually striped; normal head shields; maxillary dentition of about 14 teeth, increasing in size posteriorly, followed after a slight gap by 1 or 2 enlarged fangs; mandibular teeth subequal; no scale pits; scales smooth; subcaudals in 2 rows; hemipenis single; sulcus divided; hemipenis with basal portion spiny and distal portion calyculate; calyculate area with free proximal edge (capitate)" (Dunn, Gen., 1932).

The species in the United States, *R. flavilata*, is slender, size 8–16 inches; tail 3.2–3.5 in total length, in newborn 4 times; posterior chin shields longer than anterior ones; labials $\frac{7}{9}$ (8); scales in 17 rows; ventrals 126–131, caudals 65–77; color reddish brown with light stripes outlining above and below the dark brown band from rostral to corner of mouth; temporals 1–2. Nine species known. Synonyms: *Coronella, Dromicus, Leimadophis, Liophis*.

Yellow-lipped snake (13—Ditmars 1907),
Brown-headed snake (5—Brimley 1907)

Rhadinaea flavilata (Cope) 1871. Fig. 182; Map 47

Another common name: Yarrow's Dromicus (Yarrow 1882).

Range: Gulf strip or swampy coast from s.e. North Carolina to Indian River County, Fla.; thence w. to s. of the mouth of the Suwannee River and along Gulf of Mexico to n.w. of Galveston, Tex.—Ala.; Fla.; Ga.; La.; N.C.; S.C.; Tex. *Elevation*—Narrow coastal strip below 120 feet (Malnate); 620 feet, Texas (Netting).

Size: Adults, 215–402 mm., or 8–16 inches. For 60 adults, Allen has an average of 325 mm., his largest 402 mm. Malnate gives 377 mm. for his large female, 340 largest male, average size 299 mm. We have seen males 240–295 mm., females 255–370 mm.

Distinctive characteristics: "Scales in 17 rows, smooth . . . ; ventrals 126–129; subcaudals 66–77. . . . Reddish brown above, somewhat lustrous in life, each scale finely dotted with dark brown; belly light yellow, invading the edges of the 2 lower rows of scales; top of head a little darker than the back and indistinctly vermiculated with light brown; a faint dark band from the rostral to the temporals, slightly bordered above with yellow and below with black; labials colored like the ventrals, the upper ones slightly spotted with dark brown" (Brown, Gen., 1901).

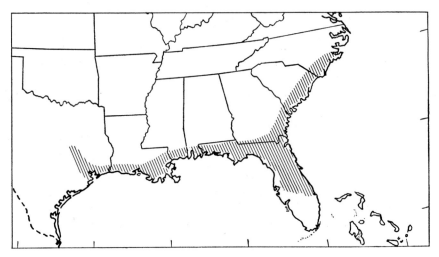

Map 47. *Rhadinaea flavilata.*

Color: Some snakes, taken in Harrison Co., Miss., Apr. 25, 1931, and received from Caribbean Biological Laboratory (S. Springer). In general appearance these small snakes are very much like some *Potamophis, Virginia, Storeria,* or even *Tantilla,* but without the pink belly. Why do all these little brown snakes seem so similar? Of course, if one sees the band through the eye, he knows that he has *Rhadinaea.*

The back of one is hazel, tawny, or mikado brown. The top of the head and rear temporal region are mars brown or auburn. The top of the head ahead of the eyes is deep olive-buff spotted with warm sepia or mars brown. Beginning on the rostral and extending through the nostril, loreal, preocular, postoculars, anterior temporal, and the upper part of the last 2 upper labials is a band of color like the back. This is bordered above and below with chestnut-brown, bister, or clove brown. These borders in turn are outlined above and below with white. The upper white border goes along the lower edge of the prefrontals, across the middle preocular, and the middle of the upper postocular, across the lower tip of the parietal and the upper rear corner of the anterior temporal, extending onto the lower post temporal. The lower white border is above the upper labials ahead of the eye and crosses them to the rear of the eye. The first 2 labials are white, each with a dark dot in the center and with dark edges above and to the rear. The 2 labials below the eye are dark-edged above but with no spots. All these labials have some wash of light grayish olive or grayish olive. The upper parts of the eye are deep olive-buff like the prefrontals and internasal, but without the spots of those regions. Through the middle extends an indistinct band of dorsal color. The lower parts have a smaller area of deep olive-buff. The pupil rim is colonial buff. The lower head is white with black spots on the mental and adjoining lower labials. The remaining undersurfaces are marguerite yellow or seafoam yellow merging into primrose yellow or chartreuse yellow.

Another snake is bay, chestnut-brown, or mars brown on the back. The top of its head is mummy brown and without spots on the prefrontals and internasals. The pupil rim is a line of orange or ochraceous-orange.

Habitat: This secretive snake is found under numerous kinds of cover in low marshy ground of cut-over pine and oak lands and cypress edges.

From labels of specimens in Malnate's monograph of 1939, we have notes such as these: "lowland form," "open pine woods," "loose damp sandy soil," "pine-woods flat with occasional gum- and cypress-surrounded ponds," "open dry flatwoods, though always in close proximity of water," "palmetto prairie with a sprinkling of pines," "under dead leaves at the base of a fence," "under surface of loose damp sandy soil," "under logs," "hiding or burrowing in the subsoil, in rotten logs; under loose bark either on living trees or on rotting trunks, or under the ground carpet of fallen leaves."

Period of activity: *First appearance*—March, April (Allen, Ala., 1932); Mar. 28 (Allen, Fla., 1939); Apr. 3, 1911, Apr. 26, 1914 (Hurter, Mobile, Ala.); Apr. 14, 1948 (L. H. Babbitt, Brooksville, Fla.); May 23 (Obrecht); May 27 (Netting). *Fall disappearance*—November (Coues and Yarrow); Aug. 19, Oct. 6 (Allen, Fla., 1939).

Breeding: Oviparous. Males 215–340 mm., females 255–402 mm. *Sexual dimorphism*—Blanchard (Gen., 1931) found keellike ridges on the dorsal scales of the anal region of adult males. *Eggs*—"A large female laid 3 eggs on August 19, 1937, measuring 23 mm. in length and 8 mm. in diameter" (Allen, Fla.). *Young*—"The eggs hatched in September, but the babies were several days old when discovered. Their average total length was 167 mm.; length of tail 41 mm." (Allen, Fla.). Before Allen's publication we had considered one specimen in the U.S. National Museum slightly beyond hatching. It is 189 mm. (USNM No. 56446, Hurter, Apr. 3, 1911, Mobile, Ala.) of which the tail is 59 mm.

Food: Tree frogs, toads, lizards, baby mice, young frogs. Allen (Fla.), Haltom (Ala., 1931), Malnate.

Venom: "It is . . . not surprising to find evidence of venom in the yellow-lipped snake, *Rhadinaea flavilata*. . . . Seldom was any prey held for less

than 45 minutes. Usually a frog would be held for about 70 or 80 minutes . . ." (Neill).

Field notes: We have seen live and preserved specimens early and late,
from Karl Schmidt's record of 1916 and Brimley's St. Louis, Mo., ones, but
have never collected *Rhadinaea* alive in the field. We have had living captives and have tried for them in North Carolina, Georgia, cent. Florida,
and at Mobile, but they always eluded us in our hurried trips.

Authorities:

Allen, E. R. (Fla., 1939)

Brimley, C. S. (N.C., 1941–42)

Campbell, G. R., and W. H. Stickel
   (Fla., 1939)

Cope, E. D. (Fla., 1877)

Coues, E., and H. C. Yarrow (N.C.,
   1878)

Löding, H. P. (Ala., 1922)

Malnate, E. (Gen., 1939)

Neill, W. T. (Fla., 1954)

Netting, M. G. (Tex., 1936)

Obrecht, C. B. (S.C., 1946)

Schmidt, K. P. (N.C., 1916; S.C., 1924)

The individual who has furnished us with our firsthand knowledge of
this form is E. R. Allen. The second specimen of this species came from
Volusia, Fla. When we came into herpetological collecting, the Brimleys
were getting a few from Bay St. Louis; then Karl Schmidt took this snake
in North Carolina, and Löding found a few in Mobile County. It continued
rare to 1936, when Netting made the startling discovery of this species in
Texas. At the time of Malnate's 1939 revision from 12 collections, he had
about 50 specimens. Imagine, then, 84 specimens collected by one farmer
in one year!

We will summarize by quoting Malnate: "Though not uncommon when
found, *flavilata* seems restricted to a definite ecological niche, and very rarely
is it found in extralimital habitats. The communities in which it lives are
essentially hygrocolous. . . . The time of its arrival and the method are
unknown, and the only datum that may be construed as evidence of an
exotic origin is the foreign position of its intergeneric allies."

LONG-NOSED SNAKES

Genus *RHINOCHEILUS* Baird and Girard (Fig. 19)

Size, medium, 18–41 inches, most caudals undivided; scales smooth with
no apical pits or 1 or 2 apical pits in 23 (25) rows mid-body, 19 (17) vent;
snout long, rostral prominent, projecting, in some uptilted; maxillary teeth
subequal 13–16, no interspace (diastema); eye moderate; 1 loreal; 1–2 preoculars; 2 postoculars. Synonym: *Rhinochilus*.

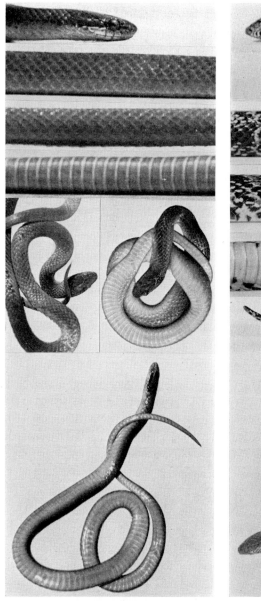

Fig. 182. *Rhadinaea flavilata,* Biloxi, Miss., S. Springer.

Fig. 183. *Rhinocheilus lecontei lecontei,* Miramar, San Diego Co., Calif., C. B. Perkins through R. H. McCauley.

KEY TO THE GENUS *RHINOCHEILUS*
(Adapted from Klauber's characterizations of 1941a)

a. Dark blotches on body usually 17 or less, their longitudinal extent at mid-body 3 or more times the interspaces; 7–9 middorsal rows uniform before lateral area of light-centered scales starts; ventral scales 200 or less, caudals average 51 in ♂, 47 in ♀; venter may be blocked with irregular dark blotches.   *R. l. antoni*
(Sonora, Sinaloa, Nayarit, and Jalisco, Mex. Intergrades with *R. l. clarus* in northern Sonora.)

aa. Black dorsal body blotches usually more than 17, their longitudinal extent less than 3x interspaces, with 3–5 middorsal rows uniform black and many scales of lateral extensions with light centers.

b. Snout sharper, with distinct upward tilt; rostral raised appreciably above nasals and internasals, prefrontals, internasals, rostral red; anterior of frontal angulate indenting between prefrontals, making suture of prefrontals short; suture between internasals shorter; posterior edge of loreal more vertical; lower average ventral scale count ♂ 200, ♀ 195.5; caudal count higher ♂ 54.3, ♀ 49, black body blotches about 25 tapering laterally as more or less regular triangles to point on or close to ventrals; 1½ (2½–1) times the intervals at middorsum. Red on middorsum not spotted with black. Interval with red block on middorsum and adjoining scales and below this the dark scales are light edged, and the interval broken below by a clearly distinguished bar; ground color of venter yellow. In the hemipenis, as contrasted with *l. lecontei* and *l. clarus,* the major spines are less thickly set and with a more gradual transition from almost spineless distal shaft to main spines of outer section.   *R. l. tessellatus*
(Nuevo León and Coahuila, Mex.; Texas w. of long. 97°, w. Oklahoma, s.w. Kansas, cent. and s. New Mexico. Intergrades with *R. l. lecontei* in s.w. New Mexico and s.e. Arizona.)

bb. Snout blunter and without a distinct upward tilt toward the point; rostral raised only slightly or not at all above the nasals and internasals; anterior of frontal straight, not indenting between prefrontals.

c. Black dorsal blotches on body, usually 25 or more, narrowing irregularly toward ventrals, less than twice the interspace red on middorsum flecked with black; lateral areas between primary dark blotches heavily mottled or spotted with black (may be faint in juveniles) and secondary blotches conspicuous, but irregular; red usually present in interspaces; ground color cream to yellow. Hemipenis rounded; forked only slightly at end; sulcus single; proximal half of shaft with tiny spines. Above this almost smooth shaft is a sudden transition to spinous area of distal half, spines close set, fairly large and recurved. Calyces fringed with small spines. Ventrals average, ♂ 206.3, ♀ 201.3; caudals 51.5 in ♂, 45.3 in ♀.

R. lecontei lecontei

(From Mendocino and Lassen Counties, Calif., southward to n. Baja California; s.w. Idaho, cent. and s. Nevada, s.w. Utah, and w. and s. Arizona.)

cc. Black dorsal blotches on body usually less than 25, with sides relatively parallel to within 4 or 5 scale rows of venter, the blotch being 5–9 scales long at that point, then tapering to a point or to line of 4–5 scales at venter or on 1st scale row. No red on dorsum between blotches; interspace immaculate or with a few faintly black-tipped or red-flecked scales. Secondary blotches absent or confined to few small spots at ends of ventrals, ground color white. Hemipenis, large spines extend more nearly to distal end; fewer calyces. Ventrals average. Males 209.2, females 205.3; caudals 53 in ♂, 46 in ♀. 5th lower labial more clearly contacts chin shields in clarus because 4 lower labials contact anterior chin shield, while in l. lecontei only 3 lower labials completely contact anterior chin shield. R. l. clarus

(The Colorado Desert, including the Coachella Valley in s. California, and the adjacent mountain slopes to the west, but excluding the irrigated areas of Imperial Valley and around Yuma, Arizona. Occasionally found interspersed with R. l. lecontei in s. Nevada, the w. Mojave Desert, and in the Wickenburg-Tucson area of s.w. Arizona. Intergrades between clarus and lecontei are found in the desert foothills surrounding the clarus area. Clarus intergrades with antoni in extreme n. Sonora, Mex.)

Long-nosed snake (17—Van Denburgh 1897),
Le Conte's snake (15—Yarrow 1882)
Rhinocheilus lecontei lecontei Baird and Girard 1853. Figs. 183–185; Map 48

Other common names: Scale-nosed snake (Cronise 1868); sharp-nosed snake; western long-nosed snake.

Range: From Mendocino and Lassen Cos., Calif., s.w. to n. Baja California; e. to s.e. Arizona; n. through w. Utah to s. Idaho; thence across Nevada to n. California.—U.S.A.: Ariz.; Calif.; Ida.; Nev.; Ut. Mex.: Baja Calif. Elevation—Coast to w. edge of desert basin, but excluding the mountains above about 4,000 feet (Klauber, Calif., 1931a). From the ocean to the mountains, but not above about 4,000 feet (Perkins); 1,000–5,400 feet (Linsdale, Nev., 1938-40); 1,700–3,500 feet (Atsatt); 3,500 feet (Little, Ariz., 1940).

Size: Adults, 20–38 inches. From two series of 65 males and 33 females

Klauber's (Gen., 1943b) measurements are: 842 mm. (tail 111) and 890 mm. (121) males, 740 mm. (97) and 749 mm. (96) females.

Longevity: 12 years 1 month (Perkins, Gen., 1954).

Distinctive characteristics: "Snout blunter and without a distinct upward tilt toward the point; rostral raised only slightly or not at all above the nasals and internasals. Black dorsal blotches, excluding those of the tail, usually 25 or more; lateral areas between the primary dark blotches heavily

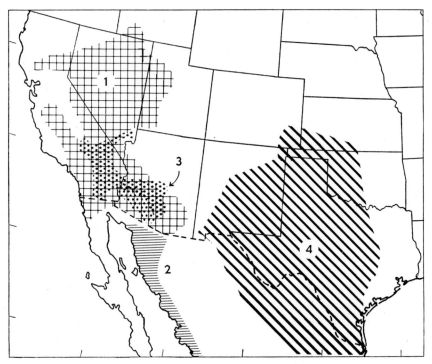

Map 48. *Rhinocheilus*—1, *lecontei*; 2, *l. antoni*; 3, *l. clarus*; 4, *l. tessellatus*.

mottled and spotted with black (may be faint in juveniles); red usually present in the interspaces; ground color cream" (Klauber, Gen., 1941). A medium, 23-rowed, red-black-and-yellow snake, with ventrals 190–217, caudals 41–60. The yellow scales usually have black centers and the black scales yellow centers. The venter is yellow.

Color: A snake from Florence, Ariz., received from J. R. Slevin and Wallace Wood, May, 1946. The back is marked with red and black saddles, outlined with and in part flecked with pale green-yellow. The red areas are flame scarlet, a middorsal area 5–7 scales wide being clear, and in the lateral portion for 5–6 scale rows part of the scales having black centers and light green-yellow edges. This area continues ventrad as a black irregular vertical bar causing the red saddle to fork on the sides. Some of the scales of this vertical bar may have yellow centers. The black saddle is 4–5 scales long on middorsum, clear for 1–3 scales width in middle and for 5–7 scale rows at either end, thus forming a black hourglass. The black area continues laterally to within 1 scale of venter, but for most of this area, i.e., 5–8 scale rows deep, the black scales have light green-yellow centers. All black scales on side of neck and face have yellow centers. Upper labials are yellow with black sutures. There is a clear black triangle on top of neck that narrows to 1 scale at rear of parietal. The tip of snout has wash of flame scarlet on rostral, nostril, loreal, prefrontals, and internasals. The eye is flame scarlet or orange-rufous. The belly is pale green-yellow. The ventrals have a sharp angle like *Elaphe*. May 18, 1942: A small *R. l. lecontei* with numerous black bands and much red between was picked up on a road near Glendale, Nev.

Habitat: This is a crepuscular or nocturnal snake. To find it in daytime, turn over any flat objects—boards, stones, debris, fallen signs. Most captures come in night searches for snakes. Both Klauber and Perkins recorded it from coast to desert except above 4,000-foot altitudes.

In 1941 Klauber (Gen., 1941) gave a good summary: "In the southwest *Rhinocheilus* is largely, but not entirely, nocturnal. . . . The following table shows the character of the road where specimens (*lecontei* and *clarus*) have been noted on the road either dead or alive. Pond, creek, river bank 2; orchard, vineyard 4; cultivated field 10; uncultivated grass 41; light brush 12; heavy brush, chaparral 38; trees, forest 1; rocks, boulders 19; rocky desert 2; brushy desert 41; sandy desert 1; barren desert 1." Another tabulation, Klauber's "Sixteen Year Census," gives coast 116; inland valleys 81; foothills 60; mountains 1; desert foothills 35; desert 3; undetermined 3. Total 311 (desert foothills and desert mainly *clarus*) (Gen., 1939a). In 1941 Klauber (Gen.) recorded for the desert 66. Finally in 1949 Fitch recorded it "four times, once as prey in a red-tailed hawk nest, once as a dried carcass found in open grassland, once under a log in a pile of granite boulders, and once crossing a road at dusk."

Period of activity: *First appearance*—Apr. 28 (Tanner, Ut., 1940); May 23 (Van Denburgh 1912a); May 13 (Ruthling); May 19 (Hardy, Woodbury and Smart, Ut., 1950); May 27 (Burt, Gen., 1935). The "Sixteen Year Census" has Jan., 2 snakes; Feb., 1; Mar., 9; Apr., 34; May, 125; June, 72; July, 34; Aug., 17; Sept., 11; Oct., 3; Nov., 1; Dec., 2. Total 311. Rank 12. Per cent 2.40 (Klauber, Gen., 1939a). *Fall disappearance*—July 22 (Van Denburgh and Slevin, Ariz., 1913); Oct. 15 (Van Denburgh and Slevin, Ida., 1921b); Aug. 9 (C. L. Evans in Phoenix); Aug. 24 (Campbell); Aug. 8 (Tanner, Ut., 1940); Sept. 20, 1949 (Woodbury and Smart, Ut., 1950). *Hibernation*—A specimen was unearthed in plowing, Dec. 13, 1926. Another was plowed out on Feb. 14, 1940 (Klauber, Gen., 1941).

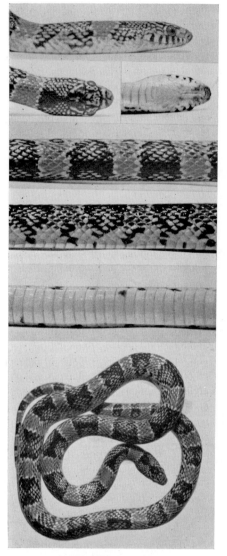
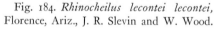

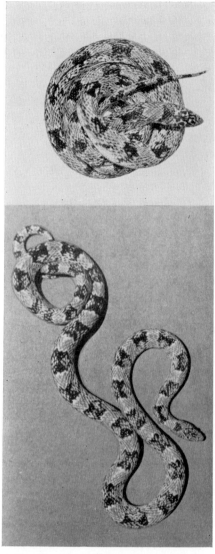

Fig. 184. *Rhinocheilus lecontei lecontei,* Florence, Ariz., J. R. Slevin and W. Wood.

Fig. 185. *Rhinocheilus lecontei lecontei:* 1, San Vicente, Tex.; 2, Organ Mts., N.M., photo by T. H. Lewis.

Breeding: Oviparous. Males to 890 mm., females 612–783 mm. *Eggs—*Number, 5–9, Conant and Downs (Gen., 1940) reports 6 eggs. "A specimen collected on June 3, 1933, contained 8 eggs about 20x7 mm. Two specimens 612 and 615 mm. long each contained 5 eggs; one 672 mm. contained 7 and another 678 mm. contained 9" (Klauber, Gen., 1941). Time, July, possibly late June. Size, Conant and Downs found in the cage July 1, 1935, 6 eggs:

37.0x15.9 mm., 36.2x16.0, 37.2x16, 41.0x15.4 mm., 35.6x15.8 mm., 30.1x15.3 mm.—average of 36.18x15.73 mm.

Young—Klauber (Gen., 1941) holds the young are hatched in the last week of August "for this is when the young of the year first appear." The smallest specimens we have seen are several in the U.S. National Museum which are 239, 244, 244, 239, 260, 242, 233, 279, 287, 245, 296 mm.; also some in the California Academy of Science, Nos. 33843-33844, of from Tucson, 238 and 242 mm., and No. 542 from St. George, Ut. 232 mm. (tail 32). This gives a range of 232–296 mm.

In another statement, Klauber reports that young just hatched are about 210 to 220 mm., the smallest 202. In his (Gen., 1943b) measurements he gives minima as follows: 202 mm. (tail 27) and 280 mm. (37) males, and 231 mm. (31) and 273 mm. (33) females.

Food: Gophers, rodents, lizards, small snakes, insects. Ruthling, Grinnell and Camp (Calif., 1917), Perkins, Klauber, Fitch.

Authorities:

Atsatt, S. R. (Calif., 1913)
Baird, S. F., and C. Girard (Gen., 1853)
Bogert, C. M. (Calif., 1930)
Campbell, B. (Ariz., 1934)
Fitch, H. S. (Calif., 1949)
Hardy, R. (Ut., 1939)
Hensley, M. M. (Ariz., 1950)
Klauber, L. M. (Gen., 1939a, 1941; Calif., 1924a, 1932)
Perkins, C. B. (Calif., 1938)
Ruthling, P. D. R. (Calif., 1915b)
Schmidt, K. P. (Baja Calif., 1922)
Tanner, W. W. (Ut., 1940, 1941a)
Van Denburgh, J. (Gen., 1897; Calif., 1912a)
Van Denburgh, J., and J. R. Slevin (Ariz., 1913; Ida., 1921b)

1938, C. B. Perkins, Calif.: "It is moderately common, . . . usually found in the brush. Large specimens are about two and a half feet long. The Long-nosed Snake is crepuscular, preferring the dusk to the daytime. As is the case with all the nocturnal or crepuscular snakes, it is often captured in the daytime by turning over boards, stones, fallen signs, or anything else that lies flat, or nearly so, on the ground."

1941, L. M. Klauber (Gen.): "Snakes of this species are not ill natured. Occasionally they will bite, but not so readily as many other colubrids. They vibrate their tails when annoyed. The juveniles will both bite and vibrate their tails; they strike quite fiercely, and their teeth can be felt. In captivity *Rhinocheilus* will burrow in sand and may remain buried for a considerable time, either with or without the snout protruding. If alarmed when emerging from the sand, and only the forepart of the body is out, they will pull backward into the sand and disappear. But they are not nearly as consistent burrowers as *Sonora occipitalis, Phyllorhynchus decurtatus perkinsi* or *Chilomeniscus cinctus,* for if rocks be available, they prefer to hide in crevices rather than burrow."

Desert long-nosed snake (Klauber 1941)

Rhinocheilus lecontei clarus Klauber 1941. Fig. 186; Map 48

Range: Foothills of desert areas; Mojave Desert to s. tip of Nevada; s. through w. Arizona to Phoenix and Tucson areas; w. to Yuma and Colorado deserts.—Ariz.; Calif.; Nev. *Elevation*—Probably many records are around 1,000 feet or above; or from 500 to 3,500 feet or more. Actually in spite of the Salton Trough area of Fenneman, we know of no record in the trough itself; 3,500 feet (Atsatt).

Size: Adults, 20-36 inches. Klauber's (Gen., 1943b) measurements of 29 males and 13 females are: mean over all, 641.79 mm. males, 586 mm. females; maxima 843 mm. (tail 120) males, 787 mm. (103) females.

Distinctive characteristics: Red usually absent; ground color white—a striking form. "A subspecies distinguished from *lecontei* and *tessellatus* by having fewer and longer dorsal blotches, and with the lateral spaces between the primary blotches either immaculate or with few spots, while the other 2 are much spotted. It also differs from *tessellatus* in not having an uptilted snout. It has relatively shorter blotches and wider interspaces than *antoni* and there are other pattern differences" (Klauber, Gen., 1941).

Color: A snake from Borego Desert near Benson's Dry Lake, San Diego Co., Calif., caught May 8, 1942. The body color is white with black dorsal saddles 7 to 9 scales longitudinally separated by white intervals (3½) scales long. There are 31 of these saddles, of which 8 are on the tail and 1 directly over the vent. The black is solid on the 5 or 6 mesal scales transversely and with lateral extensions 2 scales in width down the 8 succeeding rows surrounding the black scales, which have centers of ivory yellow or marguerite yellow. This black border is 1 scale or less below. In the rear portion of the body, the lowest scale row is white; in the forward half it bears a spot of black which extends onto end of one ventral; in the neck region onto 4 ventrals. Rarely in the front, more commonly in the rear, there are touches of scarlet or coral red in the white areas. In the last 3 intervals on the tail it is very prominent. Each upper labial has a black suture. The scales from frontal forward are pale pinkish buff because of a few flecks of scarlet or coral red, and outlined by black sutures. The black suture from eye to eye between frontals and prefrontals is prominent. The frontal is white, dark bordered; the parietals and an area for 12 scales backward are black. The scales back of the eye are white-centered surrounded by black. Under parts are pure white.

A snake from The Narrows, east of Julian, San Diego Co., Calif., received May 9, 1942; sent by Perkins to Salt Lake City, Ut.; caught 9:52 P.M., in cold and windy weather. This smaller snake has saddles of almost solid black with only a slight suggestion on the 3rd to 6th rows of scales touched with sulphur yellow. The interspaces are pure white, but with tiny bars of red at bases of some scales showing when skin is stretched. The top of head and face have some sulphur yellow, and the eye is red like that of the larger snake.

Habitat: (See *R. l. lecontei*.) Many of Klauber's and Perkins' observations apply equally to *clarus* and *lecontei*. For example: "It is seldom abroad in the daytime, evidently being active only in the evening or at night" (Klauber, Calif., 1934a). "The temperature at which *Rhinocheilus* (*clarus* and *lecontei*) has been found active at night on the desert [ranges from 62°–63° to 86°–87°] . . . They are often out when the wind is blowing" (Klauber, Gen., 1941). We recall his observing one being blown across the road.

In 1948 Johnson, Bryant, and Miller in the Providence Mts., Calif., received one specimen. "A long-nosed snake was given to us in 1938 by Mr. A. H. Thomas, who had found it in a basement on his ranch in the Joshua tree belt 5 miles southeast of Cima at 4,300 feet altitude."

Period of activity: *First appearance*—Apr. 11, 1935 (MVZ No. 18033); Apr. 28, 1940 (Tanner); May 19, 1927 (Slevin, CAS 62840); May 26, 1908 (Swarth).

Breeding: Oviparous. (See *R. l. lecontei*.) Males 760 (approx.) to 880 mm., females to 787 mm. *Eggs*—Number 5–9 (Johnson, Bryant, and Miller, Calif., 1948). Their lone specimen, a female, contained eggs 18 mm. long. *Young*—As in *R. l. lecontei*. "Young specimens just hatched measure about 250 mm.; the smallest available is 245 mm.; other small specimens are 246, 252, and 253 mm." (Klauber, Gen., 1941).

Food: Lizards, small rodents. Klauber (Calif., 1934a), Perkins (Calif., 1949).

Authorities:

Atsatt, S. (Calif., 1913)
Bogert, C. M., and J. A. Oliver (Ariz., 1945)
Garman, S. (Gen., 1883)
Hensley, M. M. (Ariz., 1903)

Klauber, L. M. (Gen., 1941; Calif., 1932, 1934a)
Perkins, C. B. (Calif., 1938, 1949)
Smith, H. M. (Gen., 1942)

1883, S. Garman: "The increase of the amount of the black on the scales tends to form bands and obliterate the original pattern."

1913, S. R. Atsatt: "No. 228 is large in size and dark brown and white in coloration with no red and no markings on the sides between the brown patches."

1932, L. M. Klauber (Calif.): "A fourth specimen further out on the Mojave at Yermo, San Bernardino Co., is entirely black and white, the red having disappeared from the center spaces. The black is nearly solid, dorsally, but spotted with white on the sides." (Not until 1941 did he describe *R. l clarus*. Nine years make a very good incubation period.)

1941, L. M. Klauber: "In *lecontei* territory there are large areas where this subspecies occurs without contamination with *clarus;* similarly there is an area (the western part of the Colorado Desert) where *clarus* is only rarely contaminated by *lecontei*. But there are fairly large areas where *lecontei* predominates and an occasional *clarus* is found; and a narrower belt wherein *clarus* predominates and an occasional *lecontei* or *lecontei*-intergrade occurs. It may be suggested that these 2 forms were once territorially separated until they had become distinct, but have now recontacted and are spreading through each other's territories, without completely merging into an intermediate pattern."

1942, H. M. Smith: "On the contrary, however, *clarus* and *lecontei* may have become differentiated in at least one other fashion—by some type of 'De Vriesian' mutation."

1942, L. M. Klauber (in a letter) stated: "Of course I knew when I recognized *clarus* as a valid subspecies . . . [that it] would lead to considerable comment and some disagreement."

1944, A. H. and A. A. Wright: One of us feels inclined to call this form *R. antoni clarus*, and one inclines to *R. lecontei clarus*. Seeing the changes which irrigation has made in 25 years and what the canal is now doing, we wonder whether the Colorado Desert purest *clarus* might not be a Salton or similar relict from the Sonoran *antoni*. Knowing first-hand the coral king snake-California-Boyle king snake complex and this *Rhinocheilus clarus* population, one of us is quite ready to accept Klauber's interpretation. Each of us knows it is easy with scarcity of material or initial studies to make seemingly profound pronouncements, but we recall the 86-year-old veteran L. H. Bailey and his study of acaulescent and caulescent specimens of the same palm.

1945, C. M. Bogert and J. A. Oliver: "Smith [cited above] seeks to reinterpret the data presented by Klauber and draws the conclusion that the genus is composed of two species, *lecontei* and *antonii,* each with a single race. The intergrades occurring in Arizona and California are interpreted as intergrades. . . . Intermediates, or 'hybrids' as Smith prefers to call them, are not rare around the periphery of the range of *clarus* and occur elsewhere as well. The fact that intergradation in this case is not confined to narrow geographic limits hardly warrants the conclusion that two species overlap, and hybridize on occasion only."

1950, A. H. and A. A. Wright: *Rhinocheilus* is not done yet. It is very variable. When we compare a young from Sonoita, Ariz., with our photograph of young from Palo Pinto, Tex., they are seemingly counterparts. Jameson and Flury (Tex., 1949) in Big Bend found ventrals clear or with dark blotches, and we in the same area in 1934 recorded dark blotches on the ventrals, but besides found dorsals looking like *R. l. lecontei* of Florence, Ariz., sometimes having hourglass spots, longer than wide.

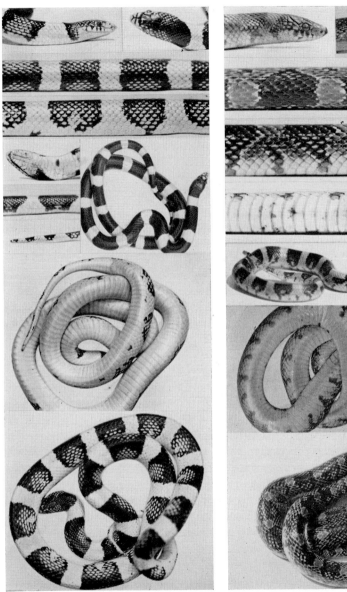

Fig. 186. *Rhinocheilus l. clarus,* near Benson's dry lake and narrows not far from Borego desert, Julian, Calif.: 1,3,4,6,7,9,10, C. B. Perkins; 2,5,8, Victorville, Calif., authors.

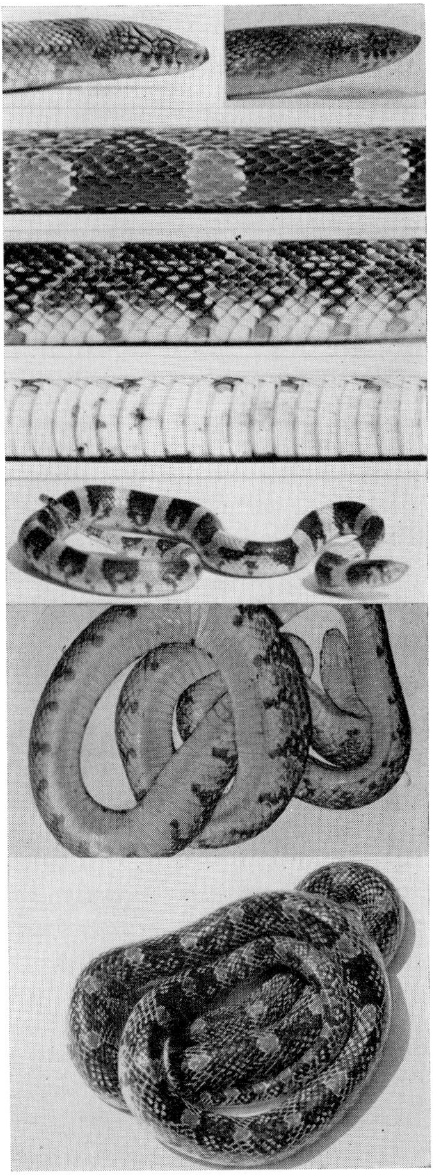

Fig. 187. *Rhinocheilus l. tessellatus:* 1,3,4,5,7, Brownsville, Tex., H. C. Blanchard; 2,8, San Antonio, Tex., Mrs. W. O. Learn; 6, young, Palo Pinto, Tex., P. Harter.

Le Conte's snake (11), Eastern long-nosed snake

Rhinocheilus lecontei tessellatus Garman 1883. Fig. 187; Map 48

Other common names: Belle snake; king snake; long-nosed snake (2).

Range: From s.w. New Mexico to s.w. Kansas; s. through w. Oklahoma and cent. Texas to Tamaulipas, Mex., and w. through Coahuila, to Chihuahua, Mex.—U.S.A.: Kan.; N.M.; Okla.; Tex. Mex.: Chihuahua; Coahuila; Nuevo León; San Luis Potosí; Tamaulipas. *Elevation*—Sea level from Brownsville to Corpus Christi; thereafter mainly 500 to 2,000 feet with some records to 5,000 feet, 2,800–5,000 feet (Bailey, N.M., 1913).

Size: Adults, 18–41 inches.

Longevity: 2 years 2 months (Conant and Hudson, Gen., 1949).

Distinctive characteristics: "Twenty-seven brilliant scarlet blotches on the body and 12 on the tail; below the scarlet blotches each scale is yellow with a black centre, while on the corresponding portion of the black areas, which extend to the 4th row, each scale has a yellow centre; many of the scales in the outer rows are tinged with red. The snout in front of the frontal plate is red, behind that black, each scale marked with yellow. Labials yellow, all the upper ones posterior to the 3rd, heavily margined with black" (Brown).

Color: A snake from San Antonio, Tex., purchased from W. O. Learn, May 5, 1925. A band on the neck, 29 dorsal spots on the body and 12 on the tail, and the tail tip are grenadine red. Alternating with these dorsal spots are larger ones of blue-violet black. In the middle of the body, the black ones are about 5 scales long and 5 wide, while the grenadine red ones may be 2 or 3 scales long and 3 to 5 wide. These red and black spots are separated by a common edge of chalcedony yellow or sulphur yellow. The grenadine red spots are clear on the dorsum, but soon become lost on the side. They fork in their course to the 2nd rows of scales about a dark vertical bar on the lower side. On the side, below the clear dorsal grenadine red spot, the scales are blue-violet black in their centers, those on the first 3 rows below the dorsal spot having cephalic dorsal edges of grenadine red and rear edges of sulphur yellow or chalcedony yellow. Those below these upper 3 rows are black with chalcedony yellow edges. Below each wholly blue-violet black dorsal spot is a collection of 9 to 14 chalcedony-yellow-centered scales, surrounded by a border, 1 scale wide, of black scales. This border extends down the lower side onto the ends of the ventrals as a vertical bar. With a similar vertical bar below each grenadine red spot, there is a continuous series to the tail tip. The rostral, 2 nasals, loreal, the lower part of the prefrontals, and almost all of the internasals are grenadine red. The lateral edge of the parietal, the supraocular, and frontal are marked with a longitudinal line of pale chalcedony yellow more or less edged with grenadine red. Each scale on the temporal region and those back of the eye and angle of mouth have pale chalcedony yellow centers with some grenadine red edges to the centers. The upper labials are pale chalcedony yellow with blue-violet black edges, the first 2 with parts of grenadine red, the others with a light touch of this red on the dorsal border if any. Some of the lower labials are marked with blue-violet black. The iris is grenadine red with outer parts of blue-violet black and with an area of that color in the lower cephalic quarter. Sometimes the grenadine red is flecked with chalcedony yellow or sulphur yellow. The ventrals are pale chalcedony yellow or sulphur yellow, clear in the cephalic region, but marked in the rear with a few scattered spots of blue-violet black.

A young snake from Palo Pinto, Tex., received from Harter in 1938. Dorsal pattern is one of black and yellow crossbands, the black ones broader. These black bands fork on the lower side in the forward part and in the rear, where the prongs are close together, sometimes uniting at tips making an enclosed spot of yellow. Along the sides the yellow bands have touches of red on the scales; the neck ring is orange; and the yellow on the tail has touches of red. The tip of the snout is yellow. The venter is ivory with a few black dots in the rear half of the body.

A letter from A. J. Kirn reads: "July 5, 1945. . . . There are 2 *Rhinocheilus* from 20 miles S.W. of Barnhart, in very S.W. corner of Irion County [Tex.]. These snakes are so different from our local ones that I thought you might be interested in comparing them." These snakes are much like ours from San Vicente on the Rio Grande in the Big Bend, and also like the ones from the Organ Mts., N.M., that Lewis photographed. See also Jameson and Flury.

May 16, 1934, San Vicente, Tex.: This *Rhinocheilus* of the Big Bend Rio Grande country looks so different from the ones of Brownsville and the San Antonio section. The red areas are longer, the black saddles narrower and hourglass-shaped, the other scales with a great deal of white or yellowish white in many ways much more like *R. l. lecontei,* a very speckled snake. (See Fig. 185.)

Habitat: This beautiful snake generally occurs in sandy deserts, rocky slopes, more or less arid brushy terrain, mainly in Lower and Upper Sonoran zones.

Much of our early and still scanty knowledge of this form comes from Texas, largely from Strecker. Jameson and Flury took several in the Sierra Vieja Range of southwestern Texas. "Two males and one female were collected from the catclaw-grama association of the Roughland belt. One male was collected from the catclaw-tobosa association of the Plains belt." Lewis (N.M., 1950) recorded it as restricted in the Organ Mts., N.M., to the Yucca grassland zone on the slopes between 4,300 and 4,000-foot contours while Milstead *et al.* (Tex., 1950) reported it from the mesquite-creosote association.

Period of activity: *First appearance*—Apr. 21, Apr. 30 (Marr); May 5 (A.H.W.); May 19, 1908 (Hurter, Tex.). *Fall disappearance*—Sept., 1916 (McAllen, Tex.).

Breeding: Oviparous. Males 498–936 mm., females 536–820 mm. *Young*— The smallest specimens we have seen are U.S. National Museum No. 2020, 216 mm. long; No. 2023, 227 mm.; No. 17394, 216 mm.; No. 82277, 231 mm.; and others to 240 mm. Stanford University (No. 6420 from Albuquerque, N.M.) has one as small as 188 mm.

Food: Rodents, lizards, young snakes. Ditmars (Gen., 1907)

Authorities:

Bailey, V. (Tex., 1905)
Branson, E. B. (Kan., 1904)
Brown, A. E. (Gen., 1901)
Cragin, F. W. (Kan., 1887)
Garman, S. (Gen., 1883; Tex., 1887)

Jameson, D. L., and A. G. Flury (Tex., 1949)
Marr, J. C. (Gen., 1944)
Maslin, T. P. (Calif., 1950)
Strecker, J. K., Jr. (Tex., 1902, 1908c, 1909b, 1915, 1928c, 1930)

PATCH-NOSED SNAKES

Genus *SALVADORA* Baird and Girard (Fig. 22)

Size medium, 20–48 inches; body long, slender, tapering; tail long ratio to total length .18–.34, average .24; head elongate, distinct; cephalic plates normal except rostral, which is thickened, widened, triangular, curved back over snout in all forms except *pulcherrima;* loreal single or divided, 1–4; preoculars 1–4; postoculars 2, 3; suboculars present in some forms; labials $\frac{8-10}{8-12}$, 0, 1, 2, 3 contacting eye; second pair of chin shields in contact or separated by as many as 3 small scales; eye large, pupil round above labials 4 + 5 to 7; scales smooth with indistinct apical pits in 17 rows (rarely 19); ventrals 177–212; caudals 66–152; maxillary teeth $9-17+3$; "hemipenis non capitate, not bifurcate, with apical calyces, sulcus single, basal spines long" (Bogert); pattern, longitudinal stripes on either side of a light vertebral stripe. Synonyms: *Phimothyra, Zamenis.*

KEY TO THE GENUS *SALVADORA*

a. Upper labials usually 8 or 8 (9); lower labials usually 9 (10); loreal 1; temporals 2 + 2, rarely 2 + 3; posterior chin shields in contact or slightly separated by 1 scale; ventrals 178–197; caudals 90–112; upper labials 4 and 5 usually in contact with eye; loreal in contact with upper labials 2 and 3; postnasal usually in contact with 2nd upper labial; rostral edge only slightly raised; lowest preocular a triangle cut off from corner of labial 4 or wedged between 3 and 4.

b. One pair of dark dorsal stripes, each 3 scales wide anteriorly, light dorsal stripe 3 scales wide in cephalic ⅔ and ½ + 1 + ½ caudad. (W. Texas and s.e. Arizona.)   *S. grahamiae grahamiae*

bb. Two pairs of dark stripes, lower one on scale row 3, upper on ½ of row 5, all of 6 and 7, and ½ of 8; light dorsal stripe (ochraceous-orange or cadmium yellow to ecru-olive caudad); preoculars 3, postoculars 2. (Oklahoma through Texas to Mexico between longitudes 97°–101°.)   *S. g. lineata*

aa. Upper labials usually 9 (10) rarely (8) 9; lower labials usually 10–11 rarely (8, 9, 12); loreals 1–4; temporals usually 2 + 3 or 2 + 3 + 4 rarely 2 + 2; posterior chin shields not in contact, widely separated by 2 or more scales; ventrals 179–212; caudals 68–103; loreal in contact with labials 3 + 4 rarely 4 + 5 or 3 only; postnasal usually in contact with upper labial 3; rostral enlarged, edges conspicuously free.

b. 2 upper labials reaching eye (usually 5 and 6); 2 pairs of continuous dark stripes; no suboculars.

c. Loreal 1; lower dark stripe confined to row 4 and not involving row 3; preocular (1) 2; scale rows 17-17-13; ventrals 179–205 (usually less than 192); caudals ♂ 76–87, ♀ 66–82. (Chisos Mountains, Tex., s.w. to n. Sinaloa, Mex., n. to El Paso, Tex., w. to Nogales, Ariz., and s. to Guaymas, Sonora, Mex.)   *S. h. deserticola*

cc. Loreals 2; lower dark stripe on rows 3 and 4; preoculars 2; scale rows 19-17-15-13; ventrals 191–204 (usually over 192, mean ♂ 198, ♀ 197); caudals ♂ 91–103; ♀ 86–100. (Baja California, Mex., from San Pedro de Martir Mts. to Cape San Lucas.)   *S. h. klauberi*

bb. 1 (usually 6th) or no upper labial reaching eye; 1 pair of continuous broad dark stripes or 1 pair breaking into 2 posteriorly or 1 or 2 pairs broken into bars.

c. 1 upper labial, usually 6th, reaches eye.

d. Light vertebral stripe 1 and 2 half scales wide; one pair of continuous broad dark lateral stripes involving scale rows 3-7, sometimes feebly divided at mid-body; top of head buffy or snuff brown almost like the dark stripes; scale rows 17-15-13; ventrals 187–201, average 193.7. (S.w. California and n.w. Baja California.)   *S. h. virgultea*

dd. Light vertebral stripe 3 scales wide; lateral dark stripe distinctly separated into 2 at mid-body, the lower stripe on scale row 3; top of head light like middorsal stripe. Ventrals 189–212, average 200. (S. tip of Nevada over s.e. California and n. Baja California to the Gulf of California, cent. and s.w. Arizona, e. to Nogales-Wilcox line, s. to Guaymas, Sonora, Mex.) *S. hexalepis hexalepis*

cc. No upper labial reaches eye owing to subocular ring; light vertebral stripe may be 3 scales wide in mid-body or from Utah to the Painted

Desert may be irregular and broken or obscured by dark bars; the lower lateral stripe on rows 3 and 4 is fainter than the upper stripe on rows 6 and 7; top of head is light like mid-dorsal area. Ventrals 191–208; average 200. (Principally Mojave Desert, Calif., and from Washoe County, Nev., s. across Washington County, Ut., to the Painted Desert in Arizona.)   *S. h. mojavensis*

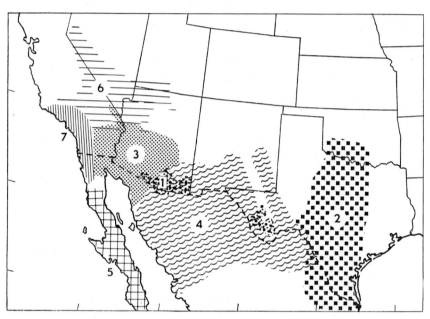

Map 49. *Salvadora*—1, *g. grahamiae;* 2, *g. lineata;* 3, *h. hexalepis;* 4, *h. deserticola;* 5, *h. klauberi;* 6, *h. mojavensis;* 7, *h. virgultea.*

Mountain patch-nosed snake, Patch-nosed snake (6)

Salvadora grahamiae grahamiae Baird and Girard 1853. Fig. 188; Map 49

Other common names: Banded flat-nosed snake; eastern patch-nosed snake; Graham's flat-nosed snake; Graham's Salvadora (Cooper 1869); Graham's snake (Cooper 1869); patch-nose snake (5); plateau patch-nosed snaked (1).

Range: Mountains and plateaus from Pecos River in Texas, through s. New Mexico across s. Arizona to a point several miles west of Nogales, Ariz., and in adjacent states of Mexico, Sonora to Coahuila.—U.S.A.: Ariz.; N.M.; Tex. Mex.: Chihuahua; Coahuila; Sonora. *Elevation*—2,800 to 6,500 feet. 2,800–5,000 feet (Bailey, N.M., 1913); above 4,000 feet (Bogert, Ariz., 1945); 5,400, 5,800, 6,500, 6,500 feet (Bogert, Gen., 1939).

Size: Adults, 20–34 inches.

Distinctive characteristics: "A *Salvadora* with edges of rostral only slightly

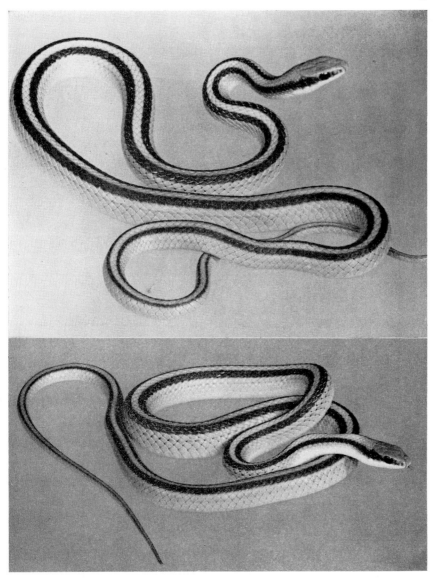

Fig. 188. *Salvadora grahamiae grahamiae,* Government Spring, Pajaritos Mts., Ariz.,
W. H. Woodin, photos by C. M. Bogert.

raised; posterior chin shields in contact or narrowly separated; 8 upper
labials (occasionally 9); ventrals fewer than in *deserticola* and *hexalepis,*
and caudals more numerous; caudals more numerous than in *lineata,* from
which it is further distinguished by the usual absence of the lateral narrow
line and by the broader dorsal light band; no supra-anal keels in adult
males" (Schmidt).

Color: We have seen this form alive at Mt. Livermore, Fort Davis Mts., in 1917 and at Rucker Canyon, Chiricahua Mts., in 1942, yet neither time did we describe it. In Schmidt's review of the Texan *Salvadoras,* H. M. Smith's notes on USNM No. 2081 are: "Median light stripe 3 scales wide in anterior ⅔ of body, 1 and 2 half scales wide on posterior third. Adjacent dark band 3 scale rows wide on anterior ⅔ of body, 1 and 2 half scale rows wide on posterior third. Each scale in these dark bands has the base jet black; the antero-lateral edge of the scales of the 2 upper rows in the dark bands is white. These white spots are confined to the scales of the median row of the dark stripe on the posterior fourth of the body. No other dark stripes."

Habitat: This form is no longer held to be a Lower Sonoran species. In 1939 Bogert (Gen.) placed it as an inhabitant of "less arid territory than *hexalepis,*" "as an inhabitant of the Mexican plateau" of 4,000 to 6,500 feet or higher altitudes. See also Schmidt under "Authorities." In 1945(a) Bogert (Gen.) placed it in "mountain islands, within the ranges of both *hexalepis* and *deserticola.*"

In 1949 came our best note on its habitat, the statement by Jameson and Flury—"Seven specimens were collected on the Miller ranch, all from rocky areas. One was taken in the catclaw-cedar association of the Plains belt. One escaped into a gopher burrow in the lechuguilla-beargrass association, and another escaped into a rodent burrow in the catclaw-cedar association. The others were from the following associations of the Roughland belt: stream bed, 2; catclaw-grama, 2; tobosa-grama, 1; creosote-bush-catclaw-black-brush, 2."

A letter dated Dec. 14, 1950, from W. H. Woodin of Tucson, Ariz., who collected the snake of the beautiful photograph given us by Bogert, said: "I collected the *Salvadora* in question on the Ruby Rd. a short distance east of Yank Springs (Sycamore Canyon) and 19.6 miles west of the junction of the Ruby Rd. with the Tucson Nogales highway, April 21, 1950." In sending us the pictures, Dr. Bogert wrote that it was collected "farther west than any published records indicate that the form occurs."

Period of activity: *Early appearance*—Apr. 1, 29, 1894 (Van Denburgh, Ariz., 1897); Apr. 28, 1892 (Stejneger, Ariz., 1903). *Fall disappearance*— Aug. 20, 1893 (Van Denburgh); Oct., 1873 (Smith, Gen., 1940a).

Breeding: Oviparous. Males 670–847 mm.

Authorities:

Baird, S. F., and C. Girard (Gen., 1853)

Bogert, C. M. (Gen., 1939, 1945a)

Brown, A. E. (Gen., 1901)

Jameson, D. L., and A. G. Flury (Tex., 1949)

Mosauer, W. (N.M., 1932)

Schmidt, K. P. (Tex., 1940)

Van Denburgh, J. (N.M., 1924b)

Van Denburgh, J., and J. R. Slevin (Ariz., 1913)

Yarrow, H. C. (Ariz., 1875)

1940, K. P. Schmidt: "In the Big Bend region of western Texas this species is represented by a form which appears to be confined to the more humid and timbered upper slopes of the mountains. Our few specimens are insufficient for a detailed comparison with the typical *grahamiae* of the Huachuca Mountains. It seems clear that the Chisos Mountains form is directly allied to that of southern Arizona; and it is believed that *grahamiae* is essentially a relict species with more or less completely isolated populations in the mountains of the Southwest."

1943: A letter from C. M. Bogert, Mar. 29, 1943, said: "It is also possible that *S. g. grahamiae* occurs in the mountains north of Globe. It might turn up near Springerville, for instance, since I have seen a specimen from a somewhat similar habitat in Valencia County, New Mexico."

Texas patch-nosed snake, Patch-nosed snake

Salvadora grahamiae lineata Schmidt 1940. Fig. 189; Map 49

Other common names: Eastern patch-nosed snake; flat-nosed snake; Graham's snake; patch-nosed snake; Rio Grande patch-nosed snake; striped mouse snake.

Range: From Hidalgo, Mex., more or less n., thence across cent. Texas to s. cent. Oklahoma.—U.S.A.: Okla.; Tex. Mex.: Coahuila; Durango; Hidalgo; Nuevo León; San Luis Potosí; Tamaulipas. *Elevation*—Sea level to 1,500 or 2,000 feet. 1,000 feet (Smith and Laufe).

Size: Adults, 20–48 inches.

Distinctive characteristics: "A *Salvadora* with rostral edges little raised, posterior chin shields in contact or narrowly separated, upper labials almost invariably 8–8, lower labials more frequently 9 than 10, ventrals few, 179 to 192 in males, 189 to 194 in females, caudals 90 to 103 in males, 91 to 93 in females. Supra-anal scales not keeled. In most of these characters *lineata* agrees with *grahamiae;* it is sharply distinguished from that form by having a well-defined lateral line, which is on the 3rd scale row anteriorly (the 2nd posteriorly). The anterior section of the nasal is usually in contact with the 2nd labial, and the dorsolateral dark stripe passes over the temporal region to the eye" (Schmidt). A medium, lithe, 17-scale-rowed attractive snake with 4 stripes, 2 dark brown dorsal and 2 lateral ones on a yellowish background. The venter is olive-buff or a light green. Ventrals 179–201; caudals 85–103. Eye in contact with upper labials $4 + 5$.

Color: We found this snake in Helotes, Tex., Apr. 6, 1925, in the branch s. and w. of the store, near where we caught *Coluber taeniatus girardi,* the ornate racer. The back is marked with a yellow stripe 1 whole and 2 half scales in width. The central scale row is deep chrome or cadmium yellow with edges of picric yellow, which is the color of the 2 adjoining half scales. On either side of this stripe is one of mummy brown, bister, or vandyke brown in which the outer edges of the scales are in part pale forget-me-not blue. On the sides below this area are 2 stripes of drab or avellaneous with the edges of the individual scales green-yellow or light greenish yellow. These 2 light stripes are separated by a thread which may be less than a scale in width and which is colored like the upper brown stripe. The top of the head is grayish olive, citrine drab, or yellowish olive. The upper and lower labials are white. The iris is black in front and rear and straw yellow above. The underside of the head is white. The ventrals are pale olive-buff, becoming on the rear half, olive-buff and under the tail, deep olive-buff.

Another snake was vetiver green on the under parts with light grape-green or grape-green on the under tail surface.

A young snake from Palo Pinto, Tex., received Sept. 8, 1938, from Harter, was colored like the adult.

If one is holding this snake by the head, it will often reach down with its tail, wrap it under one's shoes and over the instep and, looping its tail over its body, strive to pull its head free. Or when it is on the ground, it may wrap around one's heel. It must be a snake of rocky places.

Habitat: When surprised it quickly seeks the cover of rocks or flat stones in creek beds or hilly canyons. It is more common than the collections might indicate, and it is surprising there are not more notes on its exact habitat, ecological associates, and breeding habits. All in all, we believe it likes best hilly, rocky, ledgy situations, notwithstanding its type locality (Kingsville) and the Brownsville records. In 1950 Milstead and associates (Tex.) recorded three specimens of *Salvadora grahamiae* thus: "Two specimens were collected on the Blackstone Ranch. One was from the cedar savannah and one from the cedar-ocotillo association. Blair collected an additional specimen in May from cedar-ocotillo association near Gravel Springs." Northeastern Terrell County at the level of about 2,000 feet is seemingly the meeting ground of *Salvadora grahamiae lineata* and *Salvadora h. deserticola*. Without recourse to the specimens, we are assuming Milstead's specimens to be *S. g. lineata*.

Period of activity: *Early appearances*—Our dates are Feb. 24, Mar. 29, Apr. 6, Apr. 12, Apr. 25, Apr. 29; Jan. 16, 1942.

Breeding: Oviparous. Males 516–909 mm., females, 799–919 mm. Until Conant's paper appeared in 1942, we did not know the breeding habits. *Eggs*—Number, 9–10. Conant reported: "A female, from 8 miles north of Palo Pinto, Texas, deposited 10 eggs on April 1, 1941. . . . Measurements and weights of her eggs were [length 24.1 to 32.5x13.5 to 15.6 mm. width; 3.4 to 4.2 grams in weight]. Five of these eggs were adherent to one another. Probably all 10 might have been adherent in a single cluster if the snake had not moved while laying. Each of the 5 eggs which were separate had one or more pebbles from the cage floor attached to it when the clutch was found. The eggs of snakes of many genera, such as *Elaphe* and *Lampropeltis,* are coated with a fluid when deposited which, upon drying, serves as an adhesive binding the eggs together wherever they touch one another. Presumably the eggs of this *Salvadora* were similarly coated, although actual deposition was not witnessed. Snakes of other genera, such as *Coluber, Masticophis,* and *Drymarchon,* lay eggs which are not adhesive. Furthermore, the eggs of the last 3 genera are covered with small hard particles resembling crystals of salt in gross appearance. The eggs of this *Salvadora* lacked such nodules, the shells being entirely smooth. Bogert (1939, p. 177) states that *Salvadora* is most closely related to *Coluber,* a view which, based upon comparative studies of scalation and hemipenes, is shared by most herpetologists. Stejneger and Barbour (1939) placed *Salvadora* after *Coluber, Drymobius* and *Drymarchon* (in that order) and before *Phyllorhynchus* and *Elaphe,* in their check list. It is of interest to note, therefore, that the eggs of *Salvadora,* at least in the case of the single clutch here reported, are much more similar to those of *Elaphe* in the texture of the shells and in adhesive qualities, than they are to those of *Coluber."*

Young—Conant's account continued: "Four of the eggs spoiled, but the others began hatching on August 4, 1941, and the last snake escaped from its shell on August 10; on the latter date 4 young still bore egg teeth. Measurements and weights of the young were: [length 217 to 253 mm., average 234.8; weight 1.8–3.2 grams]. The young were very active, crawling about the terrarium in which they were hatched and striking occasionally when disturbed. Sometimes when held in the hand, they would vibrate their tails rapidly. Two of the young shed their skins on August 21, 2 on August 22, and 1 each on August 25 and 26. In coloration and pattern they closely resemble their parent, a fact which indicates further dissimilarity between snakes of the genera *Salvadora* and *Coluber."*

Food: Lizards, small mammals, birds. Strecker, Ditmars (Gen., 1907).

Authorities:

Bogert, C. M. (Gen., 1939)
Conant, R. (Gen., 1942)
Hartweg, N. (Tex., 1940)
Schmidt, K. P. (Tex., 1940)
Smith, H. M. (Gen., 1944; Tex., 1943a)

Smith, H. M., and L. E. Laufe (Tex., 1945)
Strecker, J. K., Jr. (Tex., 1915, 1922, 1926d, 1930, and others)

Western patch-nosed snake (17—Van Denburgh 1922), Patch-nosed snake (7—Meek 1905)

Salvadora hexalepis hexalepis (Cope) 1866. Fig. 190; Map 49

Other common names: Arizona flat-nosed snake; banded flat-nosed snake; desert patch-nosed snake (5); Graham's Arizona snake; Graham's flat-nosed snake; Graham's Salvadora (Cooper 1869); Graham's snake (Cooper 1869).

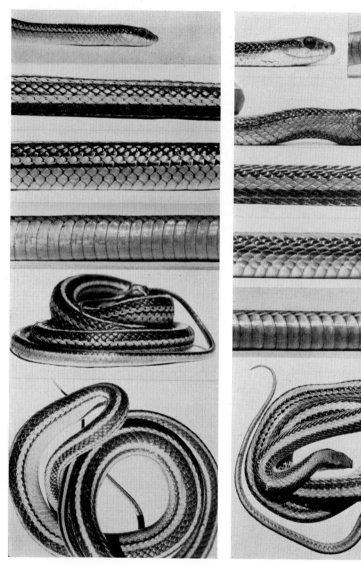

Fig. 189. *Salvadora g. lineata* Witte Museum Reptile Garden, San Antonio, Tex., Mrs. E. S. Quillin.

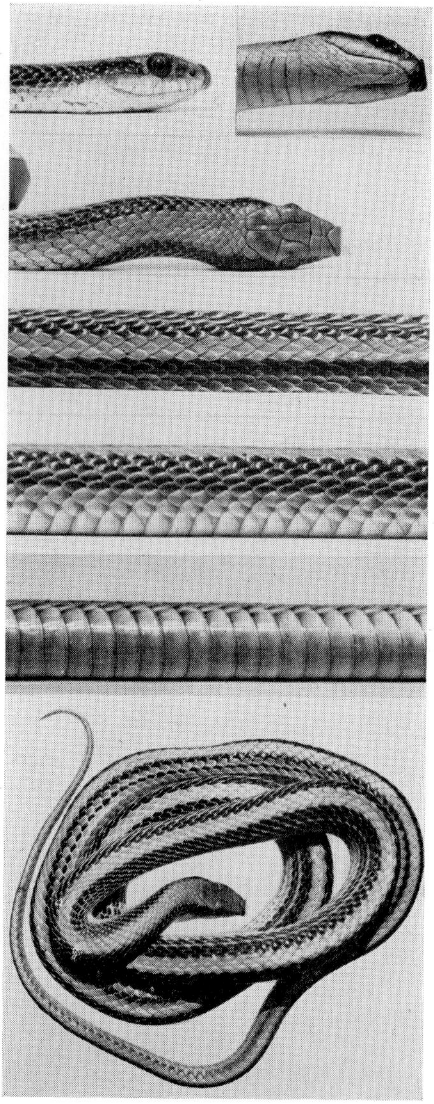

Fig. 190. *Salvadora hexalepis hexalepis,* Florence, Ariz., J. R. Slevin and W. Wood.

Range: From Providence Mts. in California s.e. to Graham and Gila Counties, Ariz.; s.w. to Guaymas, Sonora, Mex.; n.w. into mountains in n.e. Baja California, Mex., and s.e. California.—U.S.A.: Ariz.; Calif. Mex.: Baja Calif.; Sonora. *Elevation*—Below sea level to 6,000 feet. Colorado Desert (Klauber, Gen., 1939a); 1,000 feet (Stejneger, Calif., 1893); 1,500–6,000 feet (Linsdale, Nev., 1938–40); 2,800–5,000 feet (Bailey, N.M., 1913); 3,500–6,000 feet (Little, Ariz., 1940); 5,000–7,000 feet (Tanner, Ut., 1941a); sea level at La Paz to over 900 feet at Triunfo (Van Denburgh and Slevin, Baja Calif., 1921, 1921c); 2,730, 3,200 feet (Bogert, Gen., 1939); 3,300, 4,000, 5,000 feet (Johnson, Bryant, and Miller).

Size: Adults, 20–46 inches.

Distinctive characteristics: After the separation from *hexalepis* of *virgultea, deserticola, klauberi,* and *mojavensis,* we have the following characterization of it by the creator of 3 of the above subspecies: "One supralabial (usually the 6th) reaching the eye. Light vertebral stripe 3 scales in width; top of head gray; lateral stripe distinctly separated at mid-body" (Bogert, Gen., 1945a).

Color: A snake from Florence, Ariz., received from J. R. Slevin and W. Wood, May 30, 1946. There is a middorsal stripe, 3 scales wide, of olive-buff to pale pinkish buff, becoming toward tail pinkish cinnamon. The top of the head is wood brown to clay. There is a warm sepia stripe extending backward from eye on scale rows 3 and 4 and 5 and 6. On the neck for 6 inches this is a solid stripe, then on edges of rows 4 and 5 a prominent thread of olive-buff appears and continues almost to the vent, becoming in caudal section of body almost a scale wide, ceasing at the vent. The warm sepia stripe becomes on the tail a thread of saccardo's umber or buffy olive on scale row 2. All the face and rostral are like top of head except for 2 or 3 flecks of warm sepia ahead of eye. The upper labials are like ventral side of head, white. The eye is warm sepia with upper portion and part of pupil rim cinnamon. The belly is cartridge buff, as are also the first 2 scale rows. The forward part of scales of these rows and front edge and ends of ventrals are flesh color or salmon color to flesh ocher. In the rear half of the body this color covers most of the ventral surface and continues as a stripe on mid-ends of caudals.

Habitat: This is called a Lower and Upper Sonoran snake of the "desert," "Sonoran desert," "extreme desert," "Arizona succulent desert," "California microphyll desert," and "southwestern desert." It has been taken buried in the sand or in open stretches of sand. This crepuscular or nocturnal burrower has been taken along desert water courses, in greasewood plains and broad shallow washes bordered by creosote-bush flats, and on hillsides with sparse cover of bushes. In the last quarter century, the southern California group has contributed most. They have taken it in brushy desert, sandy desert, barren desert, rocky desert, grass, and cultivated fields.

Period of activity: *Early appearances*—Mar. 14, May 7, June 20, 1912 (Van Denburgh and Slevin, Ariz., 1913). The "Sixteen Year Census" has Mar., 1 snake, May, 1 (Klauber, Gen., 1939a). *Fall disappearance*—Sept. 12, 1939 (M. Storey); MVZ dates are Mar. 16 to Oct. 5.

Breeding: Oviparous. Males 684–1,014 mm., females 709–826 mm. *Eggs*— Until 1948 the only comment is that of Perkins: "The Patch-nosed Snakes lay eggs and it has been said that the embryos are further advanced when the eggs are laid than is the case with most snakes." In 1948 Johnson, Bryant, and Miller supplied much-needed information. "Two specimens from Cedar Canyon are females, both containing eggs. In one collected May 31, 1938, the eggs are 26 mm. long; in the other, collected June 4, they are 34 mm." *Young*—The smallest we have recorded in August and September were not below 300 mm.

Food: Lizards. Ruthven, Perkins.

Field notes: July 9, 1942, 20 miles northeast of Globe, Ariz., on route 60: Picked up a *Salvadora*. This is Seven Mile Wash bridge.

In a letter Mar. 22, 1943, Bogert wrote of *mojavensis* thus: "It is barely possible that intergradation (with *hexalepis*) may also occur north of Globe via the Little Colorado River."

Authorities:

Bogert, C. M. (Gen., 1939, 1945a)
Burger, W. L., and M. M. Hensley
　(Ariz., 1949)
Cope, E. D. (Gen., 1900; Ariz., 1866a)
Gloyd, H. K. (Ariz., 1937a)
Hensley, M. M. (Ariz., 1950)

Johnson, D. H., M. D. Bryant, and
　A. H. Miller (Calif., 1948)
Klauber, L. M. (Calif., 1931, 1934a)
Perkins, C. B. (Calif., 1938)
Ruthven, A. G. (Ariz., 1907)
Smith, H. M. (Gen., 1938b, 1941a)

Big Bend patch-nosed snake (Schmidt)

Salvadora hexalepis deserticola Schmidt 1940. Fig. 191; Map 49

Range: From Coahuila to Sinaloa, Mex., and n. into s.e. Arizona, s. New Mexico, and the Big Bend region of Texas.—U.S.A.: Ariz.; N.M.; Tex. Mex.: Chihuahua; Coahuila; Sinaloa; Sonora. *Elevation*—2,000 to about 4,000 feet (below Burnham's, Chisos Mts., Tex.). 2,800–5,000 feet (Bailey, N.M., 1913).

Size: Adults, 20–35 inches.

Distinctive characteristics: "Allied to *Salvadora hexalepis hexalepis* in the separation of the posterior chin shields, enlargement of the rostral, 9 upper labials, in having keeled supra-anal scales, and in pale grayish coloration; distinguished by the uniformly single loreal, lower ventral count, and the situation of the narrow lateral line on the 4th scale row instead of on the 3rd and 4th" (Schmidt). In 1950 Lewis wrote of his snakes collected in the Organ

Mts., N.M.: "I refer the 4 specimens examined to this sub-species. However, the narrow black lateral line is found on scale rows 3 and 4, not confined to scale row 4 as described by Schmidt (1940)."

Color: A snake taken from the mouth of Carr Canyon, Huachuca Mts., Cochise Co., Ariz., 5,300 feet elevation, Sept., 1948, received from Mrs. J. H. Healy, and loaned to us by C. F. Kauffeld of the Staten Island Zoological Society, May 3, 1949. There is a middorsal band, orange-cinnamon for an inch on neck, vinaceous-tawny on body, and orange-cinnamon toward tip of tail. This band is outlined on either side by stripe of black 2 scales wide on the body which extends to the postoculars and is indicated to the snout. For about 1½ inches back of the eye the stripe is 3 scales wide on the neck. Thereafter this black margin begins to divide into black margin for the dorsal band of 2 scales and a dark lateral stripe on lower half of 4th scale row. The intervening space appears vinaceous due to onion-skin pink on the bases of the scales. The same is true of the first 3 scale rows. The top of the head, ahead of the eyes is mikado brown, the frontals and parietals verona brown. From nostril to postoculars and along upper edge of supralabials is a bright area of xanthine orange. The preoculars and postoculars have a tendency toward inner rims of black outlining the eyes. The lower half of the iris is black while the upper half is cadmium orange, giving the eye a striking appearance. The lower labials and lower ⅔ of supralabials are glistening white. The chin and cephalic 3–4 inches of venter are glistening white. There is a wash of onion-skin pink on center of belly particularly prominent in the caudal half of the body, with the underside of tail buff-pink. The whole lower surface has an opalescent sheen. It is indeed a beautiful snake.

The length of body is approximately 20½ inches and tail 5 inches.

Habitat: In 1940 Schmidt said: "The subspecies *deserticola* may be associated with the West Texan creosote bush desert. Its relation to the Chisos population of *grahamiae* is evidently the same as that of *hexalepis hexalepis* to the Huachucan *grahamiae*. . . . A second species in west Texas from the desert plateaus surrounding the isolated mountain forests proves to be distinguishable from the Chisos form (*grahamiae grahamiae*) and that of southeastern Texas (*lineata*); and though it is directly allied to the Arizonian *hexalepis*, it clearly represents an undescribed form."

A note from Jameson and Flury (Tex., 1949) is our most definite: "Unlike *S. grahamiae,* this species [*Salvadora hexalepis deserticola* Schmidt] seemed to occur mainly in the Plains belt. Two specimens were taken, however, in the Roughland belt, where one each was caught in the stream bed and huisache-lechuguilla associations. The 4 specimens from the Plains belt were taken in the following associations: catclaw-tobosa, 1; tobosa-grama-blue stem, 1; creosote-bush-catclaw-blackbrush, 2."

In 1950 Lewis gave excellent descriptions of collecting spots in the Organ
Mts., N.M.: "The monolithic peaks of the Organ Range protrude from vast
bajadas . . . which slope far out into the valley. These alluvial fans, a mixture of huge boulders, smaller water-worn stones, and areas of sand, fine
gravel and earth, are deeply dissected by interconnecting dry washes. . . .
The edges of the bajadas are relatively well watered tangles of bushy vegetation set around great piles of granitic boulders. From these thickets small
trees follow the gorges upward into the mountains, and accompany the dry
washes out into the open flats." He found *Salvadora* on the flats and also on
the next level below, of which he wrote, "From the edges of the alluvial
fans a gentler and smoother slope extends between the 4300 and 4000 foot
contours. These slopes are also stream built and show yucca-mesquite-
ephedra-grassland associations . . . interspersed between areas of creosote
bush desert. . . . Also found, but not exclusively here, are the largest number of genera and species of any zone . . . *Masticophis flagellum testaceus,
Pituophis sp., Salvadora h. deserticola, Arizona e. philipi, Elaphe subocularis.*" Also exclusively in this yucca grassland belt he found *Rhinocheilus
l. tessellatus.*

Breeding: Oviparous. Males 684 mm. and up, females 709–826 mm.

Authorities:

Bogert, C. M. (Gen., 1939, 1945a)
Bogert, C. M., and J. A. Oliver (Ariz., 1945)
Gloyd, H. K. (Ariz., 1937a)
Lewis, T. H. (N.M., 1950)
Quaintance, C. W. (Ariz., 1935)
Schmidt, K. P. (Tex., 1940)
Smith, H. M. (Gen., 1941a, 1943)
Smith, H. M., and M. B. Mittleman (Gen., 1943)
Stejneger, L. (Ariz., 1903)
Van Denburgh, J. (Ariz., 1897)

1939, C. M. Bogert: Written in 1937, his paper appeared a year before
Schmidt's descriptions of *Salvadora lineata* and *Salvadora hexalepis deserticola.* We await with eagerness Bogert's subsequent papers, which we are
sure will help to elucidate our understanding of the ranges, characters, and
intergradations of this genus.

1945(a), C. M. Bogert: "On the basis of these data, as well as other evidence . . . it may be hypothesized that *deserticola* represents the most
primitive population." In his key he described *deserticola* as having "two
supralabials (usually 5th and 6th) reaching the eye. Loreal single; lower
stripe on 4th scale row; subcaudals on males 76 to 87, on females 66 to 82;
ventral scales usually less than 192 (82 per cent)."

1945, C. M. Bogert and J. A. Oliver: "This race heretofore has not been
recorded from Sonora, although the typical form (*S. h. hexalepis*) is represented by a few specimens from the state. Additional Sonoran material
referable to *deserticola* has been available, but the senior author reserves
comment upon it pending conclusion of more extensive studies of the genus
Salvadora. The race *celeris* described by Smith differs from *deserticola* only

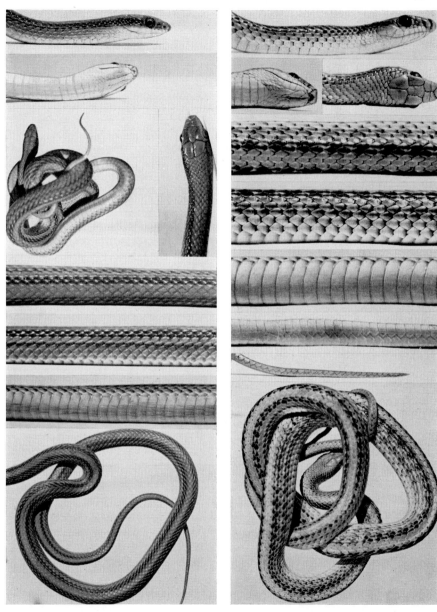

Fig. 191. *Salvadora h. deserticola,* mouth of Carr Canyon, Huachuca Mts., Ariz., Mrs. J. H. Healy through C. F. Kauffeld.

Fig. 192. *Salvadora h. mojavensis,* Mojave Desert, Calif., W. R. Lasky.

in possessing more ventrals. No other character listed in Smith's diagnosis serves to separate it. The specimen described above with 198 ventrals indicates that there is no satisfactory difference between *celeris* with 200 to 205 ventrals (2 specimens only) and *deserticola* with from 179 to 198. A difference of 2 ventrals, with so few specimens from the southern portion of the range now available, hardly suffices for recognition of *celeris*."

Mojave Desert patch-nosed snake

Salvadora hexalepis mojavensis Bogert 1945. Fig. 192; Map 49

Other common names: Western patch-nosed snake; whip snake.

Range: From Pyramid Lake, Nev., s.e. to s.e. Utah and the Painted Desert, Ariz.; w. to Mojave Desert.—Ariz.; Calif.; Nev.; Ut. *Elevation*—800 or 1,000 to 5,000 feet, possibly to 7,000 feet. 800 feet (Atsatt, Calif., 1913); 1,500–6,000 feet (Linsdale); "1,000 feet above Amargosa River" (Stejneger).

Size: Adults, 20–42 inches.

Distinctive characteristics: "No supralabials reaching the eye (owing to presence of suboculars). Lower lateral stripe on 3rd and 4th scale rows fainter than the upper stripe on the 6th and 7th rows; the entire pattern is sometimes obsolescent or, in the eastern portion of the range, cross bars obscure the vertebral stripe" (Bogert).

Color: A snake caught May 30, 1941, in the Mojave Desert, on a highway 15 miles from Mojave, Kern Co., Calif., and sent by W. R. Lasky. The background of the back is pale vinaceous-fawn. There is a dorsal band, 3 scales wide of pale vinaceous-fawn to ecru-drab bordered on either side by a stripe of clove brown or prout's brown. Beginning on the rear temporal scales and the rear of the last upper labial, there is an area 3½ to 4 scales wide of citrine-drab which extends for 2 to 3 inches and then splits up into 2 stripes. The upper one, 2 scales wide, borders the middorsal band, with the lateral edges of each scale of this clove brown stripe, pale vinaceous-fawn. This dark dorso-lateral stripe tapers to 1 scale in width 6 inches from the vent, and ceases about 1 inch caudad of the vent, giving a unicolored dorsum to the tail. The lower lateral stripe is on the 3rd and 4th scale rows, but is indistinct as such on the forward ⅔ of the body, because there the scales of the first 5 rows have bases of clove brown. On the rear third, this lateral stripe becomes prominent on the 3rd row of scales and ceases just before the vent. The top of the head, upper face plates, and rostral are light grayish olive. The upper labials and some of the suboculars are white. The iris rim is pale ochraceous-buff. Otherwise the eye is black or clove brown except for a wash of light cinnamon-drab at its top and rear. The ventral surface of the tail and forward for half the length of the body is pale ochraceous-salmon drifting through pale ochraceous-buff, to white on neck and lower side of head. The ends of the ventral plates and the first 2 or 3 rows of scales have on their forward edges a wash of light ochraceous-salmon.

Habitat: Almost nothing is recorded on habitat. Van Denburgh and Slevin found it "on the ground under a sage bush at 5 o'clock in the afternoon." Pack recorded one digging in a gently sloping hillside of dry sandy foothills. The Zion and other Utah groups have furnished the most material. They found this secretive snake to be an aggressive fighter, quite arboreal at times.

Period of activity: *First appearance*—Mar. 16, Apr. 26, May 2, May 8 (Stejneger); May, 1934 (Tanner, Ut., 1935); May 15, 1940 (Tanner, Ut., 1940); May 23, 1953.

Breeding: Oviparous. Males 800–941 mm., females 650 or 528–803 mm. *Sexual dimorphism*—In 1945(a) Bogert wrote: "Whereas the means for ventral counts and tail length ratios are virtually identical, there are evidently differences between the sexes in subcaudal counts and in the position of the lateral scale row drop at mid-body, as noted above. As in other races of *hexalepis*, strongly keeled scales are present above the anal region on sexually mature males, whereas the scales in the same region are smooth in females or very faintly keeled on larger specimens. Males probably exceed the females in size, since nearly ⅓ of 31 males measured exceed in total length the largest female in the sample." *Mating*—"A male and a female were taken Apr. 1, 1939, from beneath adjoining rocks near the creek about 4 miles northwest of Santa Cruz" (Hardy).

Eggs—Number, 5–10. "A specimen at the Museum of Vertebrate Zoology, University of California, taken on August 22, contains 8 eggs in the right and 2 in the left ovary, measuring ¾ by ⅛ inches, which had not yet passed into the oviduct" (Woodbury). "The general belief that this species is oviparous can now be confirmed. A large specimen from Zion National Park No. 75 contained 5 eggs which averaged 19.24 mm. long and 7.2 mm. wide. The 2 largest were located in the posterior part of the body and measured in length 24.5 and 26.3 mm. respectively. The 2 middle eggs were intermediate in size measuring 16 mm. each. In none of the eggs were there any indications of a developing embryo. The fact that this specimen was collected in May and contained 2 apparently fully developed eggs would lead us to believe that some of the eggs are deposited in late spring or early summer" (Tanner, Ut., 1941a).

Young—The smallest we have recorded in August and September, 306, 318, 328 mm., must be considerably beyond hatchlings.

Food: Lizards, young snakes. Woodbury, Dodge, V. M. Tanner (Ut., 1935), W. W. Tanner (Ut., 1941a).

Field notes: See under *S. h. hexalepis* above a letter of Bogert, Mar. 22, 1943, applying to a specimen we picked up northeast of Globe, Ariz.

Authorities:

Bogert, C. M. (Gen., 1945a)
Cope, E. D. (Nev., 1884)
Dodge, N. N. (Ariz., 1938)
Hardy, R. (Ut., 1939)
Linsdale, J. M. (Nev., 1938–40)
McKee, E. D., and C. M. Bogert (Ariz., 1934)

Pack, H. J. (Ut., 1930)
Stejneger, L. (Calif., 1893)
Tanner, W. W. (Ut., 1940, 1941a, 1954a)
Van Denburgh, J., and J. R. Slevin (Nev., 1921a)
Woodbury, A. M. (Ut., 1931)

1884: E. D. Cope, the versatile scholar, wrote: *"Phimothyra grahamiae* B. and G. A variety with the dorsal bands nearly obsolete, and separated by 3 rows of dorsal scales on all parts of the body. Two preoculars on one side and 3 on the other. The most northern locality for this species. (St. Thomas, Nevada.)"

Chaparral patch-nosed snake (4—Bogert 1935), Pacific patch-nosed snake (1)

Salvadora hexalepis virgultea (Bogert) 1935. Fig. 193; Map 49

Other common names: Red racer; western patch-nosed snake.

Range: Mountains and foothills of s.w. California from Santa Barbara County to San Quintin Bay, Baja California.—U.S.A.: Calif. Mex.: Baja Calif. *Elevation*—Sea level to 6,000 feet. Coast to desert foothills (Klauber, Gen., 1939); entire area except the mountains above 4,000 feet (Klauber, 1931a); ocean to desert (Perkins, Calif., 1938); 800, 2,200 feet (Atsatt, Calif., 1913); to 6,000 feet in Upper Sonoran (Bogert, Gen., 1939).

Size: Adults, 20–48 inches.

Distinctive characteristics: "A subspecies of *Salvadora grahamiae,* differing from the typical form in having the posterior pair of chin shields separated by 2 or more small scales, in possessing a divided loreal, a proportionately broader frontal, a wider rostral, its edges more detached and in having a greater average number of ventral scales. From *S. g. hexalepis,* to which it is more closely allied, it differs in having a narrower dorsal stripe paralleled on each side by a single brown band, 5 to 5½ scales wide, which may be indistinctly broken up, posteriorly only, into 2 bands. Also it differs from *hexalepis* in having a lower average ventral scale count and in usually having the 6th upper labial only in contact with the eye" (Bogert, Ariz., 1935).

Klauber's (Gen., 1943b) measurements of 23 males and 23 females are: mean over all, 678.78 mm. males, 625.70 mm. females; maxima 1027 mm. (tail 244) males, 892 mm. (200) females.

Color: A snake from Santa Ana Canyon near Orange, Calif., sent by C. W. Kern, July 10, 1939. There is a light middorsal stripe of isabella color on the neck, soon becoming colonial buff and on the tail deep olive-buff. On either side of this is an area 5 scales wide, mummy brown on the neck and forward part and prout's brown to bister toward the tail. Two-thirds of the way back, on the lower edge of the 4th row of scales, this dark band begins to be divided into two by a thread of tilleul buff. The first 2 lateral rows of scales are cream-buff toward the head, but toward the tail have centers of light ochraceous-salmon. The top of the head is snuff brown or buffy brown with the rostral dark olive-buff. The facial plates are like the top of the head. The iris is black with a pupil ring of cartridge buff. The upper labials except for their top edges are like the underside of the head. So also is the lower edge of the rostral. The underside of the head is pale cinnamon-pink or cartridge buff, which passes into cream-buff and grades through warm buff and pale ochraceous-buff to capucine buff on the rear half of the body.

The posterior pair of chin shields are not in contact. They are separated by several small scales. Loreal—2 on left side, single on right.

A snake from Glover Flat, San Diego Co., Calif., received from L. M. Klauber, May 1, 1928. There is a middorsal stripe of cream-buff, on either side of which is an area 5 scales wide of bister with the outer edges of the scales faintly pale campanula blue. The first 2 lateral rows of scales are cartridge buff and pale cinnamon-pink. The top of the head is snuff brown with the tip of head ahead of the eyes tawny-olive. The iris is dull purplish black or blue-violet black with possibly a faint pupil rim of pale olive-buff or with sparse flecking of the same or of olive-buff above the pupil. The under parts of the head and neck are pale pinkish buff or cartridge buff. The rest of the under surfaces are buff or naples yellow, becoming on the underside of the tail light ochraceous-buff.

Habitat: In 1935 when Bogert (Ariz.) described this form, he assigned it to "chaparral-covered foothills" from sea level to 6,000 feet and held it mainly terrestrial, with a predilection for brush and chaparral. As early as 1907 the Grinnells remarked its great climbing agility. Klauber (Calif., 1931a) and Perkins (Calif., 1938) placed it in "brush." In 1939 Klauber (Gen.) in his "Sixteen Year Census" summarized it thus: "Coast 14, Inland Valleys 39, Foothills 117, Mountains 2, Desert foothills 13, Undetermined 1, Total 186. . . . Snakes Encountered on the Road in San Diego County, *Salvadora grahamiae virgultea*. Alive 5, dead 56, Total 61."

Period of activity: The "Sixteen Year Census" has Mar., 5 snakes; Apr., 35; May, 53; June, 49; July, 24; Aug., 7; Sept., 8; Oct., 2; Nov., 2; Dec., 1. Total 186. Rank 15. Per cent 1.44 (Klauber, Gen., 1939). MVZ dates are Apr. 23 to Aug. 3. *First appearance*—Mar. 14, 1912 (J. R. Slevin); Apr. 20, 1924 (CAS 64320 Klauber). *Fall disappearance*—Oct. 13, 1922 (Klauber, Calif., 1928b).

Breeding: Oviparous. Males 678–1,027 mm., females 625–892 mm. *Mating*—Bogert (Gen., 1939) notes that Klauber observed a pair in captivity mating Apr. 14. Bogert had a pair mating in a laboratory in June. *Eggs*—

Fig. 193. *Salvadora h. virgultea,* Santa Ana Canyon, Calif., C. W. Kern.

Fig. 194. *Seminatrix pygaea:* 1,3,6–8, Gainesville, Fla., O. C. Van Hyning and A. H. Wright; 2,4,5, Silver Springs, Fla., E. R. Allen.

We know of no recorded description of the eggs, or their measurements, or their deposition in nature. *Young*—The smallest specimens we have seen, 300–348 mm., must be 50 to 75 mm. beyond hatching size. Klauber's (Gen., 1943b) minima are 315 mm. (tail 72) males, 280 mm. (60) females.

Food: Lizards. Perkins (Calif., 1938), Bogert (Gen., 1939).

Authorities:

Bogert, C. M. (Gen., 1945a; Ariz., 1935)

Grinnell, J. and H. W. (Calif., 1907)

Klauber, L. M. (Gen., 1939; Calif., 1931a, 1934a)

Perkins, C. B. (Calif., 1938, 1949)

Smith, H. M. (Gen., 1938b)

RED-BELLIED MUD SNAKES

Genus *SEMINATRIX* Cope (Fig. 24)

Size small, 9–20 inches; body stout, subcylindric; head small, slightly distinct; tail short (15 to 25 per cent of total length; in a brood of 8 newborn, 19–24 per cent, and in their mother, 17.6 per cent); anal divided; scales smooth, sometimes faintly keeled on tail, without pits, in 17 rows, the lowest rows widest; head scutellation normal; loreal present; oculars 1–2; temporals 1 + 2 (1); upper labials 8 (6, 7, 9); lower labials 9; ventrals 112–134; caudals 46–56 in males, 35–49 in females; maxillary teeth 19–21, increasing slightly posteriorly; mandibular teeth 20–23 subequal; "hemipenis unforked, spinose, and without papillae; 4 indistinct groups of enlarged spines near base, 2 basal hooks laterally; sulcus spermaticus single, lips not conspicuously raised" (Dowling, 1950). Synonyms: *Contia, Tropidonotus.*

KEY TO THE GENUS *SEMINATRIX* (after Dowling) Fig. 195

1. Ventrals more than 126 . . . . *S. p. paludis*
   Ventrals less than 127 2
2. Ventral pattern of short triangular markings (Pattern 4); ventrals usually less than 118 . . . . *S. p. cyclas*
   Ventral pattern not as above (Pattern 1, 2, 3); ventrals usually more than 117 . . . . *S. pygaea pygaea*

Fig. 195. Ventral patterns of *Seminatrix pygaea*: 1,2,3,4, *S. p. pygaea*, 4, *S. p. cyclas*, 3, *S. p. paludis*. Drawings after H. G. Dowling.

Red-bellied mud snake (2—Goin), **Black swamp snake**
(7—Ditmars 1907)

Seminatrix pygaea pygaea (Cope) 1871. Fig. 194; Map 50
(*S. p. paludis* and *S. p. cyclas* of Dowling are included in this account.)

Other common names: Florida miter snake (Yarrow 1882); Florida water snake; mud snake (6—Ditmars 1907); pigmy water snake; red-bellied snake; swamp (black) snake.

Range: Swampy coastal plain from s.e. North Carolina to Dade Co., Fla.; w. in n. Florida to Suwannee River; 1 or 2 isolated records in s.w. Georgia. —Fla.; Ga.; N.C.; S.C. *Elevation*—Sea level to 500 feet.

Size: Adults, 9–20 inches.

Distinctive characteristics: "A subspecies of *Seminatrix pygaea* in which the ventrals usually number more than 117 and less than 125 (M = ca 120) and the ventral color pattern usually consists of long, narrow, curved bars . . . or is immaculate" (Dowling, 1950).

A snake from Summerfield, Fla., near Ocala, received from E. R. Allen, May 2, 1951. Ventrals 126.

Color: A snake from Gainesville, Fla., received from O. C. Van Hyning, Feb. 26, 1929. The upper parts are black with a cast of dull violet-black (2) or (1). The 2 or 3 lower rows of scales are marked with a median thread of deep olive-buff or ecru-olive, which break up on the rear of these scales into clusters of light spots. In water, these rows look to have light-centered scales or appear to be marked with rows of light spots. The other scales of the dorsal surface are obscurely marked with unbroken light threads that show distinctly only under the lens. The top of the head and eye are black. The upper and lower labials are ecru-olive, citrine, or even deep olive-buff with a fine dusting of darker specks. The upper edges of the upper labials are dark. The chin shields are olive-buff, the gulars are grenadine pink or lighter, the lower neck region for 1 or 2 inches back of the head is a strawberry pink or light coral red. The rest of the under parts and underside of the tail are scarlet or jasper red. The ends of the ventrals and caudals are, like the back, black or dusky dull violet-blue or dull violet-black (1) or (2). On the body, this color extends as a bar along the cephalic edges of the ventrals, but on the caudals there are no such bars.

Habitat: This aquatic and fairly fossorial snake has been ascribed usually to the cover of logs, roots and boards along creeks or ponds or at the water's edge of small lakes, marshes, sphagnum bogs and sloughs. In recent times, the University of Florida group have found it common when they rolled up shallow mats of water hyacinths. In fact Goin remarked it "more closely correlated with water hyacinths than any other vertebrate known to me." In 1951 Neill (Gen.) found them "in shallow or fairly deep ponds overgrown with pond-cypress but with little marginal, floating or emergent vegetation."

The snakes were found beneath small piles of soggy leaves or pine needles in very shallow water.

Period of activity: *First appearance*—Feb. 15, 1897 (Brimley); Mar. 20, 1926, Apr. 25, 1924 (Corrington, S.C., 1929); Feb. 26, 1929 (Van Hyning). "I have records for February, March, May" (Goin). *Fall disappearance*— Nov. 20, 1912 (J. Hurter); January (Brimley); January (Howell); Nov. 23, 1902 (Brimley). "I have records for October, November, December" (Goin). Dowling has only 1 male for August and 2 males and 1 female for December from Payne's Prairie, Fla. *Hibernation*—"I have dug them up in winter under 2 feet of sphagnum and mud" (Carr).

Breeding: Viviparous. Males 216–355 mm., females, 240–379 mm. *Young* —Number, 3–13. Size, 95–116 mm. long. Time of birth, Aug. 20–Oct. 18. The first note on breeding was Ditmars'. A 16¾-inch specimen "gave birth to 11 young on the 20th of August; the young were as indifferent to food as the parent; their coloration was exactly like her. They were fond of laying in the water of their drinking dish; their skins were shed under water." The next came from Goin in 1943: "On the afternoon of October 18, 1939, I collected a large female which that night gave birth to 8 young. The following table gives the measurements and scale counts of the series of young. [Four males, 129, 127, 134, 128 mm. long, had 121, 123, 126, 126 ventrals, 54, 54, 53, 55 caudals, and tails 31, 29, 30, 30 mm. long. Four females, 123, 124, 124, 124 mm. long, had 127, 125, 122, 125 ventrals, 44, 45, 42, 45 caudals, tails 24, 25, 24, 25 mm. long. All 17-17-15 scale rows. The mother was 379 mm.]" In 1933 Ditmars in his *Reptiles of the World* mentioned a litter of 9 born Aug. 21. In both Conant and Bridges (Gen., 1939) and Schmidt and Davis (Gen., 1941) are references to litters of 13. Allen recorded three litters of 3 to 5 individuals.

Dowling in his interesting study gave this summary: "The smallest with enlarged eggs was 240 mm. long. There was no marked correlation of number of eggs with the size of the mother. The smallest individual (240 mm.) contained 7 eggs; the largest (356 mm.), 5. The number of enlarged eggs ranged from 2 to 9, averaging about 5 in the 11 females with enlarged eggs or embryos. The accumulated data indicate that the eggs begin to enlarge when the female reaches about 160 mm. in length, but probably they do not become mature until the female is about 240 mm. in length. The number of young is usually 5 or 6, with recorded extremes of 2 and 11."

Food: Frogs, fish, earthworms, salamanders, leeches, worms. Dowling, Carr, Ditmars.

Field notes: Aug. 18, 1922: The boys made a bet. If one skinned a skunk, the other had to do a turkey vulture. The skunk was skinned, so we began prodding the vulture skinner. At 8 P.M. he went down to the corner of two pieces of pine woods where vultures roosted. He shot a turkey buzzard, a male. In making the turkey buzzard disgorge, it first gave up a snake and the eye cups of a bird (presumably a swamp owl). We hastily examined the snake amongst the debris and thought it *Farancia*. Later we went out and dug it up for examination.

Aug. 19, 1922: A look at this form makes it *Seminatrix*, the first record for Georgia. Did the owl capture it or did the vulture capture it separately? A fine record. Probably a form inhabiting cypress bays and cypress ponds.

Years afterward we said to some friends of the Cornell Jugatae (entomological seminar), "We'll make much of this new state record. See if Prof. —— doesn't challenge it." After we had finished, the professor reacted as we expected: "How do you know the vulture didn't catch the snake in Florida and roost in Georgia? Who knows but the owl caught it in Florida? Is this borderline record a good state record?"

Mar. 31, 1934, Gainesville, Fla. (see account of *Storeria victa*): Went with the University of Florida boys to Payne's Prairie. In rolling the hyacinth mats onto the banks, we took several *Seminatrix pygaea*, 1 small *Farancia*, *T. s. sackenii*, and *S. victa*.

Authorities:

Allen, E. R. (Fla., 1941a)
Brown, A. E. (Gen., 1901)
Carr, A. F., Jr. (Fla., 1940a)
Cope, E. D. (Fla., 1871, 1875, 1889)

Corrington, J. D. (S.C., 1927, 1929)
Ditmars, R. L. (Gen., 1907)
Dowling, H. G. (Fla., 1950)
Goin, C. J. (Fla., 1943)
Loennberg, E. (Fla., 1895)

1901, A. E. Brown: "On the whole I suspect that *pygaea* is a degenerating *Tropidonotus* in process of acquiring subterranean habits. It is possible that the light line on the dorsal scales may indicate the former presence of keels, but lately lost."

South Florida mud snake

Seminatrix pygaea cyclas Dowling 1950. Fig. 195; Map 50

Other common names: For these and for other topics not treated below, see *S. p. pygaea*.

Range: "From Polk County, in central peninsular Florida, south to the tip of the peninsula" (Dowling).

Distinctive characteristics: "A subspecies of *Seminatrix pygaea* in which the ventral pattern consists of short triangular lateral markings (Pattern 4) and the ventrals usually number less than 119 (M = Ca 116)" (Dowling).

Color: A snake from the Everglades of southern Florida received from E. R. Allen, May 2, 1951. The dorsum and top of head are black; lower edges of upper labials and lower labials are isabella color. The eye is black. The mid-belly is jasper red, fading forward to carrot red on neck. The underside of head is isabella color with considerable suffusion of black on lower labials. The black of the dorsum extends as prominent bars along the front edge of each ventral ⅓ of the way across the plate, expanding in width at base of ventral; which areas are separated by narrower areas of cartridge buff, the red of belly extending laterad along front edge of the black bar. The underside of the tail is entirely jasper red. Ventrals 119.

Authority: H. G. Dowling (Fla., 1950)

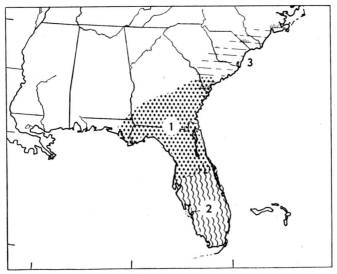

Map 50. *Seminatrix*—1, *pygaea pygaea;* 2, *p. cyclas;* 3, *p. paludis.*

Carolina mud snake

Seminatrix pygaea paludis Dowling 1950. Fig. 195; Map 50
(See *S. pygaea pygaea* for topics not treated here.)

Range: "*Seminatrix pygaea paludis* ranges from Carteret County, North Carolina, westward to the fall line in the vicinity of Columbia, South Carolina, and southward in the coastal plain to the area of intergradation with *S. p. pygaea*. The exact location of the area of intergradation cannot be determined at present because of the scarcity of specimens from critical areas, but it lies between Charleston County, South Carolina, and the Okefinokee Swamp, Georgia. The barrier between the 2 subspecies may be the broad dry sandy area which lies on either side of the Altamaha River, Georgia."—N.C.; S.C.

Distinctive characteristics: "A lone series of 7 males and 2 females has been obtained from the Carolinas. These snakes are from the Santee River, South Carolina. The ventrals range from 127 to 134, with a mean of 131.11 ± .72. This character alone is sufficient to distinguish these snakes from any of those from southern Georgia or Florida. All of the specimens have the typical Pattern 3" (Dowling).

Habitat: In 1927 J. D. Corrington made a noteworthy contribution. "On

April 25, 1924, the writer was accompanied by a small party of students on a field study at Horseshoe Lake, a fairly small and shallow body of water on the outskirts of New Brookland, Lexington County, S.C., just across the Congaree River from Columbia. The first specimen of *Seminatrix* was found here beneath a discarded automobile side curtain which lay partly in and partly out of the water, the snake being just at the water's edge. The second example was brought in by two students from Lakeview, a fairly large pleasure lake formed by damming of a small stream in Richland County, S.C. March 20, 1926, a situation some 7 miles east of Horseshoe Lake and across the river, which is here wide and rather swift flowing and rough. This snake was taken from an environment similar to that of the first time, being found under a board within a few feet of the water."

With Corrington (S.C., 1929), Jopson, Chamberlain, and others, we have considered this form to belong to any fresh-water environment of the coastal southeast—i.e., shallow marshes or prairies, open lakes and their borders, wooded swamps or cypress bogs, cypress ponds, runs, branches or branch swamps, river or river swamps. Jopson in S.C. (1927) found "5 individuals

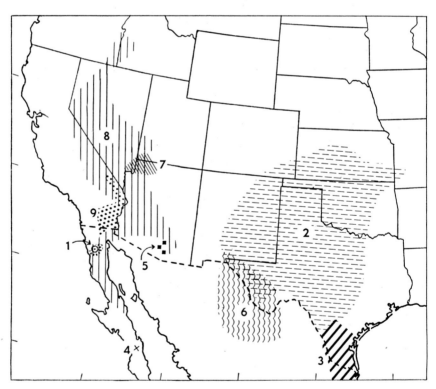

Map 51. *Sonora*—1, *bancrofti*; 2, *e. episcopa*; 3, *e. taylori*; 4, *mosaueri*; 5, *s. semiannulata*; 6, *s. blanchardi*; 7, *s. gloydi*; 8, *s. isozona*; 9, *s. linearis*.

of this species, all from cypress swamps. Four were captured while we were digging for *Siren*. One was found beneath a partially submerged log which also sheltered a small *Farancia*."

Brimley (N.C., 1941–1942) states, "It is also known to occur in middle South Carolina, and there is no particular reason why it should not occur sparingly in the coastal plain, at least in the southeastern corner."

Field notes: Apr. 26, 1950, Wilmington, N.C., in a swamp of Cape Fear River and across a creek on route No. 17: Beside the road saw a dead *Farancia* and 6 feet farther on a dead *Abastor*. Anna walked 100 feet farther on and found the prize, *Seminatrix,* beside a dead frog. These 3 in one stop. Near this area are 100–200 Liberty ships. This swamp has in blossom golden club (*Orontium*), fetter bushes, *Viburnum dentata, Bradleia, Salix marginata,* and *Lobelia boykinii.*

Authorities:

Brimley, C. S. (N.C., 1941–42)   Dowling, H. G. (Fla., 1950)
Corrington, J. D. (S.C., 1929)   Jopson, H. M. G. (S.C., 1940)

GROUND SNAKES

Genus *SONORA* Baird and Girard (Figs. 21, 23, 24)

Size small, 8–19 inches, slender; head not very distinct; anal divided; tail short; abdomen rounded; no nasal valve; snout rounded and rounded in profile; anterior margin of frontal rounded, straight, or slightly angulate; scales smooth with conspicuous light edges on lateral scales, in rows 13, 15, rarely 14 or 16; without apical pits; snout not conspicuously projecting beyond lower jaw; loreal present; nasal entire; 1 preocular; upper labials 7; temporals 1 + 2; 1, occasionally 2, maxillary foramina; maxillary teeth 11 + 3 to 13 + 3; 3 posterior maxillary teeth moderately enlarged with lateral groove; several rows of gulars between tips of chin shields and ventrals; hemipenis (after Stickel) (for *semiannulata* group): length usually 12 or 13 caudals (range 11–15); one or at most 2 of lower rows of calyces are at all spinous; calyces with short, triangular lobes (except at top of organ); 8–14 small and medium-sized spines on plane of the large basal sulcar spines and below zone of small spines; almost always with a spine beside each basal spine; spines in zone of small spines not hooked, the whole spine with only a slight sigmoid curvature; well-developed bare area between apical lobes, sulcus not forked. Synonyms: *Chionactis, Contia, Homalocranium, Homalosoma, Lamprosoma, Ogmius, Scolecophis.*

KEY TO THE GENUS *SONORA*

a. Anterior scale rows 13 rarely 14; ventrals in ♂ 126–144, in ♀ 136–153; caudals ♂ 39–50, ♀ 35–41; 9–10 or more rows of gulars between tips of chin shields and ventrals; posterior chin shields not in contact and not much different in size from adjoining gulars; temporals 1–1. Color: dorsum uniform buffy brown to light vinaceous-drab; top of head black; venter white to colonial buff. (S. Texas, n.e. Mexico.)   *S. e. taylori*

aa. Anterior scale rows 15, rarely 14 or 16, temporals 1–2.

  b. Scale rows near anus 13 (14 in only known female); ventrals ♂ 150–155 (average 152), ♀ 164; caudals ♂ 43–48, ♀ 39. Color: unbanded, grayish brown or brown. (Comondu, Baja California, Mex.)

                                                 S. mosaueri

  bb. Scale rows near anus 15 or 14; ventrals ♂ 134–168, ♀ 140–185; caudals ♂ 39–59, ♀ 31–54. Color: various.

    c. Scale rows near anus 15 in 90%, 14 in 10%; ventrals average 147 ♂–153 ♀; caudals ♂ 52 or less (39–52 (av. 43.5)), ♀ 48 or less (31–48 (av. 37)); ventrals minus caudals ♂ less than 109, ♀ less than 127 (for contrast with *S. s. semiannulata*); 4–9 rows gulars between chin shields and ventrals; posterior chin shields not much different in size from adjoining gulars and not in contact. Dorsum plain, striped, barred, or collared; in plain color form, there may be dark spot on head; bands if present 12–29 on body and tail, 10–22 on body, bands much narrower than intervals—ratio may be 1 1/2 or 2 1/2 scales to 6 1/2 scales; venter commonly clear pale yellow, but sometimes with black rings on tail in barred form, or washed with interrupted bands of vinaceous-rufous in plain form; in red-lined form of *e. episcopa*, lateral scales are edged in front with brown, and *whole top of head is vinaceous-rufous*, while in *S. s. linearis* lateral scales are edged with ivory, and snout only is orange-rufous; in plain *e. episcopa* first 4 rows are light edged, but top of head is entirely grayish olive. (Cent. Texas n. to s.e. Kansas and Missouri w. to e. Colorado and New Mexico.)   *S. episcopa episcopa*

    cc. Scale rows near anus 14 rarely 15 or 13; ventrals average higher, 151–172.

      d. Caudals less than 50 in ♂s. Black bands 21–22 on body, about 4 1/2 scales long with interspaces 4 1/2–5 scales long; ventrals minus caudals in ♂ more than 109, in ♀ (presumably over 127) (No female known) (in contrast with *S. e. episcopa*); ventrals plus caudals 197 or fewer in males; ventrals ♂ 153,

154, caudals ♂ 41, 43; posterior chin shields not in contact, not different from adjoining gulars; 4 labials contact anterior chin shield; anterior margin of frontal angulate. Color ventral surface clear chartreuse yellow. (Santa Rita Mts., Ariz.; expected in Sierra Madre Occidental, Mex.) *S. semiannulata semiannulata*

dd. Caudals 53 or more in ♂s, 45 or more in ♀s.

  e. Ventrals minus caudals 97 or fewer in males, 115 or fewer in females; tail 23% to 25.2% of total length in males, 20.3% to 21.6% in females (in preserved specimens); black bands in barred form 35–50 with many of the black scales in rows 1–3 edged with light; ventrals ♂ av. 151, ♀ av. 160; caudals ♂ 53–59 (av. 56), ♀ 46–51 (av. 48.5); color: dorsum, plain, striped, orbarred; venter commonly clear yellow (but specimen of Mulaik is barred across venter like *S. gloydi*). The striped form has top of head orange-citrine with rostral, internasal, and prefrontal olive, and the clear grenadine stripe may be 3–5 scales wide as a core of tawny dorsal area 10 scales wide. (Brewster Co., Tex.) *S. s. blanchardi*

  ee. Ventrals minus caudals 98 or more in males, 116 or more in females; tail 19.4% to 23.3% of total length in males; 16.4% to 20.0% in females; dark bands on body, if present, 19–40; in striped form lateral scales have light edges; ventrals ♂ av. 161, ♀ av. 172.

    f. Regular series of dark dorsal crossbands present, 25–50; bars and interspaces about equal.

      g. Several to all dark bands meeting on venter to form rings; posterior chin shields larger than adjoining gulars. Ventrals ♀ 178, caudals ♀ 48. *S. s. gloydi*

     gg. No or few dark crossbands meeting across belly. Black bands on body 19–40, tail 6–12, total 25–50. Ventrals ♂ av. 160, ♀ av. 171; caudals ♂ 52, ♀ av. 46; ventrals plus caudals ♂ 203 or more, ♀ 207 or more; posterior chin shields not in contact, but well differentiated from adjoining gulars; 3 labials contact anterior chin shields. Color: venter pale yellow or green with many dorsal black bars extending onto, but mostly not crossing venter. (S. Idaho, Utah, Nevada, Arizona (exclusive of range of *S. s. gloydi* and *S. s. semiannulata*). Inyo Co., Calif.) (See ff–gg for plain form.) *S. s. isozona*

    ff. No regular dark dorsal crossbands present (contrast ventrals with plain *S. e. episcopa*'s 134–162).

g. Sharp-edged dorsal scarlet stripe covering 3–6 rows strongly contrasting with olive gray to andover green scales of sides, all scales except dorsal red stripe with conspicuous light ivory yellow borders; no red on lateral scales, centers of 1st row dark, *snout orange-rufous, top of head and facial plates buffy olive*. Ventrals 168–185, caudals 45–50. Posterior chin shields not in contact and not distinctly different from adjoining gulars; 7–8 rows gulars between shield tips and ventrals; head flat; eye large. (N. Baja Calif. and Cocopal Mts., Mex., s.e. California, and w. Nevada.)

S. s. linearis

gg. Uniform back with dusky head, or top of head and face grayish olive with spots of vinaceous-rufous; or dorsal red stripe not sharp-edged, covers 7 scale rows, rows 2, 3, 4 gray with touches of rufous and thread-like light edges; 1st row yellow with 1st inch clear, then scales marked with vinaceous-rufous. Ventrals av. ♂ 160, ♀ 171, caudals ♂ 52, ♀ 46. Posterior chin shields not in contact, but well differentiated from adjoining gulars; 6–7 rows gulars between chin shields and ventrals. 3 labials contact anterior chin shields; venter barium yellow. (S. Idaho, Utah, Nevada, Inyo Co., Calif., and Arizona exclusive of range of *S. s. gloydi* and *S. s. semiannulata*.)

S. s. isozona

Miter snake (5—Strecker 1915), Great Plains ground snake (2)

Sonora episcopa episcopa (Kennicott) 1859. Fig. 196; Map 51

Other common names: Banded miter snake (3); bicolor(ed) ground snake; black-banded ground snake; Great Plains earth snake; (prairie) ground snake; Sonora; striped ground snake; Texas ground snake; yellow ground snake.

Range: From Nuevo León, Mex., to St. Clair Co., Mo.; w. through s. Kansas, s.e. Colorado, and e. New Mexico.—U.S.A.: Colo.; Kan.; Mo.; N.M.; Okla.; Tex. Mex.: Nuevo León. *Elevation*—500–5,000 feet. 750 feet (Evans).

Size: Adults, 8–15 inches.

Distinctive characteristics: "A species of *Sonora* characterized by 15-15 scale rows and the lowest number of ventrals and caudals of any 15-rowed species of the genus with which it would be confused. The color is phenomenally variable; plain, streaked, striped, barred, collared; gray, brown, black, red. Combinations and intermediates of all these variations have been seen from one locality" (Stickel, Gen., 1938).

Color: Seven snakes from Palo Pinto, Tex., received from Philip Harter and (except where otherwise noted) described May 25, 1938. One snake in the *gray and black phase:* The back is crossed by black bars covering 1½ to 2½ scales longitudinally, 17 bars on body and 6 on tail. They extend down the side to the 2nd or even 1st row of scales. The background or interspace color is light drab to hair brown, covering 5½ to 6 scales longitudinally. The top of the head from the horizontal of the eyes backward is fuscous, from the eyes forward, drab or light grayish olive. The iris is fuscous. The under parts are pale vinaceous-fawn, becoming on the lower side of the head, pale olive-buff. The upper labials may be olive-buff.

A *snake not barred,* with red stripe down back: The middorsal region for 3 scales' width is vinaceous-rufous. All the lateral scales are isabella color, edged in front with liver brown or chestnut-brown. The top of the head, from the eye along the rear margin of parietals and 2 scales rearward, is like the midback, vinaceous-rufous. So also are the rostral, internasal, and pre-frontal. The frontal, supraocular, and inner half of the parietal are drab or light grayish olive, with a dusky line through the center of the frontal and along the interparietal suture. The iris is black. The under parts are chamois on the rear, shading through deep colonial buff to primrose yellow or colonial buff on the underside of the head and the upper labials.

A *snake of uniform color:* The general dorsal color is hair brown, citrine drab, buffy olive, or grayish olive, barely showing a dorsal stripe of vinaceous-rufous in the rear half. The top of the head is conspicuously vinaceous-rufous in contrast with the hair brown or light grayish olive of the forward back. The iris is black. The plates on the rear half of the venter, but not on the tail, are prominently washed with interrupted bands of vinaceous-rufous. The forward venter is white slightly washed with the same. The underside of the head is white.

A young one, described Aug., 1938. *Uniform reddish brown above,* creamy below.

In another snake from the same place the entire upper parts are *buffy olive* except for a dusky spot on center of frontal and along the interparietal groove.

A *barred form:* A middorsal band 2 to 3 scales wide of grenadine red to carnelian red extends to the tip of the tail. The back is crossed by 21 black bars on the body and 2 partial ones on the tail, which are 1½ to 2½ scales longitudinally. You would expect 26 or more bars, but there are certain longer intervals where they are omitted. Interspaces are usually 6 to 7 scales longitudinally, but one is 13 to 14 scales. The top of the head is grenadine red or carnelian red with a half-moon of black across the front of the parietals from eye to eye. The under parts are mustard yellow on the rear, passing through pinard yellow to maize yellow or baryta yellow on throat and upper labials.

A *snake with bars widely spaced:* The general color is dark olive-buff or isabella color with no middorsal red showing except on the tail. The back is crossed with 14 irregularly spaced bars on the body, 9 good ones and 5 obscure, and 2 faint ones on the tail. One would suspect that this creature once had about 22 crossbars on the body. The rear of the top of the head is dusky. The iris is black. The rear of the venter is colonial buff. This color passes through primrose yellow to marguerite yellow on the underside of the head and the upper labials.

Variation in coloration: This is one of the most perplexing snakes to taxonomists. Consult Ortenburger, Force, and Strecker (Tex., 1929b).

Habitat: This little secretive snake is a prairie species, taken mainly in dry situations. By day, this burrower may be ploughed up or taken from under cover of stones, boards, or rocks. It may be beside or in the road, in vacant town lots, and in quarries. It is frequently collected from rocky localities and hillsides, especially sunny southern hill slopes.

In the light of the establishment of *Sonora s. blanchardi* for western Texas, we are much interested in Jameson and Flury's note (Tex., 1949) not on *S. s. blanchardi* but *Sonora episcopa* (Kennicott): "One specimen was found in the catclaw-grama association of the Roughland belt. The specimen was dark gray in color, had no black bands, and both loreals were missing." Milstead *et al.* (Tex., 1950) in the Stockton plateau wrote: "Twenty-one specimens were taken in the following associations: Cedar-Savannah 3; cedar ocotillo, 9; persimmon-shin oak, 2; cedar-oak, 3; mesquite-creosote, 2; walnut–desert willow, 2."

Period of activity: *Early appearances*—Apr., 1902 (Brown); Apr. 27–May 24 (Force); Apr. 9, 30, 1932 (Burt); Apr. 18, 1931 (S. E. Seymour); Mar. 15, Apr. 1, 3, 21, May 27, 1934 (Burt and Hoyle); Apr. 15, 1932; Apr. 23, May 21, 1933 (Burt); Apr. 17, June 19, 1938 (Evans); Apr., 1926 (Kirn).

Breeding: Oviparous. Males to 296 mm., females to 305 mm.

Food: Ants' eggs, ants, insects, small invertebrates. Strecker (Tex., 1930, 1934), Conant and Bridges (Gen., 1939), Schmidt and Davis (Gen., 1941).

Authorities:

Brown, A. E. (Gen., 1901; 1903)
Burt, C. E. (Gen., 1935; Kan., 1933)
Burt, C. E., and W. L. Hoyle (Gen., 1935)
Cockerell, T. D. A. (Colo., 1927)
Cope, E. D. (Gen., 1900; Tex., 1880)
Cragin, F. W. (Kan., 1894)
Ellis, M. M., and J. Henderson (Colo., 1913)

Evans, P. D. (Mo., 1940)
Force, E. R. (Okla., 1930)
Kennicott, R. (in Baird, Tex., 1859)
Ortenburger, A. I. (Okla., 1923)
Smith, H. M. (Kan., 1950)
Stickel, W. H. (Gen., 1938, 1943)
Strecker, J. K., Jr. (Tex., 1929b)

1880: E. D. Cope declared that Texas had 3 "well-marked color varieties, which pass into each other." (Then follows a description of 3 subspecies: *episcopa, torquata, isozona*. He has *episcopa* in Texas and *torquata* in northwest Texas.)

1901: A. E. Brown put *Contia episcopa* in 2 groups: (1) *C. e. episcopa*, rosy yellow to ashy; no crossbands; (2) *Contia episcopa isozona*, orange

Fig. 196. *Sonora episcopa episcopa,* Palo Pinto, Tex., P. Harter.

Fig. 197. *Sonora e. taylori:* 1–5, Edinburg, Tex., S. Mulaik; 6,7, Medina Lake, Tex.

with black crossbands. *"C. e. torquata* Cope rests upon degrees of color intensity which are admittedly inconstant in the 2 specimens known."

1923: A. I. Ortenburger's paper, "The Status of *Sonora semiannulata* and *Sonora episcopa,"* we considered a very significant one because 2 years later we encountered in an El Paso, Tex., field a situation similar to the one described. We still consider this article noteworthy, along with later careful papers by Stickel.

South Texas ground snake (2), Taylor's ground snake (3—Pope 1937)

Sonora episcopa taylori (Boulenger) 1894. Fig. 197; Map 51

Other common names: South Texas earth snake; Taylor's snake (3—Ditmars 1907).

Range: From Calhoun and Wilson Counties in s. Texas to cent. Nuevo León, Mex.—U.S.A.: Tex. Mex.: Nuevo León. *Elevation*—Sea level to 1,000 feet. In general *taylori* occurs in areas lower than 500 feet in altitude, whereas the records for *episcopa* indicate that it inhabits higher terrain.

Size: Adults, 10–16 inches.

Distinctive characteristics: "The general color is light brown to dark brown. In a large number of individuals the anterior and central portions of the dorsal scales are darkened, which gives a longitudinally striped appearance on the sides. The head is usually brown like the body, but in numerous individuals the top of the head is partially or entirely much darker than the body" (Mulaik).

Color: We found this snake between La Pryor and Crystal City, Tex., under a fence post in a very dry location, Apr. 2, 1925. The general color is buffy brown, which under the lens appears wood brown. The first 3 rows of scales are light vinaceous-fawn or vinaceous-buff. Between the 1st and 2nd scale rows, the 2nd and 3rd rows, and the 3rd and 4th, are faint light longitudinal lines. The top of the head is black except for rostral, internasals, and prefrontals, which are buffy olive or buffy brown. The upper labials are pale drab-gray, pallid vinaceous-drab, or white. The iris is black except for a faint more or less broken pupil rim of buffy olive or body color. The underside of the head is pale drab-gray, pallid vinaceous-drab, or white. The rest of the ventral surface is yellowish glaucous.

Habitat: About the only note on this is the Mulaiks' sentence, *"Sonora taylori* is a burrowing snake which is found most often after hard rains in spring and summer months." This form is from the semidesert or thorn savannah of Shreve, the small tree semiforest, and the South Texas tip of the coastal plain. It likes sandy country. The country from Falfurrias to Edinburg, Tex., a semidesert, is an ideal area for it.

Breeding: Oviparous. Males 270–300 mm., females up to 370 mm. *Eggs*— The only eggs of which we know, we saw ourselves. The Mulaiks tell us, "Usually about 6 eggs are laid, these measuring 20 mm. in length and 6 mm. in diameter." *Young*—The smallest specimen measures 99 m. We do not know the size of the hatchlings. The smallest we have seen was 133 mm.

Field notes: May 2, 1934, Edinburg, Tex.: Mulaik has in his laboratory a female *Sonora taylori*. It was brought in with grass. The grass he put into the waste basket. Then he looked at the snake later and found an egg. He examined the waste basket grass and found another egg. Today there is another egg in the box. I believe these are the first egg records for *Sonora taylori*. The snake finally laid 6 eggs 20 mm. in length and 6 mm. in diameter. This snake is 133 mm., of which the tail is 22 mm.

Authorities:

Boulenger, G. A. (Gen., 1893–96)
Cope, E. D. (Gen., 1900)
Mulaik, S. and D. (Tex., 1941)

Stickel, W. H. (Gen., 1938, 1943)
Strecker, J. K., Jr. (Tex., 1915)

1941, S. and D. Mulaik: We quote most of their study of 70 specimens of this snake collected from 1933 to 1939: "Scale rows on anterior 5th of body 14, and 13 posteriorly except for the following irregularities observed back of the anterior fourth of body: SM 12, 14-13-14; SM 10 and SM 33, 14-14; SM 815, 14-13-14-13; Stickel (*Copeia*, 1938: 183) reported the range of ventrals in males as from 126 to 139. The present series ranges in males from 132 to 144 with an average of 137, and for females 138 to 153 with an average of 146. Caudals range in males from 39 to 50 with an average of 45; in females from 35 to 41 with an average of 38. In the males the caudals number 29.9 percent or more of the number of ventrals, with an average of 33.2 percent; while in females they range under 28.3 percent with an average of 25.8 percent. A study of the tail and body lengths showed that in males the tail was 24 percent of the body length, or more, with an average of 25.5 percent, while in females it was less than 22 percent with an average of 20.5 percent. These appear to be significant secondary sexual characters. There are 2 pairs of chin shields, the anterior larger, about twice as long as broad; posterior pair variable, but smaller than the anterior, often separated by gular scales. Upper labials 7-7 except SM 31 which has 6-6, the loss apparently due to fusion of the 3rd and 4th. Lower labials 6-6 except SM 34 which has 7 on the right side. Nostril perforates middle of the entire nasal. Loreal 1-1. SM 19 has nasal and loreal fused. Preoculars 1-1. Postoculars 2-2, except SM 816 and SM 817 which have 1-1. Temporals 1-1 except SM 808 in which the upper labial is fused with the anterior temporal; SM 12 and SM 17, 1-2 on right side; SM 20 and SM 23, 1-2 on both sides. The anal plate is divided."

Arizona earth snake

Sonora semiannulata semiannulata Baird and Girard 1853. Fig. 198; Map 51

Range: Region of Santa Rita Mts., Ariz. *Elevation*—3,000 to 4,000 feet.
Size: The two specimens are males, 244–119 mm. in length.
Distinctive characteristics: (See "Authorities" for comment by Stickel.) In his key, Stickel has: "Ventrals plus caudals 202 or fewer in males, 206 or fewer in females. . . . Ventrals minus caudals in males generally more than 109, in females presumably average 127 (no females known); scale rows 15-14; pattern consisting of dark crossbands; known only from the vicinity of the Santa Rita Mountains of Arizona." Cope speaks of the type as possibly an abnormal specimen "remarkable in having the superciliary plate divided symmetrically on each side by a suture which cuts off a plate . . . which Baird and Girard term a third postocular."
Color: A snake from Sonoita, Ariz., brought to L. P. Wehrle's office at the University of Tucson by James E. Serven of High Haven Ranch (11 miles north of Sonoita and near the Empire Mts. and Barrel Spring), Apr. 13, 1936, and described Apr. 22, 1936. The back is crossed with bands 3½ to 4 scales long of black or dark quaker drab. The interspaces, 4 scales long, are grenadine red on the dorsum and colonial buff on the sides. The rostral, internasals, prefrontals, and forward third of the supraoculars and frontal are grenadine or light coral red. There is a black crescent across the head and through the eyes. The nuchal region is grenadine red. The upper labials are chartreuse yellow, the first 5 with their upper edges black or quaker drab. The iris is black or dark quaker drab with the upper and rear portions of the pupil rim pinkish buff or cream-buff. The lower labials, the chin, and the whole ventral surface are unbroken chartreuse yellow.
Structure: Anterior margin of frontal angulate.
A similar snake received from C. L. Evans of Phoenix, Ariz. Light bands, 2½ scales long of flame scarlet are on the middorsal region for the width of 3 or 4 scales. The under parts are white with some vinaceous tints.
Breeding: Oviparous. Male 244 mm. The other male specimen of 119 mm must be close to birth size.
Field notes: Apr. 13, 1936: In a letter, E. P. Hilton, of Hilton Ranch in the Empire Mts., wrote, "As to snakes I have seen a good many of the little red, white and black, as you describe, but do not recall of seeing any with an upturned nose [*Ficimia*]." Are these the much sought and little seen *Sonora s. semiannulata?*

Authorities:

Baird, S. F., and C. Girard (Gen., 1853)

Cope, E. D. (Gen., 1900)

Stickel, W. H. (Gen., 1943)

1900, E. D. Cope: "I suspect that the *Sonora semiannulata* of Baird and Girard was established on an abnormal specimen of this species [*C. e.*

isozonus]. That specimen is remarkable in having the superciliary plate divided symmetrically on each side by a suture which cuts off a plate whose apex reaches the parietal and which Baird and Girard term a third postocular. The muzzle was somewhat wrinkled, so as to produce folds of the integument. This led to the mistaken belief that the nasal is divided. Omitting these two characters, there remains only a slightly more protuberant rostral plate, which is not more, in my opinion, than an individual peculiarity. The coloration is identical with that of the *C. e. isozonus*. More specimens will be necessary to settle the question definitely. Should the identification here suggested prove necessary, the name of the species will stand as *Chionactis semiannulatus,* with the subspecies *episcopus, torquatus* and *semiannulatus.*"

1938: W. H. Stickel's (Gen.) *semianulata* of 1938 plus his new *S. m. miniata* make up his *S. s. isozona* of 1943 except for the Grand Canyon and Sonoita, Ariz., local populations.

1943, Stickel: "It is proposed to restrict the type locality, originally given as 'Sonora, Mexico,' to the vicinity of the Santa Rita Mountains of Arizona. . . . Since the R.O.M.Z. [Royal Ontario Museum of Zoology] Santa Rita specimen closely resembles the type specimen, while snakes from nearby Huachuca Mountains are *isozona,* it seems highly probable that the type was collected in the region of the Santa Rita Mountains, Santa Cruz County, Arizona."

1944, A. H. and A. A. Wright: On Apr. 13, 1936 a *Sonora* was brought into Prof. L. P. Wehrle's office for Dr. C. T. Vorhies. On Apr. 22, 1936, we saw it. It came from Sonoita, Ariz. Had we known that two years later Stickel would put *Sonora semiannulata semiannulata* definitely only along the eastern edge of the Santa Ritas we would have looked at the supraoculars. All we did was describe the color. What opportunities are missed in a hurried trip! Our good friends Vorhies and Wehrle would have been besieged for that specimen. A good series from Rosemount to Patagonia and even Santa Cruz is badly needed. We suspect Cope was right in 1900 in holding this type specimen abnormal, and we urge very strongly that herpetologists proceed to collect material to clear up this point. We who partially muffed on the Sonoita specimen hope the nomenclatorial difficulties of the genus *Sonora* don't have to revolve about this specimen for 90 years more.

Blanchard's ground snake (1—Conant and Bridges 1939), Big Bend earth snake

Sonora semiannulata blanchardi Stickel 1938. Fig. 199; Map 51

Other common names: Bicolored ground snake; Blanchard's western ground snake.

Range: The Big Bend region of Texas and Chihuahua, Mex.—U.S.A.:

Fig. 198. *Sonora semiannulata semiannulata,* High Haven ranch, Sonoita, Ariz.,
J. E. Serven through L. P. Wehrle.

Fig. 199. *Sonora s. blanchardi,* El Paso,
Tex., M. L. Crimmins.

N.M.; Tex. Mex.: Chihuahua. *Elevation*—4,000 to 6,000 feet. 6,000 feet (Bailey, Tex., 1905).

Size: Adults, 9–13 inches.

Distinctive characteristics: "Snout and abdomen of normal shape; 15 scale rows anteriorly and 14 posteriorly; ventrals fewer than in *semiannulata* and caudals higher than in *episcopa*. . . . The color may be uniform brownish or grayish or may have bands as in *semiannulata*, or may show intermediate conditions in which the bands are only partially present" (Stickel, Gen., 1938).

Color: A snake from El Paso, Tex., taken by Col. M. L. Crimmins, July, 1925. The back is crossed by 39 black bars with 11 more on the tail. These bars are 2, 2½, or 3 scales long and usually extend to the 1st row of scales, but on the 1st 5 or 6 scale rows, the black scales are edged with sulphur yellow or pale green-yellow. The dorsal interspaces are flame scarlet and are 2 to 3 scales long. The nuchal band is flame scarlet and is 13 scales transversely, while the next interspace band is 10 scales transversely. The others have the dorsal 6 scales of flame scarlet and those below of sulphur yellow or pale green-yellow with slight touches of salmon-orange or flame scarlet. The general color therefore is about pale orange-yellow. The top of the head from the eye backward is crossed by a crescent band of citrine-drab and black, giving a deep olive or dark olive appearance. The side of the head back of the eye is of the same color, and ahead of the eye is grayish olive. The top of the head from the eye forward is flame scarlet. The upper labials are pale green-yellow except for their dark upper edges. The outer area of the iris is dark or dusky slate-violet. The pupil rim is pale green-yellow, and an area just outside it has a few lines or spots of salmon-orange. The ventral surfaces are sulphur yellow or pale green-yellow.

Another snake taken by Colonel Crimmins, July, 1925. Middorsally is a band of clear grenadine, for the most part 3 scales wide. Just back of the parietals, it may be 5 scales wide, and in the caudal portion of the body it may be 4 or 4 and 2 half scales wide. Forward, a few of these scales may have dark central lines. This band is the bright central core of an area of tawny or cinnamon-brown which in all covers 10 dorsal scales. The forward end of each scale of this area outside the central grenadine band is black-specked. Each scale of the dorsum has hyaline edges, and every scale stands out except the dorsal grenadine ones. The 1st 5 scale rows of the side are olive-buff or the color of the adjoining venter. The general impression of the top of the head is orange-citrine. The rostral, internasal, and prefrontal are buffy olive. The other plates are the same with some grenadine. The scales of the head in the temporal region are citrine-drab with some grenadine edges. The face and labials from the eye forward are citrine-drab. The other upper labials are grenadine, olive-buff, and citrine-drab. The iris is dusky slate-violet. The pupil rim is cartridge buff or white. Just outside the rim there are a few clear specks of yellow-green or bright green yellow. The ventral surfaces in the caudal regions are light chalcedony yellow, those in the forward stretches light dull green-yellow or light chalcedony yellow.

A third snake from El Paso, Tex., taken by Colonel Crimmins, July, 1925. The back has black crossbars, 35 on the body and 11 on the tail, which cover 2 scale rows longitudinally. The background or interspace color is pale drab-gray. These areas are 2 to 3 scales long. The black crossbands extend down the side to the 2nd or even the 1st row of scales. Very few of these scales are completely black as the caudal edge is white and then hyaline. The interspace colors also have a narrow hyaline edge and then a white border with the remainder pale drab-gray with fine blackish specks. Some of the dorsal scales have each a small black spot near the caudal tip. Some of the cephalic interspaces lack the clear white borders. The top of the head from the eye forward is buffy olive while back of the eye it is olive. The side of the head is smoke gray. The upper labials are whitish except for the dorsal edges which are smoke gray. The iris is dark slate-violet. The pupil rim is pale yellow-green with a narrow area just outside where there are short lines of the same color broken but parallel to the circular rim. The chin is white. The under parts are pale ecru-drab.

Habitat: Similar to that of *S. e. episcopa.* Strangely enough, in 1950 Jameson and Flury in the Sierra Vieja Mts., which lie in the Chihuahuan province of several authors, identified their one specimen as *Sonora episcopa.* "One specimen was found in the catclaw-grama association of the Roughland belt. The specimen was dark gray in color, had no black bands, and both loreals were missing." Again we reiterate that we need from one locality and also from southern New Mexico to Chihuahua a large series, including a few broods of young, to solve the puzzling situation in the Big Bend country.

Breeding: Oviparous. Females 237–300 mm.

Authorities:

Lewis, T. H. (N.M., 1949)

Mulaik, S. (Tex., 1935)

Schmidt, K. P., and T. F. Smith (Tex., 1944)

Stickel, W. H. (Gen., 1938, 1943)

1935, S. Mulaik: "Several features about this reptile . . . diverge from characters presented by Blanchard and Strecker."

1944, K. P. Schmidt and T. F. Smith: "Our specimens, all female, exhibit the two color phases that apparently characterize this species. Our annulated example has 33 half-rings and 12 entire caudal rings, as compared with 25 + 6 in *S. s. semiannulata.* In essential characters all the specimens agree, the ventrals being 161, 161, and 153 respectively; the caudals are 46, 47 and 51. The two ringless snakes are light olive-brown with dorsal scales broadly tipped with dark brown and the top of the head dark brown."

1944, A. H. and A. A. Wright: From our own experience for 25 years, from hurried examinations of Force's mass of *Sonora episcopa episcopa* material, and from varied patterns from Palo Pinto, Tex., we have become conditioned to expecting *Sonora episcopa episcopa* with diverse color patterns! In 1925 we saw from one corner lot in El Paso, Tex., an equally diverse array of patterns in what are now called *S. s. blanchardi* or its intergrades. In 1943 *Sonora miniata miniata* became synonymized with *S. s. isozona,* a cross-banded form. Thus we have 3 forms, each with very diverse color patterns, *episcopa, blanchardi,* and *isozona.* Will the 4 forms more or less based on single color patterns—*semiannulata, gloydi, mosauri,* and *linearis*—hold? Possibly these localized populations will stand the test of time.

1949: T. H. Lewis' specimen had "dorsal color greenish yellow to brown, each scale with a large central black spot; orange-red dorsal stripe, brighter and broader posteriorly; head scales blackish to gray, edged with orange; belly pale gray-green and unmarked."

Grand Canyon ground snake (2) Gloyd's western ground snake

Sonora semiannulata gloydi Stickel 1938. Fig. 200; Map 51

Other common names: Bicolored ground snake (4); Grand Canyon earth snake; St. George ground snake.

Range: Grand Canyon region.—Ariz.; Ut. *Elevation*—2,000 to 5,000 feet.

Size: Adults, 8–14 inches. Our measurements include St. George, Ut., material not strictly *S. s. gloydi* according to Stickel's interpretation.

Distinctive characteristics: "Morphologically like *S. s. semiannulata,* from which it differs in coloration. The black bands are wider than the interspaces on the back and extend downward onto the ventrals; most of the bands completely cross the abdomen, though they are more diffuse ventrally than dorsally. The scales of the interspaces are heavily shaded with dark gray except sometimes for the lower and median rows" (Stickel, Gen., 1938). "Pattern in cross bands, with most of the body bands entirely crossing the abdomen; known only from the Grand Canyon of the Colorado River, Arizona" (Stickel, Gen., 1943). In fairness to Stickel we may state we have shown our *Sonora* map to him, but he does not agree that the St. George (Ut.) material is of *S. s. gloydi.*

Color: Two snakes from St. George, Ut., sent to Trapido by Tanner, Oct. 24, 1940. The dorsum of one is prominently barred black and orange, there being 34 black bars on the body and 10 on the tail, these 10 being encircling rings. The black bars are about the same width as the orange chrome to flame scarlet intervals which cross 8 scale rows with the lateral scale rows below the orange light chalcedony yellow, which is the color of the belly.

The black bars cover 2½ scale rows longitudinally, while the orange bars cover 3 scale rows. The black bars in the caudal half of the body extend across the venter, while in the cephalic half their ends approximate. The black of the head extends feebly from nostril to eye, then as a strong crescent crosses the top of the head involving the forward ¾ of the parietals and the rear half of frontal. The iris is black.

The larger specimen, according to Stickel's definition, is closer to *Sonora semiannulata semiannulata* since the black bars extend onto but not across the belly, and their ends do not approximate.

Habitat: In 1934 E. D. McKee and C. M. Bogert had specimens from the Lower Sonoran Zone at Indian Gardens, where Mr. Lloyd Davis said it was not rare. In Utah it has been taken at Rockville and St. George.

Breeding: Oviparous. Females to 350 mm.

Field notes and observations: This is another form of very limited range. Its type comes from Grand Canyon, but we use a specimen from St. George, Ut., to illustrate it. We question whether all the St. George material has the bands across the belly.

June 2, 1942: Visited Zion National Park. Saw Mr. Grater. He gave me a little *Sonora semiannulata*. He has one alive. This he promised to me. Saw his series of snakes. He has no *S. semiannulata* which could be called *S. s. gloydi* Stickel.

Dodge, writing in the same year (1938) as Stickel, said that the black bands of Grand Canyon material "pass over the back usually fading at the edge of the abdomen . . . ; under parts are yellowish or greenish white." Did Dodge have the specimens before him?

In 1942 we made the following notes on St. George and Grand Canyon material. At Provo, Ut., we have Brigham Young University 1257, 1922-23, *Sonora semiannulata* with 9 bands across tail, 1 on head, and 31 on body— 9 across venter of tail and 19 on body. Looks like the *gloydi* type. Smallest specimen 110 mm. (tail 20 mm.). BYU 1254, St. George, 1922 Close to *gloydi*, 172 mm. (tail 35), 28 bands on body and 9 on tail—of these, 21 on body across the belly. BYU 654 St. George, Utah, V. M. Tanner, April, 1938. One looks like *gloydi*—total of 42 bands, of which 11 are on tail. Except for neck band and head band all cross the belly, sometimes in center of gastrosteges, is light color. They had 2 jars from St. George and only 2 had pronounced bars across the venter of body.

At the Museum of Vertebrate Zoology we note No. 17580, *Sonora s. gloydi*, Bright Angel Trail, Grand Canyon, A. E. Peterson, Aug. 14, 1934. This is one of Stickel's specimens. He remarks that he has a series from St. George closer to *gloydi* than *semiannulata*, and he thought the St. George specimens intergradations. But we have seen 2 specimens from St. George with dark bands crossing belly better than this No. 17580. None of bands across the

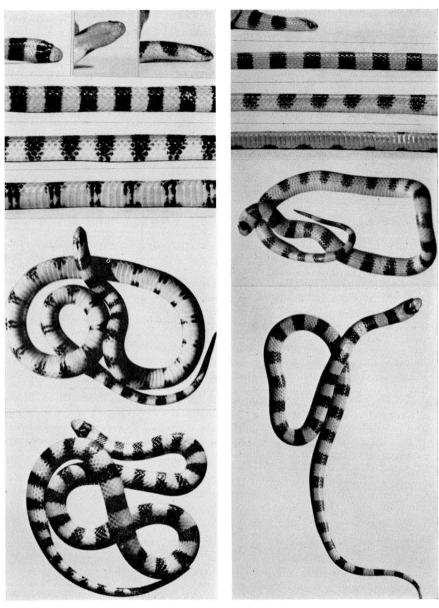

Fig. 200. *Sonora s. gloydi,* St. George, Utah, W. W. Tanner through H. Trapido.

Fig. 201. *Sonora s. isozona, semiannulata* pattern, Searles, Calif.

venter of body are complete except on the tail. Length 327 mm. (tail 57). At Salt Lake City we find that Mulaik has a small *Sonora semiannulata gloydi* from St. George, collected by H. Higgins. It's all black and white.

Authorities:

Cragin, F. W. (Kan., 1894)
Dodge, N. N. (Ariz., 1938)
McKee, E. D., and C. M. Bogert (Ariz., 1934)

Pack, H. J. (Ut., 1930)
Stickel, W. H. (Gen., 1938, 1943)
Tanner, W. W. (Ut., 1940)
Woodbury, A. M. (Ut., 1931)

1938, W. H. Stickel: *"Sonora semiannulata gloydi,* subsp. nov. Type.—MZUM 83754, collected by Mr. William Holzmark in 1936 on the Bright Angel Trail, Lower Sonora level of the Grand Canyon, Grand Canyon National Park, Ariz. Paratypes.—Grand Canyon National Park, Ariz.: Grand Canyon National Park collection 107, vicinity of Indian Gardens; UCLA 32, mouth (187) of Garden Creek; MVZ 17580, Bright Angel Trail."

Bicolored ground snake (4—Woodbury 1928),
Ringed ground snake (3)

Sonora semiannulata isozona (Cope) 1866. Figs. 201, 202; Map 51

Other common names: Banded ground snake; banded miter snake (Yarrow 1882); bicolor ground snake (7—Van Denburgh 1922); black banded ground snake; ground snake (6—Ellis and Henderson 1913); miter snake (Yarrow 1882); pinkish ground snake; Sonora ring snake; striped ground snake; Texas ground snake; vermilion ground snake (3); western earth snake.

Range: Along s. half of boundary of Idaho and Oregon; s. through Nevada to Owens Valley, Calif., to s.w. Utah to s. cent. Arizona to 28°N. in Baja California.—U.S.A.: Ariz.; Calif.; Ida.; Nev.; Ore.; Ut. Mex.; Baja Calif. *Elevation*—Mainly below 2,000 feet but possibly to 4,000 feet (see Linsdale). 3,750, 4,230, 5,500 feet (La Rivers).

Size: Adults, 9–19 inches. In one year we measured adults from 300 to 353 mm. In 1942 we saw adult specimens from 257 to 345 mm.

Distinctive characteristics: From Stickel's key (Gen., 1943) we assembled the following: "Anterior scale rows 15, rarely 14 or 16; temporals generally 1–2 (1–2 or higher on both sides in 96% of specimens)." "Caudals 53 or more in males, 45 or more in females; scale rows 15-14 (posterior scale rows counted in reference to scale row reduction in the middorsal region, disregarding lateral irregularities)." "Ventrals minus caudals 98 or more in males, 116 or more in females; tail 19.4% to 23.3% of total length in males, 16.4% to 20% in females." "With or without crossbands but if banded, few or none of the body bands cross the abdomen." "With or without crossbands, but if bands are lacking, the color of the back is the same as or changes gradually into the gray, reddish, or brown of the sides."

Color: A snake from Phoenix, Ariz., received from Vic Housholder Sept.

23, 1937, and freshly shed when described. The mid-back for about 7 scale rows is marked with a vinaceous-rufous band. The 2nd, 3rd and 4th scale rows are grayish olive with slight touches of vinaceous-rufous, and with threadlike edges of barium yellow. The 1st row of scales is barium yellow with those caudad of the 1st inch marked with vinaceous-rufous. The top of the head and face are grayish olive with spots of vinaceous-rufous. The iris is black with a few flecks of pale smoke gray in the upper half. The venter is barium yellow.

A second snake is drab on the sides, hay's russet on the back, and straw yellow on the venter. The top of the head is hair brown. The eye is black.

A snake from Searles, Calif., found May 11, 1942. The back is barred with black and orange chrome crossbands, 25 black bands on body and 8 encircling rings on tail. For 8, ahead of the vent, the black extends ⅓ of the way across the venter, being on 3 plates; the bands on forward part of body stop at ends of ventrals or slightly touch them. The black bands, olivaceous black or slate color under the lens, are 3 scales wide or ½ plus 2 plus ½. The interspaces are the same, with the orange chrome, apricot orange, or zinc orange covering 8 or 9 scales transversely. The color below this is like the ventral color, pale olivine, pale glaucous green, or pale fluorite green in the rear half of the body and almost white with a touch of seafoam yellow in the forward part. The black head crescent is made by a line from edge of rostral through nasal region, loreal, preocular, upper rim of 2nd and 3rd upper labials, 2 postoculars, crossing the rear third of supraoculars and rear half of frontal and involving the parietal except for the rear third. The plates ahead of this crescent are orange chrome to zinc orange as is, in part at least, the interval caudad of it. The eye is black with a pupil rim of pale vinaceous-fawn or pale grayish vinaceous. There is a little wash of tilleul buff on the underside of the head. We were delighted with this tiny snake.

Habitat: During the day these burrowers are found generally under rocks or other cover. They emerge just before dark. Normally, they are found in desert areas, or in relatively dry sections of prairie, or in marginal zones near woods with moderate moisture. They have been found on the banks of rivers, in back washes of reservoirs, and even in mine shafts.

Period of activity: *Early appearances*—Mar. 15, Apr. 1, 2, 3, 21, May 27, 1934 (Burt); Apr. 15, 1932, Apr. 22, 23, May 21, 1933 (Burt and Hoyle, Gen., 1935). *Fall disappearance*—July 1, 1911 (E. J. Newcomer); July 30, 1923 (Erwin); Aug. 3–9 (Van Denburgh and Slevin); Oct. 5, 1913 (A. B. Howell, Huachuca Mts.); July 12, Aug. 11, Sept. 6 (La Rivers); Sept. 11 (Storm).

Breeding: Oviparous. Otherwise no definite information is available. Carlson (CAS 17550), Cave Creek, Maricopa Co., Ariz., Apr. 20, 1910, took a small *Sonora* 110 mm. long.

Authorities:

Boulenger, G. A. (Gen., 1893–96)
Burt, C. E. (Gen., 1935)
Burt, C. E., and W. L. Hoyle (Gen., 1935)
Cope, E. D. (Ariz., 1866a; Tex., 1880)
Erwin, R. P. (Ida., 1925)
La Rivers, I. (Nev., 1942)
Linsdale, J. M. (Nev., 1938)

Mocquard, F. (Baja Calif., 1899)
Mosauer, W. (Calif., 1938)
Stickel, W. H. (Gen., 1938, 1943)
Storm, R. A. (Ore., 1947)
Van Denburgh, J. (Gen., 1922)
Van Denburgh, J., and J. R. Slevin (Ariz., 1913; Nev., 1921a)
Yarrow, H. C. (Ariz., 1875)

1944, A. H. and A. A. Wright: With the varied patterns of widespread *Sonora episcopa episcopa* in mind, we could not agree in 1938 to the recognition of *Sonora miniata miniata* for the noncrossbarred forms of central Arizona. For many years, especially from 1928 to 1937, we had received from the Phoenix area or seen both crossbanded forms (*isozona* and *semiannulata* before 1938) and the new form *miniata*. We are glad that the careful Dr. Stickel has now placed *S. m. miniata* in the synonymy of *Sonora semiannulata isozona*. We never could believe that the Arizona population and Idaho population were each *m. miniata* with *S. s. semiannulata* (now *S. s. isozona*) of Utah, Nevada, and California separating them.

Striped ground snake (6—Van Denburgh 1922)
Vermilion-lined ground snake

Sonora semiannulata linearis Stickel 1938. Fig. 203; Map 51

Other common names: Striped earth snake; (Texas) ground snake; vermilion-striped ground snake.

Range: From n.e. Baja California and s.e. California n. to Providence Mts., Calif., with pinpoints in adjacent Arizona and Nevada.—U.S.A.: Ariz.; Calif.; Nev. Mex.: Baja Calif. *Elevation*—500 to 1,000 feet, possibly 2,000 feet. Desert (Klauber, 1939a).

Size: Adults, 10–17 inches. Klauber's (1943b) measurements of 43 males and 57 females of Wood and Slevin are: mean over all 211.01 mm. for males, 209.41 mm. for females; maxima 328 mm. (tail 70) for males, 307 mm. (55) for females.

Distinctive characteristics: "Structurally similar to *miniata miniata,* but distinguished from it by having a distinct dorsal stripe, usually quite sharp-edged, contrasting in color with the sides. In life the stripe is vermilion, in preservative salmon to cream. The sides are bluish gray to brownish gray, instead of reddish to brown" (Stickel).

Color: Snakes from Potholes, 6 miles n.e. of Bard, Imperial Co., Calif., collected March 27, 1941, by L. W. Arnold. The dorsal stripe of flame scarlet is 3 scales wide in one, and in another covers 3 scales and halves of the adjoining scale rows. This stripe may end at the parietals or extend onto

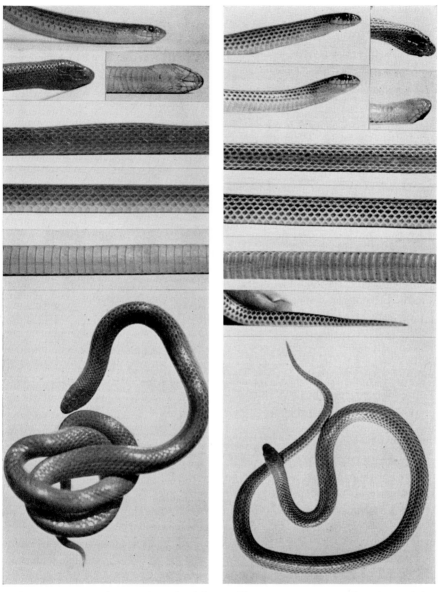

Fig. 202. *Sonora s. isozona* (*m. mineata*), plain, Phoenix, Ariz., V. Householder.

Fig. 203. *Sonora s. linearis,* potholes, 6 miles northeast of Bard, Imperial Co., Calif., L. W. Arnold.

them, and extends caudad to the tip of the tail. The same color is on the front of frontal, the prefrontals, internasals, and rear of rostral, where it may be orange-rufous. The top of the head and facial plates are buffy olive. The iris is black with a rim of pale purplish vinaceous. The centers of the scales of the 1st 3 rows are dark olive-gray and andover green, becoming dorsad in 4th and 5th rows deep olive-gray and vetiver green. Each scale has a border of ivory yellow, except those in the dorsal stripe, where it is lacking. The venter is yellowish glaucous. In one small snake, the dorsal stripe covers 4 solid rows with the adjoining rows almost covered so that almost 6 rows are flame scarlet and only 4 rows without orange. The smallest snake has only a 3-scaled dorsal stripe.

Habitat: In earlier days, this snake was thought a Lower Sonoran, desert, or other dry-land form, but several authors have felt that it preferred irrigated regions or, as one author wrote, "more moist places." In 1950 Slevin wrote: "In March 1940, the late Mr. Wallace Wood brought to me 56 Vermilion Striped Ground Snakes (*Sonora semiannulata linearis*) and 13 Desert Worm Snakes (*Leptotyphlops humilis chauilae*) which he had taken at Laguna Dam, Imperial County, California, while engaged in trapping mammals. He remarked that he made no special effort to collect these snakes but merely picked them up at odd times while he was engaged in his trapping. . . . "Through the courtesy of the Yuma Reclamation Service the latter part of April, 1941, the 21st to be exact, found us camped on the small spit of land formed by the cut made for installing the gates of Laguna Dam. Unfortunately we were unable to obtain a map of this particular piece of land nor were any figures as to the exact size available, so it will have to be described as a spit of land approximately 500 yards in length and about 40 yards in width at the widest point. A small grove of cottonwoods is situated at one end of it, the rest being covered with mesquite trees and with a heavy growth of willow and arrowweed bordering the edges. In such a limited area it was not difficult to pick out the most likely spots for hunting, and after making camp and looking over the situation in general picked up 3 worm snakes and a striped ground snake as a beginning. Next morning we started out early before the sun got too warm and by noon had 26 striped ground snakes, 99 worm snakes and 4 milk snakes (*Lampropeltis getulus yumensis*). The following day, April 23, netted 36 worm snakes and 27 striped ground snakes. On the 24th, 3 worm snakes were taken and on the 25th 1, these days being given over to working the mainland. In May 1947, while passing through Yuma, Wood and myself made a short visit to Laguna Dam more to see the keeper than to hunt, but during the couple of hours there secured 4 worm snakes and 6 striped ground snakes. Our last visit, in May 1949, was given to observing night activity, and 17 worm snakes were taken by hunting along the open trail with a gasoline lantern."

This is distinctly a southwestern desert form of Shreve's California microphyll desert or of the Colorado Valley part of Harshberger's Sonoran desert or the lower Colorado part of Fenniman and Johnson's Basin and Range Province.

Period of activity: *Early appearances*—Jan. 25, 1916 (J. Gray); June 27, 1925 (Mrs. E. C. Weaver); Feb. 8, 20–26, 1940 (Wood); Apr. 21–25, 1941 (Slevin and Wood). *Fall disappearance*—Oct. 26, 1925 (J. C. Howorth); Oct. 30, 1939 (W. F. Wood). MVZ dates are Feb. 8 to Oct. 30.

Breeding: Oviparous. Males to 328 mm., females to 376 mm. *Eggs, Young* —Practically nothing of record. The smallest records of young are 111, 116, and 126 mm. (Wood). Klauber's (1943b) measurements for the same material are: 115 mm. males; 126 mm. (tail 22) females.

Food: "The food habits are presumably similar to those of the Shovelnosed Ground Snake" (Perkins).

Field notes: 1942: Slevin, who with Taylor and one or two others, is among our master field collectors, urged us to go to the Potholes on the Colorado River for *Sonora miniata linearis*. He and Wood had taken 100 or more quickly at this locality. (Our notes on these 100 are omitted.)

Value of friends to a field collector: June 23, 1934. Dr. W. P. Taylor at Tucson provided us half a cottage at the Florida Field Station. Mr. and Mrs. Mercer lived in the other half. We lived there 2 weeks.

June 21, 1941: Previous to this date Klauber had recommended Lee Arnold of Yuma, Ariz., as a fine field collector.

May 7, 1942, Yuma, Ariz.: Coming across the most inspected state border of the U.S.A. (war or peacetime), we arrived at the Arizona side. A man stepped up, asked what we were doing, then recognized us and answered himself. "Why, I'm Mercer. How are you?" Later we looked up Lee Arnold teaching biology in the Yuma schools. "What are you after?" asked Arnold and Mercer. "We want to reach the Potholes." "Fear not," they replied. "It's a military reservation now." Our journal note follows:

May 7, 1942: Arnold had 2 sidewinders, 1 *Sonora miniata linearis* and 1 *Lampropeltis*. He gave them to me and arranged a trip to Potholes. With Mercer and Arnold to vouch for us we got passes from U.S. Reclamation Service. Went to Potholes with Mr. and Mrs. Arnold. Turned over the rocks where Wood and Slevin got their great series. I saw 6 sheds and Anna about 2. Mrs. Arnold found several sheds. In all Mr. and Mrs. Arnold caught 5 *Sonora s. linearis* and 1 *L. h. cahuilae*. The last a pigmy (later carelessly lost or something ate it). Too dry. From the holes we discovered we didn't go deep enough. Must have been more moist when Slevin and Wood dug.

Authorities:

Camp, C. L. (Calif., 1916)
Grinnell, J., and C. L. Camp (Calif., 1917)
Klauber, L. M. (Gen., 1939a, 1943b; Calif., 1931a, 1934a)
Perkins, C. B. (Calif., 1938)

Slevin, J. R. (Calif., 1950)
Stickel, W. H. (Gen., 1938)
Van Denburgh, J. (Gen., 1939a; Calif., 1931a)
Wood, W. F. (Calif., 1945)

1931: L. M. Klauber (1931a) discussed the puzzles of the southeastern Californian *Sonoras:* "Almost the same predicament exists with reference to the ground snakes, *Sonora semiannulata* and *S. episcopa.* Ortenburger (*Copeia* No. 120, p. 79, 1923) has stated that a complete series of intergrades has been found at Ardmore, Okla., between the cross banded form (*semiannulata*) and the longitudinally striped or unicolor snakes (*episcopa*). Erwin (*Copeia* No. 138, p. 6, 1925) found the two forms together in Idaho but without intergrades. I have seen both forms, but no intergrades from central Arizona; the locality data were not sufficiently definite to determine whether they were found together. From Imperial and San Diego Counties in California, and particularly from the Imperial Valley, I have seen at least 25 specimens. All were pure *episcopa,* and all distinctly striped, not unicolor, neither intergrades nor *semiannulata* specimens having yet come to light. The chances are therefore rather strong that the cross ringed form does not occur in this territory. Also in the western part of the range the two forms have differences in scutellation as well as pattern. So we have here the same alternatives considered under the black-red racer situation. To be consistent the same decision as that made in the racer problem should be adopted, and I have therefore decided to refer to *S. episcopa* in these notes as a valid species. . . . The snakes of the Imperial Valley and adjacent desert seem to be always of the *episcopa* rather than the *semiannulata* form. As they occur in a single zone, no color modifications varying with zones are to be expected."

1938: W. H. Stickel gave this form, heretofore dubbed *episcopa,* a new name, *Sonora miniata linearis,* making a specimen from Seeley, Imperial Co., Calif., his type.

SHORT-TAILED SNAKES

Genus *STILOSOMA* Brown (Fig. 19)

Size, small medium, 12–24 inches; extremely slender, width $\frac{1}{100}$ of length; tail very short $\frac{1}{10}$–$\frac{1}{15}$ of length; no loreal; head scales variable; parietals and prefrontals usually in contact with upper labials; prefrontals large, contacting labials $1 + 2$; 6 upper labials, $3 + 4$ contacting orbit, 5th is largest, contacts parietal; 5 lower labials, 5th very large; 1 pre- 2 postoculars; temporals 1-1, the anterior separated from postocular by parietal, which is very long; eye small; anal entire; scales smooth with no pits, in 19 rows; 2 pairs well-developed long chin shields closely in contact; maxillary teeth small, smooth, subequal, 10–11; mandibular teeth 12; hemipenis, calyces few and apical; ventrals 223–260; caudals 33–46. Synonym: *Stylophis.*

Short-tailed snake (13—Ditmars 1907)

Stilosoma extenuatum Brown 1890. Fig. 204; Map 52

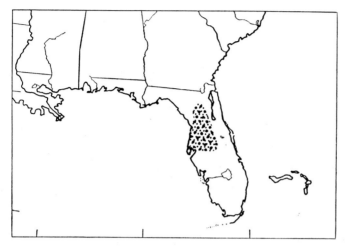

Map 52. *Stilosoma extenuatum*.

Range: Ridge and Gulf coast of w. cent. Florida from Alachua County to Polk and Pinellas counties. *Elevation*—50 to 100 feet.

Size: Adults, 12–24 inches. Our largest is 19½ inches long. We saw a large specimen (Stanford University No. 8242) taken by E. R. Allen, Aug., 1939, 485 mm. (tail 45 mm., sharp pointed). It was 5 mm. wide and 9 mm. deep. In 1950 we measured one 555 mm. in the Allen and Neill collection. The 2 smallest specimens of the 8 we have seen are 267 and 276 mm.

Distinctive characteristics: (See also the general description of the above and "Color" below.) "Color, silvery-gray, with 60 to 70 irregular dark brown dorsal blotches with narrow blackish borders, 10 to 12 on tail; interspaces mottled with pale red; belly blotched with black which extends on sides and often breaks, so forming lateral spots; the scales on sides are finely spotted with black; a dark patch on parietals; a small 1 on each side of neck; a dark postocular streak; fore part of chin and head peppered with black" (Tucker).

Color: A snake from Silver Springs, Fla., received from Florida Reptile Institute, Sept. 1, 1933. The back is marked with saddle spots of olive-brown, brownish olive, or sepia. Under the lens these scales look to be belly color with natal brown spots in the centers. There are 86 such saddles on the body and 15 on the tail. The 4 or 5 central scales of the interspaces are orange chrome, cadmium orange, or zinc orange, giving a broken bright stripe down the back. The rest of the interspace color of back and sides is smoke gray, pale smoke gray, pale drab-gray, or drab-gray. This color is produced by a white ground flecked with clove brown or blackish brown (1–3). Along the side is a series of vertical bars, alternating with the dorsal saddles, crossing the first 4 or 5 scale rows and extending onto the belly as the predominating color there. They are clove brown or blackish brown (1-3) with white borders. The top of the head is marked with a triangular spot like the saddles, but with a light center of sulphur yellow with orange-centered scales. The upper part of the iris has orange chrome and sulphur yellow spots. The rear and lower parts are close to the dorsal saddle color. The underside of the head is like the belly with a few flecks of white or smoke gray. The ventral surfaces are clove brown or blackish brown (1-3) interspersed with white.

Snake No. 35803 in the museum at Gainesville, Fla., had 67 dorsal saddles on the body and 14 on the tail.

A snake received from the Florida Reptile Institute, April 28, 1933, which died en route from Silver Springs, Fla. Interspaces between dorsal saddles sulphur yellow or barium yellow, the central scales for 4 or 5 scales in width orange chrome or cadmium orange centered. The same combination on Y-shaped spot on back of head. This sulphur yellow with orange chrome center combination gives a general cream-buff or chamois or antimony yellow appearance. The other interspaces on sides, rear, and somewhat on cephalic portion except for white margins of lateral spots, look smoke gray or pale smoke gray. This is produced by the light scales having faint specks of the belly color, which is bone brown or clove brown. This color sends a vertical bar onto sides for 4 or 5 scales. These side spots alternate with the saddle spots. The saddle spots are olive-brown, brownish olive, or saccardo's umber with bone brown or black edges. On parietal plates is a spot with sharp median caudal point. This spot has a lateral branch extending backward to the first transverse saddle with which it unites. Top of head ahead of eye grayish olive dotted with saddle-spot color. A prominent olive-brown vertical band is on edge of 4th and 5th upper labials. A horizontal olive-brown stripe is back of eye along upper edge of 5th, 6th, 7th upper labials and lower edge of 1st temporal. Iris has outer ring of olive-brown or brownish olive and around pupil an inner ring of xanthine orange, tawny, or orange-cinnamon. The underside of head is almost entirely belly color with a few white or smoke gray specks. The belly has a center of smoke gray or pale smoke gray with each side interspace encroaching on the belly color, but not quite far enough to break it on the middle line.

Abnormal coloration—Dr. Archie Carr (1934) received a unique specimen that was uniformly bright scarlet. Excitement subsided when the snake shed its scarlet coat for a normal garb, a cochineal dye having caused the livery.

Habitat: Since its description in 1890 by Brown, this snake has remained a rarity to most herpetologists. From 1934 onward we began to get more information because of Allen's success in collecting it. In 1934 Carr wrote a good account of it: "During the month that this specimen has been kept in captivity it has been handled frequently and has shown evidence of being far more intelligent and aggressive than any other of the small burrowing species that I have observed. Although most of its time is spent under the sphagnum floor of the aquarium, the snake emerges frequently to explore with its tongue the sides and bottom of its cage, even pushing with its head against the glass lid of the aquarium. When a watchglass of water is proffered, it usually immerses its head and drinks for several minutes. When handled, although alert, it seems quite unafraid, and if treated roughly it becomes enraged, coiling, vibrating its meagre tail, and striking like an irate blacksnake. Its powers of constriction and muscular control are remarkable. When it coils about my first and second fingers, I find it impossible to part them. In crawling from one of my hands to the other it bridges gaps slightly wider than half its length, and like the larger constricting snakes, it is capable of progressing several feet along a taut wire."

In 1940(a) Carr summarized its habitat thus: "High pine, upland hammocks, and rosemary scrub. . . . Specimens have been dug out of sphagnum beds.

Period of activity: *First appearance*—Jan., 1897, Apr. 19, 1909 (Brimley); Jan. 25, 1934 (Carr, 1934); Apr. 28, 1933 (E. R. Allen). *Fall disappearance*— Sept. 9, 1933 (E. R. Allen); Sept. 19, 1927 (O. Swed).

Breeding: Oviparous. Males 270–567 mm., females 300–575 mm.

Food: *Tantillas,* small snakes. Carr.

Field notes: In 1890 its describer, Brown, received it from N. P. Fry of Lake Kerr, who later supplied Brown with more specimens. For 50 years this form was largely known from 3 men, N. P. Fry, C. C. Tyler, and E. Ross Allen. To each of these, herpetologists are indebted for most of the material we have received. For example, in 1930 Conant wrote, "Returning to Eureka we spent an interesting hour looking at specimens which Tyler has preserved during the 7 years of his experience in the neighborhood. He presented us with a fine example of the Short-tailed Snake, *Stylophis extenuatus,* which he had taken two years before."

Mar. 28, 1934: Photoed snakes and turtles at E. Ross Allen's establishment. He has taken some 17 or 18 short-tailed snakes. They inhabit the sand, feed on *Tantilla coronata* and possibly other small snakes.

Subsequent years: We later learned that he had taken more of them than there were in all the collections. In fact he had specialized in them, but we doubt if he ever found as many of them as he did of *Rhadinea.*

Authorities: [1]

Brimley, C. S. (N.C., 1941–42)	Conant, R. (Fla., 1930)
Brown, A. E. (Gen., 1901; Fla., 1890)	Loennberg, E. (Fla., 1894)
Carr, A. F., Jr. (Fla., 1934, 1940a)	Tucker, H. (Fla., 1911–12)

---

[1] 1956: Highton (*Bull. Fla. State Mus.,* **1:** 73–96) examined 89 specimens which varied in sexual dimorphism in four respects. This circumscribed form (limited to an area whose greatest diameter is 125 miles) he subdivides thus:

1A. Lower labials 7; internasals and prefrontals

1890, A. E. Brown: "The general coloring of the specimen is much like that of *Rhinocheilus lecontei* but the generic and other characters render it impossible to confuse it with that or any other North American species. The fact that but one specimen has yet been collected in a region so comparatively well known as northern Florida renders it probable that the species is of extreme rarity."

1894: E. Loennberg, who referred his 3 specimens to L. Stejneger, remarked: "Mr. Brown compares the coloration of the present species with that of *Rhinocheilus lecontei* while Cope (1892) states that it 'has the coloration of the type of *Hypsiglena* or *Sibon*.' None of these comparisons seem particularly happy, while on the other hand the similarity of *Stilosoma extenuatum,* so far as color and pattern, both above and below, is concerned to *Lampropeltis calligaster* is very striking indeed. Even the head markings are almost identical."

1911–12: H. Tucker from an examination of Brown's 6 specimens (plus 4 more in the Academy of Natural Science of Philadelphia), wrote: "The color scheme strongly suggests that this reptile is derived from some member of the *Ophibolus* group, as the marking and color are almost identically those of *Ophibolus calligaster,* but the fused and unstable scalation of the head are evidences of degeneration and make it impossible to determine the probable line of descent."

1942, A. H. and A. A. Wright: Why reach for the black or patterned distant *L. r. calligaster* when *L. r. rhombomaculata* reaches northern Florida? One of us holds for *sui generis,* and the other admits the remote possibility of *L. r. rhombomaculatus* affinity.

BROWN SNAKES

Genus *STORERIA* Baird and Girard (Fig. 24)

Size small, 7–19 inches; slender; tail comparatively short; head distinct; all teeth solid, maxillary equal 14–18, mandibular 15–19; anal divided; caudals paired; scales keeled with no apical pits and in 15–17 rows; nasal entire or

---

1B. Lower labials 6 on one or both sides of head and/or internasals and
　　prefrontals fused　　　　　　　　　　　　　　　　　　　　*extenuatum*
2A. Dorsal body blotches 69 or more　　　　　　　　　　　　*multistictum*
2B. Dorsal body blotches 68 or less　　　　　　　　　　　　　*arenicola*

　Extenuatum, central peninsular—Putnam, Marion, Lake, Seminole, Orange, and Polk counties.

　Multistictum, north gulf peninsular—Alachua and Levy counties.

　Arenicola, south gulf peninsular—Citrus, Sumter, Hernando, Pasco, and Pinellas counties.

divided; loreal absent or rarely present; preoculars 1–2; postoculars 2–3; temporals 1 + 2 (3); upper labials 6–7; lower normally 7; very few or no gulars between chin plates and ventrals; ventrals 110 ♂ –148 ♀ ; caudals 35 ♀ –69 ♂ ; dorsum brown, belly white pinkish or red; hemipenis varies: in *S. occipitomaculata,* distal end expanded, flattened and smooth without much enlarged basal spines, while *S. dekayi* has the organ not expanded distally but finely spinose at that end, the spines becoming larger proximally to 1 much enlarged spine at the base of the sulcus. Synonyms: *Coluber, Ischnognathe, Ischnognathus, Tropidonotus.*

KEY TO THE GENUS *STORERIA*
(Adapted from Trapido)

a. Body scales in 15 rows, loreal absent.
  b. Supralabials 7, preocular 1.   *S. d. victa*
  bb. Supralabials 6, preoculars 2, venter red or pink.
    c. Three occipital light marks.   *S. occipitomaculata occipitomaculata*
    cc. Occiput has light ring about 2 scales wide.   *S. o. obscura*
aa. Body scales in 17 rows.
  b. Anterior temporal has horizontal dark mark. Posterior temporals often
    3. Sum of ventrals and subcaudals averages 187.   *S. d. temporalineata*
  bb. Anterior temporal not with horizontal dark mark.
    c. Anterior temporal with vertical or diagonal dark bar (occasionally
      interrupted); dorsal spots separate.   *S. dekayi dekayi*
    cc. Anterior temporal with vertical dark bar (occasionally interrupted);
      dorsal spots fused to short crossbars.   *S. d. wrightorum*
    ccc. Anterior temporal not marked with black, or with black only along
      margin; dorsal spots separate.   *S. d. texana*

DeKay's snake (88—Allen 1868), **Brown snake** (17—Abbott 1884)
Storeria dekayi dekayi (Holbrook) 1842. Fig. 205; Map 53

Other common names: Brown grass snake; DeKay's (little) brown snake; ground snake; house snake; little brown snake; rock snake; small brown snake; spotted adder; spotted (brown) snake.

Range: From s. Ontario and Quebec through New England and New York to w. South Carolina, thence n. through e. Tennessee and Kentucky into s. peninsula of Michigan.—U.S.A.: Ala.; Conn.; D.C.; Del.; Ky.; Mass.; Md.; Me.; N.C.; N.H.; N.J.; N.Y.; O.; Pa.; R.I.; S.C.; Tenn.; Vt.; Va.; W. Va. Can.: N.B.; Ont.; Que. *Elevation*—Sea level to 4,000 or 5,000 feet. 1,400–1,900 feet (Smith, Pa., 1945); 1,500–1,600, 4,000 (King, Tenn., 1939).

Size: Adults, 10–18 inches.

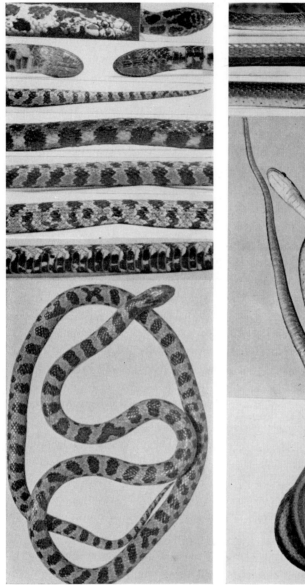

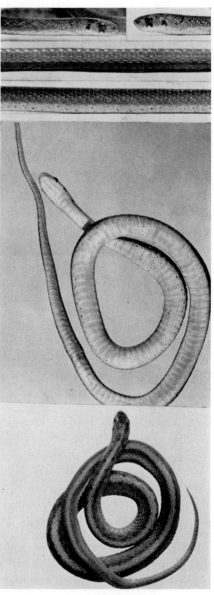

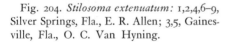

Fig. 204. *Stilosoma extenuatum:* 1,2,4,6–9, Silver Springs, Fla., E. R. Allen; 3,5, Gainesville, Fla., O. C. Van Hyning.

Fig. 205. *Storeria dekayi dekayi:* 1,2,4–6, Silver Creek, N.Y., W. C. Ritter; 3, Ithaca, N.Y.

Distinctive characteristics: "The subspecies *dekayi* is characterized by the low number of ventrals and caudals (their sum equalling 175 or less in 94 percent of specimens examined), by the discrete paired spots along the back and by the vertical or diagonal dark bar across the rear of the anterior temporal" (Trapido, Gen., 1944). "General color above grayish brown, with a somewhat lighter vertebral band margined by dotted lines; a black bar extending from the occipitals to the angle of the mouth; 2 black spots below the eye; abdomen and under parts greenish to grayish white" (Smith, O., 1882).

Color: A snake from Ithaca, N.Y., collected by Rudolf Schuster, Dec. 18, 1943. There is a very clear middorsal avellaneous band 3 scales wide outlined by pairs of sepia or natal brown spots. This band is in sharp contrast to the tawny-olive side, which bears an alternating row of spots on scale rows 2 + 3. At times there appear in the forward half of the body oblique connecting threads between the 2 series. In this subspecies as described in *S. wrightorum* there are 6 series of light lateral flecks formed of interscale color. The light dorsal band continues the length of body and tail, but the bordering dark dorsal spots may be absent in the caudal half of body. The parietal plates are rood's brown with rest of top of head buffy brown. There is a vertical bar from edge of parietal across posterior half of anterior temporal and suture of upper labials 6 + 7 and on to suture of lower labials 5 + 6. There is a spot below eye prominent on suture of upper labials 3 + 4 and somewhat on 4 + 5. The eye in lower half is natal brown, in upper half orange-cinnamon. The underside of head, pale pinkish buff to white, is clear of dark spots, the venter light vinaceous-cinnamon with an occasional spot toward the end of a ventral plate.

Habitat: A tabulation of habitat notes yields the following results: It is largely nocturnal and is found under flat stones or rocks 9, under leaves 6, under brush heaps 1, under boards 3, under rubbish 2, under trash 3, under old paper 2, roofing 2, or any dump cover 3, under logs 2, and in earth 1. It is of both moist and dry situations. Of the latter we have hillsides 3, above embankment 1, corner of rail fence 1, sides of railroads 2, second-growth woodlands 1, pine woods 2, near buildings 3, dry well-drained situations 1, fairly dry situations 1. But of moist habitats we have: about pumps 1, about sinks 1, about moist places 1, beside a pond 1, near a lake 1, along a river 1, marshy meadow 1, above freshwater marsh 1, along lake shore 1, under driftwood 1, damp portions 1, grassy swamps 1, swampy ground 1, and more. Whether it is Hartford (Babbitt), Brooklyn (Engelhardt), Newark (Trapido), Philadelphia (Abbott and Conant), or any other large city, it is the snake of the wastelands and rubbishy vacant lots. There is one record of its having been run over by an automobile. Unusual actions and habitats noted include: swimming, climbing bushes or vines, overhanging the water (Neill), face of an escarpment, swampy part of abandoned stone quarry. It is a versatile, ubiquitous, urban and rural creature.

Period of activity: *Early appearances*—Mar. 28 (Clausen); Mar. 31 (Axtell). "DeKay's Snake. Extremely common in spots in the city limits of

Northampton. For two successive years some 40 were taken at a single place each spring, just before they came out of hibernation. With them were a few *S. occipito-maculata.* Dates: 1917, Oct. 26; 1918, Apr. 17; 1922, April 8; 1923, Apr. 11" (Dunn, Mass., 1930). *Fall disappearance*—Nov. 18 (Noble and Clausen); Nov., 1915 (Bishop in Wright, N.Y., 1919b); Oct. 26, 1917 (Dunn); Oct., 1938, Oct. 10, Sept. 6, Oct. 24 (Trapido, 1940); Nov. 12, 1944 (Axtell); Oct. 6, 1912, Oct. 19, 1917, Nov. 6, 1917, Oct. 10, 1919, Sept. 8, 1921, Oct. 4, 1925 (W. De W. Miller, N.J.). "Previous to November 26, 1914, there were several drops of temperature to below the freezing point, 18 degrees above zero being reached on one occasion. On the above date, the weather was milder, the thermometer registering as high as 50 degrees. While the writer was walking near the corner of Kingsbridge Road and University Avenue, he found a young DeKay's snake (*Storeria dekayi*), about 8 cm. in length. It was quite active and when released, quickly disappeared under the dried grass" (Crandall, N.Y., 1915).

Hibernation—Noble and Clausen in their paper observed that *S. d. dekayi* tended to aggregate at all times of the year except at the gestation period, when females are found isolated. Naturally aggregation is most marked at the hibernation period. "In the fall of 1932 Mr. S. C. Yeaton found the first hibernation den on a small knoll on the edge of a swamp on the outskirts of Flushing, N.Y. The den was apparently an old rat burrow which faced south. Although the burrow was only 11 inches deep no less than 76 *S. dekayi*, 10 immature *T. sirtalis* and 1 immature *Natrix sipedon* were taken from the bottom of the single chamber which ended blindly." Axtell found that the "males predominated very greatly in the spring studies at the dens. Later the females were in great predominance. Since this summer excess of records of females includes those killed by cars, there may be a real excess of males caused by large-scale selective killing of the females in this way." In Connecticut in 1948 Finneran reported thus: "A large hibernating den is located in a built up area over which a bridge has been constructed. The bridge crosses a railroad track. The bridge is in constant use and the adjacent locale is well populated. Still the den has been used annually during the period (1940–1947) of this paper."

Breeding: Viviparous. Males 251–400 mm., females 242–450 mm. Of 524 specimens—240 males, 218 females, and 66 sex unknown—Axtell wrote: "The largest seen . . . was a female 18 inches long. There were also 17¼ and 17 inch females. A total of 15 females were 16 inches or more in length but one male attained this size, the largest being exactly 16. A total of 14 males were 14 inches or more in length." Miller (N.J., 1937) reported males 253–593 mm., females 318–526 mm.

Mating behavior—Noble has described it in considerable detail. Seemingly there are no courtship or combat dances. There are no aggressive actions of one male against another except to crowd another out of the favorable dorsal position. The male slides along the back to bring his chin in contact with the female's neck.

Gestation period—Noble concluded that mating occurred mainly from Apr. 12 to 22, though earlier Clausen (Gen., 1936) held it to be in late March and the first part of April. As has been customarily done, both computed the gestation period from these dates to the dates of parturition. In 14 litters Clausen considered 105 to 113 days the gestation period. If a female mates Apr. 2 and gives birth to 14 young July 18, the period would be 107 days. No doubt this might be true in many instances, but how about a female captured in November which laid eggs March 20? Or one in which parturition occurred June 26 (Minton, Ind., 1944)? Or what shall we say about the female which was observed mating but which, when killed immediately thereafter, was found to contain advanced embryos? Mating may occur throughout summer or fall, according to enough observations to make the statement acceptable. The gestation period is therefore not so easily computed as once thought.

At this juncture it is pertinent to quote from Trapido's (Gen., 1940) "Mating time and sperm viability in *Storeria*": "A female *Storeria dekayi* which was received in early October, 1938, from Br. Alexander Blouin of Mont-Saint-Louis College, Montreal, was kept in captivity, alone, or for a time with several garter snakes, until the 6th of December, when it was dissected. Mature spermatozoa were found in abundance in the oviducts. The specimen was taken in the last part of August, and kept in a container with 2 green snakes (*Opheodrys vernalis*) and a red-bellied snake (*S. occipitomaculata*) until they were sent to the writer. In a letter, Br. Alexander said, 'There has surely been no male DeKay's snake with the female you have since the end of August.' It is thus apparent that the male germ cells lived more than 3 months in the female genital tract."

Young—Number, 3–24. Various authorities have distributed the number of young per female as follows: 3, 14, 24 (Fowler); 5 (Noble and Clausen); 5, 8, 14, 21 (Schonberger); 8, 13, 18 (Axtell); 9 (Conant); 9–20 (Clausen); 10, 20 (Trapido); 10, 15, 23 (Conant); 11 (Hay, Minton); 11, 12, 13, 14, 16 (Judd); 12, 15, 18, 20 (Ditmars); 12 (Williams, Babcock, Conant and Bailey, Bishop and Alexander); 15 (Brimley); 16 (Harwood); 21 (Shields); 22 (Triplehorn); 27 (Littleford). Time of birth, usually last half of July and August. Mar. 20, July 28, July 31, Aug. 8 (Noble and Clausen); June 26 (Minton); July 6, Aug. 1 (Conant); July 14, 18, 20, 21, 22, 24, 25, 26, 28, 29, 30, Aug. 1 (Clausen); July 31, Aug. 8 (Ditmars); Aug. 3 (Schonberger); Aug. 4 (Harwood); Aug. 14 (Conant and Bailey); Aug. 14, 16, Sept. (Shields); Aug. 14, Sept. 14 (Axtell); Aug. 17 (Littleford); Sept. 4 (Trapido thesis); late July and August (Babcock, Trapido, Bishop and Alexander, Surface). There are records of females with embryos beyond Aug. 1. Size at birth, 3.1–4.3 inches. The following hatchling sizes are recorded: 78, 80 mm.

(Noble and Clausen); 3.5 inches (Babcock); 3¾–4³⁄₁₆ inches (Conant); 86 mm. (Conant and Bailey); 88 mm., 87–100 mm. (Triplehorn); 96 mm. (twice), 98 mm., 99 mm. (3 times); 100 mm., 101 mm. (twice), 102 mm., 103 mm., 108 mm. (Clausen); 91 mm. (Schonberger); 100–107 (Shields). "The young are very dark, with a whitish ring around the neck, and resemble the young of the ring-necked snake, but may be distinguished by their keeled scales" (Ditmars, Gen., 1929).

Littleford's records of a female only 133 mm. giving birth on Aug. 17 to 27 young, only 22 mm. long, not 85–108 mm., is startling, as is also his small female, 130 mm. with 13 young, only 33 mm.

Food: Earthworms, slugs, snails, insects, small treefrogs, fish. Surface, Holbrook, Conant (O., 1938a), Noble and Clausen, Harwood, Trapido (1944), and Judd (Ont., 1954).

One year after Trapido's study of 1944, Harwood published his study of a brood of 16 young. They hatched Aug. 4, 1943. The snakes fed daily until Sept. 16. Between then and Oct. 1 their appetites lessened markedly. The first snake shed Sept. 1, 3 weeks after birth. The range of the hatchlings was 105–148 mm. He offered them aphids, larvae of flour beetles, cabbage worms, cutworms, ant pupae, crickets, millipeds, beetle grubs, and other insects, but they were ignored. Slugs and small earthworms they seized eagerly.

Authorities:

Axtell, H. H. (N.Y., 1947)
Bishop, S. C., and W. P. Alexander (N.Y., 1927)
Clausen, H. J. (Gen., 1936)
Ditmars, R. L. (Gen., 1907, 1929; N.Y., 1905)
Harwood, P. D. (O., 1945)
Holbrook, J. E. (Gen., 1836–42)
Judd, W. W. (Ont., 1954)
Littleford, R. A. (Md., 1945)
Noble, G. K. (Gen., 1939)
Noble, G. K., and H. J. Clausen (Gen., 1936)
Shields, F. B. (N.Y., 1929)
Surface, H. A. (Pa., 1906)
Trapido, H. (thesis 1939, Gen., 1940, 1944)

In 1936, G. K. Noble and A. J. Clausen felt that the "olfactory organs alone are adequate sensory mechanism for food trailing in S. dekayi and T. sirtalis. The tongue and Jacobson's organ in combination make trailing possible, but either one of these structures alone is inadequate."

1944, H. Trapido: "The evolutionary success of Storeria dekayi dekayi is attested by its survival even within the limits of such large eastern cities as Boston, New York, Philadelphia, and Washington. Individuals are rarely seen on the surface, except perhaps at dusk when they seem most actively on the prowl for food. That the successful survival of this form in the urban situation is not alone due to their secretive habits is evident from the fact that similarly secretive snakes like Diadophis punctatus, Carphophis amoena, Tantilla coronata, and Storeria occipito-maculata have not survived in such areas."

1947: H. H. Axtell wrote a fine thesis in which he gave his conclusions on 524 specimens of this species.

Mexican brown snake (Trapido 1944)

Storeria dekayi temporalineata Trapido 1944. Fig. 206; Map 53

Range: Western coast of Gulf of Mexico from Veracruz to Mex., to s. Texas.—U.S.A.: Tex. Mex.: Puebla; San Luis Potosí; Tamaulipas; Veracruz. *Elevation*—Sea level to 500 feet, possibly to 1,000 feet, in Mexico. Trapido reports one at 5,000 feet in Puebla.

Size: Adults, 8.3–16.3 inches (Trapido, 1944).

Distinctive characteristics: "Similar to *S. d. texana* but with a higher number of ventrals and subcaudals, the labials completely or almost completely unmarked, anterior temporal with a horizontal dark mark" (Trapido, 1944).

Color: A snake from Brownsville, Tex., received Apr. 26, 1925. It is marked with an avellaneous or light drab dorsal band with pairs of black spots on either side throughout its length. The dorsal scales for 5 rows on either side of the broad median band are grayish olive. The skin between is black and marguerite yellow. Sometimes it looks as if there were 4 yellow and black lines on each side—i.e., yellow, then black, yellow, and black in a band.

A snake from Houston, Tex., received from John Wottring, Mar. 8, 1950. The dorsal band is drab outlined on either side by a row of bone brown spots. The lateral scales are light brownish olive with edges of olive-buff, except for rows 1 and 2, which are fawn and lack the light edges. The top of the head is light drab heavily flecked with bister; the nuchal spots are bister. There is a dark longitudinal line of prout's brown on the upper half of anterior temporal, across the corresponding posttemporal and involving the postocular. There is the slightest suggestion of the same color below the eye on sutures of upper labials 4 and 5, and 5 and 6. On 2 or 3 cephalic lower labials are dark pinpoints. The lower part of the iris is prout's brown with a dash of light ochraceous-buff in the upper part. The belly is vinaceous-buff, with conspicuous black pinpoints on ends of ventrals and even on subcaudals. This specimen is distinctly of the *temporalineata* pattern.

A smaller snake received in the same shipment from Houston. It bears the *S. d. texana* pattern. The dorsal stripe is drab, the lateral scales sayal brown with a very indistinct pattern. The temporal is clear gray, the spot under the eye very pronounced, and a black suture between upper labials 6 and 7 extends onto the corresponding suture of the lower labials. Below the eye between lower labials 4 and 5 is a black dot. The neck spot is distinct, but not large, and there are a very few pinpoints on the ends of the ventrals on the forward half of the body.

We observed that Trapido made one Houston specimen *S. d. temporali-*

nata x *S. d. texana,* but the larger snake of this shipment accorded with his description of *S. d. temporalineata.* If these two acquisitions came from the same vicinity, we are reminded of Taylor's observations: "It is significant that there are two subspecies of *Storeria dekayi* reported from San Luis Potosí. The two specimens of *Storeria dekayi texana* mentioned in the type description '5 miles south of Valles, District Ciudad de Valles EHT-HMS 4662, 2664' were taken in the same pile of driftwood in which was found *Storeria dekayi temporalineata* mentioned in the type description of that form as '5 miles south of Valles, E.H.T.-H.M.S. 4663.' If these are distinct, one might question the wisdom of regarding them as subspecific. Sufficient material is not at hand to determine this point."

Habitat: In 1938 Taylor and Smith reported finding these snakes "in piles of driftwood near a river bank." See "Field notes," Feb. 1, 1950, under *Storeria d. texana* below. In 1944 Trapido wrote: "No accounts of the habits of this race in Tamaulipas and Vera Cruz are available, although it is probable that it is found in much the same sort of place as *S. d. texana.* . . . It is probably principally a species of low elevations."

Breeding: Viviparous. Males 207 mm. and up, females 339–408 mm.

Authorities: Taylor, E. H., and H. M. Smith (Gen.,
Taylor, E. H. (Tex., 1949)   1938)
                                        Trapido, H. (Gen., 1944)

1950, A. H. and A. A. Wright: In the lot from W. H. Gottsch from Liberty Co., Tex., were both *temporalineata* and *texana.*

Texas brown snake (Trapido 1944), DeKay's snake (16)

Storeria dekayi texana Trapido 1944. Fig. 207; Map 53

Other common names: Brown grass snake; brown (wood) snake; De-Kay's brown snake; DeKay's ground snake; little brown snake; spotted brown snake.

Range: From Hidalgo, Mex., northward e. of the 98th meridian to Minnesota; thence e. to Wisconsin and s. to w. Louisiana.—U.S.A.: Ark.; Ia.; Kan.; La.; Mich.; Minn.; Miss.; Mo.; N.M.?; Neb.; Okla.; Tex.; Wis. Mex.: Hidalgo; Nuevo León; San Luis Potosí; Tamaulipas. *Elevation*— Mainly sea level to 1,000 feet, possibly to 2,000 or more feet. 4,000 feet (Hidalgo, E. H. Taylor); 1,000 feet (Smith and Laufe, Tex., 1945).

Size: Adults, 7.5–19 inches.

Distinctive characteristics: "This subspecies is characterized by the coloration of the anterior temporal which is not marked with a black vertical bar, nor with a longitudinal stripe. The dark occipital blotches are broader than in other subspecies and the 4th labial is usually more extensively darkened" (Trapido).

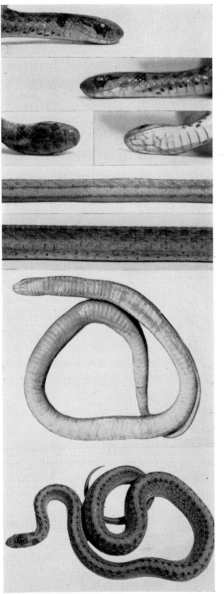

Fig. 206. *Storeria d. temporalineata:* 1–6, Houston, Tex., J. Wottring; 7,8, Boca Chica, Tex.

Fig. 207. *Storeria d. texana:* 1–3, Kendall Co., Tex., H. Trapido; 4–8, San Antonio, Tex.

Color: We found this snake close to the Medina River, near Blue Wing Lake, San Antonio, Tex., on a trip with R. D. Camp, Roy Quillin, and Ellen Schulz, Feb. 15, 1925. This snake, of last year's brood, was found under a log. The back is cinnamon-brown, verona brown, or buffy brown. There is a darker spot of olive-brown or mummy brown on either side of the neck. The color in front of this neck spot is pale vinaceous-fawn or pale grayish vinaceous. On top of the head and in front of the eye is prout's brown. The black spot below the eye is on the 6th upper labial and on 1 or 2 lower labials. The iris is ochraceous-tawny. The lower labials and chin shields are white. The neck and other under parts are pale grayish vinaceous, pale vinaceous-fawn, or vinaceous-buff; each ventral in the cephalic half of the body has a black spot on either end.

A snake from 10 miles south of the town of Liberty, Tex., received from Mr. and Mrs. Gottsch, Jan. 29, 1950. The most striking mark is the dorsal band of avellaneous or wood brown, outlined by spots of verona brown. There is an indistinct row of tawny-olive spots on the lower side of scale rows 2–5. All scales below middorsal stripe are edged with pale dull green-yellow. Scattered amongst these light edges are black linear flecks. Neither light nor dark edges are present on the tail. Top of head is bister, nuchal spots umber. Face is drab gray, supralabials drab gray and white. The anterior temporal bears no longitudinal bar. There is a vertical bar on rear of 6th upper labial and on rear of 6th lower labial. Below the eye, the sutures of 3 and 4 and 4 and 5 are dark, but there is no prominent spot below eye. Under parts of head are white, becoming pale cinnamon-pink on belly with a small black pinpoint on either end of ventral plates just below the lateral that encroaches on ends of ventral plates. These points are lacking on rear half of body.

Habitat: This common snake is usually taken under cover of stones, logs, leaves, chips, debris, and driftwood piles. Cope thought them terrestrial; others held them aquatic. They are both; they are found in fallen timber, in vicinity of river and streams, in creek bottoms, in open or deep woods, or on grassy hillsides.

Period of activity: *First appearance*—Mar. 4, 1892, Mar. 14, 1905 (Bailey, Tex., 1905); Apr. 23, 1927 (Burt, Kan., 1927); Mar. 15, 1927, Apr. 21, 1928, Apr. 6, 1929 (Gloyd, Kan., 1932); Apr. 7, 1923, Apr. 21, 1924 (Linsdale, Kan., 1927); Mar. 27, 1940, Mar. 26, 1939, Apr. 7, 1941 (Anderson, Mo., 1942). *Fall disappearance*—Nov. 24, 1927 (Strecker, Tex., 1927); Sept. 23, 1928 (Gloyd); Nov. 15, 1923, Dec. 2, 1922 (Linsdale); Nov. 4, 1922, Jan. 11, 1928, Oct., 1932 (Gloyd); Sept. 6, 1935 (Anderson). *Hibernation*—In New Braunfels, Tex., Dec. 2, 1891, Test (Tex., 1894) wrote: "This little snake . . . seems to be quite commonly found at this time of year about water courses, in the bottoms of ditches, and similar places, sometimes occurring dozens together, of all ages and sizes."

Breeding: Viviparous. Males 246–341 mm., females 190–455 mm. *Young*— Number, 3–15. Time of birth, Aug. 11–Sept. 2. Size at birth, 3.5–4.5 inches. In 1904 Branson (Kan., 1904) queried Hay's statement that this snake is oviparous.

The records are so few that we give them in their entirety: "Minnesota specimen 265, taken in Hennepin County, gave birth to 8 young in August, 1919. These young varied little in size and averaged slightly under 4 inches at birth. Specimen 145, taken in Scott County, gave birth on Aug. 11, 1935, to 15 young which varied from 4¼ to 4½ inches in length" (Breckenridge). "The young are produced alive, measuring about 3½ inches at birth. One of our Iowa specimens bore 11 young on Sept. 1 and 2, 1924" (Guthrie). The immature specimen 108 mm. long which Gloyd captured in Kansas Nov. 4, 1922, must have been a recent young.

Our best note on the reproduction of this form comes from Force: "A female . . . collected July 7, 1928, gave birth to 8 young August 13. . . . In the process of deposition the female was very active, moving around and around the cage. The tail was held erect and the young emerged steadily, about 8 seconds apart. Each was in a fine tissue bag, which immediately burst. It remained attached to the ventrals but was shed almost immediately, before the little snake had moved about the cage three times. After the first nervous activity the young, together with the female, settled down under the water pan. The bands around the neck of the young were a bright yellow and the body color a rich brown like the female. The young measured 102 and 110 mm. in length, while the adult was 270 mm. in length."

Guidry (Tex., 1953) has reported 3 born Sept. 12, 1952. Taylor reported a specimen from San Luis Potosí: "No. 269 contains 8 nearly full-time embryos which average 84 mm. in length. . . . No. 268 contains large eggs, but in none did I discern embryos. This specimen was captured May 13; the other with embryos was taken June 29" (E. H. Taylor).

Food: Insects, slugs, earthworms, spiders, cricket frogs. W. E. Taylor, Guthrie, Gloyd, Strecker (Tex., 1930), Anderson (Mo., 1942).

Authorities:

Branson, E. B. (Kan., 1904)
Breckenridge, W. J. (Minn., 1944a)
Force, E. R. (Okla., 1930)
Garman, S. (Tex., 1892)
Gloyd, H. K. (Kan., 1928)

Guthrie, J. E. (Ia., 1926)
Taylor, E. H. (Tex., 1949)
Taylor, W. E. (Neb., 1892a)
Trapido, H. (Gen., 1944)

Hay's snake (3—Pope 1937), **Florida brown snake** (3—Ditmars 1936)
Storeria dekayi victa Hay 1892. Fig. 208; Map 53

Other common names: Brown snake (Van Hyning 1933); DeKay's snake?; ground snake.

Range: Peninsular Florida to Okefinokee Swamps, Ga.—Fla.; Ga.; S.C. *Elevation*—Sea level to 200 feet.

Size: Adults, 10–17 inches.

Distinctive characteristics: "Scales in 15 rows, head plates normally as in *S. dekayi*. Ventrals and subcaudals high in number. Dorsal color brown with dark spots of varying intensity on the 6th scale row. Belly whitish, variously marked with dark flecks laterally, or almost unmarked. Head characteristically with a light band posteriorly, followed by a dark band on the occiput, labials below the orbit dark" (Trapido, 1944).

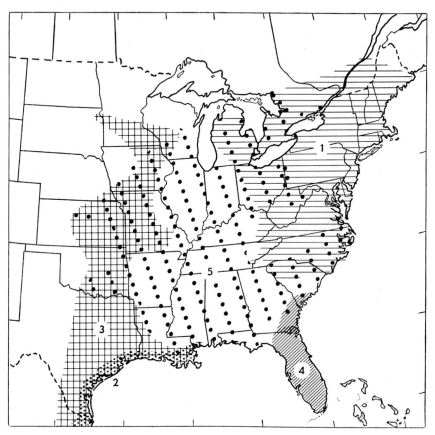

Map 53. *Storeria*—1, *dekayi;* 2, *d. temporalineata;* 3, *d. texana;* 4, *d. victa;* 5, *d. wrightorum.*

Color: A snake from Payne's Prairie, Gainesville, Fla., Mar. 31, 1934. It measures 26 cm. in body length plus 6½ cm. tail; width 1 cm. The general color is buffy brown with a middorsal band of citrine-drab 3 scales wide. On either side of this band is a row of black spots spaced every 2 or 3 scales, thus forming a double row to the base of the tail. The spots in each row are much closer together than in *S. dekayi*. One or 2 scale rows back of the parietals appears a dark nuchal band of deep grayish olive, narrowest on midback, and extending completely across sides and back from ventral to ventral. Some of the lower scales have prominent black centers; those above have dark edges. In front of the nuchal band is a light area of avellaneous, becoming vinaceous-buff or even lighter on the sides. The top of the head is citrine-drab with an obscure band of black or olive-brown extending across the top over most of the parietal and part of rear of the frontal areas. There are dottings of the same color on supraoculars and prefrontals. There is a black patch below the eye on 3 upper labials, the lower postocular, the anterior end of front temporal, expanding over half of the 4th and 5th upper labials. The 1st and 2nd upper labials and half of the 3rd are white. The iris in the ventral half is much like the darker spot below it. The upper half is buffy brown with 2 olive-buff areas. The ventrals are tilleul buff or pale olive-buff with a dot toward the end of each plate. Toward the neck there may be 3 irregular rows of these specks or dots. The underside of the tail is clear deep olive-buff

A small snake from Royal Palm Hammock, Mar. 17, 1934. The dorsal band of smoke gray is indicated for only half its length by the pairs of spaced black or chaetura drab spots, these spots being absent or indistinct in the caudal half. On the bases of the ventrals and edges of the 1st row of scales is a snuff brown or brownish olive band with a smoke gray light band above it. The black spots on the side of the neck are few, so that there is no nuchal spot. The belly is shell pink or pale vinaceous-pink, most pronounced on the lower belly, the underside of the tail becoming buff-pink or light pinkish cinnamon.

Habitat: Almost every writer has remarked the snake's aquatic tendencies, its preference for marshes, sloughs, ponds, ditches, moist localities, river swamps, creek bottomlands, and wet areas in general. It is particularly fond of water prairies and water hyacinth. It may seek cover "under logs near the water's edge."

Period of activity: *First appearance*—Mar. 17, 1934 (Wright and Wright); Mar. 31, 1934 (Carr, Kilby, Van Hyning, Jopsons, Wrights); Feb. (Loennberg).

Breeding: Viviparous. Males 252–320 mm., females 257–412 mm. *Young*—Number, 11–17. Hay, the describer of this species, observed: "The oviducts of the specimen contained a dozen eggs, each somewhat more than ¼ of an inch in length. The coverings of the eggs are extremely thin, from which I infer that the animal brings forth its young alive. This is the case with *S. dekayi*, and probably with the other species of the genus." In 1915 Wright and Bishop said of their collection: "One specimen had 17 small developing eggs, 14 being on the left side. Inasmuch as this was taken after July 15, this would doubtless indicate that this particular specimen of this ovoviviparous species would not have given birth to young until late summer or early fall." In 1940 our most definite evidence appeared. Carr wrote: "A female collected May 5, 1936, Alachua County, bore 11 young June 6, 1936. The young were 107–109 mm. in length; the coloration was similar to that of the adult, but much darker, the dorsal ground-color, the dark neck band, and the top of the head being nearly black, and the ventral surface dark gray; the light neck band was almost white and much more distinct than in adult specimens; all have 15 scale rows."

Food: Insects, gastropods. Wright and Bishop.

Field notes: Mar. 17, 1934: Came to Royal Palm Park. Went west of the house. . . . In a pine log near a ditch tore off some bark and found one of the snakes we seek, *Storeria victa*. It looks like *S. dekayi* on the belly, but it has oculars 2-2 and 15 rows of scales.

Mar. 31, 1934. Went with A. F. Carr, Tom Carr, G. Van Hyning, John Kilby, H. G. M. Jopson, and Hope Jopson, to several ponds and Payne's Prairie. First the boys waded out in the prairie about 6–10 feet and rolled hyacinths onto the bank. Left a clear area between windrow of plants and edge of prairie. Animals come out on this bare strip as the water soaks out. In this way they took many *Pseudobranchus,* plenty of *R. grylio* tadpoles, and a few *R. sphenocephala* adults and tadpoles, *Jordanella, F. chrysotis* clear and black spotted, several *Seminatrix pygaea,* 1 small *Farancia,* newts, *T. sackeni,* and *S. victa.*

Authorities:

Carr, A. F., Jr. (Fla., 1940a)   Trapido, H. (Gen., 1944)
Hay, O. P. (Fla., 1892)   Wright, A. H., and S. C. Bishop (Ga.,
Loennberg, E. (Fla., 1895)   1916)
Neill, W. T. (Ga., 1950a)

1892, O. P. Hay: "This species appears to differ from *Storeria dekayi* in the smaller number of dorsal scales (15 instead of 17) in the greater proportional width of the scales, in the somewhat greater number of ventral plates, and in the presence of the 2 rows of spots on the abdomen. . . . It is possible that the animal which I here describe as new is a specimen of *S. dekayi* with a smaller number of scales than usual, but until there is other evidence of this, it seems better to regard it as different."

1940(a), A. F. Carr, Jr.: "Variation in specimens of *victa* which I have examined has embraced all the characters of *dekayi* except the two additional scale-rows of the latter."

1944, H. Trapido: "There is much variation in the intensity of the markings on the head and belly."

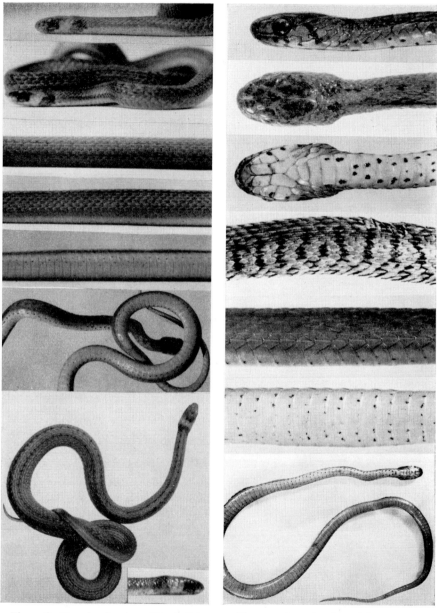

Fig. 208. *Storeria d. victa,* Royal Palm Park and Payne Prairie, Gainesville, Fla., G. Van Hyning, T. and A. F. Carr, J. Kilby.

Fig. 209. *Storeria d. wrightorum,* New Orleans, La., R. Roecker.

Central brown snake, DeKay's snake (39)

Storeria dekayi wrightorum Trapido 1944. Fig. 209; Map 53

Other common names: Brown (grass) snake; DeKay's brown snake; grey-bellied brown snake; grass snake; ground snake; little brown snake; little grey snake; small brown snake; worm snake; Wrights' brown snake (Trapido 1944).

Range: From s. Virginia and North Carolina s. around the Appalachian highland to s. Georgia, thence n. in Mississippi basin to Michigan and Ontario; west to e. Kansas and e. Oklahoma.—U.S.A.: Ala.; Ark.; Fla.; Ga.; Ia.; Ill.; Ind.; Kan.; La.; Mich.; Miss.; Mo.; N.C.; O.; Okla.; Pa.; S.C.; S.D.; Va.; W. Va.; Wis. Can.: Ont. *Elevation*—Sea level to about 2,000 feet.

Size: Adults, 8–17 inches.

Distinctive characteristics: "*Storeria dekayi wrightorum* is similar to *S. s. dekayi* but differs in that the dorsal spots are fused to form short dorsal crossbands, and the sum of the ventrals and subcaudals is 176 or more (91 percent of specimens examined)" (Trapido). "From ash-gray to chestnut brown above, with a pale dorsal stripe, on each side of which is a series of brown spots; the latter may encroach upon the median stripe, and occasionally unite across the middle line; sometimes they are wanting. Beneath pale gray, with 1 or 2 small black specks near the outer margins of each ventral scute. Head brown above, with a faint iridescence. On each side of the neck, at the base of the head, is an obliquely-placed black or brown bar, the 2 occasionally meeting above. Smaller black bars across the temporals and superior labials of each side extend to or slightly beyond the angle of the mouth. Posterior margins of the 3rd and 4th supralabials black. Infralabials pale, or touched with black at the margins" (Garman).

Color: A snake from New Orleans, La., received from R. M. Roecker, Dec. 18, 1943. The sides are snuff brown with a dorsal band 2½–3 scales of tawny-olive or sayal brown. The dorsal bands across this tawny-olive area are broader at their lateral ends and sometimes appear no more than a dark edging to the scale bases of the meson. These dorsal spots and bars are warm sepia. Along the sides are faint alternating bars linked with dorsal bars by oblique threads. In the rear half of the body, dorsal bars are obscure or absent. The tail and 1½ inches forward are uniform sayal brown with no spots. The tail, standing out distinctly, looks regenerated. Below the ends of the dorsal crossbars along the sides, the skin between the scales bears 2 or 3 rows of flecks of seafoam green. Above this series, between ends of dorsal bars, but not on median band, are 3 more such rows of flecks, but somewhat obscured. The lateral color involves scale row 1 and extends onto ends of ventrals forming there a clearcut line of lateral color. The top of the head is warm sepia with parietal spots obscurely outlined. There is a black bar across the suture of the last 2 lower labials and last 2 upper labials crossing anterior temporal near its posterior border. This dark spot is on its front somewhat edged with mikado brown. Below the eye, on sutures of upper labials 3 + 4, and 4 + 5 is a bowing spot of same color. On sutures of lower 3 + 4 and 4 + 5 are 2 spots of the same, extensions of upper labial marking. The eye in lower half is vandyke brown and in upper half pinard yellow. The ventral color proper is pale cinnamon-pink on outer parts and pale pinkish cinnamon in the center. This color extends to lower side of head becoming there pale pinkish buff to white. There is a tendency for ventrals to have a collection of 2 spots toward either end with a few irregular ones in the center. These spots become more intense and reduced to 2 on ventrals 3 to 10, thereafter continue backward as 4 rows of spots with no perceptible clear central area. No spots on underside of head except the lower labial ones.

Abnormal coloration—Albinism. In 1947 Smith, near Charleston, Ill., recorded that "a small albino was found near the college campus in 1942."

Habitat: Like *S. d. dekayi* it is recorded in back yards of dwellings, in gardens, in city lots, and in the debris areas of cities and towns. Also like the northeastern form it is found under boards, stones, logs, rubbish, and bark, and among leaves. Many early writers placed it in dry situations. However, all these dry or semidry references are in more or less moist areas. In the open country apart from urban areas, it is surely of the moist situations. If an observer says "upland woods," he appends "along a ravine." Terms such as "near water, river, swamps, ponds, lake, pool, meadows" enter most every habitat note. The adjectives *wet, moist, swampy, marshy, damp,* are prevalent in the characterizations. Neill (Ga., 1950a) pronounced it less aquatic than *S. d. victa,* which inhabits river swamps and creek bottomlands while *s. d. wrightorum* is of the meadows and forests.

Period of activity: First appearance—Feb. 10, Mar. 22 (Corrington, S.C., 1929); Mar. 20, May 3, 24 (Hurter). *Fall disappearance*—Nov. 8, 1929 (Allen, Miss., 1932); Oct. 8, 17 (Evermann and Clark); Sept. 1, Oct. 15, 26, Nov. 1, 13 (Hurter); Oct. 8 (Mittleman, Ind., 1947). Brimley's "Seasonal Catch" (N.C., 1925) at Raleigh may apply to this subspecies as well as to *S. d. dekayi:* Jan., 3 snakes; Feb., 2; Mar., 8; Apr., 10; May, 9; June, 6; July, 2; Aug., 1; Oct., 5; Nov., 5; Dec., 1. Total 52.

Hibernation—An interesting observation on winter mortality by Bailey is: "A hibernation den of *Storeria dekayi* (Holbrook) was discovered quite by accident on March 22, 1939. . . . While searching the edge of the roadway embankment, Silas S. Sharp and I noted 2 or 3 live specimens emerging from small burrows. A number of these passageways were excavated and found to contain numerous additional snakes. About a dozen active specimens were secured between the surface and 18 inches underground, and 20 dead individuals, including juveniles and adults, were taken from the same passageways. . . . All of the dead snakes were within 10 inches of the surface. They were in various stages of decomposition and obviously many had been dead for a considerable time. The mortality here was evidently due to winter kill during hibernation."

Breeding: Viviparous. Males 247–350 mm., females 282–405 mm. *Mating*—Conant records a pair in mating position as early as Mar. 28 and takes a female in October with 24 large eggs and conjectures that "such might be indicative of a late summer or early fall mating."

Young—Number, 3–24. The broods, embryos, eggs, or hatchling young have been given as 3, 9, 10, 11, 13, 15, 23, and 24. Time, last of July and early August. Size, 3.2–4.2 inches. "New-born specimens of Georgia *wrightorum* are scarcely distinguishable from those of Florida *victa,* both being nearly black above and gray below, with a conspicuous white neck-ring" Neill (Ga., 1950a).

Food: Earthworms, slugs, insects, froglets, toadlets. Parker (Tenn., 1937), Surface (Pa., 1906), Boyer and Heinze (Mo., 1934).

Authorities:

Bailey, R. M. (Ia., 1948)
Conant, R. (O., 1938a)
Davis, N. S., Jr., and F. L. Rice (Ill., 1883)
Evermann, B. W., and H. W. Clark (Ind., 1920)
Garman, H. (Ill., 1892)
Hay, O. P. (Ind., 1892)
Higley, W. K. (Wis., 1889)
Hurter, J. (Mo., 1911)
Pope, C. (Ill., 1944)
Trapido, H. (Gen., 1944)

Red-bellied snake (114—Macauley 1829), Storer's snake (23—Butler 1887)

Storeria occipitomaculata occipitomaculata (Storer) 1839. Fig. 210; Map 54

Other common names: Brown snake (9); copper snake; ground snake (4); little brown snake; little red-bellied snake; red-bellied brown snake; red-bellied DeKay's snake; red-bellied garter snake; red-bellied ground snake; red-bellied Storeria; spot-necked snake; spotted-neck snake; Storer snake; Storer's brown snake; Storer's grass snake.

Range: From the Maritime Provinces and Quebec, w. to Manitoba, southward to w. Louisiana and cent. Georgia, e. to the Atlantic coast, and n. and n.e. to the Maritime Provinces—U.S.A.: Ala.; Ark.; Conn.; D.C.; Del.; Ga.; Ill.; Ind.; Kan.; Ky.; La.; Mass.; Md.; Me.; Mich.; Minn.; Miss.; Mo.; Neb.; N.C.; N.D.; N.J.; N.Y.; O.; Okla.; Pa.; R.I.; S.C.; S.D.; Tenn.; Tex.; Vt.; Va.; W. Va.; Wis. Can.: Man.; N.B.; N.S.; Ont.; P.E.I.; Que. *Elevation*—Sea level to 5,000 feet or more. Sea level to 1,500 feet (Manville, Me., 1939); 1,500–4,950 feet (King, Tenn., 1939); 2,000 feet (Weber, N.Y., 1928); 2,250, 4,050 feet (Barbour, Ky., 1950); 3,800 feet (Dunn, N.C., 1917); 1,400–1,600 feet (Smith, Pa., 1945).

Size: Adults, 7.5 or 8–16 inches. All lengths are below 16 inches except one.

Longevity: 2 years 2 months (Conant and Hudson, Gen., 1949).

Distinctive characteristics: "The subspecies *occipitomaculata* is characterized by the 3 light spots on the occiput, the light mark on the 5th labial scale interrupted by black on the lower margin of the scale, the moderate amount of black pigment over much of the dorsum and rear of the head, and the red belly. The dorsal scales are keeled, and in 15 rows. The loreal is

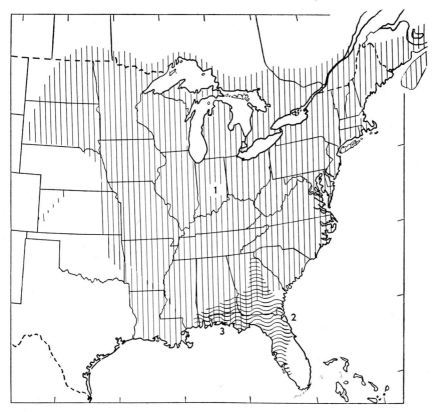

Map 54. *Storeria*—1, *occipitomaculata;* 2, *o. obscura;* 3, *o.* (intergrades).

absent, the preoculars normally 2; the postoculars normally 2, the upper labials normally 6, and the lower labials 7" (Trapido, 1944). "Olive or chestnut-brown above, uniform, or with a dorsal ash-gray stripe, and a similar stripe on the outer rows or dorsal scales, the latter more obscure than the dorsal stripe, or wanting altogether. Beneath salmon-red, fading anteriorly into light gray. External margins of the ventral scutes with distinct blackish submarginal spots, forming a longitudinal series for each side. Head above reddish brown, faintly iridescent, with 3 occipital pale spots, the median much the largest. Fifth supralabial pale" (Garman).

Color: A snake from Ithaca, N.Y., taken Oct. 2, 1935. Along the back, the middle 3 rows of scales are tawny-olive or buckthorn brown, forming a light brownish stripe outlined by a dark border on the 6th row of scales. This border is cinnamon-brown, sudan brown, warm sepia, or bister. On the 2nd to 6th rows is saccardo's umber or dresden brown. The top and sides of the head are mikado brown or russet. There is a spot back of the parietals and a lateral spot on either side below it of ochraceous-buff, clay color, or cinnamon-buff. These spots are separated by the color of the top of the head or by the color of the border of the dorsal stripe. On the upper half of the 5th upper labial and extending obliquely to the rear of the eye is a white spot. The iris is more or less like the top of the head in color with an area over the pupil of clay color or cinnamon-buff. The lower side of the head is whitish with black punctae and with a partial wash of cinereous or plumbeous. On either end of the ventrals and below the 1st row of scales is a band of light sky blue, pale blue, or a darker shade verging into cinereous or plumbeous. This gray or plumbeous area is more or less specked with black.

Abnormal coloration—We have seen "brown snakes" or "ground snakes," brown, gray, frequently all black, rarely reddish, once or twice almost orange, and once albino. In the period of 1900–14 we could walk on our campus to suitable areas and find a black one or two. They still appear from time to time. It is not surprising then that Surface in 1906 and Spencer in 1915 in Pennsylvania, Brimley in 1942 in North Carolina, Allen in 1901 in New Hampshire, Gloyd in 1928 in Kansas, or Babbitt in 1932 in Connecticut recorded black, blue black, almost black, on both back and belly. In North Carolina in 1924 Myers recorded "one small erythristic female. This peculiar individual was nearly as bright red on the back as on the belly." On the belly we may have just as decided changes. We have mentioned black-bellied individuals. We also find rare individuals dark blue, yellow, orange, or white. Other persons also have recorded such colors. For example, in 1931 at Syracuse, N.Y., Corrington described a "white-bellied red-bellied snake," and Pickens (1927c) in South Carolina remarked about a "yellow-bellied red-bellied snake."

Habitat and habits: Various authors have given this snake as in woods 7 or in wooded regions (pine woods 4; heavily wooded regions 2; deeply wooded areas 2; higher wood 2; more wooded 2; upland woods 2; dry upland woods 1; sandstone wood, open oak-hickory woodland, pine barrens, pine ridges, aspens, shady rocky woods, hilly forested region, hemlock grove). This somewhat nocturnal snake we usually find under cover as follows: under stones or rocks 23; under logs 17; under boards 12; among or under leaves 6; beneath bark 4; in lumber piles 2; under wood 2; in woodpiles 1; in dwellings 2; under debris 1; under old heaps of debris, tar paper, auto parts, roots, leaf mould, fallen timber, sphagnum mat, and rotten stump.

A glance at the above habitats will satisfy the reader that it lives more in the upland hilly ridges than in the lowlands. We believe this conclusion in spite of these captures as follows: near river 4; damp meadow 2; shore of lake 1; on moist ground 1; sphagnum mat, edge of swamp, edge of bog, and marshy country. In contrast, there are such habitats as sandy ridges, hilly regions, hillsides, flat dry area, under limestone rocks, stony ground, and limestone hill.

This species may frequent abandoned dwellings 2, fallen houses 1, deserted barns, and old buildings. It has been recorded in open fields 5, open pastures 3, semiopen areas, rarely plowed fields 2. From the above summary it is observable that it may be on the edge of wet places or marginal to open areas, such as in roads 5, beside roads 4, at edge of dirt roads 1, under fallen fence posts, along fences, in exposed fire lanes. Unusual records are: swimming 10 or 15 feet from shore, atop a tangle of poison ivy, climbing up a honeysuckle 15 feet to a window ledge. All in all, it is widespread in distribution and habitat, but most likely to be found in high, hilly, stony, wooded areas. In Ithaca, N.Y., favorite spots were a gravel pit and a stone quarry.

Axtell (N.Y., 1947) found that his 119 specimens appeared "to be less specialized in habitat than with most species. We have collected it in numbers at some of the highest and driest localities and likewise at some of the lowest and wettest."

Period of activity: *Early appearances*—Mar. 31, 1945 (Axtell); May 3, 9, 16, 23 (Gloyd); May 15 (Pope); Apr. 28 (Evermann); May 9 (Evans); Apr. 8, 11, 20 (Dunn); Mar. (Fowler); May 8 (Small); Apr. 15, May 23, June 3, 4, (Hurter); Mar. 24, May 26 (Gloyd); Mar. 16 (Dundee). Some of our early dates at Ithaca, N.Y., are: Mar. 17, 1903; Apr. 28, 1907; May 18, 1908; Apr. 18, 19, May 18, 1908; Apr. 27, 1912; Apr. 17, 1913; Apr. 18, 21, 22, 1915. *Fall disappearance*—Sept. 7 (Atkinson); Sept. 27 (Evans); Oct. 25 (Wright); Sept. 11 (Weber); Oct. 12 (Dunn); Aug. 31, Sept. 5 (Bishop, Alexander); Sept. 11 (Engelhardt); Sept. 26, 1944, Oct. 28, 1945, Nov. 2, 1944 (Axtell). We have at Ithaca such late dates as Oct. 11, 22, 1912; Oct. 12, 1913. On Oct. 17, 1950, we saw several DOR near Springville, N.Y. Brimley (N.C., 1925) reports in his "Seasonal Catch" of snakes at Raleigh: 1 in February, 7 in April, 1 in May, 2 in July, 1 in September, 2 in October, 2 in November, and 1 in December.

Hibernation—In 1844 Linsley (Conn.) remarked: "I have seen several of the spotted neck snake here in autumn, usually 9 to 10 inches long, turned out of ground where they had eventually intended to pass the winter."

We give one of our field notes: On January 8, 1950, Heinz Meng called up to say that near Perry's coal yard, Ithaca, N.Y., a friend dug up in a gravelly area 65 *Storeria occipitomaculata*. He wanted to know if they were ever black underneath. He had one black all over and one with a yellow belly.

For Criddle's remarkable story, see *Opheodrys v. blanchardi*. In his famous anthill he took 100 or more *Storeria occipitomaculata;* measurements of 75 varied from 112 to 303 mm.

Breeding: Viviparous. Males 182–359 mm., females 211–383 mm. *Sexual dimorphism*—In 1863 Verrill (Me.) thought that possibly the fact that some specimens are reddish brown above and others slate colored indicated a sexual difference, but no one else has held this belief. Trapido found the males had 42–61 caudals and the females 35–54.

Mating—For 40 or more years we have not believed wholly in the gestation period as customarily interpreted—spring mating to hatching. Delayed fertilization, fall mating, parturition without yearly mating we recognized. We are glad that some of our students—such as Trapido, Rahn, McCauley, Bishop, Wimsatt, Alexander—have contributed publications on this subject. The following notes show that besides spring mating we may have midsummer or fall mating: "On July 9, 1921, a pair in coitu was found in a clump of *Taxus* in the wood near Buffalo Camp. Dissection of the female, which was preserved at the time of capture, showed well developed embroys. . . . L. Eggleston coll." (Bishop and Alexander).

"During the fall of 1938 the writer dissected specimens of *Storeria occipito-maculata* and made smears of the fluid in the reproductive tracts of both males and females. The vas deferens of males, without exception, had mature spermatozoa, which were extremely active in a drop of normal saline solution on a microscopical slide. On October 20, a female, which had been taken on October 10, was dissected and its left oviduct removed and washed with a normal saline solution. This wash was found to be swarming with actively swimming spermatozoa. Several days later 3 other female snakes were dissected and air-dried smears prepared from the fluid in their oviducts with the same results—each had an abundance of sperm present. One female, examined on October 24, had only scattered blood cells, epithelial cells, and bacteria in the fluid of the oviduct; there were no sperm. This year (1939) a pair of *Storeria occipito-maculata* taken by Mr. John Belkin at Varna, near Ithaca, New York, on September 6 were in coitus. Additional records of matings other than in the spring are those of Bishop (1927) for *Storeria occipito-maculata* on July 9, and Dymond and Fry (1932) for *Opheodrys vernalis* in August" (Trapido, 1940).

Young—Number, 1–21. 1–14 (Blanchard, Fowler); 2 (Myers); 3, 15 (Conant); 3, 11, 13 (Loomis and Jones); 4, 5, 7, 9 (Ruthven); 5, 6, 7, 8, 9, 14, 18 (Breckenridge); 6 (Minton, Cohen); 6, 7 (Gloyd, Corrington); 6, 8, 9 (Langlois); 6, 9 (Bishop and Alexander); 7 (Brimley); 7, 12 (Wright and Allen); 7, 12, 17, 21 (Axtell); 8, 10 (Lamson); 10 (Hahn); 10, 14 (Lowe); 12 (Guthrie); 14 (Weber). "The number of young at a birth, as shown by 7 broods, varies from 1 to 13 with an average of 7.18± a standard deviation of 2.54. More than two thirds of the broods in northern Michigan comprise 4 to 9 young inclusive" (Blanchard).

Time of birth, June 18–Sept. 26. June 18 (Brimley); June 30, July 17, July 19, Sept. 5, 7, 9 (Breckenridge); July 24 (Gloyd); Aug. (Logier, Langlois, Wright and Allen); Aug. 22, 28 (Bishop and Alexander); Aug. 23 (Lamson, Conant, Cohen); Aug. 29 (Weber); early Sept. (Eckel); Sept. 4 (Ditmars, Gibbs, Axtell); Sept. 7, 10, 19, 26 (Ruthven). "Most of the young are born about Aug. 10 to 23, but they may appear as early as late July and as late as September 5" (Blanchard). There are records of advanced embryos July 24, Aug. 4, Aug. 6, Aug. 10, Aug. 23, and as late as Sept. 10.

Size at birth, 45–100 mm. (1.8–4 inches). 3, 4 inches (Surface); $3\frac{3}{16}$, $3^{11}\!/_{16}$ inches (Bishop and Alexander); 81–89 mm. (Langlois); $3\frac{1}{4}$ inches (Ditmars); $3\frac{1}{3}$ inches (Small and Lett); $3\frac{5}{8}$ (Conant). "The range of variation in length at birth is 67 to 98 mm., although no single brood shows a variation of more than half this number" (Blanchard). According to one author, the newly born "are so tiny that it has been said of them, 'a large earthworm appears quite gigantic in comparison'" (Funkhouser, Ky., 1925). Another has said: "They are so small that one could easily coil on a dime" (Guthrie, Ia., 1926). The circumference of a dime is about $2\frac{1}{8}$ or $\frac{3}{16}$ inches or about 55 mm., 12 mm. lower than Blanchard's size. At first we questioned it, but since we chanced on Ruthven's (Mich., 1906) record of a 45-mm. newborn hatchling, we must believe it.

Three of the best detailed accounts of breeding are by Ruthven in 1906, Langlois in 1925, and Blanchard in 1937, all in Michigan. Some of the southern records may show breeding a little earlier in the season.

Food: Insects, slugs, earthworms, myriapods, sowbugs. Axtell (N.Y., 1947).

Defense: As Trapido, Hamilton, and others have noted, this species has a facial (labial) defense. Independently, Axtell (N.Y., 1947) wrote, "When *Storeria occipitomaculata* is first captured, it often appears to become very angry, lifting the upper labials and laterally exserting the teeth of the upper jaw, at the same time pressing the side of the head against its captor in such a way that the teeth often catch momentarily, producing a very slight pricking which can scarcely be detected as applied to human skin. This pricking effort has apparently not been noticed even by herpetological writers." Warburton (Ont., 1951) recounted several defensive and intimidation traits of this species.

Authorities:

Bishop, S. C., and W. P. Alexander (N.Y., 1927)
Blanchard, F. N. (Mich., 1937)
Criddle, S. (Man., 1937)
Garman, H. (Ill., 1892)
Hallowell, E. (*Proc. Acad. Nat. Sci.,* 1847, pp. 278–279)
Storer, D. H. (Mass., 1839)
Surface, H. A. (Pa., 1906)
Trapido, H. (Gen., 1940, 1944)

1937, F. N. Blanchard: From his significant paper we quote the first paragraph of the summary: "Ordinarily these snakes first become parents at the age of 2 years. The minimum length of adults in northern Michigan is about

Fig. 210. *Storeria occipitomaculata occi-pitomaculata,* Ithaca, N.Y.: 1–5, authors, 6, A. B. Klots.

Fig. 211. *Storeria o. obscura,* H. Trapido, Gainesville, Fla.

220 mm. Both sexes probably mature at about the same size, but females may grow to a greater length. The largest male measured 295 mm., the largest female 325 mm."

Florida red-bellied snake (Trapido 1944), Red-bellied snake (5)

Storeria occipitomaculata obscura Trapido 1944. Fig. 211; Map 54

Another common name: Crane snake.

Range: From Charlotte Co., Fla., n.w. to s.e. Mississippi, thence n.e. across s. coastal Alabama and Georgia to Oconee Co., S.C.—Ala.; Fla.; Ga.; Miss.; S.C. *Elevation*—Sea level to 500 feet, seldom to 750 feet.

Size: Adults, 7–12 inches.

Distinctive characteristics and color: Characters of *S. c. occipitomaculata,* but differing as follows: the top and sides of the head are black, with the occasional exception of the portion before the eyes and the anterior portion of the 5th supralabial, which is white to the lower margin of the scale. The anterior tip of the 1st labial is also sometimes white. The occiput is marked with a light ring about 2 scales in width, joining the light color of the venter laterally. The dorsal body color varies from light tan to black. Ventrals fewer and subcaudals more numerous than in *S. o. occipitomaculata* (Trapido).

Habitat: Carr wrote of its habitat and habits: "Upland and mesophytic hammock; under bark and logs and in leafmold. . . . Not common; I have seen 5 living specimens. . . . Fossorial, apparently burrowing chiefly in leaf mold; I have found 2 in piles of debris at the bases of magnolia trees."

This southeastern-mesophytic-evergreen-forest, Sabalian, or swamp coastal form remains little known. Too few records are at hand even to outline its range satisfactorily, to say nothing of its habits or preferred habitats.

Period of activity: *First appearances*—Apr., 1893 (Loennberg); Jan. 14, 1911, Feb. 22, 1911 (Blatchley); Apr. 17, 1937 (Carr). *Fall disappearance*—Sept., Oct., 1930 (Allen, Miss., 1932).

Breeding: Viviparous. Males 197–215 mm., females 231–260 mm. *Young*—Only one note is of record, Carr's: "A female, collected at Gainesville (Fla.), Apr. 17, 1937, had 8 large but incompletely developed embryos in the oviduct."

Food: Slugs, earthworms, insects, snails. Wright and Bishop, Haltom (Ala., 1931).

Authorities:

Blatchley, W. S. (Fla., 1932)
Carr, A. F., Jr. (Fla., 1940a)
Loennberg, E. (Fla., 1895)

Trapido, H. (Gen., 1944)
Wright, A. H., and S. C. Bishop (Ga., 1916)

1944, H. Trapido: "At the periphery of the range of *obscura,* i.e. in the panhandle of Florida and in western Georgia, specimens are found with the head coloration as described above, but with occipital spots not fused to form a neck ring. Such snakes are regarded as intergrades between the typical subspecies *occipitomaculata* and subspecies *obscura*. Similarly modified specimens have also been seen from further west along the Gulf."

BLACK-HEADED SNAKES

Genus *TANTILLA* Baird and Girard (Fig. 24)

Size small, 6–20 inches; slender; head flat and not very distinct; eye small; tail short; anal divided (except sometimes in *T. c. wagneri*); caudals paired; scales smooth, without pits, and in 15 rows; no loreal; upper labials 6 or 7; posterior maxillary teeth slightly enlarged, separated by an interspace, grooved (no poison gland—C. B. Perkins [Calif., 1938]); oculars 1-1 (2); nasals 2; ventrals ♂ 112–174, ♀ 123–190; caudals ♂ 42–73, ♀ 35–67; dorsum brown, venter with considerable red or pink; "hemipenis—caliculate, not capitate, fusiform" (Cope). Synonyms: *Homalocranion, Homalocranium, Scolecophis.*

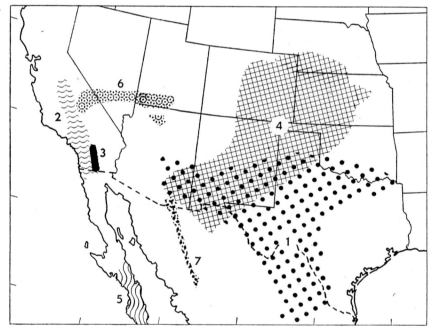

Map 55. *Tantilla—1, atriceps; 2, e. eiseni; 3, e. transmontana; 4, n. nigriceps; 5, planiceps; 6, utahensis; 7, w. wilcoxi.*

KEY TO THE GENUS *TANTILLA*

a. With head cap much darker than dorsal scales. Oculars 1–2. Upper labials usually 7 (with 6th approximately as long as 5th). White color present, though sometimes faint except in *T. n. nigriceps* and *T. n. fumiceps* and some individual *T. wagneri.*

   b. Head cap with vertical lateral extensions to labial margin, often across suture of 6th and 7th labials; posterior tip of last labial commonly light; white collar usually conspicuous, and crossing tips of parietals (except in black-headed *wagneri* where white is suffused); large-bodied; secondary temporal elongate; mental usually contacts chin shields.

   c. White collar bordered behind by broad black band 3–4 scale lengths in width. Light temporal area forms indentation into head cap; venter buff to flesh pink; teeth 16.

   d. White collar well defined, but sometimes interrupted on midline; 1st 4 labials commonly dark; black on nape usually to 5th scale behind parietals. Ventrals 131–141 in ♂, 139–148 in ♀; caudals 42–51 in ♂, 41–46 in ♀. Maximum size recorded 324 mm. (South Carolina to s.e. Louisiana, thence north into w. Kentucky.)   *T. coronata coronata*

   dd. White collar commonly heavily clouded with dark; black usually not extending beyond the 4th scale behind parietals (even in black-headed specimens white spot back of eye visible). Anal may be entire; (mental not in contact with chin shields in our specimen). Ventrals ♂ 119–129, ♀ 123–145; caudals ♂ 50–67, ♀ 41–59. Maximum size recorded 240 mm. (Florida.)
                                                       T. c. wagneri

   cc. Posterior black border of collar very narrow (1–1 1/2 scales), sometimes reduced to dotted line. Lateral extensions of head cap to labial border on 6th and 7th labials. White nuchal collar crossing tips of parietals and 2 scales on neck being 2–3 scale lengths in width; no light indentation into dark cap in area behind eye; labials light; eye large, posterior nasal contacts preocular; coral red below; teeth 14; labials 7–7 (6), ventrals 148–164, caudals 58–69. Maximum size recorded 349 mm. (In U.S., Huachuca and Patagonia Mts.)   *T. wilcoxi*

bb. Head cap without lateral vertical extensions to labial margin; ant. to last supralabial. White collar poorly defined or absent; slender bodied; eye small; mental in contact with or separated from chin shield; ventrals red.

   c. No white band bordering head cap; head cap not extending behind or below angle of mouth; cap extending 2–5 scale lengths behind parietals; upper labial margin and lower half of temporal light; mental plate usually separated from chin shields by 1st pair of labials; prefrontal may penetrate between nasal and preocular to meet labial; temporals longer than broad, but not extremely elongate.

      d. Anterior of frontal obtusely angulate; labials 7–7; teeth 13; prefrontal and labial separated or not. Ventrals ♂ 136–150, ♀ 150–163; caudals 43–62 ♂, 35–58 ♀. Maximum size recorded 350 mm. (S. Nebraska and w. Kansas to e. Colorado, s. through Oklahoma and Texas to New Mexico and Arizona.)   *T. nigriceps nigriceps*

     dd. Anterior of frontal very obtusely angulate, approximately straight across; labials 7–6; teeth 14; prefrontal and labial usually meet; ventrals ♂ 130–138, ♀ 137–150; caudals ♂ 43–52, ♀ 39–44. Maximum size recorded 224 mm. (S.-cent. Oklahoma through cent. Texas to Tamaulipas, Mex.)   *T. n. fumiceps*

 cc. Dark head cap usually bordered behind with narrow and often faint white band. Mental usually contacts chin shields except in *T. planiceps*.

    d. Dark head cap crossing 3–5 scale rows on nape with white collar about 1 scale length usually on 6th and 7th scale rows; mental separated from chin shields; posterior nasal united with anterior above nostril and usually in contact with preocular; temporals elongate; labials: upper 7 (last largest), lower 6; anterior of frontal obtusely angulate; ventrals 134–141; caudals 49–61; maximum size recorded 260 mm. (Lower half of Baja California, Mex.)   *T. planiceps*

   dd. Dark cap extending 1–3 scale lengths behind parietals; mental usually contacts chin shields.

      e. Cap diagonally crossing last 1–2 labials and extending below angle of mouth, sometimes onto lower throat; other upper labials conspicuously light; frontal angulate anteriorly; teeth 15; prefrontal and labial separated.

        f. Labials 7–7 (rarely 6); color: all dorsal scales have punctations; venter red; ventrals ♂ 165–174, ♀ 174–190; caudals ♂ 58–69; ♀ 53–66. Maximum size recorded 373 mm. (S.e. Alameda Co., Calif., and Fresno, Calif., south to San Quintin, n. Baja Calif.)   *T. eiseni eiseni*

       ff. Labials 7 (6)–6 or 7; color lighter than *eiseni;* lowest 2 scale rows without punctations; tail shorter than *eiseni;* venter red; ventrals ♂ 175–184, ♀ 190–197; caudals ♂ 62–68, ♀ 60–66; maximum size recorded 302 mm. (East of mts. on desert slopes of San Diego Co., Calif., to Palm Springs, Riverside Co., and along e. base of San Bernardino Mts., Riverside Co., Calif.)   *T. e. transmontana*

ee. Cap not covering last upper labial margin and not extending below angle of mouth; cap forms a straight line along middle or upper edge of labials, leaving border light.

 f. Cap extending 1-1 1/2 scale lengths posterior to parietals; white collar not edged with dark behind; prefrontal and labial separated; labials 7-7; teeth 13; primary and secondary temporals elongate; anterior of frontal very obtuse, merely curved; coral red below; ventrals ♂ 123-149, ♀ 138-158; caudals ♂ 54-73, ♀ 51-67; maximum size recorded 270 mm. (Oklahoma and w. Texas to s.e. Arizona, Tucson region to Roosevelt Dam). *T. atriceps*

 ff. Cap extending 1-2 scales posterior to parietals, truncate in rear; light collar not edged behind with dark; black cap extends downward on side to middle of eye and forward to front of supraocular (C.A.S. 65378); mental broadly in contact with chin shields; labials 7-6; prefrontal and labial in contact; ventrals ♂ 153-160, ♀ 163-174; caudals ♂ 59-73, ♀ 50-64; maximum size recorded 297 mm. (S.w. Utah w. into Sierra Nevada Mts. in California.) *T. utahensis*

aa. Without black head cap; without white nuchal collar; oculars 1-1; upper labials 6 (when 7, the 6th much shorter than 5th); secondary temporal small, scalelike; slender bodied; teeth 15; mental touches chin shields at a point; 1st labials taper to same point; venter red; upper labials 4, 5, 6 and part of 1st temporal pink in life (bleaching white in alcohol); tips of triangular preocular, prefrontal, posterior nasal, and 2nd labial meet at common point; anterior margin of frontal very obtusely angulate or curved. Ventrals ♂ 112-127, ♀ 126-138; caudals ♂ 44-57, ♀ 36-48; maximum size recorded 225 mm. (Missouri and e. Kansas [except in the north], south to extreme s. Texas, w. to about the 98th meridian.) *T. gracilis*

(See "Distinctive characteristics" below in the accounts of northern *T. g. hallowelli* and the southern *T. g. gracilis*.)

Gunther's black-headed snake, Texas black-headed snake

Tantilla atriceps (Gunther) 1895. Fig. 212; Map 55

Other common names: Black-headed tantilla; Mexican black-headed snake; Sonoran tantilla.

Range: From s. Oklahoma to s.e. Arizona, thence s.e. to Mexico (Coahuila, Nuevo León, and San Luis Potosí), thence n. through the w. half of Texas to the Red River.—U.S.A.: Ariz.; N.M.; Okla.; Tex. Mex.: Coahuila; Nuevo León; San Luis Potosí. *Elevation*—500 to 5,000 feet. 2,800-5,000 feet (Bailey, N.M., 1913); 3,500-6,000 feet (Little, Ariz., 1940).

Size: Adults, 6.5–10 inches.

Distinctive characteristics: "Body generally light above and below; a dark brown head cap, truncate posteriorly, extending 1 or 1½ scale lengths posterior to parietals; cap not extending below angle of mouth; a faint light collar covering about 1 scale length, not bordered posteriorly by a distinct black line; 7 upper and lower labials; 1 preocular; 2 or rarely 1 postoculars; 2 elongate temporals, separating labials and parietal; prefrontals and labials separated; mental in contact with chin shields, rarely not (type); ventrals 123 to 158; caudals 55 to 70 (males 54 to 70, females 51 to 64)" (Smith). "Black of head extending only 1 or 2 scale lengths behind parietal suture, its posterior margin not pointed and but slightly, if at all, convex, narrowly bordered behind with white, the black not extending below angle of mouth onto gular scales; mental plate usually in contact with anterior chin shields between the 1st lower labials (in general contrast with *nigriceps*); like *nigriceps* in number of ventrals, but caudals more numerous. A small species, the total length varying from 96 to 230 mm. (*nigriceps,* 120 to 350 mm.)" (Blanchard).

Color: A snake from Bisbee, Ariz., received from H. A. Smith, June 12, 1946. The dorsum is buffy brown or wood brown with the 1st 4 or 5 lateral rows of scales light edged. There is a black or raw umber nuchal band crossing the rear tips of the parietals and 1½–2 scale rows of the neck, extending forward across temporals 1-1 to the eye and as a solid mass on side of head 2 scales wide to level of angle of mouth and forward to the end of last supralabial. It demarcates a striking white area on upper and lower labials. This black neck ring is bordered caudad with a white ring 1 scale wide which may be olive-buff or marguerite yellow on middorsum. The top of the head is citrine-drab or buffy olive; internasals, rostral, and prenasals olive-buff. This makes the head rather striking with olive rostral contrasting with citrine-drab dorsal head and black neck ring bordered white. The eye is black or raw umber. The under side of head and 1st 6 or 8 ventrals are white, the other ventrals and underside of tail brazil red.

Habitat: It is found under flat stones or rocks, under dry heads of sotol, in road banks. One was found swimming in a small stream and one in a run-off tank. "This species does not appear to prefer any particular association. It does not seem to be limited by the amount of rock coverages, although 5 of the 7 specimens were taken under rocks. These 7 specimens were collected from 4 associations. Two specimens were collected in May from under rocks in the cedar-ocotillo association; 3 were taken under rocks in the persimmon–shin oak association; 1 was found in a gopher (*Cratogeomys*) burrow in the mesquite-creosote association; 1 taken in September, was found under a sotol stump in the cedar-savannah association. The remains of a half-grown millipede were in the stomach of one individual" (Milstead, Mecham, and McClintock, Tex., 1950).

Period of activity: *Early appearances*—Mar. 26, Apr. 1, Apr. 28, 1912 (Van Denburgh and Slevin). *Hibernation*—Found hibernating in gravel along a road bank Dec. 24, 1936 (Little, Ariz., 1940).

Breeding: Oviparous. Males to 243 mm., females to 221 mm. The smallest that Blanchard mentioned was 96 mm. The smallest we have seen was Brigham Young University No. 2941, ♂, 138 mm. (tail 31), collected by Fred Karchner in 1938, at Benson, Cochise Co., Ariz.

Enemies: (See Vorhies, in "Habitat and habits," under *Micruroides euryxanthus* below.)

Authorities:

Blanchard, F. N. (Gen., 1938)

Boulenger, G. A. (Gen., 1893–96)

Gunther, A. C. L. G. (Gen., 1885–1902)

Murray, L. T. (Tex., 1939)

Schmidt, K. P., and D. W. Owens (Tex., 1944)

Schmidt, K. P., and T. F. Smith (Tex., 1944)

Smith, H. M. (Gen., 1942c)

Van Denburgh, J., and J. R. Slevin (Ariz., 1913)

1913, J. Van Denburgh and J. R. Slevin: *"Tantilla nigriceps* Kennicott. A species of *Tantilla* was found to be fairly common along the Santa Cruz River near Tucson (Ariz.), where 11 specimens were collected between March 26 and April 1. One (No. 34171) was secured in Ventana Canyon, near the base of the Catalina Mts., April 28, 1912. They are much smaller than *Tantilla wilcoxi,* and have fewer gastrosteges and no posterior dark border on collar. . . . This Arizonian *Tantilla* is readily distinguished from the Californian *Tantilla eiseni* by its smaller number of gastrosteges (135 to 148 against 167 to 181 in *T. eiseni*). . . . *Tantilla wilcoxi* has a larger number of gastrosteges (148 to 157) and the white collar crosses the parietals."

1939, L. T. Murray: *"Tantilla atriceps* (Gunther) B.U.M. 6422 a, b, 6436, 6437, 6438 Basin, Chisos Mts. (Tex.). These 5 specimens are variable in scutellation and in coloration. . . . Each specimen falls within the limits of *atriceps* as defined by Blanchard."

1944, K. P. Schmidt and T. F. Smith: Nineteen specimens from the Basin, Cattail Canyon, and Casa Grande.

1944, K. P. Schmidt and D. W. Owens: Mex. Chihuahua.

1944, A. H. and A. A. Wright: San Diego, Tex. If Taylor and Smith did not have specimens from 4 miles west of Saltillo, Coahuila, and 102 kilometers north of San Luis Potosí, we might feel inclined to question the type locality "Nuevo Leon. W. Taylor Esq. (P)" for this species. Cope described a new species of lizard, *Lysoptychus lateralis* (now synonymized with *Sceloporus couchi*), from San Diego, Tex., and ever thereafter the range of the species was thought to be from southern Texas to San Diego, California. We rather doubt if it came from San Diego, Tex. Doubtless *Hypopachus cuneus* and *Sonora taylori* actually came from San Diego, Tex., but that will always be somewhat confused. The S. and B. *Check List's* inclination to give Taylor type-locality material as "Duval Co.—Nuevo León" shows that this confusion was recognized in its authors' minds. (See *Sonora taylori, Tantilla planiceps*.) As a consequence we must confess we are surprised that the British Museum authors in their *Check List* did not also credit this species to San Diego, Duval Co., Tex. With Smith's record of *T. n. nigriceps* in Chihuahua how does *atriceps* cut across the *nigriceps* range to reach southeastern Arizona?

1954, W. W. Tanner (Ut.): Excerpts follow: "In studies of *T. utahensis* and *T. nigriceps,* comparisons were made with 18 *atriceps*. . . ." "These comparisons indicate that typical *atriceps* and *utahensis* are distinguishable only on the basis of ventral totals (ventrals *atriceps,* male 130–147, female 145–157; ventrals *utahensis,* male 153–160, female 163–172). The dark head cap of both species extends only one or two scales posterior to the parietals, is rarely convex, and is edged by a narrow light line which is not always distinct. In a few specimens of each species the cream colored border is obvious, especially in live or recently preserved material. The relationship of the mental, first pair of infralabials and chin shields is much the same in both species, although there are more *atriceps* than *utahensis* with the first infralabial making contact on the midventral line. . . . On the basis of the few specimens examined, one is not able in all cases to use as key characters the color patterns designated by Blanchard (loc. cit.) for *atriceps* and *nigriceps.* This may be further complicated by an overlapping of ventral counts, especially in the females. The present study points to the need for an extensive comparative study of the *Tantilla* of at least Arizona, New Mexico and Utah. Such a study may clarify whether *atriceps* and *utahensis* are species or subspecies, indicate the true position of *wilcoxi,* and also indicate whether—and if so to what extent—*nigriceps* and *atriceps* are sympatric species."

Crowned Tantilla (14—Yarrow 1882), Crowned snake (6—Corrington 1929)

Tantilla coronata coronata Baird and Girard 1853. Fig. 213; Map 56

Other common names: Ground snake; southeastern black-headed snake; Tantilla; Tantilla snake.

Range: From extreme s. cent. Virginia to n. edge of Florida, w. to n.e. Louisiana, n. to extreme s. Indiana.—Ala.; Fla.; Ga.; Ind.; Ky.; La.; Miss.; N.C.; S.C.; Tenn. *Elevation*—Mainly sea level to 500 feet. 1,000–1,500 feet (King, Tenn., 1939).

Size: Adults, 8–13 inches.

Distinctive characteristics: "A light band on back of head crossing tips of parietals and bordered behind with a broad black band, 3 or 4 scales'

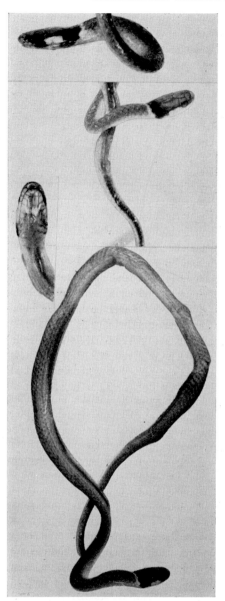 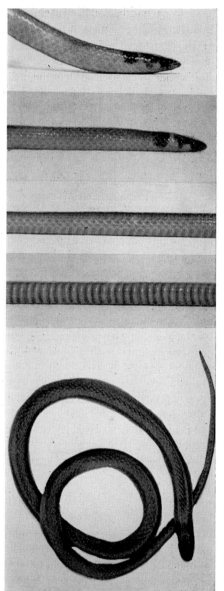

Fig. 212. *Tantilla atriceps,* Bisbee, Ariz., H. A. Smith, photos by J. H. Fenner.

Fig. 213. *Tantilla coronata coronata,* Auburn, Ala., H. Good.

length in width, usually extending to the 5th dorsal scale behind the head on the midline; similar to *wilcoxi,* but with broader black band (½ to 1½ scale lengths wide in *wilcoxi*), and with fewer ventrals and caudals. Black of head extending laterally towards last upper labial, sometimes reaching labial border across last 2 upper labials, and extending below eye nearly or quite to the labial border. The maximum length known is 324 mm." (Blanchard, Gen., 1938). A small taupe-colored snake with a pointed nose (A.H.W.).

Color: A snake from Auburn, Ala., received from H. G. Good, Apr. 19, 1928. The dorsum is snuff brown or cinnamon-brown. Under the lens, the snuff brown is minutely dotted with a pale pinkish buff border and translucent scale edge. The 2 lowest rows of scales are light vinaceous-lilac or purplish vinaceous. A nuchal collar 3 scales wide and the top of the head are dusky slate-violet (in general, appearing black). These 2 areas are separated by a band of vinaceous-buff, cream-buff, or cinnamon-buff, which extends across the neck just behind the parietals. The side of the head has 2 light areas of white, vinaceous-buff, or pale olive-buff. One spot is on the 5th and 6th upper labials and the lower border of the 1st temporal and lower postocular and on the posterior lower labials. Then the lower part of the light nuchal band appears as a spot. Thus, in sequence, the face is dark, then light, dark at the angle of the mouth, light at one nuchal band, dark at the other, and finally the snuff brown of the body color. The iris is dusky slate-violet. On the underside of the head, the gulars and chin shields may be plumbeous or deep plumbeous. The rest of the under parts are pearl gray, french gray, or sometimes cinereous or pallid purplish gray in the central area.

A snake from St. Petersburg, Fla., received from Fry, Apr. 16, 1928. The upper parts are cacao brown, vinaceous-fawn, or vinaceous-cinnamon.

Another snake, under the lens, has no light collar, but viewed in general is slightly light.

Habitat: This secretive burrower usually has been found under flat stones, logs, boards, bark, and other cover along southern rocky slopes, moist heavily wooded slopes, wooded hills, and rocky hillsides. In 1949 Minton in Indiana wrote: "These snakes were collected along the crest of the Knobstone Escarpment from Rennis Spring about 5 miles north of New Albany to Barrel Chute Knob on the Floyd-Clark County line west of St. Joseph. Their habitat seems restricted to the immediate vicinity of the bare claystone slopes, which give this area the local name of Bald Knobs. With the exception of one individual coiled in the sun at the base of a sandstone ledge, all specimens were found under logs or stones. They are found in drier situations than are *Carphophis* or *Diadophis,* the other small snakes of the area. In Floyd County, *Tantilla* seems to be associated with *Cnemi-*

dophorus sexlineatus quite consistently. It has been found in all but two of the known *Cnemidophorus* colonies and *Cnemidophorus* has been collected at all sites where *Tantilla* has been found. This association seems to be based on the preference of both reptiles to a dry habitat. . . . Three of the specimens were secured following periods of heavy rain."

The old terms "Atlantic southern" (Le Conte, Ecol., 1859) and "Eastern southern" (Binney, Ecol., 1862–65) apply well to this inhabitant of dry places, for this form occurs in every southern state east of the Mississippi and south of the Ohio. It is mainly of the Lower Austral life zone.

Period of activity: *First appearance*—Apr. 5, 1936 (King, Tenn., 1939); May 6, 1905; May, 1909 (Brimley, N.C., 1941–42); May 29, 1938 (Minton, Ind., 1944); May 1 (Snyder, Ala., 1945); Mar. 29 (Minton, Ind., 1949). *Fall disappearance*—July 10, 1905, Oct. 28, 1916 (Brimley, N.C., 1941–42); Oct. 16, 1933 (Minton, 1944). "Seasonal Catch" at Raleigh—May, 1 snake; Oct., 1. Total 2 (Brimley, N.C., 1925). *Hibernation*—"Several specimens [were] taken during the winter months below the surface of the ground on the interior of pine stumps" (Allen, Miss., 1932).

Breeding: Oviparous. Males 165–233 mm., females 176–324 mm. Minton in 1944 held that this is "presumably an egg-laying species," but in 1949(a) he reported: "A specimen collected May 30 showed 2 or 3 eggs visible through the semi-translucent ventral plates. Unfortunately this snake escaped before the eggs were laid." The smallest we have seen were 112 and 115 mm. and were taken in early spring. They were doubtless from the year before or older. Minton (1949a) measured males 76 and 86 mm. and a female 80 mm. long.

The most detailed observations are those recently given by Neill (Gen., 1951): "The crowned snake is unusually abundant on certain wooded hillsides bordering a small stream on the northwestern outskirts of Augusta, Richmond County, Georgia. Here during April and early May I have found on perhaps a dozen different occasions, a pair of crowned snakes, intertwined and sometimes in coitus. These breeding pairs were always beneath a scrap of bark at the base of a rotting tree stump. Later in the year, specimens were not to be found beneath such scant cover; they could be collected only by digging into piles of decaying bark scraps, by uprooting rotten stumps, or by overturning large rocks and boulders on the wooded hillsides. At the above mentioned locality there once stood an enormous tangle of pine. This huge tree died and its branches and portions of the trunk broke off and fell to the ground, leaving today a 15-foot stump, protruding from a hillock of rotting wood-pulp and partially decayed fragments of bark. On one occasion I discovered the nest and eggs of a crowned snake in a mound of debris. Near the base of the old stump, a small mass of wood pulp and rotting bark scrap protruded slightly above the level of the remainder of the mound; and in this mass, beneath two overlapping bark fragments, was a cup-shaped depression containing 3 small white eggs. The depression was smooth-walled and looked as though it had been scooped out by the snake. The eggs were unusually small for snake eggs, in keeping with the small size of *Tantilla coronata*. They were not elongate, but more nearly oval in shape. One of them was opened and found to contain a well-developed embryo of the crowned snake, probably nearly ready for emergence. Unfortunately, the remainder of the eggs desiccated.

Food: Insects, centipedes, earthworms, Minton, Brimley (N.C., 1941–42), Haltom (Ala., 1931).

Field notes: Apr. 7, 1934: Out with Löding and Van Aller, two good old line naturalists of the Brimley type. To the Bellingrath Azalea gardens in which Löding helped. We went by the river in the undeveloped part. Under oaks Anna saw a movement she took to be *Leiolopisma laterale*. It was in the fallen oak leaves. Made a clear circle around it. Apparently missed it. Then lo and behold my left hand was holding down her supposed ground lizard, which proved to be *Tantilla coronata*. Just a moment before, Löding said, "We ought to find *Tantilla* here."

Authorities:

Baird, S. F., and C. Girard (Gen., 1853)

Blanchard, F. N. (Gen., 1938; Tenn., 1922)

Brown, A. E. (Gen., 1901)

Minton, S. A., Jr. (Ind., 1944, 1949a)

1949(a): S. A. Minton, Jr., found from a review of other data plus his own that "there are 131–141 ventrals, 41–51 caudals, neck bands 1–5 scales wide, length 76–211 mm. in males and 139–148 ventrals, 37–50 caudals, neck bands 1½–4½ scales wide, 80–264 mm. length of females." His specimens from Indiana were "characterized by slightly smaller size, narrower black neckband, and a low number of subcaudals in both sexes."

Southern Appalachian black-headed snake

Tantilla coronata mitrifer Schwartz

Too recent except for a brief notice is A. Schwartz's *Tantilla coronata mitrifer,* which occurs in the southern Appalachians (i.e., N.C., e. Tenn., n. w. S.C.). He characterizes (S.C., 1953) it thus: "A darkly-colored race of *Tantilla coronata* in which the postocular ventral extension of the black cap tends not to reach the upper labial border, the black collar does not extend farther posteriorly than the fourth row in the midline behind the parietal plates and with more ventral (132–147) and less subcaudal scutes (35–46) on the average than the remaining two species." These two subspecies and particularly *c. wagneri* are so variable we wonder whether some day we may not return to one form.

Florida crowned snake (3—Conant and Bridges 1939),
Florida black-headed snake

Tantilla coronata wagneri (Jan) 1862. Fig. 214; Map 56

Other common names: (Wagner's) crowned snake; Wagner's miter snake.
Range: E. and w. Florida. *Elevation*—Sea level to 150 feet. 850[+] feet
(King, Tenn., 1939); about 500 feet (Minton, Ind., 1949a).
Size: Adults, 7–10 inches.

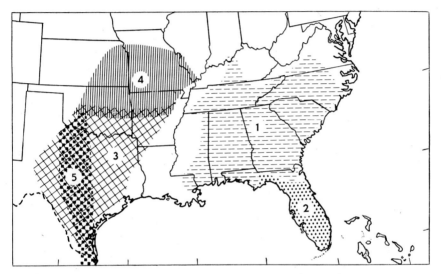

Map 56. *Tantilla*—1, *c. coronata;* 2, *c. wagneri;* 3, *g. gracilis;* 4, *g. hallowelli;* 5, *n. fumiceps.*

Distinctive characteristics: "Head pattern like that of *coronata* but the
white band more often nearly obliterated with dark pigment, and the black
usually not extending beyond the 4th scale behind the parietals in the midline; ventrals fewer, caudals more numerous than in *coronata;* size smaller.
The maximum length known is 240 mm." (Blanchard).
Color: A snake from Silver Springs, Fla., received from E. R. Allen, July
11, 1939. The back is light cinnamon-drab or wood brown. The 1st 2 or 2½
scale rows of the sides are light vinaceous-fawn. The head is black or nearly
so, as is the 4th scale row behind the parietals. This dark color, where most
intense, is deep olive or black. Ahead of the prefrontal, the head is buffy
brown, as it is also back of the center of the prefrontal. There is a prominent
bar of olive-buff across the rear of the rostral and internasals, extending half
way down onto the nasals. There is a touch of the same color on either side
of the median suture between the prefrontals. On the rear tip of each parietal, there is a deep olive-buff spot. The black of the head crosses the eye and

extends below it to the labial border and onto the 2nd, 3rd, and 4th lower labials, crossing the 2nd, 3rd, and 4th upper labials. The 4th upper labial, eye, upper postorbital, and supraocular are black. There is a light area on the 5th and front half of the 6th upper labials and the front edge of the 1st temporal. Then the dark of the upper head comes down across the back of the 1st temporal and wholly on the last temporal onto the rear of the 6th upper labial and covers all of the 7th except the caudal tip extending to the labial border. The dark of the upper head at its very rear again extends laterally, leaving a light neck area between the tip of the last upper labial and the 3rd row of scales back of the parietals. Thus the dark area crosses the eye, then after a light interval, crosses the 6th and 7th upper labials, and after another light area extends down on the neck. The iris is black. The belly is pale vinaceous-fawn or pale grayish vinaceous and the under surface of the tail olive-buff or pale olive-buff.—Mental not in contact with chin shields.

A snake from Englewood, Fla., received from Fraser, Apr. 14, 1941. The dorsum is kaiser-brown. The top of the head is dresden brown with frontal and supraoculars chestnut-brown. This with the black iris gives the impression of a very dark band across the head. The light head stripe crosses the tips of the parietals and 1st row of scales. It is formed by the light center of each scale and a light spot on the rear of each parietal. The 3 succeeding rows are solid black, which extends to, but scarcely involves the lowest scale row. The venter is pale flesh color.

Habitat: Conjectural writing covers much print but actual notes on the habitat of this snake are a mere handful. This burrower is held to have few preferences as to habitat. It is dug up or found under stumps, debris, or customary cover. One writer reports it most numerous in upland hammocks or in open woods. It seems to be restricted to Florida, to the Floridian section of the s.e. mesophytic evergreen forest, or to the s. cent. Floridian part of the swampy coastal plain.

Period of activity: *First appearance*—Apr. 14, 1941, Mar. 28, 1934 (Wright and Wright).

Breeding: Oviparous.

Field notes: Apr. 16, 1928, Eustis, Fla.: Van Hyning says that when the workmen were grubbing for the airport at Eustis, he had them watch carefully. They took *Tantilla* in the surface layer, *Eumeces egregius* near the surface, but *Neoseps reynoldsi* and *Rhineura* 6–10 inches or more down.

Mar. 28, 1934, Silver Springs, Fla.: With E. R. Allen. He has taken some 17 or 18 short-tailed snakes. They inhabit the sand, feed on *Tantilla coronata* and possibly other small snakes.—A beautiful *Tantilla coronata* with a black head was just brought in.

Authorities:

Blanchard, F. N. (Gen., 1938)
Carr, A. F., Jr. (Fla., 1940a)

Garman, S. (Gen., 1883)
Jan, G. (Gen., 1862–63)
Loennberg, E. (Fla., 1895)

1862, G. Jan: *"Homalcoranium wagneri.* The relative position of the supralabials is in this species identical with that observed in *H. melano-cephalum,* which it resembles likewise in coloration. It differs from it, however, in the mental, which is in contact with the chin shields, and in the internasals, which are a little more oblique in relation to the loreal. In our museum there are two specimens of this species, both with a white stripe which, however, in the larger individual, collected in Florida by Prof. Wagner, is found on the occiput, while in the other, the source of which is unknown, it is actually on the nape."

1938, F. N. Blanchard: "Jan's description appears composite, but as he emphasized a specimen from Florida, and as the species was referred to the synonymy of *coronata* by Boulenger, it seems preferable to adopt Jan's name *wagneri,* for this well distinguished species, designating the cotype from Florida as the lectotype."

1940(a): A. F. Carr wrote of *T. c. coronata:* "The region of intergradation between this race and *T. c. wagneri* must be north of Alachua County, since I have seen but 1 Florida specimen (from Gainesville) which I could refer to *coronata.* However, I have examined only 2 specimens from the Pan Handle. Ecological differences between the 2 races are probably slight."

1942, A. H. and A. A. Wright: This "well distinguished species" of Blanchard has bothered us for a third of a century or more. He said, "Jan's description appears composite." Most assuredly any considerable collection of *wagneri* would have a very diverse range of head-color characters. Once when he was in the field in Florida with us, O. Van Hyning said that in the same area one could find a very divergent lot with clear white band, clouded band, or no light band. According to coloration, specimens from Florida often appear *coronata* and specimens from *coronata*'s range appear *wagneri* on first appraisal. To a person inept in sexing these small snakes and in overcoming the difficulties of counting 125–150 ventrals on a squirmy live snake, the locality proves at times a godsend. In fact, even the expert welcomes it. *Tantilla c. coronata* is different from the other *Tantillas* of the U.S., but is *T. c. wagneri* well defined? Hand an expert a *coronata,* and he might have to know from which side of the Florida state line the specimen came.

Jan gave *T. c. wagneri* an entire anal; yet a divided anal is the rule in *Tantilla.* The other plates vary, e.g., the postnasal-preocular contact. In *T. atriceps,* Gunther has them in contact; Boulenger in contact or narrowly separated. In Cope, Baird and Girard, and Brown they are in contact in *T. c. coronata,* yet Cope's drawing from Baird and Girard has separated them. In *T. gracilis* Gunther has them in contact or separated. In *T. eiseni* Stejneger has them in contact; Brown has them almost separated. In *T. nigriceps* and *T. planiceps* they are described as *usually* in contact. In the same way the mental in *T. atriceps* is in contact with anterior chin shields, according to Smith; usually in contact, according to Blanchard; separated, accord-

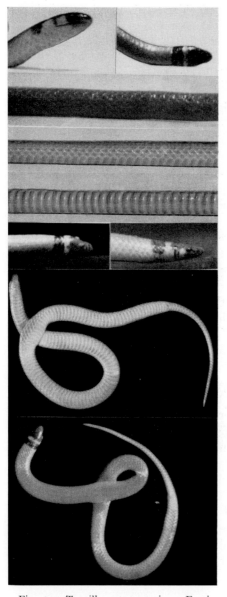

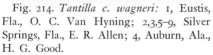

Fig. 214. *Tantilla c. wagneri:* 1, Eustis, Fla., O. C. Van Hyning; 2,3,5–9, Silver Springs, Fla., E. R. Allen; 4, Auburn, Ala., H. G. Good.

Fig. 215. *Tantilla eiseni eiseni,* San Diego, Calif., L. M. Klauber.

ing to Gunther. In *T. wilcoxi* Smith has it in contact, occasionally not; Stejneger in contact. Van Denburgh says that infralabials just meet. In *T. n. fumiceps* the mental is usually separated from the chin shields; rarely not separated according to Smith; well separated, according to Blanchard. In other words, the authorities are not wrong. We have burrowing snakes, and it is hard to find head plates which do not vary. In this connection the discussion by Smith of the numerical variation of ventrals in Blanchard's 50 specimens of *T. atriceps* is apropos.

California Tantilla (12—Grinnell and Camp 1917), California black-headed snake (5)

Tantilla eiseni eiseni Stejneger 1896. Fig. 215; Map 55

Other common names: (Black-headed) Tantilla; Eisen's black-head snake (4—Ditmars 1907).

Range: From Fresno Co., Calif., to n. Baja California, Mex.—U.S.A.: Calif. Mex.: Baja Calif. *Elevation*—Sea level to 3,000 feet. Coast to desert foothills (Klauber, 1931a); except in high mountains, from ocean to desert foothills (Perkins, 1938); 2,800 feet (Stephens, Calif., 1918); 410 feet (Klauber).

Size: Adults, 10–15 inches. In 1943(b) Klauber (Gen., 1943b) gave the following range of length over all. Minima 264 mm. (tail 45) for males, and 234 mm. (tail 35) for females. Maxima 738 mm. (tail 114) for males, and 1,054 (tail 137) for females.

Distinctive characteristics: "Supralabials 7; posterior nasal in contact with preocular; temporals elongate 1 + 1; 1st pair of sublabials not in contact behind mental; ventrals 176–181; subcaudals 58–65; head blackish, bounded behind by a white collar about 3 scale lengths from parietals" (Stejneger). "Black of head extending below angle of mouth onto gular scales (as in *planiceps*, sometimes nearly encircling the throat), reaching about 2 scale lengths behind parietal suture and narrowly bordered posteriorly with white; the white band sometimes with black dots behind it. Ventrals more numerous than in *planiceps* and *atriceps* (165 or more). Differing from *atriceps*, further, in that the black cap extends 2 to 3 scale lengths behind parietal suture, instead of 1 to 2, and in that the posterior white border is wider. A large species, varying in total length from 130 to 373 mm." (Blanchard). Klauber's (Calif., 1944) revision has *eiseni* with ventrals 164–175 in males and 169–182 in females, and *transmontana* with ventrals 175–184 in males and 190–197 in females.

Color: A beautiful little snake from San Diego, Calif., received from L. M. Klauber, July 18, 1928. The back is avellaneous, wood brown, fawn color, mikado brown, or verona brown. The first 2 rows of scales are lavender, pallid brownish drab, or pale drab-gray, as are also the upper labials. The rostral, internasals, and prefrontals are drab. The rest of the top of the head, including 4 rows of scales caudad of the parietals and the oculars and area back of the eye to the top of the last 2 supralabials, is mummy brown, black, raw umber, or carob brown. The iris is the same. The under part of the head is lavender, pallid brownish drab, or pale drab-gray, while the rest of the ventral surfaces are coral red, light jasper red, scarlet-red, or rose doree.

Habitat: Perkins (1938) and Klauber (1931a, 1934a, 1939a) have supplied most of our information. They found this very small, secretive, nocturnal snake from coast to desert foothills, but not in the high mountains. It is frequently recorded from road building areas, diggings, and excavations. From Klauber's study of reptile life in the southwest (1939a), we quote: "Monthly distribution of snakes found alive on the road at night. *Tantilla eiseni* June 1, Total 1." "Sixteen Year Census," "*Tantilla eiseni*. Coast 21, inland valleys 12, foothills 7, mountains 1."

Period of activity: *First appearance*—Feb. 27, 1923, May 16, 1926, May 16, 1929 (Klauber, 1931a). "Sixteen Year Census" (*eiseni + transmontana*) has Feb., 4 snakes; Mar., 2; Apr., 3; May, 12; June, 12; July, 6; Aug., 1; Sept., 2; Oct., 1; Nov., 1; Dec., 1. Total 45. Per cent 0.35 (Klauber, 1939a). *Fall disappearance*—Sept. 27, 1897 (Stephens, 1918); Aug. 23, 1925 (Klauber, 1931a).

Breeding: Oviparous. Males 277–375 mm., females 211–373 mm.

Food: Earthworms. Perkins (Calif., 1938).

Field notes: (We examined the *Tantilla eiseni* at the Museum of Vertebrate Zoology and at the California Academy of Sciences.)

Authorities:

Blanchard, F. N. (Gen., 1938)
Brown, A. E. (Gen., 1901)
Klauber, L. M. (Gen., 1939a; Calif., 1924a, 1931a, 1934a; Baja Calif., 1924b)

Perkins, C. B. (Calif., 1938, 1949)
Stejneger, L. (Calif., 1896)
Van Denburgh, J. (Gen., 1922)

1896, L. Stejneger: "The present species differs from all our North American *Tantillas* with 7 supralabials, in being proportionally much longer and slenderer, and the number of ventrals and subcaudals is greatly in excess of that of our other species."

1934(a), L. M. Klauber: "It can be readily distinguished from all other snakes in this vicinity by its black head and pinkish unicolor body. Often there is a white collar back of the head. The color of the underside is pink and is unspotted."

Desert black-headed snake

Tantilla eiseni transmontana Klauber 1943. Map 55

Range: Borego, San Diego Co., Calif., and Palm Springs, Riverside Co., Calif. *Elevation*—1,270 feet, at Yaqui Well; 1,600 feet, in Sentenac Canyon (Klauber, Gen., 1939a).

Size: *Adults*—Klauber's type is 302 mm. (12 inches) long.

Distinctive characteristics: "A desert slope subspecies of *Tantilla eiseni* characterized by a higher number of ventral scutes, a shorter tail, and lighter color than the cismontane form. *T. e. transmontana* has a higher ventral scale count than any other known *Tantilla"* (Klauber, Calif., 1944).

Color: "The following color description refers to the specimen as preserved in alcohol. The top of the head is purplish-black, although the rostral and internasals are lighter. On the sides the dark color touches only the tops of the supralabials, except posteriorly where an extension of the dark area is carried down across the last supralabial to a point behind, and below the angle of the mouth. The dark color on top of the head reaches a distance 2 scales behind the parietals. Here there is a transverse band very slightly lighter than the ground color, no doubt the vestige of the usual *Tantilla* ring. On the under surface of the head there are some faint punctations on the edges of the infralabials; the 3rd and 4th infralabials are heavily punctated where they abut the genials. The body is cream-colored throughout, both dorsally and ventrally. Fine brown punctations are faintly in evidence on the 7 middorsal scale rows. A dark streak of the vertebral process shows through the skin; there is a rather marked middorsal groove. . . . In these paratypes there is some variation in the amount and extent of dorsal pigment. The pigmented dorsal rows vary from 7 to 13, the punctations being most in evidence middorsally. . . .

"*Tantilla eiseni transmontana* subsp. nov. Desert Black-headed Snake. Type.—No. 29,273 in the collection of LMK, collected on the road 1 mile east of Yaqui Well, San Diego County, California, by Charles E. Shaw and Cyrus S. Perkins, June 6, 1938, at 8:10 P.M. Five paratypes are available from San Diego County and one from Riverside County. . . . *Description of the Type.*—Adult male. Length over-all (before shrinkage in preservative) 302 mm.; tail length 70 mm. The scale rows are 15-15-15; all scales are smooth. The ventrals are 182; anal divided; there are 68 subcaudals, all divided. The plates on top of the head are normal. The nasals are divided; there are no loreals. The supralabials are 7-7, and the infralabials 6-6. The preoculars are 1-1; postoculars 2-2. The temporals are 1 + 1, 1 + 1" (Klauber, 1944).

Habitat: "Desert foothills or desert side of the mountains," say Klauber and Perkins. "No definite localities of this subspecies are known except those where the type and paratypes were collected. Eventually it will no doubt be found along the desert base of the mountains from San Gorgonio Pass in Riverside County southeastward well into Lower California. While *transmontana* may occur along the eastern base of the San Bernardino Mountains and in the Little San Bernardinos, it has not been collected in either. Further north we may expect to find *utahensis;* at least such is the case in the Panamints and in the Kingston Range. Without doubt *eiseni* and *transmontana* intergrade through San Gorgonio Pass in Riverside County and via some of the San Diego passes. Three specimens from Snow Creek, on the north slope of Mt. San Jacinto, Riverside County, are considered intergrades, as they show characters of both subspecies" (Klauber, 1944).

Period of activity: *First appearance*—The San Diego Natural History Museum specimen from La Puerta was plowed out February 27 (Klauber, Calif., 1924a).

Breeding: Oviparous. Males to 302 mm.

Authorities:

1944, L. M. Klauber: *"Transmontana* has more ventral scutes and is a lighter colored snake than *eiseni.* The change in color is produced both by their being fewer punctated dorsal scale rows and by the punctations of *transmontana* being lighter and more widely spaced. This parallels the change which takes place in the modification of *Leptotyphlops humilis humilis* into *L. h. cahuilae* in passing from the coast to the desert; also in the worm snakes there is an increase in the longitudinal dorsal scales corresponding to the increase of the ventrals in *Tantilla.* . . . With respect to the coloration it may be said that the lightest of the coastal specimens is darker than the darkest of those from the desert, although this is not true of the specimen from Palm Springs, which is an intergrade as far as pattern is concerned. In *eiseni eiseni* all 15 rows are usually punctated, although the side rows are lighter than the middorsals. Occasionally the spots are carried onto the edges of the ventrals. *Transmontana,* besides being lighter, usually has at least 2 unmarked lateral rows on each side. The heads of the coast specimens are also darker, and the underjaws are usually more heavily punctated, although this is not always the case. The light collar is generally more clearly outlined in the coastal specimens, but the difference is not infallible. The general color divergences are apparent in the live specimens as well as the preserved. Three specimens from Snow Creek, on the north slope of Mt. San Jacinto, are available. In color they are light, like *transmontana,* and their ventral scutes fall within the *transmontana* range, the counts being 179, 180, and 183 (all males). However, in tail-length proportionality they resemble the coastal subspecies; I therefore consider them intergrades."

Graceful Tantilla (23—Yarrow 1882), Southern slender black-headed snake

Tantilla gracilis gracilis Baird and Girard 1853. Map 56

Other common names: Black-headed snake; brown sand snake; little brown snake; miter snake; red-bellied snake; sand snake (6); slender black-headed snake (3); slender dark-headed snake; slender snake; slender Tantilla; Tantilla (6—Ortenburger 1927).

Range: The area comprised by e. Texas except s. tip, the s. one-fifth of Oklahoma, the s.w. quarter of Arkansas, and the n.w. tip of Louisiana.— Ark.; La.; Okla.; Tex. *Elevation*—Sea level to 2,000 feet.

Size: Adults, 6 or 7-9 inches.

Distinctive characteristics: "Head usually little if any darker than the body; dark cap, when present, concave medially and extending posteriorly on the sides; supralabials 6; preoculars 1; ventrals usually 115–127 in females, 106–119 in males; caudals usually 33–41 in females, 40–50 in males; ratio of tail length to body length—.160–.200 in females, .200–.235 in males" (Kirn, Burger, and Smith).

Color: We found this snake at "The Slide," 8 miles west of Helotes, Tex., on Bandera road, Feb. 19, 1925. The upper parts are sayal brown to snuff brown. The first 2 scale rows are whitish or pale drab-gray. The top of the head is bister. The 4th, 5th, and 6th upper labials and the lower part of the 1st temporal are livid pink. The ventrals and subcaudals except for the first 23 are english red or brazil red. The rear margin of each belly plate is whitish or pale drab-gray.

Habitat: This agile species has been taken in diverse localities: in rocky stretches, on rocky hillsides, under logs and stones, under strips of bark in woods near streams, in rotten wood in a pine forest, under limestone rocks in a moist situation, in a small valley, in bottomlands, and at the foot of plains.

Period of activity: *Early appearances*—Apr., 1928, Apr., 1927 (Strecker); Apr. 13 (Marr); Mar. 8, 16, 17, 18, Apr. 2, 15, 24, 1931 (Strecker); May 5 (Bailey); Mar. 8, 1921 (MVZ No. 12536). *Fall disappearance*—Aug., 1915 (Strecker).

Breeding: Oviparous. *Eggs*—Number, 2–3. In 1926 Strecker wrote: "I have no knowledge of their breeding habits nor can I find anything has been placed on record regarding them. Near San Antonio, Texas, under a stone under which was found a female *Tantilla* was also discovered 3 small reptilian eggs which had been crushed in the turning of the stone. Therefore I judge this species to be *oviparous*." Among the numerous kindnesses of Kirn was his allowing us to examine his material from time to time. On Apr. 25, 1934, at Somerset, Tex., we made these notes: "Two eggs (this is the usual number laid). Egg 1.8 cm. x 0.6 cm. Cylindrical form for 1.4 cm. of its length."

Young—About 4 inches long. Of the Kirn material we note that a baby snake hatched in July. Another from Somerset was 96 mm. (tail 20) long. One had only 6 mm. of tail left. How did it happen?

Food: Insects, sowbugs, slugs. Strecker.

Authorities:

Baird, S. F., and C. Girard (Gen., 1853)
Blanchard, F. N. (Gen., 1938)
Burt, C. E. (Tex., 1936)
Garman, S. (Gen., 1883)
Gunther, A. (Gen., 1885–1902)
Kirn, A. J., W. L. Burger, and H. M. Smith (Gen., 1949)
Strecker, J. K., Jr. (Tex., 1926c and many more)

1944, A. H. and A. A. Wright: In 1935 Force from one region in Oklahoma counted 499 *Tantilla gracilis* and secured ventral counts from 115 to

138 or a range of 23. This range may be changed somewhat with material from other regions, but it is a satisfying number for an understanding of the variations. In 1925, when Blanchard gave us a key to *Tantilla,* he assigned 111–133 ventrals to *T. gracilis* and 136–161 ventrals to *T. nigriceps* and *T. planiceps.* And in 1936 Burt, utilizing this distinction, stated: Ventrals 133 or less = *T. gracilis gracilis.* Ventrals more than 133 = *T. gracilis nigriceps. T. nigriceps fumiceps* has as few as 130, and *gracilis* now is known to have as many as 138, but *nigriceps nigriceps* still begins at 136 and ends at 163. In Schmidt and Smith's 1944 Big Bend paper (Tex.) they mentioned 8 male *T. atriceps* 137–147—just within the corrected range they gave for *T. n. nigriceps,* namely 136–150. A difficult distinction to make! Suppose these *Tantillas* of western Texas varied as much as *T. c. wagneri* in head markings or as *Sonora s. blanchardi* in color pattern. Blanchard in 1938 stated: Ventrals 141 or less (both sexes) *T. kirnia.* Ventrals 145 or more (both sexes) *T. nigriceps.* With more material and Schmidt's correction of 136–150 for males of *nigriceps,* the key becomes difficult to use.

If we could have enough of them, we believe that *T. n. fumiceps* (when more than 1 female and 7 males are measured) will vary 18–25 ventrals, as do most of the other forms in the U.S. Of *T. planiceps,* Blanchard gives 2 measurements of 2 specimens. We are sure we have seen a greater variation in *T. n. fumiceps,* for we knew it as a "funny" *nigriceps;* we saw it at Kirn's home just before it was dubbed *kirnia,* and 7 years later regretted the change to *fumiceps.* The ventrals may vary more than 11, probably nearer 22 or more. The following data may show our basis for belief in a variation of 19–33 ventrals or an average of 27 per form: *T. atriceps,* 25 ventrals; *T. coronata* and *c. wagneri,* 29; *T. eiseni* and *e. transmontana,* 32; *T. g. gracilis,* 27; *T. nigriceps* and *n. fumiceps,* 33; *T. utahensis,* 19; *T. wilcoxi* and *w. rubricata,* 24; average 27.

The ventrals in the *atriceps, nigriceps,* and *fumiceps* group are not of much value until we get a comparable number of *fumiceps* specimens, and when they come, the picture will be more confused than ever. We coursed over the southwest for 28 years, and to an old campaigner no one taxonomic key (even ventral or caudal counts) can unlock all. In some of the other subspecies and species, the ventral count seems a valuable tool. Too much reliance should not be placed on it when the material is scanty.

Hallowell's Tantilla, Northern slender black-headed snake
(C. B. Perkins)

Tantilla gracilis hallowelli Cope 1860. Fig. 216; Map 56

Other common names: (Most of names in *Tantilla gracilis.*)
Range: From s. of the Canadian River, Okla., extending roughly e. along

the 34°30′ parallel to the Mississippi River, n. to mouth of Missouri River, w. to Kansas—thus including the area comprised of the e. third of Kansas, e. Oklahoma except the southern fifth, the n. half of Arkansas, and the s. two-thirds of Missouri (s. of the Missouri River).—Ark.; Ill.; Kan.; Mo.; Okla. *Elevation*—500 to 2,000 feet.

Size: Adults, 7–10 inches.

Distinctive characteristics: "Size small: post-nasal occasionally separated from preocular by prefrontal; oculars 1-1; temporals 1-1; upper labials 6; 15 rows of scales; ventrals 112–137; subcaudals 41–51. Length 215 mm. (tail 43). Reddish or greenish brown above, some scales speckled with darker; belly salmon color in life; top of head dark brown; labials yellowish" (Brown). "These beautiful little snakes are usually a rich brown color above, with the head slightly darker. Below they are varying shades of salmon pink, except under the chin and the anterior end of the body and the ends of the ventrals, which are white. They are being made the subject of special observations" (Force, Okla., 1930). "Similar to *T. g. gracilis* except in the following respects: ventrals 128–138 in females, 120–129 in males; caudals 42–51 in females, 51–56 in males; ratio of tail length to total length .200–.250 in females, .235–.280 in males" (Kirn, Burger, and Smith).

Color: Similar to that of *T. g. gracilis.*

Habitat: This beautiful little snake is found ideally on sandy or rocky hillsides wooded or not. Force (1935) found specimens in moist sandy soil under limestone rocks, along creek banks, on wooded slopes, and along sandy roadsides. They have been taken from flat elevated grassy plains, in rockless woods, in decaying logs and stumps on a hill's crest, on the southwestern exposure in foothills and hillsides of the Ozarks, and under stones in prairie ledges.

Period of activity: *Early appearances*—Apr. 1, 2, 3, 15, June 4, 1934 (Burt, Gen., 1935); Apr. 3, 22, 23, 29, May 6, 15, 1933 (Burt and Hoyle, Gen., 1935); Apr. 7, 9, 11, 13, 30, May 1, June 2, 1932 (Burt, Kan., 1933). "The majority of individuals are taken after the rains in April and May. Only a few are found in March and June" (Marshall in Force, Okla., 1935). *Fall disappearance*—Sept. 1, 1933 (Burt and Hoyle); Sept. 23, 1932 (Burt, Kan., 1933). "Practically none [are found] in July, August and September, but occasionally a few may be taken in October or early November if it is rainy during this season" (Marshall in Force).

Breeding: Oviparous. *Sexual dimorphism*—Force (1935) measured males from 85 to 205 mm. and females from 90 to 230. The females attain the larger size. The males 85–125 she considered juveniles, those 125–175 mm. 1 to 1½ years old, and those 175–205 mature, 1½ to 2½ years old; the females 85–125 she considered juveniles, those 125–185 mm. 1 to 1½ years old, 185–320 mm. mature, 1½ to 2½ years old. She felt that the number of caudals subtracted from the number of ventrals gave an index of sex. "Thus all examples in which this figure is less than 80 proved to be males, and all those in which it is more than 81, females."

Mating—"Observations made by the writer on the size of the gonads of tantillas collected in every week from the middle of February until the first of June indicate May as the time of mating. The males of mature size, i.e., 174 mm. or longer, collected in Oklahoma between May 1 and June 1 had well developed testes, 5 to 9 mm. long. Early in the spring they are much smaller. Females collected before May 1 had ova 0.5 to 5.0 mm. in length. Those collected on May 20 show ova 5, 7, 9 and 21 mm. in length as well as others of microscopic size. No mature female (i.e., over 190 mm.) collected before May 10 had deposited eggs, whereas 6 females of this size collected on May 20, 24, and 28 had laid. These data, together with the information previously noted concerning the greatest activity of both male and female in the field, make it seem probable that the first half of May may be the usual time of mating. It is an interesting fact, possibly related in some way to mating activities, that in March and May from two to three times as many males as females are found, whereas in April the females are twice as numerous as the males" (Force, 1935).

Eggs—Number, 1–4, usually 2 or 3. Time of deposition, mid-June to mid-July. In the same year (1930) that she announced she was making a special study of this form, Force wrote: "Three females under observation deposited 2 and 3 eggs respectively between June 22 and June 25. They were smooth in texture and irregular in shape. The color was ivory to yellowish white, with the germinal disk distinctly visible. They measured 15 to 24 mm. in length and 4.2 to 6.5 mm. in diameter. A female, collected by Mrs. A. E. Gilmore, laid 1 egg July 8 and a second July 11, of similar size, color and texture." From Force's final paper (1935) we quote: "Proof of oviparity was furnished by the writer in 1928. Since then dissection of 265 females, 10 of which had laid eggs, has shown that the most common numbers in a set are 2 and 3. Complements of 1 and 4 have been noted in some cases. Deposition of the eggs has not been seen; the eggs have always been discovered in the morning in the moistest part of the cage, even in the water pan. The eggs are laid from the middle of June to about the middle of July. June 13 is the earliest date noted for a set of normal eggs of females collected in Oklahoma. Other dates recorded are June 18, 19, 22, 25, and 26. Marshall, however, reported (Nov. 4, 1929) a set laid on July 9. One set of abnormal eggs was laid on July 8 and 11. These records of egg-laying are all from females collected after May 20. In 7 females collected between July 1 and 3, 1928, the anterior oviduct looked as if eggs had recently been deposited. The date of hatching has been obtained for a few eggs laid by females that had been transported to northern Michigan. Such eggs, kept in laboratory surrounded

Fig. 216. *Tantilla gracilis hallowelli,* Arkansas, D. L. Gamble.

Fig. 217. *Tantilla nigriceps nigriceps:* 1,6, Mesilla, N.M., R. F. Crawford; 2–5,7, Colorado Springs, Colo., A. A. Allen.

by damp, rotten wood, hatched Sept. 17 (1930) and Sept. 7 and 14 (1932). The length of the periods from laying to hatching were 83 and 84 days. If, as is likely, the eggs are laid earlier under natural conditions, the hatching time in Oklahoma is probably earlier than September 1. Furthermore, Oklahoma's warmer climate as compared with northern Michigan should hasten hatching. The young snakes emerged from the eggs in about 1 day after slitting the shell (in the 2 instances observed). Two young measured at birth 77.5 and 92.0 mm. in total length."

Young—In the Museum of Vertebrate Zoology is No. 11114 from Manhattan, Kan., May 13, 1927. It is 95 mm. long (tail 18). It cannot be too far beyond a hatchling of the previous year. From Smith in 1950 we learn that the eggs are 13 to 26x4 to 6 mm. in size, hatching in September. Force's evidence indicates possible hatching before Sept. 1 and its extension into October.

Food: Insects, centipedes, spiders, sowbugs, slugs. Force (1935).

Authorities:

Branson, E. B. (Kan., 1904)

Brown, A. E. (Gen., 1901)

Burt, C. E. (Gen., 1935; Kan., 1933)

Cope, E. D. (Gen., 1860–61a)

Cragin, F. W. (Kan., 1885a)

Force, E. R. (Okla., 1930, 1935)

Garman, S. (Gen., 1883)

Hallowell, E. (Tex., 1854)

Kirn, A. J., W. L. Burger, and H. M. Smith (Gen., 1949)

Smith, H. M. (Kan., 1950)

Strecker, J. K., Jr. (Tex., 1926c)

Great Plains black-headed snake, Black-headed snake
(4—Yarrow 1882)

Tantilla nigriceps nigriceps Kennicott 1860. Fig. 217; Map 55

Other common names: Black-headed Tantilla; Kennicott's black-headed snake; mitre snake (2); sand snake; Sonoran Tantilla (2—Ortenburger 1927); Texas black-headed snake (4—Ditmars 1907).

Range: From w. Kansas and e. Colorado, s. through w. Oklahoma, the panhandle of Texas, and e. New Mexico to s.e. Arizona and Chihuahua, Mex.—U.S.A.: Ariz.; Colo.; Kan.; Neb.; N.M.; Okla.; Tex. Mex.: Chihuahua. *Elevation*—2,000 to 5,000 feet or more. 2,800–5,000 feet (Bailey, N.M., 1913).

Size: Adults, 9–14 or 20 inches.

Distinctive characteristics: "Black of head extending 3 or 4 scale lengths behind parietal suture, posterior border of black cap very convex or even pointed behind in the median line, but not extending laterally onto the last 2 upper labials, nor reaching nearly or quite to the labial border below the eyes; not extending laterally onto the gulars, and not bordered posteriorly with white; like *atriceps* in number of ventrals, but caudals less numerous; mental plates usually excluded from contact with anterior chin shields by 1st lower labials (in contrast with *atriceps*). A larger species than *atriceps,* 120 to 350 mm. (*atriceps,* 96 to 230 mm.)" (Blanchard).

Color: "The coloration of the light individuals is light above and below, with a black cap on the head. The black cap is broadly convex or pointed (V-shaped) posteriorly, extending back onto the 3rd or 4th scale from parietal suture. Laterally the black extends down onto the upper edges of the 2nd, 3rd, 4th, 5th and 7th upper labials, covering the upper half of the 1st temporal and the entire 2nd temporal" (Loomis and Jones).

Habitat: Like other *Tantillas,* it is a flat-rock hillside form. In Nebraska, Loomis and Jones recorded them "8 inches below the surface of the soil on top of a bluff," "on highschool grounds," "in a basement," "crawling on a black-top road following a light shower shortly after dark." Some have been found under heaps of cattle dung, swimming in a canyon, in garden diggings or pipe-line trenches.

Period of activity: *Early appearances*—Apr., 1932 (Burt, and Hoyle, Gen., 1935); Apr. 18, 1931, Apr. 24, 1931 (Burt, Tex., 1936); May, 1947 (Loomis and Jones). *Fall disappearance*—Dec., 1914 (Ellis and Henderson, Colo., 1915); Dec. 1, 1950 (Loomis and Jones). "It has been reported here (Colo.) only once before, . . . in December, 1914, when it was found in a trench being dug for a pipe line" (Rodeck, Colo., 1936). *Hibernation*—"The two specimens from Ness County (Kan.) were found 8 feet under the ground on January 13, 1934" (Tihen, Kan., 1938).

Breeding: Oviparous. Adults, 225–400 mm.

Food: Insects, earthworms, spiders. Ellis and Henderson (Colo., 1913), Branson, Guthrie (Ariz., 1926).

Authorities: [1]

Blanchard, F. N. (Gen., 1938)
Branson, E. B. (Kan., 1904)
Brown, A. E. (Gen., 1901)
Burt, C. E. (Tex., 1936)
Ellis, M. M., and J. Henderson (Colo., 1913, 1915)
Hudson, G. E. (Neb., 1942)
Kennicott, R. (Gen., 1860–61)
Loomis, R. B., and J. K. Jones, Jr. (Neb., 1951)
Smith, H. M. (Kan., 1950)
Taylor, E. H. (Kan., 1929b)

1944, A. H. and A. A. Wright: No one has made a range map of the *nigriceps* complex of Texas. When Blanchard resurrected *T. atriceps* and established *T. kirnia* (*fumiceps*), it seemed a solution, but the bounds of these forms are uncertain. It would be a contribution if the data sheets of Blan-

---

[1] 1956: From a single specimen taken 6 miles s.s.e. of Alpine, Tex., at 5,000 feet, S. A. Minton (*Fieldiana,* Zoology, **34:** 449–452) described a new *nigriceps* type as *Tantilla cucullata.* His diagnosis is: "A *Tantilla* with an almost uniformly black head, the pigmentation including the chin and labials and terminating 3 to 4 scales posterior to the parietal; no light nuchal collar; mental barely in contact with anterior chinshields; ventral 167; subcaudals 82." This may possibly help in the solution of the west Texas puzzling *Tantilla* ranges.

chard's unfinished manuscript were published, particularly for these 3 forms. Anyone can quarrel with our venturesome maps of them. Burt would put the east line of *T. n. nigriceps* from Cooke County, northwest of Dallas, to Del Rio, Val Verde County, much farther east than our eastern line (s.w. corner of Oklahoma to e. of El Paso). Possibly some of Burt's problematical *T. gracilis* and some *T. nigriceps* are Blanchard's *T. kirnia* and *T. atriceps*. We do not wonder that Burt was perplexed. Smith's record for *T. n. nigriceps* at Rio Santa Maria near Progresso, Chihuahua, Mex., is not far from the type locality, Fort Bliss. Glance at our map and see how *atriceps* sticks like a thumb between the Nebraska to Arizona range of *nigriceps* and the little tail south of New Mexico and west of El Paso. Is *T. n. nigriceps* absent in this range of *T. atriceps*? Have we two populations of *T. n. nigriceps* severed by *T. atriceps*? If we worry about the type locality, Fort Bliss for *T. nigriceps* and western Texas, see the complication Smith posed in 1942 in *T. atriceps* (Gen.): "The species (atriceps) rather obviously is in the process of either differentiation of two incipient subspecies (species), or of assimilation of two previously distinct species. It is difficult to know into which category *atriceps* should be placed. While the specimens from extremes of range are easily distinguished, the character of the species in the broad area between (including northern Coahuila, western Texas) is not known except from a series from a single locality (Chisos Mts.). These exhibit no great range of variation (20, both sexes), but unfortunately straddle the middle of the range of counts of the whole species, so that some are very typical of Mexican specimens, others (the majority) typical of Arizona specimens (range 132 to 151). While it admittedly remains possible that two subspecies may be satisfactorily distinguished when larger series from more numerous localities are available, it does not seem practical to attempt subdivision of the species at present."

Kirn's dark-headed snake (3—Ditmars 1939), Texas black-headed snake

Tantilla nigriceps fumiceps (Cope) 1860. Fig. 218; Map 56

Range: Comanche Co., Okla., s. through cent. Texas to n. Tamaulipas, Mex.—U.S.A.: Okla.; Tex. Mex.: Tamaulipas. *Elevation*—Sea level to 2,000 feet.

Size: Adults, 7-9 inches.

Distinctive characteristics: "Gastrosteges 132; a divided anal; urosteges 42, Total length 5 inches; tail 1 in. . . . . Coloration. Above uniform pale brown, shading out into dirty white beneath. The top of the head including the oculars and temporals, and for 4 scales back of the occipitals, blackish brown. Rostrals, prefrontals and upper labials, pale brownish" (Cope). "Allied to *Tantilla nigriceps* but smaller in size, and with a lower number of ventrals and caudals in both sexes. Ventrals in males 130–138, caudals 43–48; in the 1 female specimen 141 and 39. Total length from 132 to 224 mm. in 8 specimens examined" (Blanchard).

Color: A snake from Blue Wing Lake near San Antonio, Tex., Mar. 2, 1925. The dorsal scales are fawn color or mikado brown with the first 2 rows and the ends of ventrals white. The rostral and prenasals are like the dorsal scales. The top of the head including the eye, the upper edges of 2nd and 3rd upper labials, the postnasals and upper parts of 2 temporals are black or blue-violet black. The iris is black. Each ventral except the first 3 or 4 and the subcaudals have centers of etruscan red or dragons-blood red. The posterior margin of each ventral plate is whitish or grayish like the side coloration.

Period of activity: *Early appearances*—Mar. 18, Apr. 6, 15, 24, 1931 (Burt).
Breeding: Oviparous. Adults, 175–225 mm.

1944, A. H. and A. A. Wright: In 1925 we met A. J. Kirn through his old field-naturalist partner, R. D. Quillin. In 1934 at his home in Somerset we examined his material and made the notation, *"Tantilla nigriceps* 9 miles east of Pleasanton, Texas. 20.6 cm. (tail 4.2 cm.). Dug up 3 inches underground under loose top soil on hard under soil." Surely it is Blanchard's subsequent type. We were glad to see a deserving modest enthusiast honored, and we hated to have the name go into synonymy. With the naming of *kirnia* we have in the U.S.A. 9 black-headed species and subspecies, but only one plain unicolored *T. gracilis*. How fitting it would be if A. J. Kirn, a Texan who knows *Tantillas* in the field, should treat us to a few new forms of *T. gracilis*.

Authorities:

Blanchard, F. N. (Gen., 1938)   Cope, E. D. (Gen., 1860–61)
Brown, B. C. (Tex., 1951)   Smith, H. M. (Gen., 1938c; Tex.,
Burt, C. E. (Tex., 1936)   1941h)

1936, C. E. Burt: "The coloration of the head is so highly variable in Texas sand snakes that it can scarcely be given diagnostic importance by working herpetologists. As the above tables indicate, eastern specimens (*gracilis*) frequently have black or intermediately colored heads and western ones (*nigriceps*) may have light colored brown cephalic scutes."

1938, F. M. Blanchard: "Mr. A. J. Kirn stated, 'In life the middle of the belly was pink from about the 24th ventral to the tip of the tail, paler forward to the 10th ventral, and without color from chin to this point.'"

1941(h), H. M. Smith: *"Scolecophis fumiceps* Cope (*Proc. Acad. Nat. Sci.* 1850: 371) described without definite locality data (erroneously stated 'Probably China') seems to be the same as *Tantilla kirnia* Blanchard (*Zool. Ser., Field Mus. Nat. Hist.* 20, 1938: 373–4), which it long antedates. The type of *fumiceps* is in the U.S. National Museum, not in the Museum of Comparative Zoology as stated by Cope. . . . Since the chief difference between typical *nigriceps* and *kirnia* lies in ventral counts 146 to 159 in males of the former, 130 to 138 in the latter, *fide* Blanchard, the conspecificity of *fumiceps* and *kirnia* seems rather certain. The subspecies accordingly retains its identity as *Tantilla nigriceps fumiceps* (Cope)."

1951: B. C. Brown makes significant additions to the range of distribution and changes the ventral and caudal scutellation numbers. "All 4 of the *Tantilla nigriceps* were found in junk yards in typical mesquite chaparral country. Two were under old cardboard, 1 under a piece of gypsum wallboard and the fourth was in the ground under a small cactus. All were collected near noon on warm sunny days during the winter and moved rapidly attempting to escape when first uncovered."

Sonoran Tantilla (5—Van Denburgh 1922), Utah black-headed snake
Tantilla utahensis Blanchard 1938. Map 55

Other common names: Blanchard's black-headed snake; California Tantilla.

Range: From s.w. Utah w. into the Sierra Nevada Mts. Calif.—Calif.; Nev.; Ut. *Elevation*—2,000 to 5,000 or more feet. 6,000 feet (Slevin, Calif., 1931).

Size: Adults, 6 or 7–15 inches.

Distinctive characteristics: "Much like *atriceps*, but a larger and more elongate species with more ventrals and with a relatively short tail. The ventrals in *utahensis* range from 153 to 160 in males (130 to 147 in *atriceps*) and from 163 to 172 in females (145 to 157 in *atriceps*). The total length of the specimens of *utahensis* examined ranges from 128 mm. to 297 mm.; in *atriceps* it ranges from 96 to 230 mm." (Blanchard).

Color: A snake from Saint George, Ut., received Apr. 25, 1945, from Ross Hardy of Dixie Junior College. The back is tawny-olive, the tip of snout (rostral, internasals, nasals, prefrontals) the same; the top of the head (frontal, supraoculars, parietals) is verona brown or bister, this color intensifying into sepia on temporals, postoculars, upper portion of upper labials, and 1st row of scales back of parietals. Back of these sepia postparietal scales is an indistinct collar of pale pinkish buff (narrow to the naked eye, but actually suffusing 2 rows of scales). The lower half of the upper labials, and the lower labials are also pale pinkish buff. The eye is black, underside of head white, and belly scarlet, the scarlet beginning on the 10th ventral as a small spot and increasing in size caudad, in midlength covering ½ of ventral, and near vent, where widest, all but the tips of the plates, and on tail all but outer edges. These outer edges of ventrals and caudals and 1st row of scales have 2nd row in center of length of pallid mouse gray.

Notes on structure: Mental barely contacts chin shield at tip only. Two points of 1st pair of labials touch at apex of mental. Four rows gulars between tips of chin shields and 1st ventral. Posterior chin shields in close contact. Anterior edge of frontal slightly curved.

Habitat, habits, food: In 1931 Slevin recorded (Calif.) taking one in the "Panamint Mountains, Inyo County, May 4. It was captured late in the afternoon while crossing a trail at an elevation of 6000 feet." The same year Woodbury wrote: "Little is known of the habits of this snake. It is probably a burrowing form, which may account for its rarity in reptile collections. V. M. Tanner found specimens near St. George under old logs; and I found one under a rock on a very rocky hillside in the Virgin Mountains near St. George." In 1935 Tanner said that several had been studied, but nothing discovered about their food habits.

Breeding: Oviparous. Males 214–270 mm., females 167–215 mm.

Field notes: June 3, 1942, St. George, Ut.: Find 4 Tantilla sheds in an area and, mighty hunter that I am, I land not a snake. Wrong season, technique, man—will have to depend on boys and local people for them.

June 4, 1942: Here we are in St. George, came down from Zion June 3— came with hope we might find *Lepto. utahensis* and *Tantilla utahensis*. They have both eluded us. In one spot Bert found 4 sheds and later when he was showing me the spot, I found one. It was like smelling the dinner but not being allowed to eat. This spot is at the foot of Red Mountain just above the winter home of Brigham Young. There is a certain amount of moisture as there was a narrow irrigation ditch a hundred feet away and a pipe leaking and forming a wet spot in the farm road—30 feet away. This pipe went up to a house standing on overhanging bluff just above where we found the sheds. Below the exposed bluff was a claylike talus slope. At the foot of this was grass and on it were shrubs and some grass clumps. Here at the foot around a group of large stones in the grass were the sheds. A little lower by the farm roadside was a fairly large rough-shaped porous stone. Sticking in this was a shed. We broke up the stone. It was very hard but found no snakes in the channels.

Authorities:

Blanchard, F. N. (Gen., 1938)	Tanner, W. W. (Ut., 1954)
Pack, H. J. (Ut., 1930)	Woodbury, A. M. (Ut., 1931)

1938, F. N. Blanchard: *"Tantilla utahensis* sp. nov. *Type* from St. George, Washington County, Utah. Adult female. No. 55214 California Academy of Sciences. Collected by V. M. Tanner."

1944, A. H. and A. A. Wright: We have tabulated the data on all the material of Brigham Young University, California Academy of Sciences, and Museum of Vertebrate Zoology of University of California. We regret that space does not permit us to publish it here.

1954: W. W. Tanner on one trip collected 18 of these rare snakes. They were taken in the Kanab area, Ut., in three rocky spots. The elevations were above 5,000 feet. He also described a specimen from the north rim of the Grand Canyon.

Arizona Tantilla (2—Van Denburgh, 1922)

Tantilla wilcoxi wilcoxi Stejneger. Map 55

Other common names: Arizona black-headed snake (Pope 1937); Wilcox's black-headed snake; Huachuca black-headed snake.

Range: S.e. Arizona and w. Chihuahua, Mex.—U.S.A.: Ariz. Mex.: Chihuahua. *Elevation*—3,000 to 5,000 feet.

Size: Adults, 7–14 inches.

Distinctive characteristics: *"Tantilla wilcoxi,* new species. *Diagnosis*—Eye more than half as long as the snout; frontal less than twice as broad as the posterior border of the supraocular; 7 upper labials; 2 postoculars; frontal 6-sided, anterior angle obtuse, posterior acute; ventrals about 150; 2 pairs of chin shields, anterior pair longer than posterior; rostral much broader than deep; frontal once and a half as long as broad, longer than interparietal suture; 1st lower labials not in contact behind the mental; posterior nasal and preocular large, broadly in contact; a white collar 2 scales wide just behind the parietals and taking in their extreme posterior angle, followed by a narrow dark band only 1½ scales wide" (Stejneger, Ariz., 1903).

Breeding: Oviparous. Males 214–270 mm., females 175–215 mm.

Authorities:

Blanchard, F. N. (Gen., 1938)
Smith, H. M. (Tex., 1942a)
Van Denburgh, J. (Gen., 1922)

Van Denburgh, J., and J. R. Slevin (Ariz., 1913)

1903, L. Stejneger (Ariz., 1903): *"Type*—No. 19674, U.S.N.M.; Fort Huachuca, Arizona; Dr. T. E. Wilcox, coll. *Description of the type*—Head broad, especially across the temples, much wider than neck; eye large, more than half as long as the snout, and nearly twice as large as its distance from the commissure; rostral much wider than high, the portion visible from above equals the internasal suture; internasals short, less than half as large as the prefrontals, the lower border of which is wedged in between posterior nasal and preocular, but not in contact with supralabials; frontal 6-sided, the anterior angle obtuse, the posterior acute, the lateral sides converging backward, its width about ⅔ its length and less than twice the width of the supraoculars, its length equaling the interparietal suture, though slightly shorter than the parietals; supraoculars, rather larger, their width more than half that of the frontal; parietals as long as their distance from tip of snout; nasals and preocular of about equal size, the latter broadly in contact with posterior nasal; 1 preocular; 2 postoculars; temporals 1 + 1, long and narrow; supralabials 7, 7th very high, 3rd low, 4th nearly twice as wide as 3rd, both entering eye; infralabials 7, 4 in contact with anterior chin shields, 1st pair not in contact with each other behind mental; anterior chin shields very long, much longer than 2nd; 15 rows of smooth scales; 3 pairs of scales between posterior chin shields and ventrals; ventrals 152; anal divided; 40 caudals (tail defective). Color (in alcohol) very pale brownish gray, without stripes, lighter underneath; top of head dark brownish gray, the dark color barely encircling the eyes and descending broadly to the commissure at the suture between the 6th and 7th supralabials; a white semicollar just behind the parietals taking in their extreme posterior angle, 2 scales wide, followed by a dark-brownish gray band only 1½ scales wide. Total length 184 mm.; tail (defective) 40 mm." (Thirteen years later Barbour named the San Luis Potosí form *T. deviatrix*.)

1913, J. Van Denburgh and J. R. Slevin: *"Tantilla wilcoxi* Stejneger. The only example of this species secured is a fine large specimen removed from the stomach of a *Diadophis regalis* caught in Ramsey Canyon, Huachuca Mts., July 29, 1912. . . . This species may be distinguished from *T. nigriceps* by the position of the light collar, the larger number of gastrosteges, and the meeting of the first infralabials."

1922, J. Van Denburgh: "This snake may be distinguished from the other members of the genus which occur within the area under consideration by the number of its gastrosteges and the position of the light nuchal collar. The gastrosteges are more numerous than in *T. nigriceps* and *T. planiceps* but fewer than in *T. eiseni*. The collar does not involve the parietal plates in any of these species."

1938, F. N. Blanchard: "Diagnosis—Distribution of dark pigment on head similar to that in *coronata*, but white band behind it bordered by a dotted dark line instead of a band 3 or 4 scale lengths in width, as in *coronata*. Ventrals and caudals more numerous than in *coronata*. The maximum length is 347 mm. Range—Huachuca Mountains, Arizona."

1940, E. H. Taylor and I. W. Knobloch (Ariz., 1940): "Four specimens of this rare species (from Ariz. and Chihuahua) (Nos. 18967–18970) are in the collection, and are, I believe, the southernmost records. The following data apply to the above specimens respectively: ♂, ♀, ♀, ♀; ventrals 155, 164, 159, 159; subcaudals 62, ?, 67, 64; mental touches chin shields; narrowly on one side, narrowly on one side, broad contact with both, broad contact with both."

1942, H. M. Smith: "Ventrals 149 to 164; caudals 62 to 69. *Mexican Localities:* Mojarachic, Chihuahua. *Specimens examined:* 6. *Remarks:* This species is well differentiated from *bocourti*, which it resembles in color, by the shape of the secondary temporal. The narrow posterior border of the light color, lack of sharp differentiation between white labial area and dark coloration of top of head, and absence of an indentation in the dark area behind the eye differentiate this species from others of the group."

1944, A. H. and A. A. Wright: Inasmuch as Stejneger's type specimen and

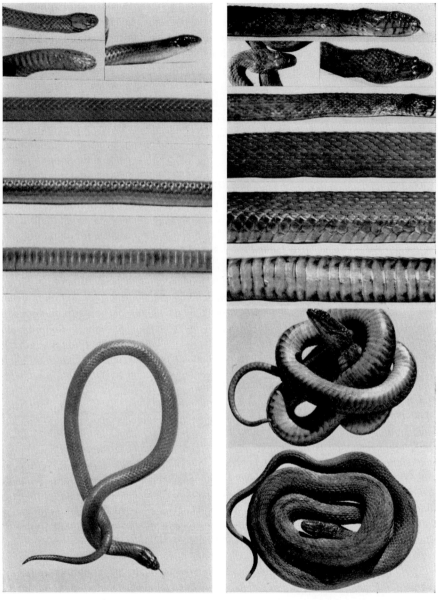

Fig. 218. *Tantilla n. fumiceps,* Somerset, Tex., A. J. Kirn.

Fig. 219. *Thamnophis angustirostris,* Pine Top, Ariz., W. Chapel.

Van Denburgh and Slevin's lone specimen (CAS 34757), have been well described, we append only one extra note concerning 34757, limiting ourselves otherwise to Slevin and Wood's specimen captured in the Huachuca Mts. (May 4, 1941). It is orange under the tail; tip of parietals is white; white band is about 2 scales or 1 and 2 halves wide. The black border behind is ½ scale wide. The dark of the black border goes down to the 3rd row of scales. The upper labials are free of black except for a beautiful half moon under the prominent eye and the last supralabial and the rear of the one ahead of the last. The edges of some forward infralabials are clouded. Scales of head have a tendency to bear just short of the tip a dark spot made up of an aggregation of flecks. Dorsum of tail is orange brown. Total length 173 mm. (tail 42).—Van Denburgh and Slevin in 1913 did not give the total length of No. 34757. It is 349 mm. (tail 81).

GARTER SNAKES, RIBBON SNAKES

Genus *THAMNOPHIS* Fitzinger (Fig. 20)

Size, small medium to large medium, 10–57 inches; small medium in *butleri* to large medium in *gigas;* form slender in ribbon snakes, moderate in general to chunky in *gigas;* head slightly distinct; anal entire; caudals paired; scales keeled, except 1st row, which is smooth or weakly keeled, in 17 to 23 rows, without pits; head plates normal; loreal present; rostral normal; nasals divided; preocular single except in 5 forms—*elegans biscutatus, e. couchi, ordinoides ordinoides* in the northern part of its range, and *hammondi,* all of which frequently have 2, also in *angustirostris,* which frequently has 3; postoculars usually 3; temporals commonly $1 + 2 + 3$ (in *butleri* $1 + 1$); upper labials 6, 7, 8, or 9, eye resting on $3 + 4$, $4 + 5$ or $5 + 6$ in *angustirostris* and *megalops* (in *angustirostris* the lower postocular may crowd in until only 1 labial contacts eye); anterior pair of chin shields usually shorter (exceptions—may be equal or anterior longer in *ordinoides* and *elegans*); gulars separate chin shields; 0–1 row gulars between tips and ventrals; pattern in general 3 light stripes long or short, faint or distinct, on darker ground and usually when light enough exhibits longitudinal rows of black spots; maxillary teeth like *natrix* rather abruptly longer near the posterior end; hemipenis—extends to 14th caudal (13th to 17th); the organ is simple; sulcus unbranched, 5 large basal spines on basal third of organ, which distal to these is studded with minute recurved spinules in more or less oblique rows decreasing in size toward the tip; individual spinules well separated; no calyces, flounces, or papillae; lips of sulcus not prominent. Ventrals 132–184; caudals 51–134. Synonyms: *Atomarchus, Chilopoma, Coluber, Eutaenia, Eutainia, Leptophis, Natrix, Nerodia, Phamnovis, Prymnomiodon, Stypocemus, Tropidonote, Tropidonotus, Vipera.*

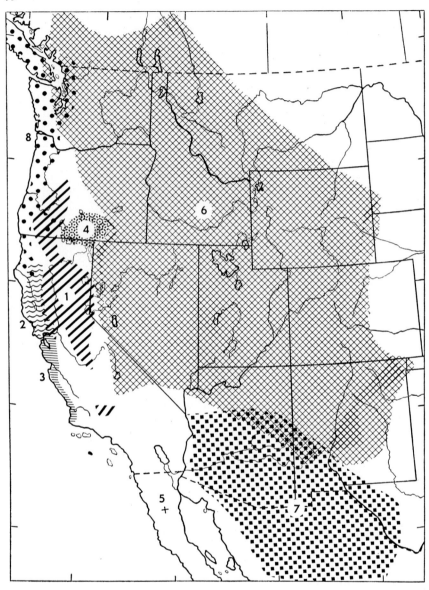

Map 57. *Thamnophis*—1, *e. elegans;* 2, *e. aquaticus;* 3, *e. atratus;* 4, *e. biscutatus;*
5, *e. hueyi;* 6, *e. vagrans;* 7, *eques megalops;* 8, *o. ordinoides.*

KEY TO THE GENUS *THAMNOPHIS*

a. Stripes usually absent, or dorsal may be evident on neck; 6 rows of small numerous dorsal spots; eye over 5th, or 5th and 6th upper labials; lowest postocular encroaches on orbitolabial contact; upper labials 8; frontal contacts preocular; preoculars 2 or 3; postoculars 3. Ventrals 161–177. Caudals 69–87.   *T. angustirostris*

aa. Lateral stripe conspicuous or faint; dorsal stripe present or absent; spots, if present, in 4 rows or fewer.

   b. Light lateral stripe anteriorly involving scale rows 3 and 4.

      c. Tail more than 0.27 total length; form slender; scale rows 19; temporals 1 + 2; eye over labials 4 + 5.

         d. Upper labials 7; tail 1/3 total length or more, average 0.33 (0.29–0.36); color velvety black or deep brown with 3 prominent yellow or orange stripes.   *T. sauritus sauritus*

       dd. Upper labials 8; lateral stripes normally more prominent than dorsal.

         e. Tail normally 1/3 of length or less (0.25–0.35); color brown, dorsal stripe yellow, brown, or red.   *T. s. proximus*

        ee. Tail normally 1/3 of length or more (0.32–0.38); color brownish or olive; dorsal stripe frequently absent; if present, green or olive-gray.   *T. s. sackeni*

     cc. Tail less than 0.27 total length.

       d. Scale rows 19–17; lateral stripe on rows 2 and 3 and 4; upper labials 6–7; temporals 1–1; head small, not very distinct; eye over labials 3 + 4.

         e. Upper labials usually 6, rarely 7; scale rows 17–17–17.
                                           T. r. brachystoma

        ee. Upper labials usually 7, rarely 6; scale rows 19–19–17 (15).
                                               T. r. butleri

       dd. Scale rows 21–19–17; lateral stripe on rows 3 and 4; upper labials 7–9.

         e. Upper labials usually 7 (8); lower labials usually 9 (10); scale rows 19–21–19–17; eye over labials 4 + 5; plains and prairie regions.

            f. Two rows of alternating blotches between lateral and dorsal stripes larger and less numerous than those in *haydeni;* average 84 inches.   *T. radix radix*

          ff. Head broader and more depressed in front than in *radix radix;* spots smaller, average 93.   *T. r. haydeni*

ee. Upper labials usually 8 (9); lower labials 10–11; scale rows 21–19–17 or 21–21–17; eye over labials 5 + 6; Mexican plateau region.   *T. e. megalops*

bb. Light lateral stripe not involving scale row 4.

c. Light lateral stripe anteriorly on row 3 only; upper labials 8; scale rows 21–19–17; prominent yellow light post-oral vertical crescent and a similar oblique bar back of the eye; black nuchal spots; 6 rows dorsal spots, the 1st lateral row below the lateral stripe.

d. Ventrals 155 or less in 88% ♂'s and 155 or less in 95% ♀s; caudals 73 or more in 77% ♂'s and 72 or less in 89% ♀s.
       T. marcianus marcianus

dd. Ventrals 156 or more in 93.2% ♂'s and 156 or more in 80% ♀s; caudals 70 or more in 97% ♂'s and 69 or less in 79.5% ♀s.
       T. m. nigrolateris

cc. Light lateral stripe on scale rows 2 and 3.

d. Upper labials 7 (rarely 6, 8); eye over labials 3 + 4 (except in *concinnus*, in which it is over 4 + 5).

e. Scale rows 17–17–15; ventrals average fewer than 153 (135–162); lower labials 8–9 (occ. as 7, 10); dorsal stripe normally bright yellow or red; lateral stripe faint or absent; eye small.
       T. ordinoides ordinoides

ee. Scale rows 19–19–17; ventrals average more than 153 (137–167); lower labials usually 10 (occ. as 9, 11); oculars 1–3; eye large.

f. Pattern spotted, without red interspaces; dorsal and lateral stripes often absent; usually 2 rows of alternating spots on each side; ground color light greenish or olive; distinct black spot on each end of ventrals.   *T. sirtalis sirtalis*

ff. Pattern, if spotted, has red interspaces, spots when present form 2 rows on either side, but seldom distinct, sometimes merged into bands, often with no interspaces; ventral end spot absent, inconspicuous, or slightly evident anteriorly.

g. Venter dark—bluish slate, slate black, or black; dorsal ground color black; dorsal stripe narrow, occasionally absent, normally on median row; if on adjacent half rows, usually invaded by black; black spots on ends of ventrals obscure or absent.

h. Head red (scarlet to cinnamon-rufous); labials marked with scarlet; dorsal stripe normally 1 and 2 half scales wide; lateral stripe reduced or absent, sides with vertical bars of scarlet or jasper red; eye over labials 4 + 5.   *T. s. concinnus* hh. Head dark or black, labials green with black wedge suture spots on uppers; dorsal stripe green or blue, normally confined to middorsal row; dorsal ground color jet black; red, if present, mainly on interspaces between scales; forward portion of venter glaucous-blue to dusky green-blue; regular 3-striped pattern. *T. s. pickeringi*

gg. Venter light; pale green; lateral stripe of scale rows 2 and 3, often +1, gently merges into light ventrals; dorsal stripe 1 and 2 half rows broad with straight lateral edges rarely invaded.

   h. Top of head red or burnt sienna; stripes prominent, dorsal and lateral stripes green.

      i. 4 lateral stripes: dorsal stripe pale blue-green; upper black stripe; intermediate scarlet or brazil red stripe; another black stripe; lateral glaucous-light blue stripe—a blue-green and red striped snake; venter light dull glaucous-blue. San Francisco peninsula to San Mateo Co., Calif. *T. s. tetrataenia*

     ii. No more than 3 stripes; dorsal stripe is striking green; upper black stripe with lateral black blotches attached, interspaces red; lateral green stripe not dissimilar to dorsal stripe; area below lateral stripe and on corners of ventrals lincoln green—a green-striped snake. (Humboldt Co. to northern San Diego Co., Calif.) *T. s. infernalis*

  hh. Top of head black, dark brown, or ivy green, dorsal and lateral stripes tending toward yellow, buff, or orange and often strikingly dissimilar; little or no black on venter.

      i. Top of head black or dark brown; red interspaces much less than the black areas, so that dorsal ground color is almost entirely black, the red confined to interspace bars a scale or less long; dorsal stripe chamois to light brown, lateral stripe sulphur yellow, area below stripe and corners of ventrals brown. *T. s. fitchi*

     ii. Top of head ivy green; ground color dark olive to dull reddish brown; 2 rows lateral spots (sometimes all distinct), those of the upper row usually fused as a black border for dorsal stripe, those of the lower row distinct and clearly outlined with english red, scarlet, or orange red, or united above with the upper black band; dorsal stripe glass green, reed yellow, or orange-rufous, lateral stripe cream-buff, area below and corners of ventrals buffy olive. *T. s. parietalis*

dd. Upper labials 8; eye over 4 + 5 (except *cyrtopsis*, in which it may be over 3 + 4 (5)).

  e. Prominent black nuchal spot clearly separated from dorsal spots; scales between spots with longitudinal black centers and sulphur yellow or pale green-yellow edges; 6 rows of dorsal spots, the lowest row of either side below the lateral stripe; this lowest row on scale rows 1 and 2 extends onto ends of ventrals, encroaches on lateral stripe, and with the spots above also encroaching, causes the stripe to be scalloped; spots are square and normally touch at corners in mid-body; 2 prominent vertical white bars on head, 1 back of eye and 1 at angle of mouth; eye large; ventral end spots present; scale rows 19–17. *T. cyrtopsis cyrtopsis*

  ee. No prominent black nuchal spots or nuchal spots merging into dorsal stripes; dorsal spots, if prominent, in 4 rows (*atratus, hammondi, vagrans*), but may be absent; no series of spots below the lateral line; spots if present, rounded, smaller and usually not touching at corners; no prominent postorbital and postrectal bars or crescents; eye small; ventral end spots usually absent. *elegans* group

   f. Dorsal line short, indistinct, or absent.

    g. Dorsal stripe absent; preocular usually divided into 2 plates; lateral line distinct, naples yellow or warm buff; ground color brownish olive; eye relatively large; lower labials 10; scale rows usually 21. *T. e. hammondi*
Dorsal black markings reduced; no conspicuous black crescentic neck markings; lateral lines absent; uniform dull brown dorsal surface. *T. digueti*

(Baja California)

   gg. Dorsal stripe present, but often faint and confined to anterior part of body.

    h. Scale rows 19 either at neck or mid-body; dorsal stripe very narrow, dull, and indistinct but discernible on anterior half of body; may lack lateral stripe; ground color pale gray or brown checkered with black spots; venter vinaceous-tawny to pink under the tail; 1 preocular. *T. e. hydrophila*

   hh. Scale rows 21–23; lateral stripes may be faint or lacking.

    i. Usually clearly defined dorsal spots and heavy black pigmentation on a gray venter; dorsal stripe absent or faint for the body length; scale rows 21. *T. e. vagrans*

    ii. Dorsal spots usually absent or poorly defined and confined to anterior part of body. Dorsal stripe may be reduced to bare indication on neck.

    j. Scale rows 23 or 22 at point 1/3 distance from head to vent; lateral stripe buffy olive, present or absent; venter light, buffy olive or brownish with pale yellow or green in center and on throat; lower labials average 10; size often very large —over 3 feet.   *T. e. gigas*

    jj. Scale rows 21, 20 at point 1/3 distance from head to vent; dorsal stripe and dorsal surface may be checkered with large squarish black markings which frequently touch at corners, alternating with paler areas, or merge so that whole dorsum becomes black with bare suggestion of dorsal stripe on neck; venter heavily marbled or completely washed with black; lower labials average 11; seldom 3 feet in length.   *T. e. couchi*

ff. Dorsal line long, present over most of body.

  g. Dorsal stripe edges sharp, not encroached on by body color; stripe yellow, bright yellow, or orange yellow; normally prominent 3-striped snakes.

    h. Scale rows 19; dorsal ground color brown, gray, or black, with 2 rows of dark spots on either side; black nuchal spots merging with the dorsal ground color; pale blue-green, red, or yellow lateral stripe present or absent; upper labials, chin, and ventral surfaces usually tinted with yellow greens and blue greens.

(Old atratus group)

[After Fox, Calif., 1951.]

    (i. Stout: 6th and 7th upper labials taller than long.

      j. Pointed snout; internasals usually longer than broad, pointed anteriorly, in narrow contact with rostral; 6th and 7th upper labials relatively large and taller than long; slightly stout. Scales 15–19–15, little or no red in ground color; orange ventral suffusions. (Coastal and great valley s. of San Francisco Bay.)   *T. e. atratus*

      jj. Blunt, short snout; internasals shorter than wide, blunt anteriorly, and in broad contact with rostral; 6th and 7th upper labials appreciably taller; spots usually distinct; terrestrial. Scales 19–21–19. Considerable reddish brown or red in ground color; red ventral suffusions. (Santa Barbara, Calif., to Oregon state line.)   *T. e. terrestris*

    ii. Relatively long slender body, head, and gape; 6th and 7th upper labials relatively straight, neither strikingly elevated nor enlarged; pointed internasals and narrow rostral; no red; dorsal spots indistinct, salmon ventral suffusions; aquatic. (N. of San Francisco Bay.)   *T. e. aquaticus*) hh. Scale rows 21 (occasionally 19, 23); dorsal ground color glossy black; no red in the pattern; venter drab-gray sometimes marked with black; nuchal spots merge with dorsal ground color, bright dorsal stripe; pronounced lateral stripe of bright yellow; (a ribbon snake in appearance); upper labials, chin, and ventral surfaces tinted with gray and olive; ventrals 154–185; caudals 72–101. (San Bernardino Mts. and Sierras to Oregon.)   *T. elegans elegans*

    i. Ventrals 149–160; caudals 66–82; upper labials frequently 7, lower frequently 9; dorsal stripe borders invaded by spots; ground color grayish brown, the young and some adults having spots. (Sierra San Pedro Mártir, Baja Calif.)   *T. e. hueyi*

gg. Dorsal stripe invaded by dorsolateral spots.

  h. Scale rows 19 either at neck or mid-body; dorsal stripe very narrow, dull, and indistinct and may be confined to anterior half of body; ground color pale gray or brown checkered with black spots; venter vinaceous-tawny to pink under the tail; 1 preocular. *T. e. hydrophila*

  hh. Scale rows over 19 (21–23).

    i. Dorsal stripe dull yellow brown or gray often broken; lateral stripe faint or buff; ground color brown; usually clearly defined dorsal spots; dull upper labials often without dark sutures; venter gray or orange usually heavily pigmented with black medially; preoculars 1; scale rows 21–20–19; ventrals 148–182; caudals 67–95.   *T. e. vagrans*

    j. Dorsal stripe yellow, conspicuous even if invaded; ground color grayish brown; upper labial whitish; venter immaculate or slightly spotted; lateral stripe sharply defined; scale rows 21; ventrals 149–160; caudals 66–82. (Sierra San Pedro Mártir, Baja Calif.)   *T. e. hueyi*

  ii. Dorsal stripe distinct, lemon yellow or orange yellow; dark nearly black ground color obscuring spots; pale upper labials often with black sutures; venter light olive gray and buff clouded with black; preoculars frequently divided into 2; scale rows 21, 22, 23.

T. e. biscutatus

Long-nosed garter snake (1—Yarrow 1882),
Brown-spotted garter snake (8—Van Denburgh 1922)

Thamnophis angustirostris Kennicott 1860. Fig. 219; Map 58

Other common names: Long-headed garter snake (2); Mexican highlands garter; red-spotted garter snake; red-spotted Chilopoma; (western) spotted garter snake.

Range: From highlands of cent. and s.e. Arizona and s.w. New Mexico south to Mexico (Chihuahua and Durango). An isolated record in Palo

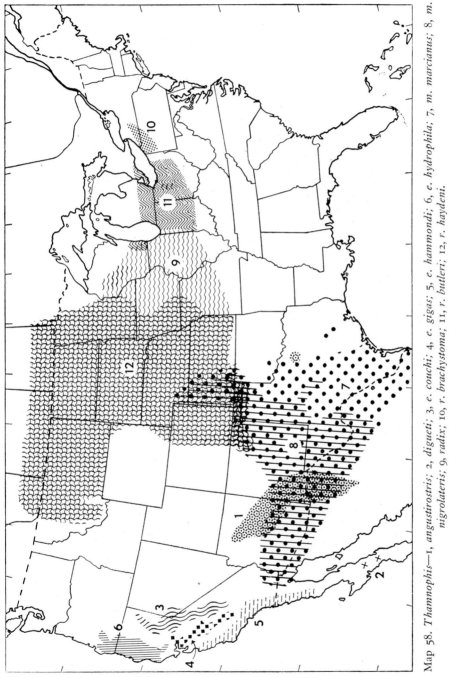

Map 58. *Thamnophis*—1, *angustirostris*; 2, *digueti*; 3, *e. couchi*; 4, *e. gigas*; 5, *e. hammondi*; 6, *e. hydrophila*; 7, *m. marcianus*; 8, *m. nigrolateris*; 9, *radix*; 10, *r. brachystoma*; 11, *r. butleri*; 12, *r. haydeni*.

Pinto Co., Texas.—U.S.A.: Ariz.; N.M.; Tex. Mex.: Chihuahua; Durango. *Elevation*—2,000 to 6,000 or 7,000 feet. 6,000 feet (Van Denburgh); 5,000–5,500 feet (Woodin, Ariz., 1951).

Size: Adults, 10–34 inches.

Distinctive characteristics: Combine the following three characterizations by Cope (Gen., 1900). "Second row of scales keeled; the first keeled or smooth; orbit above 2 labials, lateral stripe when present, on 2nd and 3rd rows of scales. Temporal scales, 1–2. One preocular; a large temporal bounding occipital; frontal narrow, touching preocular; head long; labials all longer than high; tail 3¼ in length. . . . *E. angustirostris* Kennicott. . . ." "Second row of scales keeled; orbit bounded below by a single labial. Scales in 21 rows; superior labials 8. Temporals 1–3. Oculars 3-3; labials longer than high; rostral subtriangular; muzzle narrow; 7 rows of spots; no stripes. *E. multimaculata* Cope." "Like the last; but rostral a transverse oval with free borders; loreal nearly entering orbit; and labials narrower. *E. rufopunctatus* Cope."

One distinctive structural feature is that the supraocular tapers to a point where it meets the preocular and leaves a broad contact between frontal and preocular. The narrow snout, oblique face, and protruding eyes (which appear almost entirely on the dorsal aspect as viewed from above) and 6 rows of spots give a distinctive appearance. Anal plate entire (A.H.W. and A.A.W.)

Color: An adult snake from Payson, Yavapai Co., Ariz., received from William Chapel, Oct. 29, 1936. The background of the back is prout's brown, bister, or saccardo's umber, with 6 rows of spots of warm sepia or mars brown. Sometimes 2 middle spots join, forming saddles; sometimes they are opposite as pairs; often they alternate and touch at a corner or not at all. When united, they form transverse or oblique bands 6 to 8 scales transversely and 1 and 2 half-scales long. As separate spots, they are 3 to 4 scales wide. With these 2 dorsal series, there is on either side a series of alternating spots on the 4th to 7th or 8th scale rows. And alternating with this lateral row is a suggestion of a third on the 2nd and 3rd scale rows, these being indicated below by indefinite black edges or oblique lines on the 1st and 2nd scale rows and across the ends of the ventrals. The first 2 scale rows and the ends of the ventral plates are buffy olive or citrine-drab. The top of the head, face, temporal region, and 1st 4 upper labials are brownish olive or buffy olive. The upper labials back of the eye, namely 5th, 6th and 7th, have each an oblique black line extending from the rear suture to the middle of the top. Above the black line, the plate is like the top of the head, and below the line it is ecru-olive. The 8th plate has 2 oblique lines of black across it. Many scales back of the angle of the mouth bear black apical specks. The outer rim of the eye is like the face except for the black upper part next to the supraocular. The pupil rim is broad, covering a large part of the iris and is ochraceous-buff or even ochraceous-orange in its upper third. The lower labials are olive-ocher with black sutures. The lower side of the head, the chin shields, and gulars, are deep colonial buff to mustard yellow; the neck is deep colonial buff; the other ventral plates are ecru-olive. After about 13 ventrals, there is a little indication of a black spot on either end of each plate. They are not very distinct as such and soon extend across the plate as a narrow striated black cephalic border. This continues to the vent. The subcaudals are buffy olive with borders of cream-buff.

A half-grown snake received Oct. 30, 1936. The general impression of its color is saccardo's umber, with the lowest row of spots more clearly defined than in the adult. The labials are more striking than in the adult, the lower ones and the upper ones back of the eye being deep colonial buff to mustard yellow, the sutures sharply outlined with black. The first 4 upper labials are deep colonial buff below outlined above by a dark semicircle, with their upper portions like the face. The rear upper labials have upper rims like the temporal region, and the last one bears 2 horizontal black lines as in the adult and very little deep colonial buff. The venter is yellower than in the adult. The interspaces between the lateral scales are black.

We can find no indication of a dorsal stripe or of a lateral stripe in either the adult snake or the half-grown one.

Habitat: Three authors have seen this form in sufficient quantity to help us give its habitat. Van Denburgh and Slevin (Calif., 1913) took 18 specimens in Oak Creek, Ariz., a "mountain stream running through a deep canyon with many oak trees. . . . These were found in the stream either on rocks or in the water." All sought to dive to the bottom and made no attempts to bite.

Seemingly, this Mexican highland form is in Starker's (Ecol., 1950) temperate pine-oak forest and mesquite-grassland areas or in Chihauhuan and Sierra Madre (Harshberger, Ecol., 1911), Apachian and Chihuahuan (Dice, Ecol., 1943) zones.

Period of activity: *Fall disappearance*—Sept., 1938; Sept. 1-4, 1912; Oct. 29, 1936.

Breeding: Viviparous. Males to 581 mm.

Food: Toads. Woodin (Ariz., 1951).

Authorities:

Cope, E. D. (Gen., 1886; in Yarrow, Ariz., 1875; N.M., 1883)
Kennicott, R. (Gen., 1860–61)
Ruthven, A. G. (Gen., 1908)
Smith, H. M. (Gen., 1942)
Taylor, E. H., and I. W. Knobloch (Ariz., 1940)
Trapido, H. (Tex., 1942)
Van Denburgh, J. (Gen., 1922)

1944, A. H. and A. A. Wright: For 20 or more years we have held this form to be more *Natrix* than *Thamnophis*, yet we retain it in *Thamnophis* until a better understanding of it is possible. Like other *Thamnophis* the scales are without pits, which are present in *Natrix*. Divided or entire anals may not be very important as generic differences, especially as we permit divided and entire annals to reside in the same genus, *Trimorphodon*. In reviewing the whole literature of U.S. herpetology, we see what strained relationships earlier authors indulged in and how far astray they went at times. Let's withhold judgment until we have more material. Is this form anything like *Natrix harteri?*

Note on Smith's hybrid hypothesis: Once *multimaculata* and *rufipunctata* were held to be synonyms, and most authors thought *melanogaster* related to *angustirostris*. But these supposed parents, *rufipunctatus* and *melanogaster,* are Mexican; not from Texas to Grand Canyon. All this *angustirostris* material is north. Withhold judgment! In the last quarter century we have seen all the old and new museum material from Washington to San Francisco. We are intrigued by Smith's solution but nevertheless must remain conservative. In the same spirit, we wonder if the lone Texas specimen could by any chance have come from Arizona or New Mexico.

Ocellated garter snake (Yarrow 1882), Spotted garter snake

Thamnophis cyrtopsis cyrtopsis (Kennicott) 1861. Fig. 220; Map 59

Other common names: Brown garter snake (7—Ditmars 1907); checkerboard garter; collared garter snake; Couch's garter snake (Yarrow 1882); green-bellied garter; Reuss' garter snake; white-bellied garter snake (12—Van Denburgh 1922). ("White-bellied garter snake" [12] and "brown garter snake" [7] are first and second on the basis of book names, often decided on from the appearance of alcoholic specimens, but in life the belly is grape green, water green, corydalis green, pinkish vinaceous, salmon flecked, etc.)

Range: From s.w. Utah, s. and e. through e. Arizona to Sonora, Mex., s along Sierra Madre Occidental to n. Nayarit, e. to San Luis Potosí, n. to Coahuila and w. cent. Texas; thence n.w. through New Mexico.—U.S.A.: Ariz.; N.M.; Tex.; Ut. Mex.: Chihuahua; Coahuila; Durango; Nayarit; San Luis Potosí; Sonora. *Elevation*—1,000 to 8,000 feet. 4,000–8,000 feet (Bailey, N.M., 1913); 4,800–6,500 feet (Coahuila); 5,700 feet (Bailey, Tex., 1905).

Size: Adults, 17–37 inches.

Distinctive characteristics: "*E. cyrtopis* Kennicott. *Spec. char.* Form very slender but little stouter than that of *E. saurita,* but with shorter tail, ¼ the total length. Head large. Eye very large. Superior labials 8, 6th and 7th largest. Three postorbitals, upper much the largest. Scales in 19 rows. Color above olive brown, with 2 alternating series of elongated spots between the stripes, giving the appearance of a zigzag line. Dorsal stripe whitish, narrow, distinct to the tip of the tail. Lateral stripe on the 2nd and 3rd rows, of the

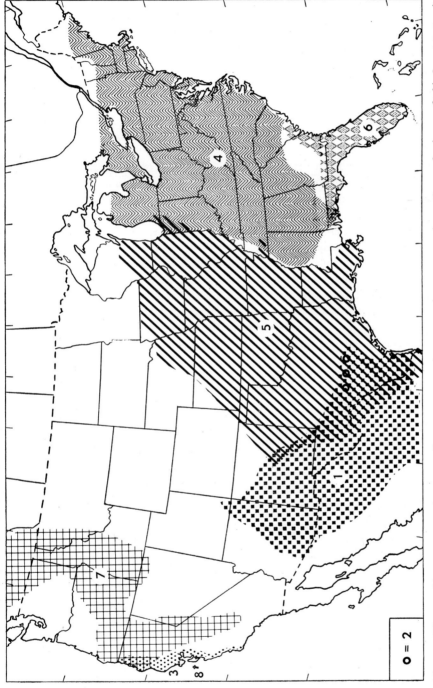

Map 59. *Thamnophis*—1, *c. cyrtopsis*; 2, *c. ocellata*; 3, *e. terrestris*; 4, *s. saurítus*; 5, *s. proximus*; 6, *s. sackeni*; 7, *s. fitchi*; 8, *s. tetrataenia.*

O = 2

same color, broad, distinct from head to anus. A series of black spots on the 1st dorsal row; abdomen greenish white. Orbitals whitish; occipital spots obsolete" (Kennicott). "This race differs from *E. eques* of the southern part of the Mexican Plateau chiefly in the greater average number of ventral scales. In *e. cyrtopsis* 86% of the males have 167 or more ventrals, and 100% of the females have 163 or more ventrals; in *e. eques* on the other hand, only 3% of the males have 167 or more ventrals, and only 3% of the females have more than 162 ventrals. . . . Very rarely do 7 supralabials occur in *e. cyrtopsis,* while in *e. eques* 7 occur as frequently as 8" (Smith, Gen., 1942b).

Color: A snake from Fern Canyon near Alpine, Tex., July 11, 1925. There is a dorsal stripe which is at first bittersweet orange, becoming after an inch or so salmon-orange and rearward pale yellow-orange or pale orange-yellow. The lateral stripe is pale ochraceous-buff, becoming pinkish cinnamon toward the vent. There is a pair of large black nape spots. Then between the dorsal and lateral stripe, there are first 7 large quadrate black spots, then 2 rows of alternating black square spots. The scales of the intervals between these spots are black with sulphur yellow or pale green-yellow edges. For the first 9 black spots, the lateral stripe merges with the interval color, and in that region, the lower portion of the interval is pale ochraceous-buff while the 5 rows of scales on either side of the dorsal stripe have longitudinal black centers and pale green-yellow edges. The skin between the scales is pale turquoise green. Below the lateral stripe is a row of black spots alternating with those just above the line. These lower spots are connected by an olive-gray or light mouse-gray line. The top of the head is dusky olive-green, the parietals marked with a central spot of white encircled with black. There is a white vertical band in front of the eye, another just back of the eye, and a third at the angle of the mouth. The scales back of and below the angle of the mouth are pale pinkish cinnamon. The iris is dusky olive-green, like the top of the head, with a pupil rim of white, cartridge buff, or pale olive-buff.

The labials have black rear edges. The throat is white, the venter corydalis green or water green with pea green or deep grape green in the center of each ventral from neck to vent.

A snake from Madera Canyon near Alpine, Tex., July 12, 1925. The top of the head is deep olive or dark olive; the iris dark olive with some vinaceous-rufous in the upper part and a pupil rim of light vinaceous-cinnamon. The belly is pale grayish vinaceous on the sides with the center of the plates grape green. The underside of the tail is water green. In a large snake from the San Antonio region, the black spots merged, and the light edges of interval scales were not apparent.

Habitat: Many authors have associated this species with rocks and boulders of canyon streams. Others have found it on low flats of the mesquite association, on the tops of talus slopes, on dry plains 2 miles from water, in chaparral-woodland or pine-fir zones, and in Upper Sonoran localities. Woodin's (Ariz., 1950) summary follows: "This is by far the commonest snake in many canyons and mountain streams of southern Arizona. It seems to prefer mountainous and hilly areas and is uncommon far from water, unless it be dried up stream beds. Specimens when captured generally make good use of their scent glands but seldom bite. It appears to be the smallest of our garter snakes with the average adult size probably less than 24 inches."

We too had a small form from Sonoita, Ariz., which we designated *T. c. cyrtopsis,* and as we read a dozen or more earlier accounts we wonder whether the Arizona *cyrtopsis* are our large Texas *cyrtopsis* or whether *cyrtopsis* and *marciana* identifications are still mixed up in 1950.

In 1949 in the Sierra Vieja range in Texas, Jameson and Flury wrote: "This species was found very commonly around the pockets of water in the stream bed association of the Roughland belt. Of 102 specimens taken on the Miller ranch in 1948, all were from the stream bed association except for one from a lake in the toboso-grama association and two from the catclaw-cedar association at the mouth of ZH Canyon. . . . Four additional specimens taken in 1947 by Blair, Miller and Walker were all from the stream bed association."

Period of activity: *Early appearances*—Mar. (Quaintance, Ariz., 1935); May 9, 1910, May 10–18, 1912 (Van Denburgh and Slevin, Ariz., 1913). *Fall disappearance*—Aug. 19 (Campbell, Ariz., 1934); Sept. (Quaintance); Sept. 1–3 (Van Denburgh and Slevin); Sept. 17 (MacCoy, Ariz., 1932). MVZ dates are May 31 to Sept. 13.

Breeding: Viviparous. Males 429–470 mm., females 504–764 mm. *Young*— On Sept. 1–3, 1912 (CAS 35256–35265), Slevin took *T. c. cyrtopsis* between 245–281 mm., some measurements being 256 mm. (tail 69), 281 mm. (tail 70), 269 mm. (tail 67), 268 mm., 245 mm. (tail 61)—probably newly born young of the year. In 1932 Mosauer (N.M., 1932) wrote: "About July 20, the creek in Dark Canyon suddenly began to swarm with young *Thamnophis,* apparently newborn. They were of 230–270 mm. total length."

Food: Fish, frogs, treefrogs, toads, and tadpoles. Ruthven (Ariz., 1907), Mosauer (N.M., 1932), Campbell (Ariz., 1934), Jameson and Flury, Woodin (Ariz., 1950). Fouquette (Tex., 1954) found its chief food to be amphibian.

Authorities:

Cope, E. D. (Gen., 1883–84; Baja Calif., 1862; Tex., 1880)

Hensley, M. M. (Ariz., 1950)

Jameson, D. L., and A. G. Flury (Tex., 1949)

Smith, H. M. (Gen., 1939a, 1942b, Tex., 1951)

Strecker, J. K., Jr. (Tex., 1933)

Yarrow, H. C., and H. W. Henshaw (Ariz., 1878)

1933, J. K. Strecker, Jr.: (From 1917 to 1942 we have several times visited, camped, and collected in the Marnock neighborhood and there made the acquaintance of *T. cyrtopsis ocellata* many a time. Strecker's respect for

Marnock, his kindly interest, and the historic nature of the area prompts us to quote the first paragraph of "Collecting at Helotes, Bexar County, Texas.") "To a naturalist, there is always something fascinating about a visit to the type locality of an interesting species of animal. On the banks of Helotes Creek, 22 miles northwest of San Antonio, is located the old stone Marnock homestead, where, for more than 40 years, abode Gabriel Marnock, pioneer Texas herpetologist. Marnock settled in what was at that time almost virgin territory and he found himself surrounded by numerous species of amphibians and reptiles of great interest, many of them of considerable rarity. Here, within a stone's throw of his home, he discovered the type specimens of the frogs described by Cope under the names of *Lithodytes* (now *Eleutherodactylus*) *latrans* and *Syrrhophus marnockii,* the skink *Eumeces brevilineatus* Cope, the little variegated gecko many years later named *Coleonyx brevis* by Dr. Stejneger, and a variety of garter snake named by Cope *Eutaenia cyrtopsis ocellata.* The garter snake has long since lost its distinctive name, *ocellata* now being regarded as a synonym of *Thamnophis eques* (Reuss), but the others have maintained their validity through the years."

1944, A. H. and A. A. Wright: Much of the *marcianus* literature is based on misidentification. In 1907 R. L. Ditmars brought out his very useful and well-illustrated *The Reptile Book* (2d ed., 1908). His Plate LXX labeled *Eutaenia elegans marciana* is *T. c. cyrtopsis.* On page 229 of the second edition he speaks of it as "larger" and "stouter" than other *Eutaenia elegans* subspecies. *T. marcianus* is in general almost as slim as a ribbon snake. On page 230 he refers to its "handsome form" and "checker board pattern." He most certainly has *T. c. cyrtopsis.* The nondescript *T. marcianus* would never have thus caught his eye. On page 230 he says, "In dimensions, Couch's Garter Snake is rather smaller than *marciana";* whereas it is often much larger, and at times 2–3 times as stout. We fear this mistake has led many astray.

Nearly thirty years later it still appears in the same garb: "Rather stout," "heavier . . . than *sirtalis* or *ordinoides,"* "most strongly spotted of any of the garter snakes," "attractive snake," "my favorite," etc. Ditmars is still describing *T. c. cyrtopsis* for *T. marcianus.*

Confusion existed before and continued after Ditmars. (About half of the literature on this species is by Strecker, 1901–1930.) For the ten years 1897–1908 or possibly much longer his familiarity with this species was limited (witness his 1908 remarks). We are fearful that some of his "dry," "handsome," "spotted," "mouse" *marcianus* specimens are *T. c. cyrtopsis* on which he had few notes, although in central Texas it is common.

Fig. 220. *Thamnophis cyrtopsis cyrtopsis:* 1,5,6, Classen's Ranch, 17 miles north of San Antonio, Tex., R. and E. Quillin; 2,3,7, Brownsville, Tex., H. C. Blanchard; 4, San Antonio, Tex.; 8, Devil's River, above Juno, Tex. (1,5,7—*ocellata*).

Fig. 221. *Thamnophis elegans elegans,* Mt. Shasta, Calif., C. B. Perkins.

Ocellated garter snake; Edward's plateau spotted garter snake

Thamnophis cyrtopsis ocellata (Cope) 1880

For his "Geographic variation in the garter snake, *Thamnophis cyrtopsis*" Milstead (Tex., 1953) examined 707 specimens. He interpreted the Arizona, New Mexico, Utah, and extreme w. Texas material as *T. c. cyrtopsis* and that of the Edwards plateau of Texas as *T. c. ocellata*. We, too, have always inclined to the *T. c. ocellata* point of view for these scalloped lateral-striped specimens of central Texas. (Note our Fig. 220, No. 5). "This subspecies is found in cedar brakes, on limestone ledges, and on rocky hillsides, not necessarily in the vicinity of water. It is usually found in the same ecological associations with *Syrrhophus marnockii* and *Gerrhonotus liocephalus infernalis*. . . . A number of specimens of *ocellata* have been collected on limestone ledges near Austin, Texas, which support dense populations of *Syrrhophus*. It is possible that the frog forms a good part of the diet of the garter snake. One specimen from Austin contained a partially digested *Leiolopisma laterale*."

Mountain garter snake (14—Van Denburgh 1922)
Elegant garter snake (7—Cooper 1869)

Thamnophis elegans elegans (Baird and Girard) 1853. Fig. 221; Map 57

Other common names: Boyd's garter snake (5); California garter snake; single-striped garter snake.

Range: High slopes of Sierras of s. Oregon and n. California; also San Bernardino Mts., Calif.—Calif.; Nev.; Ore. *Elevation*—3,000 to 8,500 feet. 4,500–6,500 feet (Linsdale, Nev., 1938–40); 3,300, 3,500, 4,500, 5,200, 5,300, 5,600, 6,800 feet (Grinnell, Dixon, and Linsdale); 2,000, 2,500–3,000, 3,500, 5,000, 5,100, 5,500, 6,000, 5,500–6,200, 6,500, 6,700–8,600 feet (Fitch, Gen., 1940); 4,000 feet (Stejneger); 5,000, 5,900, 6,200, 6,500, 6,700, 6,700, 7,750, 8,000, 8,600 feet (Van Denburgh and Slevin, Gen., 1918); 5,500–6,800 feet (Grinnell, Calif., 1908).

Size: Adults, 11–32 inches.

Distinctive characteristics: "*Eutainia elegans* B. and G.—Resembles *E. proxima*, but belongs to a different section. Black above, light beneath. A broad ochraceous dorsal stripe, with 2 lateral, greenish white, light beneath. Dorsal scales 21" (Baird and Girard, Gen., 1853). "Normally with 8 supralabials; 21 or sometimes 19 rows of scales; dorsal line very distinct, narrow; dorsal spots lacking or not evident, being hidden by the dark ground color, not invading the edges of the dorsal line; gastrosteges rarely marked with black or slate; preocular almost always single; infralabials very rarely more than 10" (Van Denburgh and Slevin, Gen., 1918). A good diagnosis is Fitch's (Gen., 1940).

Color: A snake from Mt. Shasta, Calif., received Aug., 1936, through the kindness of C. B. Perkins. The background of dorsum of body and tail is black or mummy brown. The dorsal stripe on the neck is salmon-orange, becoming along the body light orange-yellow or pale orange-yellow and on the rear half of the body buff-yellow to picric yellow. In front, the dorsal stripe is on the median scale row and ½ scale on either side; in the rear half, on median scale alone. There is a pinard yellow lateral stripe on the 2nd and 3rd scale rows which becomes on the rear half of the body light buff or pale ochraceous-buff. Just below the dorsal yellow stripe are vertical series of 3 pale turquoise green horizontal flecks, and alternating with them just above the lateral stripe is a lower series of 2 flecks. These become evident as the snake inflates or the skin is stretched, at which times these flecks indicate the 2 rows of dark spots characteristic of garter snakes. Just below the lateral stripe the lowest row of scales has a series of vertical black, mummy brown, or chocolate spots, which are larger than the spots on the ends and inner edges of the ventrals. Thus the impression is given of 2 rows of dark spots below the lateral stripe. The top of the head and the temporals are black or mummy brown. The lower part of the rostral, the nasals, loreals, preoculars, and upper labials are light grayish olive or grayish olive. The upper labial sutures, 3-4, 4-5, 5-6, have vertical black edges. Back of each eye, the lower 3rd postocular and half of the 2nd is pinard yellow like the lateral stripe. The iris is cinnamon-brown or prout's brown with a pupil rim of cream color or light buff. The underside of the head and throat are pale smoke gray to white. The rest of the ventral surface is drab-gray with a wash of pallid vinaceous-drab.

Habitat: The reports of the different University of California and Sierran groups have given us a good idea of this beautiful mountain garter's habitat. Normally, it is associated with mountain streams and waters. It has been found near a clover field, in a dry well, on a ridge of yellow pines, 1 mile from permanent water, and in dry woods. In 1940 Fitch (Gen.) summarized "the available habitat data for *elegans:* Of 106 snakes, 7 only were found in the water, 67 were found in riparian associations, and 22 in dry situations away from water. Many of those found in riparian associations or in the water were in localities where streams are partly or wholly dry at some times of year, indicating that a permanent water supply is not an ecologic necessity for *elegans.* . . . The subspecies *elegans* is most characteristic of the Transition Life Zone but also occurs throughout the Upper Sonoran and Canadian Life Zones. It has been found most often in the vicinity of streams in open woods of yellow pine or oak associations, but occurs under varied climatic conditions and in widely different plant associations."

This is well named the mountain garter. It is a sleek form reminding us easterners of our ribbon snake. Back in the old days when the park was closing for the season we used to receive some of the live snakes from the

Yosemite; we struggled with the identification of this form. Was it *T. s. infernalis* or *T. e. elegans?* We dare say if the average present-day herpetologist were presented live *T. s. infernalis* and *T. e. elegans,* he might at first be puzzled if he had not the locality data. But the former is distinctly in coastal California while the latter is of the high Sierras and northward and eastward into Oregon and Nevada. *T. e. elegans* is our favorite garter of the whole west, as the ornate garter is in Texas and the ribbon snake in the northeast. With appearance so striking, it is difficult to remember that *T. e. elegans* has 21 scale rows, 8 upper labials, eye over $4 + 5$, while *T. s. infernalis* has 19 scale rows, 7, 8 upper labials, eye over $3 + 4$.

Period of activity: *Early appearances*—May 23, 1925 (Grinnell, Dixon, Linsdale, Calif., 1930); Apr. 10, 12, 1942 (A.H.W.). *Fall disappearance*—Aug. 25-31, 1913 (Van Denburgh and Slevin); Aug. 31, 1891 (Stejneger); Aug. 27, 1917 (A.H.W.); Sept. 2, 1937 (Klauber). MVZ dates are Mar. 21 to Oct. 1.

Breeding: Viviparous. Males 370–590 mm., females 420–640 mm. 1955, J. D. Cunningham (*Herpetologica,* **11:** 152) reported 4 young in one brood and 11 eggs in a large female.

Food: Slugs, toads, tree frogs, lizards, frogs, mice, earthworms, salamanders, shrews, fish. Fitch, Grinnell, Dixon, and Linsdale. 1955, J. D. Cunningham found this form ate beetles, tree frogs and toads, lizards, ants, and spiders.

Authorities:

Brown, A. E. (Calif., 1903)
Cunningham, J. D. (Calif., 1955)
Fitch, H. S. (Gen., 1940; Ore., 1936)
Grinnell, J., J. Dixon, and J. M. Linsdale (Calif., 1930)
Grinnell, J., and T. Storer (Calif., 1924)

Hallowell, E. (Calif., 1854)
Klauber, L. M. (Gen., 1938)
Ruthven, A. G. (Gen., 1908)
Stejneger, L. (Calif., 1893)
Yarrow, H. C., and H. W. Henshaw (Ariz., 1878)

1853, S. F. Baird and C. Girard (Gen., 1853): "The species is readily distinguished from its nearest analogue, *E. infernalis,* by the darker color of the sides, the ochraceous dorsal stripe, smaller head, number of dorsal scales, etc. It has a strong resemblance to *E. proxima* in distribution of color, but is stouter and shorter, and has the lateral stripe on the 2d and 3d rows, not on the 3d and 4th. El Dorado Co., Calif." 167 ventrals, 57 caudals, 21 scale rows, 23½ inches body, 4½ inches tail.

Northern California coast garter

Thamnophis elegans aquaticus Fox 1951. Map 57

Range: "California coast from Golden Gate to Gualala River at Mendocino Co. line; Coast Ranges in this area as far north as South Fork of Eel River; southern and southeastern tributaries of Eel River, and narrow area extending northward into southwestern Trinity County to southern tributaries of Trinity River; along north shore of San Francisco Bay eastward to Sacramento Valley and northward into Lake and Colusa Counties" (Fox, Calif., 1951).

Distinctive characteristics: "Aquatic garter snake with relatively long slender body, long head and gape, pointed internasals, and narrow rostral. Relatively straight upper labials, neither strikingly elevated nor enlarged in region of 6th or 7th. Yellow, orange, or orange-yellow dorsal stripe ranges from at least ½–1½ scale rows to 3 full scale rows. Lateral stripe always present and distinct (except in certain intergrades with *hydrophila*), light olive-buff frequently olive-yellow or apricot-orange spots. Head mostly dark olive, with or without black pigment in parietal region; upper labials usually olive, fading ventrally to pale buff or cream of lower labials; usually an apricot-orange area covering cheek behind jaw. Chin usually pale cream or pale yellow, although many specimens have lemon-yellow throat. Iris gray or drab, dark olive, or nearly black; darker pigment extensive, giving general impression of extremely dark back, although some specimens have faint patches of lighter olive. Ventral surface usually of various shades of light blue or green, becoming darker posteriorly; varying amounts of pale salmon in central portions of ventral scutes, the color tending to increase in amount posteriorly. Dorsal scale rows 19-19-15 or 19-19-17, rarely 19-21-17. Ventral scutes range from 142 to 167 in females, 147 to 167 in males; caudal scutes from 63 to 82 in females, 74 to 93 in males" (Fox).

From 1903 to 1922 we were perplexed by the so-called *T. o. elegans* of the western coast ranges. In 1922 Van Denburgh recognized his confusion and limited *T. o. elegans* to the Sierras and San Bernardino Mts. We suspect that this form *T. e. aquaticus* is part of what we, following Van Denburgh, called *T. o. elegans*. We must have seen it, yet it seemingly is the only garter of the U.S. we have not handled alive.

Middle California garter snake,
Black garter snake (3—Yarrow 1882)

Thamnophis elegans atratus (Kennicott) 1860. Fig. 222; Map 57

Other common names: Pacific coast garter snake (2—Wade Fox); single-striped garter snake; western garter snake.

Range: Previous to 1951 its range was interpreted as "coastal region of California from Del Norte to Santa Barbara Counties." In 1951 Fox (Calif.) restricted it to the coast and great valley south of San Francisco Bay. *Elevation*—Sea level to 3,000 feet.

Size: Adults, 15–24 inches. Klauber's (Gen., 1943b) standard body length for 61 males and 63 females of the San Francisco region was 450 mm. In 1948, Fox's (Calif.) adult females were 410–560 mm., whereas the males were 326–466 mm.

Distinctive characteristics: "A short, somewhat stout garter snake with pointed snout and remarkably uniform head scales: almost always 8 upper labials, 10 lower labials, 1 preocular, and 3 postoculars on each side. . . . Internasals usually longer than broad, pointed anteriorly, and in narrow contact with rostral; 6th and 7th upper labials relatively large and taller than long, resembling those of terrestrial races rather than those of other aquatic races, in which rows of upper labials are practically straight. Broad orange or orange-yellow dorsal stripe usually covers at least $\frac{2}{3}$ to $1\frac{2}{3}$ rows of scales, frequently 3 full scale rows, and occasionally only central row involved. Lateral stripes absent in blue-black individuals from San Francisco peninsula, but elsewhere usually present and conspicuous pale yellow. Top of head usually olive, dark olive or blue black; chin and throat bright lemon yellow, this color usually extending to or over lower labials; upper labials generally pale yellow. Iris very dark, almost black except for loose silvery network in most specimens. Dorsal ground color blue black, black, or dark olive with distinct or indistinct black spots; no red spotting. Ventral surface varies from deep blue to pale blue or green; in most specimens central part of each ventral scute irregularly blotched with Salmon-Orange or Capucine Orange. Blotching begins in anterior third of body and increases posteriorly. Maximum number of body scale rows, 19; always 19 at neck and thoracic regions; almost always 15 at posterior end of body, rarely 17. Ventral scutes range from 145 to 169 in males and from 138 to 167 in females; caudal scutes range from 70 to 89 in males and 64 to 82 in females" (Fox, 1951).

Color: A snake collected $2\frac{1}{2}$ miles west of San Bruno, San Mateo Co., Calif., Sept. 18, 1953, by Bill Reimer and Peter Thorngreen and loaned by Wade Fox, Oct. 19, 1953. The dorsal orange stripe is, on the neck, salmon-orange, 3 scales wide, beginning on the parietals as 2 small spots. On the body, this stripe is ochraceous-orange $\frac{1}{2} + 1 + \frac{1}{2}$ scales wide, and loses little of the intensity of color or prominence to the vent. On the tail, it is ochraceous-tawny. The lowest 3 lateral scale rows are saccardo's olive, the lateral stripe being formed by pale dull green-yellow upper edges of 2nd and 3rd rows. Between dorsal and lateral stripes are 2 rows of alternating black or fuscous-black to mummy brown spots, the upper ones square and larger, the lower smaller and round. The scales of the ground color between these spots are edged above with pale dull green-yellow like the lateral line. On the lower edges of 1st and 2nd rows of scales are 2 rows of black spots. The ends of the ventrals are olive-citrine, becoming in the middle portion courge green, and on the underside of the head light chalcedony yellow. The rear half of the venter becomes more dusky and on the midline of the tail is a line of chamois. The top of the head is olive, upper labials light yellowish olive, and lower labials clear dull green-yellow. The iris is chestnut brown with a thin lighter pupil rim. When held in hand, the 2 rows of dorsolateral spots show plainly, but the general appearance of the snake at ease is an orange-striped black (*atratus*) snake.

Habitat: In 1940 Fitch published an extensive statement, but doubtless it includes in part *T. e. terrestris* and *T. e. aquaticus:* "Habitat data are available for 84 individuals. Although these data are difficult to classify, it may be said that 30 snakes (about 36 per cent) were found away from the near vicinity of water, though usually in damp places where thick vegetation provided abundant shelter; 52 (about 62 per cent) were within a few yards of a permanent water supply, and most of these were in dense riparian growths. Only two snakes were seen in the water, and these were not foraging. Individuals were often alarmed in situations where they might easily have escaped into the water, but almost without exception they took refuge beneath plant cover or in holes in the ground. A few individuals were found in dry situations such as chaparral-covered hillsides, but none was found more than a few feet from thick vegetation. In ecologic preferences *atratus* is essentially restricted to meadows with high grass, to riparian thickets, and to clearings with second growth."

In 1951 Fox described its habitat thus: "*T. e. atratus* is basically an aquatic garter snake. Throughout its range there are not as many large rivers and swift streams as there are in the ranges of *hydrophila* and *couchii*. Most of the *atratus* specimens which I collected were taken in the vicinity of ponds, lakes, or small streams. This limited sluggish-water habitat may account for the fact that the body is shorter and stouter than it is in races like *hydrophila* which inhabit larger swifter streams. The different head shape of these two races may also be correlated with this difference in habitat, or possibly with the difference in feeding habits. *Hydrophila,* with a longer snout and jaw feeds mostly on fish, whereas *atratus* feeds chiefly on tadpoles and frogs. . . . I found no indication that the character of the vegetation is of any vital significance to these snakes. They occur in areas of dense vegetation and in areas of sparse vegetation such as Pinnacles National Monument."

Period of activity: Mar. to Oct. 1; MVZ dates are Jan. 1 to Dec. 2.

Breeding: Viviparous. Males 308–604 mm., females 380–590 mm. *Young*— Before Fox's 1948 study the only evidence of small ones we could find was: 1, Mar. 17, 1909, 212 mm., Williams; 1, Apr. 7, 1911, 225 mm., Slevin; 1, May 22–26, 1911, 186 mm., Slevin.

"Eleven broods of *atratus* ranged from 4–14 and averaged 6.4 young per brood. It is difficult to decide whether the difference in number of young between the two species (*ordinoides* and *atratus*) is a specific difference in itself, or merely a result of the larger size attained by *atratus*" (Fox, Calif., 1948). The size of hatchlings is unrecorded. In his study of the effect of temperature on the development in *T. e. atratus*, Fox (1948a) placed 12 ♀ s in a cool room and 12 ♀ s in a warm one. In the 1st and 2nd weeks in August, 8 broods appeared (108 individuals); in the 1st and 2nd weeks in September, 3 broods appeared.

Food: Slugs, small rodents, salamanders, treefrogs, small snakes, lizards, birds, fish. Thompson (Calif., 1917), Burt and Burt, Fitch (Gen., 1940).

Authorities:

Brown, A. E. (Gen., 1901; Calif., 1903, 1905)

Burt, C. E. and M. D. (Ariz., 1929)

Cooper, J. G. (Gen., 1860)

Cope, E. D. (Gen., 1900)

Fitch, H. S. (Gen., 1940, 1948)

Fox, W. (Calif., 1948, 1948a, 1951)

Grinnell, J., and J. M. Linsdale (Calif., 1936)

Grinnell, J., J. Dixon, and J. M. Linsdale (Calif., 1936)

Thompson, J. C. (Calif., 1914, 1915, 1917)

1905, A. E. Brown: "A collection of 20 or more living *E. elegans* received by the Zoological Society from Santa Cruz County, just south of San Francisco, contains 4 examples of the *vidua* color-form. These correspond with the one type of *atrata* in the Academy's collection, and with the detailed description of the two in the National Museum with which Dr. Stejneger had kindly supplied me."

1948: W. C. Fox (Calif.) concludes from the wealth of material from Del Norte County that "in view of the evidence presented in this paper it is necessary to make certain changes in the nomenclature of this group of garter snakes. The races *elegans, atratus, biscutatus, hueyi, vagrans, hydrophila, couchi,* and *gigas* are classified as subspecies of *Thamnophis elegans,* while *Thamnophis ordinoides* is considered to be a monotypic species."

1948, H. S. Fitch (Gen.): "As a somewhat parallel example, *atratus* and *ordinoides,* closely similar and replacing each other geographically, have always been classed as subspecies, but recently findings by Fox (1948: 120) indicate that they actually overlap slightly in ranges without intergradation."

1953, A. H. and A. A. Wright: On Oct. 19, 1953, Wade Fox sent us a fine *T. e. atratus* black with a broad orange dorsal stripe. With it at hand we note that our original plate of *T. e. atratus* is correctly identified and that Van Denburgh's Plate 88 is within Fox's concept of *T. e. atratus.*

Klamath garter snake (8—Van Denburgh and Slevin 1918),
Cope's garter snake (2—Van Denburgh 1897)

Thamnophis elegans biscutatus (Cope) 1883. Fig. 223; Map 57

Other common names: Northwestern garter snake (1); Washington garter snake.

Range: Klamath lakes basin, upper Klamath River, Warner lakes basin in s. cent. Oregon and n.e. California.—Calif.; Nev.; Ore. *Elevation*—2,000 to 5,000 feet.

Size: Adults, 19–39 inches. Klauber's (Gen. 1943b) standard adult body length for 107 males and 95 females is 600 mm.

Distinctive characteristics: "Maximum number of scale rows on anterior portion of body 23 or 21, 5th (when 23 are present) of variable length; confined to anterior half of body; 6th extending posteriorly beyond mid-body;

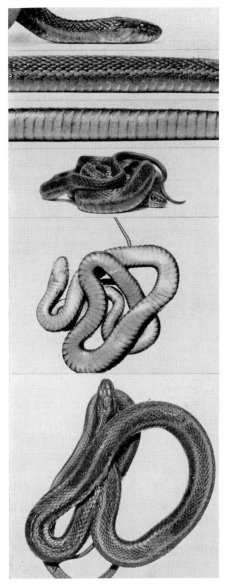

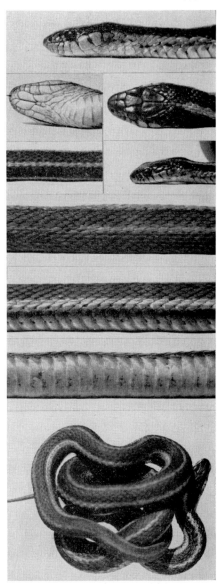

Fig. 222. *Thamnophis e. atratus,* San Francisco, Calif., L. M. Klauber.

Fig. 223. *Thamnophis e. biscutatus,* 5 miles west of Beatty, Ore.

4th extending more than ⅔ the distance to the anus; supralabials 8, 8; infralabials 10, 10; preocular frequently divided by horizontal suture on one or both sides; gastrosteges 184–160 (average for males 173.1, for females 166.1); dorsal stripe yellow and distinct, dorsal ground color dark brown, nearly black, in large part obscuring superimposed black spots; iris dark, heavily pigmented with narrow, pale, yellowish margin encircling pupil; size large (head and body length of 700 mm. often attained or exceeded); body thick in proportion to length" (Fitch).

Color: A large snake, with broken tail, from 5 miles west of Beatty, Ore., Apr. 6, 1942. The back is chaetura black, and if the skin is stretched, the 2 rows of alternating square spots show. The dorsal stripe is ochraceous-buff on the neck, but soon becomes buckthorn brown. The lateral stripe, obscure on the tail, is mustard or primuline yellow on the neck, becoming cream color and then light buff, but having the upper scale edges of primrose yellow with rows of black dots above and below it. There are similar but more obscure rows bordering the dorsal stripe, giving it a chain appearance instead of cleancut straight edges. The top of the head is bone brown, the prefrontals, internasals, and upper portion of rostral olive-brown. The upper labials behind the eye are pale olive-buff or tilleul buff, and ahead of eye light grayish olive with the lower part of rostral the same. Beginning with the 2nd upper labial, the upper portion of the suture is marked with black. The eye is almost black with a pupil rim of colonial buff. In 1 eye there is a patch of vinaceous-russet above the pupil; in the other is a wash of the same above the pupil. Below the lateral stripe the 1st scale row and ends of ventrals are drab, which color extends onto ventral plates as drab-gray. The cephalic end of each 1st-row scale bears a rather prominent black spot, and the front outer corner of each ventral a less prominent one. The underside of head and neck is white, followed by olive-buff, each ventral having a caudal edge of tilleul buff, and the whole venter washed with pale drab-gray.

Habitat: In 1883 Cope found this snake "in the swamp vegetation on the borders of the lake [Klamath]." In 1903 Brown placed this species at "Klamath Lake . . . where the rainfall is heavy." In 1922 Van Denburgh wrote: "Perhaps nowhere else in the world are snakes so abundant as formerly near Klamath Falls. We counted 180 on a small rock about a yard in diameter in Link River, and, at another point on the same river, caught 14 with one grab with both hands. . . . Most of these snakes are of this subspecies." In this connection the article "Snakes in Oregon" (*Science,* n.s. 2 (1934); 730–731), is pertinent: "In the vicinity of Klamath River, Klamath County, Oregon, a certain species of *Eutaenia* swarm by the scores, by the hundreds, and by the thousands. They are found mostly along the water courses in the grass or sunning themselves on the bare rocks or driftwood in the streams or on their banks." In 1940 Fitch characterized its habits and habitat thus: "All were found near margins of permanent streams or rivers. With few exceptions (8 individuals) these snakes were found within 10 feet of the water and many were in the water. Three were collected along the Sprague River in flat meadow-land. All others were taken along boulder-strewn stream edges in canyon bottoms."

Period of activity: *Early appearances*—Apr. 5, 6, 1942 (A.H.W.); MVZ's first date is April 14. *Fall disappearance*—Sept. 9, 1909 (Van Denburgh); MVZ's last date is Sept. 13.

Breeding: Viviparous. Males 490–797 mm., females 570–922 mm. *Young*— The only published note is that of Fitch: "That the breeding season may extend over several weeks in a given locality was indicated by the fact that 2 large female *biscutatus* of approximately the same size gave birth to broods on Aug. 13, 1934, and Sept. 13, 1934, respectively. Both were collected at Klamath River near Keno, Klamath County, Oregon, on July 29, 1934, and in captivity were kept together under exactly the same conditions." These notes we made in 1942: The Museum of Vertebrate Zoology has young born Sept. 8, 1934, that are 217, 217, 226, 226 mm. long. It also has the mother (No. 18086), taken July 5, 1934, which bore young in May, 1935. The California Academy of Science has specimens measuring 230, 235, 260, 275, 276 mm.

Food: Fish, toads, frogs, leeches, lamprey. Fitch, Van Denburgh (1922).

Field note: Apr. 8, 1942: Klamath Falls Chamber of Commerce and the snake postcard. We hear of a picture postcard purported to be of Klamath Falls showing a wagon load of snakes heaped to overflowing and squirming off at all sides and all angles. Although we can't blame them, unfortunately the Chamber of Commerce took these cards so thoroughly out of circulation that we couldn't find one. What a collection and how much "food for thought" the load would have provided!

Authorities:

Brown, A. E. (Calif., 1903)   Ruthven, A. G. (Gen., 1908)
Cope, E. D. (Ore., 1884)   Van Denburgh, J. (Gen., 1897, 1922)
Fitch, H. S. (Gen., 1940)

1940: H. S. Fitch excluded the *vagrans* forms of Puget Sound and his *hydrophila* material from s.w. Oregon and n.w. California from the *biscutata* range. We believe he proceeded wisely.

1942, A. H. and A. A. Wright: With difficulties in identifying Warner Lake and extreme s.e. Oregon material, and remembering Ruthven's comment that 2 preoculars are present sometimes in specimens found along the w. edge of the Sierra Nevadas and n. to British Columbia, we believe this name should be restricted to Klamath Lake and adjoining areas. We cannot hold it to be the most distinctive of the *elegans* group, as Cope once believed.

Couch's garter snake (6—Cooper 1896),
Sierra Nevada garter snake

Thamnophis elegans couchi (Kennicott) 1859. Fig. 224; Map 58

Other common names: Black water snake; Couch water snake; fish snake; giant garter snake (6—Van Denburgh 1922); moccasin garter snake.

Range: From the foothills of the great valley of California over the Sierra Nevadas into Douglas and Washoe Cos., Nev.—Calif.; Nev. *Elevation*— 600 to 5,000 or more feet. 600 and 1,000 feet (Grinnell, Dixon, and Linsdale); 4,500–4,900 feet (Linsdale, Nev., 1938–40); 600–7,750 feet (Van Denburgh); 3,900, 3,900, 4,400, 5,900, 6,000, 6,000 feet (Fitch, Gen., 1940).

Size: Adults, 17–42 inches.

Klauber's (Gen., 1943b) standard adult body length for 15 males and 16 females is 500 mm.

Distinctive characteristics: "Maximum number of scale rows on anterior part of body ordinarily 21 (rarely 23), the 5th (when 21 are present) continuous from head back to midbody; supralabials 8, 8; infralabials 11, 11 (or reduced to 10 on one or both sides); preocular often divided; dorsal stripe dull yellow suffused with dusky coloring, usually absent on posterior part of body and on tail; lateral stripes distinct, dull yellow; dorsolateral area between dorsal and lateral stripes brown with 2 rows of alternately placed black spots usually larger than interspaces so that their corners overlap slightly; these spots tend to be square; supralabials brownish superiorly, pale inferiorly, marked posteriorly with black areas which do not form typical triangular wedge marks but are elongated and may tend to form a longitudinal bar; top of head brown; infralabials and genials often marked with black; ventral surface ochraceous, often heavily marked with black; lower postocular and region behind corner of mouth pale, contrasting with dark color or other portions of head; gastrosteges average more than 176 in males and more than 172 in females, posterior labials relatively small, 6th often convex posteriorly and rounded on its upper hind corner; anterior height of nasal markedly exceeds combined contact of both internasals with rostral; muzzle long and pointed; head narrow posteriorly; eye relatively large, often protruding beyond profile of labials as seen from dorsal view; iris yellowish brown, pupil small, its diameter exceeded by width of iris" (Fitch, Gen., 1940).

Color: A snake from Yosemite Museum given us by A. Harwell, July 22, 1934. The background of the back is dark olive-gray down to the 3rd row of scales, where there are olive-buff interspace lines, though they are not sufficient to form a lateral stripe. There is a faint dorsal stripe of cinnamon-buff on the neck for about 1½ inches. On either side of the back are 2 obscure rows of alternating square black spots. From the 3rd row of scales extending some distance onto the belly plates is a clear area of deep olive or citrine-drab. The top of the head is deep olive with an olive-buff parietal suture spot. The upper labials are deep olive or citrine-drab, with the sutures of both upper and lower labials margined with black except between the 6th and 7th. The iris is wood brown or pinkish cinnamon. The lower side of the head is cartridge buff succeeded by pale pinkish buff, which in turn on the body becomes orange-cinnamon and on the tail verona brown. Most of the ventral plates have black suture borders extending across the belly but most prominent toward the sides. Down midbelly are clusters of dark specks. The type of belly coloration suggests *Thamnophis e. vagrans*.

A snake from King's River caught on a trip with L. F. Hadsall, R. H. Boyer, and G. A. Faris, Apr. 22, 1942. The general color is black or dark olive. There is a slight suggestion of a honey yellow dorsal stripe for about an inch. The lower labials and to a less extent the upper are olive with a touch of buffy olive, and all labial sutures more prominently black than in *T. e. gigas*. The outer edge of the iris and rim of pupil are fuscous with intermediate ring of smoke gray suffused with fawn color. The underside of the head is pale dull green-yellow, becoming on 1st ventral and gular plates light chalcedony yellow. After the 1st 5, the ventrals have heavy black front borders, and after about 20, the entire ventral surface is black except for a very narrow posterior edge of light olive-gray.

Habitat: In 1918, in the days when this form included the recent *T. e. gigas*, Van Denburgh and Slevin wrote: "It ascends the valley of the Kern River to an altitude of some 6,000 feet, and, doubtless, crosses through Walker Pass to the east side of the Sierra Nevada where it occurs in Owens Valley and about Pyramid Lake and Lake Tahoe." In 1924 Grinnell and Storer (Calif.) found it in the "meadows of Yosemite Valley." In 1930 Grinnell, Dixon, and Linsdale found that "these snakes frequented brush and driftwood at the edges of streams." In 1949 Fitch (Calif.) recorded that "subsequent findings at the Experimental Range (Fitch *1941*) indicated a wider range of tolerance for drought conditions than had been recognized before, since most of the foothill streams, supporting abundant populations, went dry in early summer. During the hot, dry months of summer and early fall the snakes were rarely seen, even in the streamside situations where they abounded in late March, April, May, and early June. In two small reservoirs where water remained, a few were in evidence throughout the summer, but there were no striking concentrations. Evidently most of the garter snake population remained through the dry season in the vicinity of creek beds, but became much less active, prowling in the sheltered, damp situations where amphibians might be found."

This species, described from Pitt River, Calif., is from a region variously described as the California Sierra Nevada district, east edge of the San Joaquin district, the edge of the great valley (Mulford, Ecol., 1937–38), and the Sierra Nevada edge of the California trough (Fenneman, Ecol., 1931).

Period of activity: *First appearance*—Apr. 24, 1939 (Fitch, Calif., 1949). MVZ dates are Mar. 27 to Dec. 3.

Breeding: Viviparous. Males 430–580 mm., females 440–900 mm. Previous to 1949 the smallest specimens we could find were 272, 273, 356, and 386 mm., surely far beyond hatchling size. In 1949 Fitch (Calif.) wrote: "Breeding in *T. e. couchii* probably occurs in early spring, and the new born young may appear in late July, considerably earlier than the young of other local snake species. They then have as much as 3 months for feeding and growth before entering their first hibernation." The smallest snakes he had for his growth study and size and sex groups were 201–250 mm.

Food: Fish, amphibians. Fitch (1940, 1949).

Field notes: Apr. 22, 1942: with Dr. L. F. Hadsall, R. H. Boyer, and G. A. Faris we went up King's River road. In one place beside the road saw two *T. o. couchi.* Caught one of them. The Couch's garters are in grass at stone's edge. In Sycamore Creek, where Hadsell once got me *T. o. couchi,* we took two small ones along the bank. One of the boys found a dead one with a pronounced lateral stripe. It was 3 ft. long and had a vinaceous *"hydrophila"* cast to the venter with blackish down the middle.

Authorities:

Brown, A. E. (Calif., 1903)
Fitch, H. S. (Gen., 1940; Calif., 1949)
Grinnell, J., J. Dixon, and J. M. Linsdale (Calif., 1930)
Kennicott, R. (Gen., 1859)
Stejneger, L. (Calif., 1893)
Van Denburgh, J. (Gen., 1922)
Van Denburgh, J., and J. R. Slevin (Gen., 1918)

Back in the past, this form was sometimes confused with *T. e. hammondi, T. e. elegans,* and *T. e. vagrans,* and it was supposed to intergrade with the last two.

Giant garter snake (6—Van Denburgh and Slevin 1918), Couch's garter snake

Thamnophis elegans gigas Fitch 1940. Fig. 225; Map 58

Range: Floor of Great Valley of California from Sacramento and Antioch southward to Buena Vista Lake. *Elevation*—Sea level to 500 feet or more.

Size: Adults, 29–57 inches.

Distinctive characteristics: "Maximum number of scale rows on anterior part of body usually 23, of which the 5th on each side is of variable length and usually short, 21 rows continuous from head posteriorly well beyond mid-body; supralabials 8, 8; infralabials 10, 10 or occasionally 11 on one or both sides; gastrosteges fewer than 170 in males and fewer than 165 in females; size large (largest form of the genus), with a head and body length in adults often exceeding 700 mm., occasionally exceeding 1000 mm.; ground color dull brown; dorsolateral black spots reduced in size and well separated;

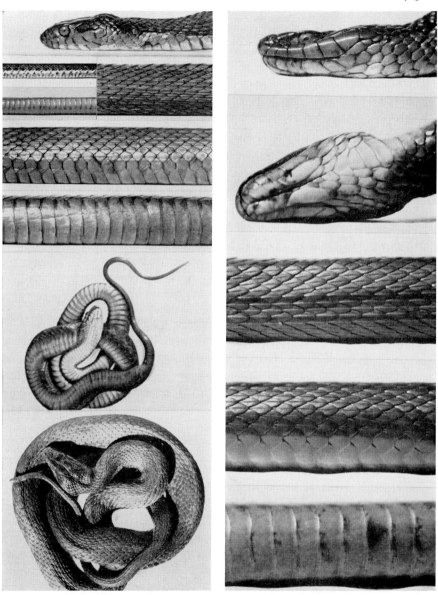

Fig. 224. *Thamnophis e. couchi:* 1,4–8, Yosemite Park, Calif., C. A. Harwell; 2, born in Ithaca of ♀ 1; 3, Swamp Lake, Tuolomne Co., Calif., C. H. Brown.

Fig. 225. *Thamnophis e. gigas,* 2 miles north of Richvale, Calif.

head brown with no contrasting facial markings; parietal spots absent or faint; ventral surface brownish; lateral stripe often not developed; head elongate, narrow posteriorly, with pointed muzzle" (Fitch).

Color: A snake from near White's bridge crossing of the Fresno slough near Fresno, Calif., Apr. 20, 1942. The general ground color is saccardo's olive or buffy olive. The dorsal stripe is weak, heavily encroached on by the ground color, barely perceptible in the posterior portion, and gone on the tail. Toward the neck it is olive-ocher soon becoming isabella color. The scales of the lateral stripe are buffy olive with edges of reed yellow. Above the lateral stripe is a row of black spots made up of black edges of 2 adjoining scales of ground color. Then follows an interval of 3 scale rows of ground color; then the 9th, 10th, and 11th rows have black edges so arranged as to form oblique dark areas 3 scales wide with equal intervals of ground color. In the 11th row these spots interrupt the outline of the dorsal stripe, are weak on rear of body and absent from tail. The top of the head and the face are buffy olive, the parietal spot obscure and with a black margin. On outer middle of parietal, on parietotemporal edge of 2nd row, and on temporolabial edge of 2nd and 3rd rows are black spots. The upper and lower labials are deep olive-buff with posterior margins at sutures with threads of black. The iris on its outer portion is buffy olive, but around pupil below and in front is a broad band of reed yellow replaced close to the pupil by deep colonial buff. The throat plates and chin shields are chartreuse yellow passing through light grape green and vetiver green to andover green under the tail. On the body proper the above colors are only in the center of the venter, and the color of the 1st scale row, saccardo's olive or buffy olive, extends onto ventrals for some distance. Note: Scale rows 23.

A big snake from 2 miles north of Richvale, Calif., caught in the road Apr. 11, 1942, hasn't enough scale rows for a normal *T. e. gigas,* but it matches the color. Tom Rodgers, who worked with Fitch, pronounced it *T. e. gigas,* as we did in our field notes (see below) at that time.

Habitat: There are two records to be noticed, Van Denburgh and Slevin in 1918 and Fitch in 1940. The first: "Where conditions are favorable, these snakes often attain enormous size. No. 43256 measures 55½ inches, of which 12¼ inches represent the tail. No. 43259 has the same measurement to anus, but the tail is 1¼ inches shorter. These snakes were secured at Buena Vista Lake, where they live in patches of tules out in the lake and doubtless eat fish. Although they may be seen in considerable numbers sunning themselves on the broken-down tules, they are hard to shoot, for they are very shy and slide into the water at the least alarm. Several were seen which appeared to be larger than any secured by us. The largest specimens sometimes show no lateral lines or other markings. Specimens of similar size occur in the marshes of Los Baños."

The second: "On April 10, 1936, I hunted these snakes along irrigation canals between Buttonwillow and Tupman, Kern County. . . . Although they were fairly common, catching them by the usual method of stealthily approaching and seizing them by hand proved to be an impossibility, partly because of the habitat conditions under which the snakes were found, but chiefly because of their alertness and timidity. The canals where the snakes were seen were usually about 15 feet wide, with nearly vertical banks and with a current of slightly turbid water several feet deep. The banks were usually overgrown with tules, willows, and weeds, making it difficult to find the snakes. The 1st one seen was probably well over 4 feet in length. It was basking in a clump of dead brush over the water, but it took instant alarm upon sighting me about 30 feet distant, and plunged into the canal with a loud splash. . . . The wariness of these snakes is probably correlated with their open habitat. Water is usually shallow in this habitat; rocks and logs that might serve as shelter are absent both under water and along the shores; trees and bushes are absent along the edge of the water, and the snakes are not screened from view from above. Under these conditions they are in constant danger from herons, marsh hawks, and other predatory birds which might drop down upon them or seek them out in the shallow water. Alertness and wariness are perhaps more necessary to them than to snakes in upland habitats, which often are screened from view by overhanging vegetation, and which have tangles of brush, driftwood, boulders and deep pools immediately available for shelter. . . . In the region where it occurs soil temperatures are often so high that surface foraging would be impossible for a strictly diurnal snake; thus the aquatic niche is the only one open to snakes of this species. No member of the *elegans* group within the species occurs within the geographic range of *gigas*" (Fitch).

This form is distinctly of the great valley part of the Pacific semidesert (Shreve, Ecol., 1921) or trough of the Pacific border province or California trough (Fenneman, Ecol., 1931) or central California valleys (Mulford, Ecol., 1937–38) species.

Period of activity: *First appearance*—The MVZ dates are Apr. 15 to Nov. Some individual dates of this museum are: Apr. 15, 1936, Fitch at Dos Palos; May 16, 1914, H. C. Bryant at Gadwell; May 13, 1939, J. Davis at Los Baños.

Breeding: Viviparous. Males 500–740 mm., females 550–1,080 mm. The smallest specimen we have seen was 191 mm. (tail 73) long. It was taken Sept. 9, 1922. Was it a hatchling of the year?

Food: Fish, frogs, newts. Fitch.

Field notes: Apr. 20, 1942, with Dr. L. F. Hadsall and Culbertson: We had been so unsuccessful in getting *T. e. gigas* near Los Baños that we asked Hadsall and Culbertson about them. The latter said he went out Saturday, Apr. 18, with his class to White bridge across Fresno slough west of Fresno. Many giant garters there. Here he saw the snakes, which had climbed up on the dead tule masses. In one instance he counted 5 sunning themselves.

On approach they drop into the water. Along the slough they encountered one snake on a limb 15 or 20 feet above the edge of the slough. We started along this slough and could occasionally see the snakes, but we constantly heard them slithering down into the tules. We concluded it was useless to try to catch them in the tules. We started abreast, Culbertson at the edge of slough, Hadsall at the crest of the embankment, and I in between. Hadsall was 15 ft. from the edge of the water. Presently he yelled, "Here's one." We all appeared to help. On this same crest farther along in the grass was a second one. We returned along this crest. When we approached the old crest, there was Anna with another snake spotted at the base of a bush. This we pinned. It had a more distinct dorsal stripe.

Authorities:

Fitch, H. S. (Gen., 1940)
Van Denburgh, J. (Gen., 1922)

Van Denburgh, J., and J. R. Slevin (Gen., 1918)

1918, J. Van Denburgh and J. R. Slevin: "Garter snakes from the San Joaquin Valley and Lower Sierra Nevada have been referred usually to *T. vagrans* or *T. hammondii*. This has never been satisfactory, for, although the San Joaquin snakes resemble both these subspecies, they are not typical specimens of either, but rather may be said to combine characters of both."

1940, H. S. Fitch: *"T. o. gigas* may be regarded as a recent derivative of *couchii,* which has differentiated in response to the special set of environmental conditions obtaining on the floor of the Great Valley of California."

Southern California garter snake (3—Klauber 1934), California garter snake (12—Van Denburgh 1897)

Thamnophis elegans hammondi (Kennicott) 1860. Fig. 226; Map 58

Other common names: Hammond's garter snake (7—Cooper 1869); Pacific garter snake; water snake.

Range: W. California and adjacent Baja California, Mex.—U.S.A.: Calif Mex.: Baja Calif. *Elevation*—Sea level to 8,000 feet. 800–7,500 feet (Grinnell and Camp); coast to the fringe of the desert foothills as far as permanent water is present (Klauber, Calif., 1931b); ocean to desert foothills (Perkins, Calif., 1938); 800, 1,700, 4,500, and 8,000 feet (Atsatt, Calif., 1913); 5,500, 6,500 feet (Grinnell, Calif., 1908); 5,000–7,000 feet (Van Denburgh and Slevin).

Size: Adults, 16–42 inches. Klauber's (Gen., 1943b) standard adult body length is 450 mm. for 19 males and 25 females from northern Baja California and also 450 mm. for 168 males and 153 females from San Diego Co., Calif.

Distinctive characteristics: "Twenty-one rows of scales. Form rather slender; head long, narrow posteriorly; snout elongate and narrow, but rather obtuse. Postorbitals 3, the upper much the largest. Eight upper labials,

6th largest; its posteroinferior angle much elongated. No dorsal stripe; lateral stripe olive yellow on the 2nd and 3rd rows. Back uniform dark olive brown or blackish, without distinct spots. Abdomen whitish olive, lighter anteriorly, and a dark line along the middle posteriorly" (Kennicott). "The upper surface is dark with no central stripe. The side stripes are yellow and not always distinct. Above these stripes is a series of black squarish spots with yellowish spots between. Specks of white are found in both yellow and black spots. This side coloring is almost unnoticeable in old specimens, except when distended with food. The belly varies from dull yellow to dull orange-red" (Perkins, Calif., 1938).

Color: A snake from San Felipe Creek, Sentenac Canyon, Calif., from L. M. Klauber, Mar. 25, 1928. The upper parts are in general light brownish olive, brownish olive, or deep olive with no conspicuous alternating square spots. The usual 2 rows of square spots on either side of the dorsum show on the neck and forward part when the body is flexed. They are chestnut-brown or burnt umber. In general, one scale may be darker and alternate with another similar one of an adjoining row. When the skin is stretched, the dorsal scales reveal some light yellow-green interstices. There is a lateral stripe of naples yellow or warm buff with the centers of the scales ochraceous-tawny, tawny-olive, raw sienna, or cinnamon-rufous. Below the lateral stripe and extending onto the ventrals is a grayish olive or deep grayish olive area. There is a small black spot on every other scale of the 1st scale row. This series of spots is close to the ends of the ventrals. On either side of the neck is a postparietal or lateronuchal spot, narrow and elongate, of chestnut-brown, burnt umber, or almost black which borders above the naples yellow of the lower neck. The top of the head is dark greenish olive. The minutely dark-edged parietal spot is colonial buff or primrose yellow. The lower labials and some upper labials are ecru-olive, light yellowish olive, or grayish olive with black sutures. The iris is cartridge buff with a wash of pale pinkish buff, succeeded by a circle of benzo brown or dark vinaceous-drab. The upper edge of the iris is cinnamon or fawn color. The underside of the head and neck is chartreuse yellow, primrose yellow, or seafoam yellow. The centers of the ventrals are honey yellow to chamois, ochraceous-buff, or light orange-yellow. The subcaudals are citrine-drab with the meeting of the plates on the middle line forming an irregular line of deep olive or dark olive. The black spots on the ends of the ventrals are revealed only when the body is flexed.

Habitat: In 1938 Perkins wrote: "The Garter Snake is never far from water, into which it dives at the first sign of danger. If not caught before entering the water, the chances are in favor of the snake, which swims to the bottom or behind a clump of plants, and remains perfectly still until the search is abandoned."

Period of activity: *Early appearances*—Mar. 29–July 1, 1931; Mar. 16, 22,

28, Apr. 27, May 4, 6, 1925; May 15, June 2, 3, 1926; Apr. 9–17, 1927 (Linsdale). The "Sixteen Year Census" gives Jan., 5 snakes; Feb., 32; Mar., 169; Apr., 389; May, 507; June, 520; July, 394; Aug., 97; Sept., 68; Oct., 32; Nov., 15; Dec., 2. Total 2,230 (Klauber, Gen., 1939a). MVZ dates are Jan. 9 to Sept. 11.

Breeding: Viviparous. Males 373–729 mm., females 388–989 mm. *Young*—Number, 16–25. In 1930 Bogert recorded that "1 of these garter snakes found in a creek near Culver City gave birth to 16 young on September 8, 1928." In 1931(a) Klauber published this journal note: "Oct. 30, 1927. 25 young were born in captivity." The smallest specimens we have seen were 238 and 263 mm. long—quite manifestly beyond hatchling size.

Food: Fish, amphibians, earthworms. Yarrow and Henshaw, Van Denburgh, Grinnell and Grinnell, Bogert, Klauber (Calif., 1931a, 1934a), Von Bloecker (Calif., 1942).

Authorities:

Bogert, C. M. (Calif., 1930)

Fitch, H. S. (Gen., 1940)

Grinnell, J. and H. W. (Calif., 1907)

Grinnell, J., and C. L. Camp (Calif., 1917)

Kennicott, R. (Gen., 1860)

Klauber, L. M. (Gen., 1939a; Calif., 1924a, 1931a, 1934a)

Linsdale, J. M. (Baja Calif., 1932)

Perkins, C. B. (Calif., 1938, 1949)

Ruthven, A. G. (Gen., 1908)

Stephens, F. (Calif., 1921a)

Van Denburgh, J. (Gen., 1897)

Van Denburgh, J., and J. R. Slevin (Gen., 1918)

Yarrow, H. C., and H. W. Henshaw (Ariz., 1878)

Oregon gray garter snake (5—Fitch 1936)

Thamnophis elegans hydrophila Fitch 1936. Fig. 227; Map 58

Other common names: Moccasin; water snake.

Range: Coastal from Umpqua River in Oregon to Gualala River in California and inland to Shasta River and Sacramento Valley.—Calif.; Ore. *Elevation*—Sea level to 5,000 feet. 800, 1,400, 1,900 feet (Fitch, Gen., 1940); a specimen taken by Linsdale at Deer Lick Spring, Shasta Co., Calif., was from a 3,000-foot elevation.

Size: Adults, 14–29 inches, according to the describer, Fitch. In Oregon in 1939 Gordon gave 30 inches. Klauber's (Gen., 1943b) standard adult body length is 500 mm. for each of two series: (1) 49 males and 42 females from s.w. Oregon; and (2) 56 males and 58 females from Humboldt and Mendocino Cos., Calif.

Distinctive characteristics: "A member of the *couchii-hammondii* series within the species, having tendency toward reduction of maximum number of scale rows on body from 21 to 19; ground color gray, dorsal stripe present, and lateral stripe faint or absent" (Fitch, 1936).

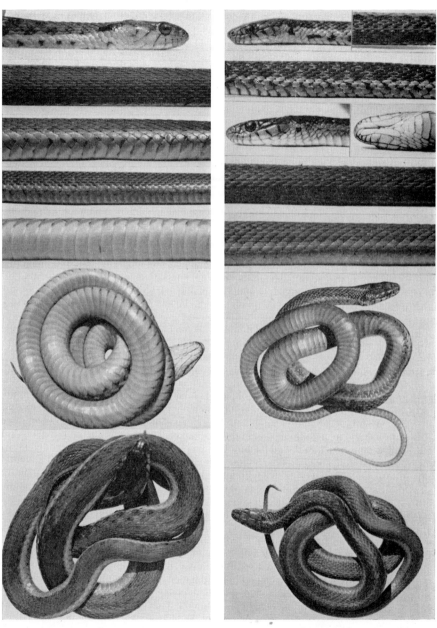

Fig. 226. *Thamnophis e. hammondi*: 1–3, 5–7, San Diego, Calif., C. B. Perkins; 4, Sentenac Canyon, San Felipe Creek, Calif., L. M. Klauber.

Fig. 227. *Thamnophis e. hydrophila,* Trail Creek, Ore., 4½ miles north of Trail.

Color: Two snakes from Trail Creek, Ore., 4½ miles n.w. of Trail (elevation 1,433 feet) where Route 227 crosses the creek, Apr. 8, 1942. The back of the larger snake is chaetura drab or fuscous. When the skin is stretched the 2 rows of alternating spots become evident because of flecks of pale veronese green on the edges of scales between the spots and also on the skin between. The middorsal stripe for about ½ an inch just back of the parietal is ochraceous-orange, then becoming a thin thread of yellow ocher to dresden brown. The lateral stripe on side of head and the gulars below angle of mouth are ochraceous-orange, the stripe soon becoming ochraceous-buff, and in the caudal half of body deep olive-buff. The top of head is uniform buffy olive, the preoculars, prenasals, postnasals, loreals, lower postoculars, and upper labials are tea green, the black suture lines of the last extending to the margin of the mouth. The iris is sandford's brown or cinnamon-rufous. The underside of the head is white or marguerite yellow, as are the first few ventrals. The center of the belly is vinaceous-tawny, becoming buff-pink on the tail. The first row of scales is citrine-drab, the skin between being prominently black. This citrine-drab extends onto the ventrals as oblique triangles with bases on their rear edges. Note—Posterior chin shields are much longer than anterior and are widely spreading.

On the smaller snake the 2 rows of square spots are very prominent. The dorsal stripe on the neck is baryta yellow.

Habitat: Most of our evidence comes from Fitch. In 1936 he wrote: "This snake is widely distributed and abundant within the area, but it is locally confined to the vicinity of permanent streams having rocky beds. I have collected altogether more than 120 specimens, mostly on boulders at the edge of the water, or in midstream or crawling and swimming among rocks under water, in search of food." In his 1940 monograph he wrote: "In its geographic distribution *hydrophila* coincides roughly with the area occupied by the "Klamath Mountain" system (Jepson, 1925: 10) of northwestern California and southwestern Oregon, including the Yolla Bolly, Scott, Salmon, Marble and Siskiyou Mountain ranges. This region is characterized by metamorphic rocks, mainly schists and granites, older and harder than the rocks found in most of the coast ranges, and predominantly gray, of probable significance in relation to the gray ground color of *hydrophila*. Throughout its range *hydrophila* is closely restricted to streams having rocky beds."

Period of activity: *First appearance:* May 15, 1936 (Linsdale); May 12, 1934 (Fitch); Apr. 15, 1936; Apr. 19, 1934 (Fitch). MVZ dates are Mar. 23 to Oct. 2.

Breeding: Viviparous. Males 330–580 mm., females 350–610 mm. *Mating*—Fitch (1940) recorded the following: "Several records are at hand for individuals of *Thamnophis ordinoides* mating in the wild, as follows: . . . Apr. 13, 1934, south fork of Cottonwood Creek, Tehama County, California (*hydrophila*). . . . On August 31, 1936, a captive male *hydrophila* showed unmistakable courting reactions toward a female of the same subspecies. Both had been collected about a month before at Trail Creek, Jackson County, Oregon. The female had given birth to a brood of young only 4 days before the courting behavior was observed. Copulation did not occur."

Young—The Museum of Vertebrate Zoology has young 225, 226, 230 mm. long, taken by Fitch, Apr. 19–May 12, 1934. One taken by Camp on July 5, 1913, measures 213 mm.; one taken Aug. 2, 1936 by Fitch measures 220 mm.; and one taken by Cook, July 1–12, 1940, measures 249 mm. On Trail Creek, Apr. 15, 1936, Fitch took a female which gave birth to young Aug. 27, 1936. Of MVZ No. 22331 we have the note, "7 young recently born."

Food: Fish, frogs, salamanders. Fitch (1936).

Field notes: Apr. 7, 1942: Went in evening to the home of Mr. and Mrs. Chester Fitch, Sr., parents of H. S. Fitch. What a lovely home overlooking so many pear orchards in bloom or approaching bloom. . . . He directed us to Trail Creek and said that he would later send us some *T. o. hydrophila* if we didn't get it this early in the season.

Apr. 8, 1942: Ate at Trail, Ore. The restaurant keeper said there were water snakes out of hibernation. We went along looking at all kinds of places. . . . Came to 61808.2 bridge. Just before it I asked a man about the snakes, whether they were here and whether they were out. He said he called them water moccasins and that they could swim in the water. I had no more than finished my conversation when 50 yards ahead of me, my discouragement was over. Here spread out on the edge of a large stone, next to water edge was my game. It was easily *T. o. hydrophila*. Took no chances— approached so slowly. I pinned him with my right stick and my left hand at the same time, both landing simultaneously. Had to have it. When I saw the underside there was no mistaking it for *biscutatus*. The rusty or vinaceous red belly is outstanding. Rows of spots, faint dorsal stripe and little pale green fleck were all apparent when it was on the rock. 4:10 P.M. Left car at bridge. Anna stayed at the bridge. Above this bridge some distance about 5 feet from edge, a snake started for creek, but went under a large stone 2 ft. from water. I turned over the stone toward the water as a barrier and caught snake coiled under the rock. Hurrah! the second one! Big as life, I returned to the bridge to find Anna all agog. Excitedly she asked, "What is my surprise?" Never meaning it, I said, "Have you *Rana boylii* eggs?" "Yes, I saw them laid," said she.

Authorities:

Fitch, H. S. (Gen., 1940; Ore., 1936)   Van Denburgh, J., and J. R. Slevin
(Gen., 1918)

Coastal California garter

Thamnophis elegans terrestris Fox 1951. Fig. 228; Map 59

Range: "Narrow strip along California coast from Santa Barbara County northward around east side of San Francisco Bay, continuing along coast to Oregon border. Range essentially that given by Fitch (1940) for *Thamnophis ordinoides atratus*" (Fox, Calif., 1951).

Distinctive characteristics: "Slightly stout garter snake with blunt, short snout; internasals shorter than wide, blunt anteriorly, and in broad contact with rostral; rostral broad; upper labials appreciably taller in region of 6th and 7th. Usually 8 upper labials and 10 lower labials, but not infrequently 7 and 9, respectively. Preoculars characteristically single but occasionally divided. Most frequently 3 postoculars, although 2 and 4 may occur. Dorsal stripe yellow or yellow orange; appears to occupy exactly ½–1½ scale rows, but appearance of regularity created by covering of the outer half of 2 lateral rows by uppermost row of dorsolateral black blotches. Consequently, on many specimens, scales of lateral rows between consecutive blotches [are] either yellow on both sides of keel, or red or olive on outer half. In specimens with essentially black dorsolateral region almost every scale of 2 lateral rows [is] black on outer half. Lateral stripes conspicuous, dull olive-yellow, but frequently varied amounts of red spotting superimposed on this. Top of head usually olive brown or dark olive with small amount of black on parietals; upper labials pale yellow to olive-buff; lower labials and chin approach cream buff. Iris brownish or sepia, sometimes appearing yellowish gray. Dorsolateral region either reddish brown with 2 distinct rows of regularly alternating black blotches and, at times, additional red spots; or black, dark olive or olive-brown with more or less indistinct black blotches. In reddish-brown individuals frequently interscale color outside of black blotches also reddish; otherwise these areas between blotches form characteristic interscale light spots. At Dillon Beach, Marin County, small numbers of individuals with blue-gray color phase occur; blue-gray ventral surface and dorsolateral regions apparently the only difference between these individuals and those with normal coloration. Ventral surface varies from pale shades of green to blue, with various amounts of red spotting. A few specimens lack red, but most have at least a few flecks somewhere on body. Scale rows at neck almost always 19, rarely 21; maximum number in body region either 19 or 21, rarely 21; maximum number in body region either 19 or 21; at posterior end of body characteristically 17, in rare instances 15. Ventral scutes range from 148 to 178 in males, 146 to 178 in females; caudal scutes from 71 to 90 in males, 61 to 88 in females. These numbers vary considerably in different parts of range" (Fox, Calif., 1951).

Color: A snake from San Francisco Co., Calif., received from Slevin, Sept., 1940. The dorsal background is mahogany red or brazil red, marked with a straw yellow or primrose yellow middorsal stripe 1 whole and 2 half scales wide. There is a pale glaucous-green lateral stripe on the 2nd and half of 3rd scale row. Below this, the 1st lateral row of scales and ends of ventrals are grayish olive with a few flecks of brazil red. Every alternate scale of this row has a black forward tip. The tip of each adjoining ventral and the interstices are black. Between the dorsal and lateral stripes are 2 rows of alternating black or mummy brown spots on 6½ rows of scales. The upper row is more elongate than deep and lies snugly against the mid-dorsal stripe. On the rear half of body, these spots almost merge, giving a dark border to the dorsal stripe. The lower row is about 3 scales deep and about 1½ scales long. The top of head, facial plates, and temporals are olive or deep olive. There are 2 black nuchal spots. The upper and lower labials are light lumiere green with black sutures between 4th and 5th and 6th. The underside of head and lower part of rostral are light lumiere green. The iris is black with pupil rim of ivory yellow. The belly is light niagara green, its center flecked with dusky bluish green. This flecking begins ahead of the first third of the body and is heaviest on the rear, with very little or none on the tail. Amongst this dusky bluish green are some flecks of brazil red. The underside of tail is water green or corydalis green.

Originally our color description and plate of *T. e. atratus* were from a Slevin specimen which we considered coloration type C of Van Denburgh's *T. o. atratus*. This now becomes positively Fox's new *T. e. terrestris*. He sent us on Oct. 19, 1953, a beautiful specimen which was taken Sept. 18, 2½ miles west of San Bruno, San Mateo Co., Calif., by William Reimer and Peter Thorngreen.

Wandering garter snake (36—Cronise 1868),
Western garter snake (6—Bailey 1913)

Thamnophis elegans vagrans (Baird and Girard) 1853. Fig. 229; Map 57

Other common names: (Gray) garter snake; Great Basin garter snake; green garter snake; large-headed striped snake; spotted riband snake.

Range: From coastal British Columbia s. on w. border of the Great Basin to Owens Valley; e. across Nevada to n.w. New Mexico; n. in the Rockies to s.w. South Dakota; n.w. across Saskatchewan into Alberta, Can.—U.S.A.: Ariz.; Calif.; Colo.; Ida.; Mont.; Neb.; Nev.; N.M.; Ore.; S.D.; Ut.; Wash.; Wyo. Can.: Alta.; B.C. *Elevation*—1,000 to 10,500 feet. 2,000 feet (Blanchard, Wash., 1921); 2,200–8,500 feet (Linsdale, Nev., 1938–40); 3,500, 3,500–6,000, 6,000+ feet (Little, Ariz., 1940); 4,000–9,500 feet (Bailey, N.M., 1913); 4,100, 4,300, 5,000, 5,000, 6,000, 7,800, 8,000, 8,400 feet (Taylor, Nev., 1912); 6,000–10,000 feet (Brown, Gen., 1901)?; 5,300, 5,800, 8,000 feet (Stejneger, Ida., 1891); 7,600, 8,000 feet (Ruthven, Ut., 1932); 7,600 feet (La Rivers, Nev., 1942); 7,000, 8,000 feet (Cary, Colo., 1911); 9,000 feet (Stej-

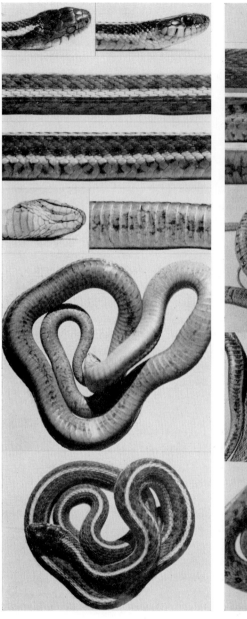

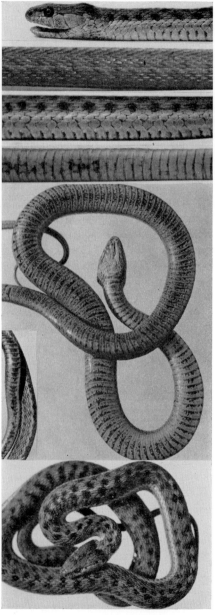

Fig. 228. *Thamnophis e. terrestris,* San Francisco, Calif., J. R. Slevin.

Fig. 229. *Thamnophis e. vagrans:* 1,3,5,7, Oak Creek Canyon, Delta, Utah, L. M. Klauber; 2, Jackson Hole, Wyoming, Mr. and Mrs. A. B. Klots; 4, Winslow, Ariz., W. Chapel; 6, Pullman, Wash., D. J. Leffingwell.

neger, Ariz., 1890); 9,000, 10,000, 10,500 feet (Rodeck, Colo., 1936); 10,000 feet (Van Denburgh, N.M., 1924b); (Blair, Colo., 1951); 1,000–7,300 feet (Ferguson, Ore., 1952).

Size: Adults, 12–36 inches. Klauber's (Gen., 1943b) standard adult body length for 66 males and 73 females is 500 mm. Hebard's (Wash., 1950) sizes of sexually mature snakes are: males' body length 380–510; tail length 130–170 mm.; females' body length 460–615, tail length 128–178 mm.

Longevity: 3 years (Mrs. R. B. Alves).

Distinctive characteristics: A customary way of describing this common variable snake is: lateral stripe on 2nd and 3rd row of scales; 8 upper labials; dorsal stripe faint, discontinuous, invaded, or absent; venter gray with some black in mid-venter, etc. Fitch in 1940 described it well for Pacific coast states, but it does not portray the species in its widespread distribution. Possibly some day someone will derive the *elegans* complex rather from *vagrans* than from the high mountain species center. Sometimes it has no black specks or black on venter; sometimes it has anal plate divided like *Natrix;* and so it goes.

Color: A snake from El Paso, Tex., 1925. The upper parts are citrine-drab with 3 rows of squarish spots of black or olive-brown. The dorsal stripe is barium yellow, becoming light grayish vinaceous a short distance back of the head. The lateral stripe is like the dorsal with interscale skin of light dull green-yellow. Below the lateral stripe is an area of hair brown to light drab with interscale skin of black. There is a black transverse band across the neck, ahead of which, the top of the head is yellowish olive or deep olive. There is a sulphur yellow spot in front of the eye on the preocular area. The upper labials are light drab with the upper rear corner of each blackish. The iris is army brown with a pupil rim of chamois. The chin is white. The ventrals on their cephalic edges are black or dusky slate-violet in the middle, followed by smoke gray and this in turn by light drab.

We had 12 snakes from William Chapel caught in the Hart Canyon region of Arizona. These varied greatly. Several suggest *T. angustirostris* at first glance, but have 4 instead of the 6 rows of spots of that form.

The larger of two snakes from Steen Mts., Ore., received from Donaldson, Aug. 6, 1936, through Stanley Jewett, Jr. The back is brownish olive, the dorsal stripe indistinct, being dark olive-buff in front and deep olive-buff, avellaneous, or vinaceous-buff toward the rear. The lateral stripe is deep olive-buff. The 1st row of scales and the edge of the 2nd row are light brownish olive, brownish olive, or drab. The top of the head is hair brown. The upper labials are grayish olive. The rear 3 or 4 of the lower labials are somewhat tinged with the same color. The iris is olive-brown, lower portion being somewhat grayish olive. The pupil rim is chalcedony yellow. The chin and lower side of the head are white or pale olive-buff. The ventral surfaces are mineral gray with the ends of the plates deep grayish olive and the centers dull greenish black (2). These central spots are on the front margins of the ventral plates and toward the rear become light celandine green or deep medici blue. The underside of the tail is drab-gray or light drab.

Abnormal coloration—Tanner (Ut., 1929) reported melanistic specimens from Utah, and Svihla (Wash., 1936) reported an abnormally colored specimen. In 1947 Johnson (Wash.) mentioned spotted and unspotted specimens, and Hebard (1950) discussed a dimorphic color pattern. Frankly, this species throughout its range could well be called polymorphic in color.

Habitat: We have at least 35 to 40 habitat notes on this very widespread and common garter. Almost everyone places it in or near water. The tabulation follows: rivers 7 authors; streams 7; creeks 7; ponds 5; lakes 5; marshes 4 (marshy areas 2, ground 1, grassy 1); swamps 2; valleys 2; springs 2; meadows 2; dry ground 2; hole in ground 1; rodent burrow 1; water holes 1; sound 1; crater of peak 1; roadside pool 1; irrigating ditch 1; pool 1; cold bog 1; cultivated area 1; moist places—truly an aquatic form. This form occurs from the Upper Sonoran zone through the Transition to the Canadian zone.

Period of activity: *Early appearances*—Apr. 24, 1908, May, 1908, June 12, 1914 (Ellis and Henderson, Colo., 1915); May 22, 1910 (Ellis and Henderson, Colo., 1913). "In the spring these snakes occur in great numbers along streams, where they can be seen lying in clusters enjoying the warm sunshine after their winter's hibernation" (Pack). *Fall disappearance or appearances late in the season*—Sept. 14, 1934 (Knowlton, Ut., 1946); Oct. 5, 1915 (Grinnell and Storer, Calif., 1924); Aug. 12, 14, 17, 20 (Cockerell, Colo., 1910); Sept. 1-3, 1912 (Van Denburgh and Slevin, Ariz., 1913); Aug. 29-30, 1919 (Van Denburgh and Slevin, Ida., 1921b); Oct. 2 (Stejneger, Ariz., 1890); Aug. 4, 20, 30, Sept. 8, 18, 20, 22, 1890 (Stejneger, Ariz., 1891); Aug. 1, 1900, Aug. 24, 1903, Sept. 16, 1904, Aug. 23, 1904, Sept. 6, 1907, Aug. 23, 1909, Sept. 4, 1911 (Ellis and Henderson, Colo., 1913). *Hibernation*—"Winter is passed in a crevice or burrow usually in the bank of a stream. An abandoned muskrat burrow is an ideal place. Here they sleep, massed together in considerable numbers. A few years ago while plowing deeply along a creek bank on March 15, a muskrat burrow was opened up from which a mass of 35 snakes was removed. All sizes were represented" (Pack).

Breeding: Viviparous. Males 510-715 mm., females 588-974 mm. Common as it is, we find only 8 notes. *Young*—Number, 8-19. Time of birth, June 10-Sept. 10. Size, 5-7.7 inches. In 1912 Taylor in Nevada reported taking a female July 31 with eggs near hatching. In Colorado, Ellis and Henderson in 1913 recorded a female's giving birth to 10 young shortly after June 27, 1890. In Nevada, Richardson took 4 females with large eggs May 25-27, June 27, July 3 and 4. Five young specimens from Tallac taken June 10-24 had yolk scars. In 1915 Ruthven and Gaige in Nevada recorded 3 pregnant females having 8, 10, and 12 young on Aug. 25, Sept. 2, and Sept. 10. In 1930 Pack in Utah noted that the adults disperse after breeding. The next year Woodbury (Ut., 1941) found a female in Zion National Park giving birth to 14 young on Sept. 4. The small specimen, 259 mm., taken by Johnson July 23, 1937, in Grant Co., Ore., is seemingly considerably beyond hatching size. The smallest we have seen (1942) is Brigham Young University No. 320 taken Aug. 14, 1933, by Beck. It measures 122 mm. V. M. Tanner's brood of 16 was born July 29, 1944. They ranged from 167 to 192 mm. in length and from 1.4 to 2.4 grams in weight. Hebard (1950) reported 9–19 in broods of spotted and nonspotted young. His newborn males were 167–213 mm. long, females 168–215 mm.

Food: Fish, frogs, mice, young birds, lizards, earthworms, salamanders, and insects. Thirty or more authors have contributed to this topic, among them, Blair, Ellis and Henderson, Fitch, Grinnell and Storer, Hebard, Knowlton, Minton, Ortenburger and Freeman, Richardson, Ruthven and Gaige, Schonberger, Storm and Pimental, V. M. and W. W. Tanner, Taylor, Van Denburgh and Slevin, Wood, and Woodin.

Authorities:

Baird, S. F., and C. Girard (Gen., 1853)
Brooking, W. J. (Ore., 1934)
Cope, E. D. (Mont., 1872)
Coues, E., and H. C. Yarrow (Mont., 1878)
Cowan, I. McT. (B.C., 1937)
Fitch, H. S. (Gen., 1940)
Hebard, W. B. (Wash., 1950, 1950a, 1951a)
Linsdale, J. M. (Nev., 1938)
Lord, J. K. (B.C., 1866)
Pack, H. J. (Ut., 1930)

Richardson, C. H. (Nev., 1915)
Ruthven, A. G. (Gen., 1908)
Ruthven, A. G., and H. T. Gaige (Nev., 1915)
Stejneger, L. (Calif., 1893)
Tanner, V. M. (Ut., 1949)
Tanner, W. W. (Ut., 1949, 1950)
Van Denburgh, J. (Gen., 1922)
Van Denburgh, J., and J. R. Slevin (Gen., 1918)
Yarrow, H. C. (Gen., 1882–83; Ariz., 1875)

Mexican garter snake (9—Bailey 1913), Arizona garter snake (5—Ditmars 1907)

Thamnophis eques megalops (Kennicott) 1860. Fig. 230; Map 57

Other common names: Arizona ribbon snake; Emory's garter snake.

Range: Mountains and other elevated regions of w. Texas, w. through s.w. New Mexico and cent. Arizona; s. into Mexico along edge of plateau to s. Durango; e. through Guanajuato and San Luis Potosí to s. Hidalgo.— U.S.A.; Ariz.; N.M.; Tex. Mex.: Baja Calif.; Chihuahua; Coahuila; Durango; Guanajuato; Hidalgo; San Luis Potosí; Sonora. *Elevation*—3,000 to 8,000 feet. 4,000–8,000 feet (Bailey, N.M., 1913).

Size: Adults, 18–39 inches.

Distinctive characteristics: *"E. megalops* Kennicott. *Spec. char.* Form shorter and stouter, with proportionally shorter tail than in *E. proxima,* which this species resembles. Tail ¼ of the total length. Eye very large, greater than in *E. proxima.* First dorsal row of scales broader, each scale as high as long, and less strongly carinate. Dorsal stripe narrow, covering 1 and less than 2 half rows of scales. Color uniform brownish ash, with the 3 longitudinal stripes whitish yellow. Head olive ash" (Kennicott). "The subspecies is separated from *m. megalops* largely on the basis of caudal counts. In caudal counts of males, 95% of *m. macrostemma* have 78 or less while 93% of *m. megalops* have 79 or more; in females there is no overlap. In ventral count of females, 71% of *m. macrostemma* have 158 or less, while 70% of *m. megalops* have 159 or more; the overlap in males is complete. In total counts, of males, 95% of *m. macrostemma* have 242 or less, while 93% of *m. megalops* have 243 or more; in females of *m. macrostemma* 80% have 221 or less, while in *m. megalops,* 100% have 222 or more" (Smith, Gen., 1939a).

Color: A snake from Hart Canyon, Winslow, Ariz., received from W. C. Chapel, Lakeside CCC Camp, Oct. 1, 1933. The dorsal stripe starts at the head as seafoam yellow or cartridge buff, soon becoming ecru-olive or grayish olive. The lateral stripe on the 3rd and 4th scale rows, or on the 3rd and the lower half of the 4th, is smoke gray or much like the belly color. Between these stripes are 2 rows of alternating, rather obscure dark spots. The more or less obscure interspace color is grayish olive. Below the lateral stripe, the scales are grayish olive with a vertical, broken Y or irregular black spot opposite the end of every alternate ventral plate. On the 1st 2 rows, the clear grayish olive areas and black spots are prominent. At the cephalic end of the dorsal stripe and 1 scale back of the parietals a black nuchal spot extends diagonally down either side to the 4th row of scales. The top of the head is deep olive or olive minutely dotted with black on the frontal and on the central portion of the parietals. This deep olive extends to the nuchal spots. Back of the last labials there is a postoral crescent of the same color as the lateral stripe or like the belly. The rostral and nasals are ecru-olive or grayish olive. The preoculars and upper labials are oural green, pale olivine or greenish glaucous. The upper labial sutures, the labiotemporal sutures, the front margin of the preocular, and the rear margin of the postocular are margined with black. The iris is mainly cinnamon-brown clouded with black, slightly tawny above and with a pupil rim of primrose yellow, pinard yellow, or antimony yellow. The underside of the head is white. The ventrals are lichen green, court gray, or pale dull glaucous-blue. The underside of the tail may be tinged as well with smoke gray or drab-gray. There is a small black spot near either end of each ventral adjoining the suture. Sometimes these spots stretch out as narrow black edges to the plates.

Habitat: Few notes are available. The shores, margins, and edges of lakes, pools, ditches, running streams, and stagnant pools have been recorded, but we need more information about this particular species. The last and best note is that of Woodin in 1950: "I have found this snake to be very common along the system of irrigation ditches near the Rillito wash north of Tucson. At one spot in particular 3 or 4 could generally be seen, lying above a valve controlling the flow of water out of a tank or artificial pond. When cornered, these snakes frequently flatten the body and lunge repeatedly at the intruder. Large specimens incline to considerable stoutness, and I have taken individuals at least 39 inches in length. I have never seen *T. e. cyrtopsis* in this valley habitat, nor have I ever taken *T. s. megalops* in a canyon or mountain stream locale. This difference in environment preference is quite striking in the Tucson area at least, although the two forms may quite possibly occur together in intermediate areas such as washes close to the mountain bases."

This Mexican highland form falls largely in Starker's (Ecol., 1950) temperate pine-oak forest, mesquite-grassland, and desert vegetation areas

Breeding: Viviparous. *Young*—The only note we know of is that of Woodin. His one sentence is therefore significant: "One brood of 25 *T. s megalops* was born June 15; the young averaged about 9½ inches."

Food: Fish, frogs. Van Denburgh and Slevin (Ariz., 1913).

Field notes: June 22, 1934, thru Ruby to Arivaca: In the middle of the creek saw the cast skin of *Thamnophis megalops* we probably lost Sunday. Nearby Anna espied a garter snake, but by the time I arrived, it had gone down.

June 25, 1942: Our 32d wedding anniversary. Today we went to Arivaca to catch *Thamnophis megalops*. I knew exactly where I saw two last time— 8 years ago. I go there, water almost gone. Right where it ought to be, it is— but a mummy, killed a week or so ago. Too bad. Went length of this creek and irrigation ditch. Saw plenty of meadow frogs. . . . To think we traveled 125 miles to get a mummy. So it is.

Authorities:

Cope, E. D. (N.M., 1886)
Ellis, M. M., and J. Henderson (Colo., 1913, 1915)
Franklin, D. (Ariz., 1914)
Kennicott, R. (Gen., 1860–61)
McLain, R. B. (Baja Calif., 1899b)
Myers, G. S. (Ariz., 1932)

Schmidt, K. P. (Baja Calif., 1922)
Smith, H. M. (Gen., 1939a, 1949a; Tex., 1949)
Van Denburgh, J., and J. R. Slevin (Gen., 1918; Ariz., 1913)
Woodin, W. H., III (Ariz., 1950)

1949(a): H. M. Smith used the name *T. subcarinata megalops* instead of *T. macrostemma megalops*.

1951: H. M. Smith (Tex.) used the name *T. eques megalops* instead of *T. subcarinata megalops*.

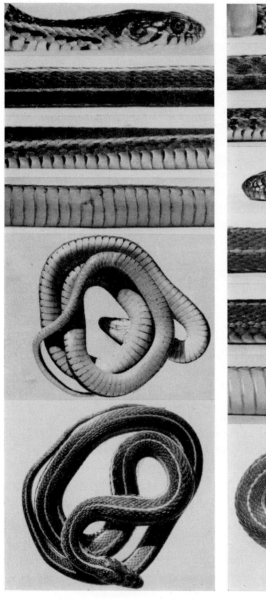

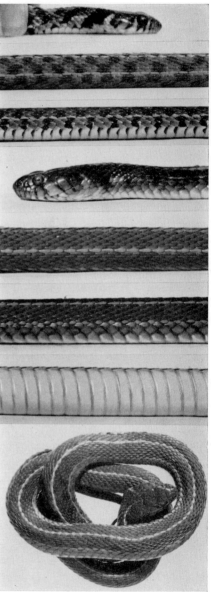

Fig. 230. *Thamnophis eques megalops,*
Hart Canyon, Winslow, Ariz., W. Chapel.

Fig. 231. *Thamnophis marcianus marcianus:* 1–3, Palo Pinto, Tex., P. Harter; 4–8,
Somerset, Tex., A. J. Kirn.

Marcy's garter snake (36—Yarrow 1875)
Spotted garter snake

Thamnophis marcianus marcianus (Baird and Girard) 1853. Fig. 231; Map 58

Other common names: Desert garter snake; garter snake (2—Strecker 1902); Marcy garter snake; mouse snake.

Range: From s. Oklahoma through cent. Texas to Mexico.—U.S.A.: Okla.; Tex. Mex.: Coahuila; Nuevo León; San Luis Potosí; Tamaulipas. *Elevation*—Sea level to 3,000 feet.

Size: Adults, 13–41 inches.

Distinctive characteristics: "Prominent color light brown; a vertebral paler line and one lateral on each side, more or less indistinct. Three series of square black spots on each side of about 56–60 in each series, from occiput to anus. Sides of head black, with a crescentic patch of yellowish posterior to the labial plates. Three and sometimes 4 black vittae radiating from the eye across the jaws. A double white spot with a black margin on the suture of occipital plates" (Baird and Girard, Gen., 1853). Dorsal scale rows 21-21-19-17. Ventrals (male) 146–158 (av. 152.4 ± 2.92), 155 or less in 88 per cent of specimens; (female) 140–162 (av. 149.1 ± 3.92), 155 or less in 95 per cent of specimens. Caudals (male) 64–81, 73 or more in 77 per cent of specimens; (female) 61–77, 72 or less in 89 per cent of specimens. Combined ventrals and caudals (male) 214–236 (av. 225 ± 5.38), 231 or less in 86.6 per cent of specimens; (female) 207–239 (av. 217.7 ± 6.31), 221 or less in 76 per cent of specimens. Supralabials 8-8, infralabials 10-10, preoculars 1-1, postoculars 3-3 or 4-4. Maxillary teeth 21–24, usually 23 or less; dentary teeth 27–29. Lateral stripe on 3rd dorsal scale row anteriorly, and on 2nd and 3rd, or 2nd only, posteriorly. Dorsal stripe occupying ½ or more of the vertebral scale row, and usually about half of each of the paravertebral scale rows. A yellowish postrictal crescent" (Mittleman).

Color: A snake from Rio Medina near Blue Wing Lake, Tex., Mar. 1, 1925. The dorsal stripe is warm buff or cream color except on the neck, where it is picric yellow. The lateral stripe is pale ochraceous-salmon or pale ochraceous-buff. There are 2 rows of alternating square black spots between the dorsal and lateral stripes and a 3rd alternating with the 2nd below the lateral stripe. The areas between the dark squares appear light yellowish olive, the scales being buffy olive in their centers and courge green on the outer edges. The top of the head is olive-green or yellowish olive with a parietal spot of picric yellow encircled with black. The nuchal collar is black with an area of sulphur yellow on the lateral stripe region and oil yellow in the interspaces. The iris is cinnamon-rufous or tawny above and below, dark or blackish in front and behind, with a pupil rim of light ochraceous-salmon. The labials and the under parts of the head are cartridge buff. The 3rd, 4th, 5th, 6th and 8th upper labials have black sutures. The edges of the ventrals are cartridge buff, the under parts in general deep olive-buff.

Habitat: With too little positive evidence at hand, we can say only that it is an inhabitant of creek and river edges and river bottoms and has a predilection for the vicinity of water.

Period of activity: *Early appearances*—Mar. 19, 1947 (Taylor, Tex., 1949); Mar. 1, Apr. 15, 1925 (A.H.W.). *Fall disappearance*—Nov. 6, 1946 (Taylor).

Breeding: Viviparous. Males 335–621 mm., females 322–887 mm. *Young*—About the only evidence we have is James McCallion's note (Tex.) of 1945: "There were 3 gravid females of this species in the collection. One gave birth to 18 living young on July 24, 1942. The 2nd gave birth to 16 young, 1 dead, on July 30, 1942. The 3rd gave birth to 12 young on Aug. 2, 1942. One young of the last litter differed in color and markings from the others in that the ground color was uniformly green instead of the usual black spots between the stripes." The smallest Marcy's garter we have seen was in Kirn's material in 1934. It was 200 mm. in length.

Food: Frogs, toads, fish, earthworms. Ditmars (Gen., 1907), Kirn. Amphibians, earthworms, lizards. Fouquette (Tex., 1954).

Authorities:

Bailey, V. (Tex., 1905)
Baird, S. F., and C. Girard (Gen., 1853; Okla., 1854)
Brown, A. E. (Gen., 1901)
Garman, S. (Tex., 1887)

Hartweg, N., and J. A. Oliver (Gen., 1938)
Mittleman, M. B. (Gen., 1949)
Shannon, F. A., and H. M. Smith (Tex., 1949)
Smith, H. M. (Gen., 1942b)

1905, V. Bailey: "There are specimens of this plain little striped snake from Brownsville, Santa Rosa Ranch (Cameron County), Corpus Christi, Victoria, Sequin, Sycamore Creek, Devils River, Paisano, and Boquillas. It is the common garter snake of the whole arid Lower Sonoran zone of western Texas, apparently reaching its eastern limit at Victoria."

Sonoran garter snake, Marcy's garter snake

Thamnophis marcianus nigrolateris (Brown) 1889. Fig. 232; Map 58

Range: From extreme s.w. Nebraska, w. Kansas, and n.w. Oklahoma through panhandle of Texas to Big Bend; s. into Chihuahua, Mex., w. to Sonora, Mex., and Colorado River Valley of California; e. across s. half of Arizona and New Mexico.—U.S.A.: Ariz.; Calif.; Kan.; Neb.; N.M.; Okla.; Tex. Mex.: Chihuahua; Durango; Sonora. *Elevation*—Sea level to 5,000 feet. 2,800 to 5,000 feet (Bailey, N.M., 1913); irrigated area in the Imperial Valley and the bank of the Colorado River (Klauber, Calif., 1931a).

Size: Adults, 12–36 inches. Klauber's (Gen., 1943b) standard adult body length for 16 males and 24 females is 500 mm.

Distinctive characteristics: "Essentially similar in all respects to *T. mar-cianus marcianus,* except as follows: ventrals (male) 153–173 (av. 161.1 ± 3.85), 156 or more in 93.5% of specimens; (female) 150–166 (av. 156.8 ± 3.21), 156 or more in 80% of specimens. Caudals (male) 69–82, 70 or more in 97% of specimens; (female) 62–83, 69 or less in 79.5% of specimens. Combined ventrals and caudals (male) 225–255 (av. 236 ± 5.85), 232 or more in 76.7% of specimens; (female) 213–241 (av. 225 ± 5.38), 222 or more in 74.5 % of specimens. Maxillary teeth 21–24, often 24" (Mittleman, Gen., 1949). That is, ♀ s ventrals 156 or more, caudals 69 or less; ♂ s ventrals 156 or more, caudals 70 or more.

Color: "A golden yellow stripe occupies the median row of scales from nape to tip of tail, widening slightly on the edges of the contiguous rows at the anterior end; a lateral stripe of same color, very indistinct anteriorly, where it is mostly confined to the 3rd row, but better defined on the posterior third of the body, where it invades the upper half of the 2nd. Color above the laterals, brownish-olive with 2 series of alternating dark spots (66 pairs, in this specimen from head to anus), the lower series on the 4th, 5th, and 6th rows, the upper on the 7th, 8th, and 9th, below the lateral lines, the 1st and lower half of the 2nd rows (anteriorly, occasionally to the lower half of the 3rd) with the ends of the abdominal scutellae, are lustrous pitch-black. The upper surface of the head in front of the occipitals is greenish-olive; behind that, to the neck and the sides of the head, including the 7th and 8th superior labials, blackish-brown, slightly maculated with dull chestnut just behind the occipitals; the dorsal yellow line being slightly indicated on the dark patch. Beneath white, with a creamy tinge anteriorly, becoming pale greenish on the subcaudals. The labials are margined with blackish-brown; a postoral cream-colored crescent with the concave side forward; a similar band passing down on the post-orbitals widens on the 6th upper labial and runs into the throat color and a third light band is indicated on the anteorbital, becoming lost on the 4th upper labial. Iris bright copper color" (Brown, Ariz., 1890).

Habitat: Before 1949 some of the habitats given were as follows: in a cultivated field on the bank of a wash, in vicinity of streams, in mud puddles, on the desert a mile or more from the river, at the edge of an irrigation ditch in a vegetable garden, and in a marshy pond. In 1949 Jameson and Flury in the Sierra Vieja Range, Tex., found that "this species seems to be restricted to the vicinity of more or less permanent water in the Plains belt, but it may extend up the stream bed association into the Roughland belt. Of 5 specimens taken on the Miller ranch, 2 at a lake in the tobosa-grama association, and 2 at a tank in the catclaw-cedar association, 4 were active on nights of light rain. . . . One specimen was taken early in the morning from the old field association of the Rio Grande district." In 1950 Woodin in Arizona wrote that "this snake can be collected during the daytime especially by turning over boards and the like, but it is essentially a night prowler. . . . It seems to prefer low drainage areas; I have never collected this snake in the mountains."

Period of activity: *First appearance*—Apr. 17, 22, 24, 25, 26, 29, 30 (Marr, 1944); Apr. 3, 1931 (T. C. Zschakke). *Fall disappearance*—Sept. 29 (Marr). MVZ dates are Mar. 21 to Sept. 2.

Breeding: Viviparous. Males 325–650 mm., females 350–700 mm. *Young*— For this race as for *T. m. marcianus* only one note is available. In 1950 Woodin in Arizona reported: "One brood of 12 was born July 5, the young averaging a little over 8 inches; another brood of 18, born July 15, averaged about 8 inches."

Food: Spadefoots, frogs, lizards. Ortenburgers (Ariz., 1927), Jameson and Flury, Woodin.

Authorities:

Brown, A. E. (Gen., 1901; Ariz., 1890)　　Ruthven, A. G. (Ariz., 1907)
Jameson, D. L., and A. G. Flury (Tex.,　　Van Denburgh, J. (Gen., 1922)
　1949)　　Van Denburgh, J., and J. R. Slevin
McLain, R. B. (Calif., 1899a)　　　　(Gen., 1918)
Mittleman, M. B. (Gen., 1949)　　Woodin, W. H., III (Ariz., 1950)

1901, A. E. Brown: *"E nigrolateris* A. Brown was based upon an individual from Tucson, the most striking character of which, apart from obvious abnormalities, was the extension of the preocular upward to meet the frontal. Since then I have examined several *marciana* which exhibit a tendency in this direction."

Puget garter snake (10—Fannin 1898), Red-striped garter snake

Thamnophis ordinoides ordinoides (Baird and Girard) 1852. Fig. 233; Map 57

Other common names: Black garter snake; Boyd's garter snake; Cooper's garter snake (Yarrow 1882); garter snake (6—Hardy 1927); narrow-headed garter snake (4); Pacific Coast garter snake; Puget Sound garter snake (4); small-headed striped snake; western garter snake.

Range: From Vancouver Island and mainland southward w. of Cascade Mts. to Del Norte Co., Calif.,—U.S.A.: Calif.; Ore.; Wash.　Can.: B.C. *Elevation*—Sea level to 4,000 feet.

Size: Adults, 14–26 inches, based on data from Thompson in 1917, Fitch in 1940, Fox and Fitch in 1948.

Period of activity: *Early appearances*—May, 1929 (Logier); Apr. 15, 1932 (Hart, B.C., 1934); May 20–27, 1935 (Fitch, Gen., 1940); late April and early May (Fox, Calif., 1948a); Apr. 20, 1940 (J. R. Slater); March 27 (MVZ). *Fall disappearance*—Aug. 27, 1921 (Patch, B.C., 1922); Dec. 4 (Newcome, B.C., 1931); Oct. 1, 1933 (Hart); Oct. 9, 1937 (Slater); Oct. 13 (MVZ).

Breeding: Viviparous. Males 244–527 mm., females 308–603 mm. Hebard

Fig. 232. *Thamnophis m. nigrolateris:* 1–5, Peña Colorada, southwest of Marathon, Tex.; 6,7, Toyahvale, Tex.

Fig. 233. *Thamnophis ordinoides ordinoides,* Corvallis, Ore., Dr. and Mrs. K. Gordon and authors.

(Wash., 1950a) gives sexually mature males as 388–605 mm. and females as 450–717 mm. *Young*—We regret that Fox in his two fine 1948 studies of *T. ordinoides* and *T. e. stratus* did not give us the number of young, the size at birth, or the time of birth. Of *T. ordinoides* he had 22 broods and of *T. e. stratus* 13. In the Stanford University Museum we have seen 2 specimens, one 115, the other 120 mm., which looked to be embryos. Slater has a specimen, No. 3308, 153 mm. long, from north of Victoria, B.C. On Sept. 5, 1899, Allen and Burcham took one 155 mm. long from Chetwood and Silet River. On Sept. 3, 1890, near Philomath, Burcham took a 165-mm. specimen. On Aug. 13, 1925, Klauber received from Blairs, Wash., a 186-mm. specimen and on the same day from Tacoma, Wash., a 188-mm. specimen. The California Academy of Science has Slevin's 199-mm. specimen taken June 6, 1911. Recently Hebard (1950a) found that young males at birth were 152–180 mm. long and females 146–179. The nearest approach to a complement number is Van Denburgh and Slevin's. They give the scale variation of 6 females and their embryos. These six have complements of 8, 8, 12, 12, 12, 18.

Distinctive characteristics: "Normally with fewer than 8 supralabials and fewer than 10 infralabials. Scales usually in 17, sometimes 19 rows. Gastrosteges fewer than in the more southern races. Coloration very variable, striped, spotted or unicolor, often with some red. Preoculars usually single. Size small." (Van Denburgh and Slevin). Also the eye is over labials 3 and 4. According to Fox's (1948) paper, *Thamnophis ordinoides* has a 17-17-15 dorsal scale formula; ventrals, males 138–160, females 134–159; caudals, males 61–82, females 55–72; red dorsal stripe normally; 2 rows of dorsolateral spots almost absent, traceable, or only fairly developed.

Color: A snake from Eatonville, Wash., received from L. M. Klauber, July 18, 1928. The dorsal stripe is grenadine red or scarlet. The lateral stripe is empire yellow, pale lemon yellow, or light greenish yellow with that on the tail oil yellow or javel green. The color between these stripes is chestnut, kaiser brown, or argus brown with 2 rows of black alternating spots which are less distinct on the rear. The top of the head is olive-citrine. There is grenadine red, scarlet, or dragons-blood red on the parietal spot and along the margins of the head plates to the rostral. The upper labials are yellowish glaucous. There is a black stripe from the postocular backward. The iris is black with a pupil rim of dragons-blood red, or dorsal stripe color. The under part of the chin is yellowish glaucous, the venter soon becoming light grape green, then deep grape green, citrine-drab, and finally deep olive, dark plumbeous, or neutral gray. The center of each ventral is marked with an irregular patch of brazil red, nopal red, or dragons-blood red.

Abnormal coloration—In 1934 Hart in British Columbia, where *T. ordinoides* is more brightly colored than in Washington, described a melanistic specimen. The diversity in color is expressed by Hebard (Wash., 1950a) thus: "The populations in the southernmost part of the range in northern California and southern Oregon usually have a red dorsal stripe which may be obscure; have dull indistinct lateral stripes; a pale greenish or bluish dorsal ground color; and a pale immaculate or red-spotted ventral surface. Populations from the interior valleys of Oregon west of the Cascade Mountains have a dark ground color; yellow dorsal stripe, distinct lateral stripes, and lack extensive pigmentation on the ventral surface. Those in northwestern Washington usually have a dark, nearly black ground color; a narrow dorsal stripe; distinct, pale lateral stripes; and heavy black pigmentation on the ventral surface." This northern group Hebard divides into 2, the melanistic of Washington central counties and the brighter colored one of northern Washington and British Columbia.

Habitat: This snake has been taken within a few feet of water, along a canal, beside ditches overgrown with bushes, along a road, in the vicinity of dense forests, near a stagnant pool, and on open gravelly beach says one author, but in open woods rather than beach says another. It is a native of the humid Transition zone and is a coastal form. In 1942 in Oregon we found it the commonest at the coast; at Eugene and Corvallis *concinnus* was the more common, and eastward in the mountains only *concinnus* was found. It is a Pacific coast species (Sargent, Ecol., 1884) or better, a North Pacific coast species (Mulford, Ecol., 1937-38) along the west slope of the coast mountains (Cowan, B.C., 1937) "in a region of great moisture, with a rainfall of from 50 to over 100 inches" (Brown, Calif., 1903).

In a recent appraisal, Hebard (1951a) held that *T. ordinoides* "inhabits the dense undercover which borders the humid forests of the Puget Sound lowlands. They were not found on the forest floor; but rather, in adjacent meadows, clearings and right-of-way of highways and railroads. They were seldom found far from the protection of the dense thickets. The usual habit on warm sunny mornings was to curl up in or on the grass bordering the thickets. Upon being alarmed they would glide quickly into the impenetrable thickets of blackberry brambles or bracken. Meadows and pastures which had been much trampled by livestock were conspicuously devoid of any snakes."

Food: Salamanders, frogs, slugs. Fitch (Gen., 1940), Hebard (1951a).

Authorities:

Baird, S. F., and C. Girard (Gen., 1852-53, 1853)
Brown, A. E. (Gen., 1901)
Fitch, H. S. (Gen., 1940; Ore., 1936; Calif., 1941a)
Fox, W. (Calif., 1948, 1948a, 1951)
Gordon, K. (Ore., 1935, 1939)
Hebard, W. B. (Wash., 1950, 1951, 1951a)
Logier, E. B. S. (B.C., 1932)
Thompson, J. C. (Calif., 1914, 1915, 1917)
Van Denburgh, J. (Gen., 1897, 1922)
Van Denburgh, J., and J. R. Slevin (Gen., 1918)

1944, A. H. and A. A. Wright: In 1942 we made these cursory notes on live material. In Corvallis, with K. Gordon (live *T. s. concinna* in hand): *T. o. ordinoides*—top of head and general coloration of back olive-brown. It has a dorsal stripe of deep colonial buff and a lateral stripe of ecru olive. Below ecru olive is an olive-brown band on 1st row of scales and on the bases of the gastrosteges. No red. In Tacoma, with Slater (*T. s. pickeringi* at hand): *T. o. ordinoides* from near Spanaway Marsh. Blue belly. 6–7 small snakes. Only 2 have red in dorsal stripe. Lighter underneath than *T. s. pickeringi* specimens.

1948, W. Fox: "*Thamnophis ordinoides* is considered to be a monotypic species."

1948, H. S. Fitch (Gen.): "In my revision, a weak link in the demonstrated chain of intergradation was recognized in the relationship of *ordinoides* and *atratus*. . . . Fox (1948: 113–20) has brought forth evidence to prove conclusively that *ordinoides* and *atratus* are specifically distinct."

Prairie garter snake, Transition garter snake

Thamnophis radix radix (Baird and Girard) 1853. Fig. 234; Map 58

Other common names: Black-spotted garter snake; common garter snake; Hay's garter snake (9); plains garter snake (29—Ditmars 1907); Racine garter snake (13—Coues and Yarrow 1878); ribbon snake; Say's garter snake; striped snake (Kennicott 1853); western garter snake.

Range: Extreme w. Indiana, s.w. through n. $\frac{2}{3}$ of Illinois and Missouri; n. through e. Iowa, s.e. Minnesota, and s.w. Wisconsin.—Ill.; Ind.; Ia.; Minn.; Mo.; Wis. *Elevation*—500 to 1,500 feet.

Size: Adults, 16–36 inches.

Longevity: 2 years 1 month (Conant and Hudson, Gen., 1949).

Distinctive characteristics: "The ground color varies from dark olive to dark brown. One dorsal and 2 lateral stripes are present; the lateral stripes are on the 3rd and 4th scale rows, and the dorsal occupies the vertebral and $\frac{1}{2}$ of each adjacent row. There are 2 rows of alternating blotches, larger than those of *haydeni* but not as numerous, between the lateral and dorsal stripes; and another row of blotches on each side between the lateral stripes and the ventral scales. Parietal spots are usually present. The scales are normally arranged in a pattern of 19-21-19-17 rows. . . . The ventrals in 423 males vary from 138 to 175 (mean 157), and in 436 females from 135 to 174 (mean 151). In 421 males the subcaudals range from 67 to 83 (mean 75), and in 400 females from 54 to 74 (mean 65)" (Smith, 1949). Upper labials 7 (8), lower 9 (10).

Color: A snake from the Vivarium Building, Champaign, Ill., received from Hobart Smith, July 26, 1950. There is a dorsal stripe 1$\frac{2}{2}$ scales wide, the cephalic 3–4 inches capucine yellow, then clouded to mars orange, then orange-cinnamon or mikado brown toward the vent, by which time it has become a thin line which is lost on most of the tail. On scale row 3 and slightly touching row 4, anteriorly and in mid-body is a flecked lateral stripe of picric yellow. Between these stripes are 2 rows of square alternating spots of jet black; the interspaces between the upper ones being natal brown, first appearance is of an almost continuous band. The interval color between the lower dorsal series is indicated by sets of 3 viridine green edges on the scales. Below the lateral stripe is a row of black spots which alternate with the lower dorsal row. Intervals are natal brown. In the forward half of body they extend onto scale row 2, in the rear portion occupying about 1 scale on scale row 1 with 1 scale as interval. The top of the head is black. The underside of head is seafoam yellow, as are the lower halves of the upper labials. Sutures of upper labials 2–6 bear prominent black marks. The upper rim of the iris is avellaneous and pale olive-buff, front and rear black or bone brown. The belly is tea green to vetiver green with black lines from scale row 1 extending onto venter for about ¼ inch on almost every ventral plate. The center is clear of marks but somewhat clouded.

Abnormal coloration—Albinism. May (Ill., 1952) recorded a newly born albino from Chicago, described it, and made observations on its reactions, particularly its feeding habits.

Habitat: In 1893 and in 1911 Hurter took these abundant snakes in wet prairies inundated by the Mississippi and Missouri Rivers. They frequent ditches along the roads, the shores of ponds and bays, vicinity of marshes, sloughs, mud-bottomed streams, wet meadows, and bogs. In 1950 Seibert (Ill., 1950) reported that in a 3.2-acre tract near Chicago he took 298 *Thamnophis radix*, 78 *Opheodrys vernalis,* and 7 *Thamnophis sirtalis* (*ordinatus*). From May 20 to Nov. 20, 13.8 per cent of the *radix,* 15.4 per cent of the *vernalis* were discovered.

Period of activity: *First appearance*—Apr. 15, 22, 29 (Hurter); Apr. 15, 1912 (Hankinson, Ill., 1917). *Hibernation*—In 1941 Lueth reported that "the upper limit of temperature tolerance for *Thamnophis radix* in captivity during the spring of the year is between 40°C. and 42°C. . . . The lower limit of temperature tolerance for *Thamnophis radix* and *Natrix sipedon* is approximately 0°C." In 1944 Pope wrote: "Small groups of hibernating individuals are found in post holes and under sidewalks in defunct real estate developments in the Chicago region."

Breeding: Viviparous. Males 410–745 mm., females 575–845 mm. *Sexual dimorphism*—"In some specimens of *radix,* small tubercles are infrequently found on the prefrontal and internasal scutes, although many and somewhat larger tubercles are found on the chin shields of the same specimens" (Smith, 1946). The females have fewer ventrals and caudals than the males and are much larger. Pope places sexual maturity in males at 16 inches, females 23.

Mating—One of the most detailed studies of courtship-and-mating behavior of American snakes appears in the notes of our old classmate A. C. Weed (in D. D. Davis, Gen., 1936). The female mated twice with one male, and immediately afterward with a second. This reveals the difficulties of determining genetical ratios.

In Iowa in 1926 Guthrie said: "The young are produced alive as in all garter snakes, 35 having been found in one of our specimens. They measure 7 inches at birth." In 1941 Schmidt and Davis, who know this form well, stated: "Mating has been observed in April and May, and young are born in late July and through August and September. Broods number from 13 to 40 and the young measure about 7 inches." In 1944 Pope reported: "From 6 to 40 babies are born at a time; 20 may be considered the average number until more data are available. Mating has been noted in the Chicago area from April 19 to May 24, births during the first week of August. Autumn mating has been recorded. . . . Twenty-nine of 42 newborn from 3 local broods measure from $6\frac{3}{8}$ to $7\frac{1}{4}$ inches." In 1947 Smith (Gen.) reported on "navel closure time" as follows: "Although this opening is usually found near the 140th ventral in both sexes, it may occur from the 124th to the 150th ventral in females, and from the 133rd to the 156th ventral in males. The navel scar has been reduced by about one-third of its area within 48 hours after birth, and only a small tip of the umbilicus is evident. . . . The average time for the [complete] closure . . . [is] about 96 hours."

Food: Fish, frogs, toads, earthworms, insects, carrion. Hurter, Guthrie, Pope.

Authorities:

Conant, R. (Ill., 1950)
Conant, R., E. S. Thomas, and R. L. Rausch (O., 1945)
Cope, E. D. (Ind., 1889)
Guthrie, J. E. (Ia., 1926)
Hurter, J. (Mo., 1911)
Lueth, F. X. (Gen., 1941)
Pope, C. H. (Ill., 1944)
Ruthven, A. G. (Gen., 1908)
Smith, A. G. (Gen., 1946, 1949)

1922, A. C. Weed (Ill.): "This is a very common snake in the vicinity of Chicago. We have not yet actually taken it in Indiana, but it is very common on the west side of Wolf Lake a few hundred feet from the Indiana line. There are 2 distinct color patterns, which are about equally common. In 1 the lateral stripe is confined to the 3rd and 4th rows of scales on the forward part of the body and to the 3rd row the rest of the way. In the other form, there is more or less ticking of light color on the scales above and below the lateral stripe. In many specimens this is so arranged as to make it appear that the stripe is on the 2nd, 3rd, 4th and 5th rows of scales. At the region where the other form has the lateral stripe reduced to the 3rd row of scales this one has it on the upper half of the 3rd and the lower half of the 4th. At first this might be considered as a tendency toward *Thamnophis butleri,* but none of our specimens shows any tendency to a reduction of the scale rows. The scale rows are 21 in all cases."

Fig. 234. *Thamnophis radix radix,* Champaign, Ill., H. M. Smith.

Fig. 235. *Thamnophis r. brachystoma,* Horseheads, N.Y., H. and R. Axtell.

1936, A. C. Weed and D. D. Davis: "During the time of active courtship and mating, none of the snakes paid any attention to the observer's presence, allowing a cautious approach to within 4 or 5 feet without taking alarm. This behavior was in sharp contrast to their wariness immediately before and after mating activity. The dominance of the smaller of the two males over his larger companion of the same sex was striking and consistent."

Short-mouthed snake, New York dwarf garter snake

Thamnophis radix brachystoma (Cope) 1892. Fig. 235; Map 58
(*T. brachystoma*, Schmidt, *Check List*, 1953.)

Other common names: Eastern Butler's garter snake. Also all the names listed under Butler's garter snake below are applied.

Range: Upper Alleghany drainage area in s.w. New York and n.w. Pennsylvania; e. to Genesee Valley and Elmira, N.Y.—N.Y.; Pa. *Elevation*—500 to 2,000 feet. About 1,900 feet (Hassler).

Size: Adults, 10–21 inches.

Distinctive characteristics: "A garter snake in which the dorsal scales are reduced to *17 rows throughout;* the head not distinct from the neck; and the dorsal interstripe blotches are greatly reduced or absent. The ventral scales vary from 134 to 146 (mean 140) in males and from 132 to 146 (mean 139) in females. The subcaudal scales vary from 57 to 72 (mean 67) in males, and from 51 to 64 (mean 59) in females" (Smith, 1949). This small snake has a lateral stripe on the 2nd, 3rd, and 4th rows anteriorly and on the 3rd and 4th posteriorly. Its head is small; the upper labials are normally 6. The back may be black or brown, the dorsal stripe prominent or almost absent; the belly is grayish olive.

Color: A snake from Horseheads, N.Y., received from Harold and Rachel Axtell, May 5, 1946. The background of the back is argus brown or cinnamon. The middorsal stripe is pale orange-yellow bordered irregularly with black flecks. The lateral stripes are warm buff. The lowest 1½ scale rows form a band of russet. The top of head, face, and temporals is snuff brown. There is a parietal spot or suture of pale orange-yellow surrounded by black. The pupil is surrounded by a ring of vinaceous-rufous except in the lower forward corner, where it is broken with black. This ring is surrounded by a black rim. The tongue except for a black tip is vinaceous-rufous. The underside of the head is light pinkish salmon, which extends onto first 10–15 ventrals and also onto upper and lower labials. The ventrals are deep grayish olive to light grayish olive flushed on the ends with cinnamon-drab.

Habitat: The various recorded habitats for this form are: in a low wet meadow bordering a creek, beneath a low clump of grass in wet situations, in the vicinity of streams, under stones, on a pasture hillside bordering a creek, under planks in a pasture, in piles of stones on banks or terraces within about ¼ mile of a marsh. They are usually near if not in the water. Of his colony near Horseheads, N.Y., Axtell wrote: "Most of the specimens have been found in piles of stones, sometimes scarcely larger than good-sized gravel, usually on banks or terraces within about ¼ of a mile of a marsh of several acres. Thirteen adults were collected in a row of stone piles along a terrace between 2 adjacent homes in the residential section of Horseheads.

At most of the localities where this species was seen, the common garter and DeKay's snakes were much more common than the Butler's."

Breeding: Viviparous. Males 290–440 mm., females 250–506 mm.

Field notes: Outside our Gainesville and Castile, N.Y., experience we have never taken it in the field. In fact we never sought it. In 1936 Mrs. Wright and I were searching cemeteries and turning over fallen gravestones for records. To her field note we appended: "Whatever avocation or search, one may find interesting by-products. To find my first N.Y. Butler's snake alive in this incidental fashion is typical of how material and information accumulate. This ought to be a typical hunting ground for snakes, i.e., old cemeteries."

1947: At this writing our assistant, Axtell, has several alive from northwest Pennsylvania. Several students through the last 20 years have brought them from Warren to Coudersport, Pa., and from Alleghany State Park to beyond Olean in New York.

Authorities:

Axtell, H. (N.Y., 1947)
Bishop, S. C. (N.Y., 1927)
Bishop, S. C., and W. P. Alexander (N.Y., 1927)
Brown, A. E. (Gen., 1901)
Cope, E. D. (Gen., 1900; Pa., 1892)
Hassler, W. G. (N.Y., 1932)
Noble, G. K., and H. J. Clausen (N.Y., 1936)
Ruthven, A. G. (Ind., 1904)
Smith, A. G. (Gen., 1945a, 1949)
Stone, W. (Del., 1906)
Whittaker, C. C. (Mich., 1905)

1892, E. D. Cope: "A collection of alcoholic specimens from near Franklin, Venango County, Pennsylvania, on the Alleghany River, sent me by Miss Anna M. Brown, contains a *Eutaenia,* which appears to represent a specific form which I have not previously seen. The single specimen is small, but not young, and it belongs to the group of which *E. sirtalis* and *E. leptocephala* are members. . . . The absence of spots on the gastrosteges distinguished it from most of the subspecies of *E. sirtalis.* The general form is that of *Tropidoclonium,* and the distinctness of the two nasal plates is the only feature which separates it from that genus."

1901, A. E. Brown: "Examination of the type of *E. brachystoma* Cope leaves little ground for regarding it as anything more than dwarfed and shortened *E. sirtalis.*

1905, C. C. Whittaker: "The Status of *Eutaenia brachystoma.*" Detailed comparisons in which *brachystoma* and *butleri* are held to be synonymous.

1947: H. H. Axtell's discovery of this species in the Susquehanna drainage area 60 miles east of the Alleghany-Susquehanna divide was a great event. At first he thought it an introduction. Later he felt that this colony of 64 specimens deserved to be a subspecies by itself.

1950: R. Conant (Ill.) pointed out that the easternmost record of *T. butleri* is a misidentification. "M. Graham Netting, of the Carnegie Museum, has devoted much thought and study to *Thamnophis brachystoma,* and he believes that its natural distribution does not extend much farther west or south than Polk, Venango County, Pennsylvania. This snake is unbelievably abundant right up to the edge of its range, and then it stops abruptly. It is very common at Polk, yet Paul Swanson has encountered only 1 or 2 specimens during 18 years of residence a few miles south of that city. Netting believes that the few specimens which have turned up beyond the area of extraordinary abundance (including the one from Sandy Lake, Mercer County, Pennsylvania) may have been accidentally transported into those localities, possibly in the balled roots of shrubs or trees."

1950, N. Richmond: No one today knows this form better than Richmond, who has considerable unpublished material from his U.S. Fish and Wild Life service in n.w. Pennsylvania.

Schmidt's 1953 *Check List* returns to the concept of *brachystoma* and *butleri* as separate species.

Butler's garter snake (41—Butler 1891), Short-mouthed snake (4—Clark 1903)

Thamnophis radix butleri (Cope) 1889. Fig. 236; Map 58
(*T. butleri,* Schmidt, *Check List,* 1953.)

Other common names: (Butler) garter snake; striped snake; western dwarf garter snake.

Range: S.e. Wisconsin, s. Michigan, s.w. Ontario, n. ⅔ of Indiana, and n. half of Ohio.—U.S.A.: Ill.?; Ind.; Mich.; O.; Wis. Can.: Ont. *Elevation*—Mainly 500 to 1,500 feet.

Size: Adults, 10–25 inches.

Longevity: 2 years (Conant and Hudson, Gen., 1949).

Distinctive characteristics: "A garter snake with 19 scales at the neck and mid-body and 17 anterior to the anus; the head is not distinct from the neck; the dorsal interstripe blotches are reduced numerically and in size. The ventral scales vary from 132 to 147 (mean 140.4) in males and from 129 to 147 (mean 137.9) in females; the subcaudal scales vary from 57 to 71 (mean 64) in males, and 51 to 63 (mean 56) in females" (Smith, 1949). Upper labials usually 7.

Color: A snake from Ann Arbor, Mich., received from Norman Hartweg, Apr. 3, 1929. The background color of the back is black, with the first 1½ rows of scales and the ends of the ventrals chestnut-brown, mars brown, or almost chocolate. At times, they may be bone brown, burnt umber, or bister. This brown side is a conspicuous characteristic of this snake. There is a dorsal and a lateral stripe of buff-yellow, yellow ocher, or warm buff. The top of the head is black, the upper labials are orange-buff to light orange-yellow. The iris is bister, warm sepia, or like the brown of the first $1\frac{1}{2}$ scale rows. The pupil rim is cinnamon, pinkish cinnamon, or orange cinnamon. Toward the head the yellow lateral stripe merges into the orange-buff or light orange-yellow of either side of the ventral surface of the neck. The gulars match the neck, while the chin shields and the first 2 ventrals are cartridge buff or ivory yellow. The brown of the lower side extends for $\frac{1}{4}$ inch or more along the rear of each ventral, leaving on the end of each plate an interval which is flesh ocher or rufous. The middle of the ventral plates is olive-citrine, yellowish olive, or citrine-drab. The center of the plate has an indistinct rear edge of light quaker drab to deep quaker drab or plumbago gray to dark plumbago gray.

Habitat: Previous to 1908, some habitats given were: beside a rail fence crossing an open and very wet pasture; in a group of willow and alder bushes; in a very wet swamp on the margin of a lake; in decaying timber in a clearing, near a drainage ditch. Several later authors have studied it extensively: Clark; Ruthven (Gen., 1908); Logier; Conant (O., 1938); and the Chicago group of Davis, Schmidt, Pope, and others.

In 1908 Ruthven summarized thus: "In southern Michigan I have only taken it in the immediate vicinity of water, either about the margin of swampy places or on the banks of streams. . . . I have found them most frequently by overturning boards, etc., in such places, although they are also found crawling about in the long grass and herbage. It is in disposition a rather sluggish snake, seldom attempts to defend itself, and when surprised is usually easily captured."

Of it Logier in 1939 wrote, "The scene of most of our activity was at the thicket or 'swamp' known locally as 'Skunk's misery,' which has been set aside as a game preserve. . . . At twilight on our 1st evening, while searching the grassy margins of this road where the grass had been cut and raked into bundles, we noticed a small garter-snake disappearing under one of these bundles. . . . On the following evenings, July 6 and 7, a total of 27 more specimens was taken at this clearing and for a short distance along the same side of the road (the opposite side to the ditch). . . . It soon became apparent that Butler's garter-snake was active only in the evening from about sundown till dusk and was not to be found abroad at other times, at least during the hot weather."

The best summary of it in Ohio is from Conant (1938): "Butler's garter snake is locally common and shows a tendency to form large colonies in favorable habitats. In certain parks and marsh lands in and near Toledo it was very abundant and as many as 62 were collected in a single day."

Period of activity: *Early appearances*—Apr. 9 (Ruthven, Mich., 1912); Apr. 20, 23, 29, May 7, 12 (Clark); Mar. 18 (Ruthven, Ind., 1904). "Specimens were collected in every month except December. There was a decided peak in April during which month, over 3 times as many were taken as in any other month. . . . Butler's garter snake leaves hibernation between March 24 and April 20; Apr. 3 and 4 were about average dates" (Conant, O., 1938). *Fall disappearance*—Sept. 22 (Ruthven, Ind., 1904).

Breeding: Viviparous. Males 250–565 mm., females 260–572. *Mating*—In 1912 Ruthven (Mich.) described the mating in considerable detail: "The method of courtship is exactly as described for *T. sirtalis.*" Conant (O., 1938) wrote: "Breeding activities began immediately; a pair was found in coitu Apr. 4, 1930 and on numerous occasions pairs placed together in cages early in April began courting at once. Reproductive instincts appeared paramount to all others at this time of the year and specimens, which showed little concern for the observer, often were found prowling about. Males far outnumbered females in spring collections and the reverse was true in mid-summer." In 1949 Finneran reported some field observations and experiments on sexual aggregation in this species in the spring and on males trailing or heading to the aggregation area.

Young—Number, 4–16, average 8 or 10. Time of birth, June 1–Sept. 1. Size, 5–7.25 inches. In 1904 Ruthven (Ind.) stated: "Its breeding habits are unknown; in one specimen (U. of M. Mus. Cat. No. 31612) taken May 28, 1904, at Sandusky, Ohio, there are 8 eggs in each oviduct, about 20 mm. long and 12 mm. broad. In another specimen (U. of M. Mus. Cat. No. 31624) taken June 3, 1904, at Ann Arbor, Michigan, there are 7 eggs in the right and 5 in the left oviduct. These eggs are about 12 mm. long and 10 mm. broad." In 1907 and 1908 Ditmars (Gen.) recorded a female 19¾ inches long which had 12 young born August 4, the young being 5⅜ inches long. In his 1908 monograph Ruthven (Gen.) recorded: "Females taken in July are usually pregnant, and the number of young is apparently small. In the specimens examined the number of embryos is about 12 to 15. One specimen which was taken in late July, 1905, and kept in captivity gave birth during the 1st part of August to 10 young." In 1915 he gave the period of gestation as 104, 113, 144 days, or a range of 40 days.

Conant (O., 1938) added considerably to our knowledge of this form: "Butler's garter snake is ovoviviparous. Three litters of young were born at the Toledo Zoo. A female 17 inches in length from Toledo was bred April 4, 1930, and gave birth to 5 young July 2, 1930; the newly born young averaged 6¼ inches in length. A female from near Bono, Lucas County, 25 inches in length, bore 14 young, July 28, 1931, which varied from 6½ to 7⅛ inches in length. Another, 22¼ inches in length, collected at Toledo, was bred March 23, 1934, and had 4 young, plus 4 dead (but well developed) embryos and 2 infertile ova July 3, 1934. Her living young ranged from 5⅝ to 6 inches in length. A specimen in the Ohio State Museum, 16⅝ inches in length, collected near the Clifton Gorge, Green County, on June 6, 1933, gave birth to 4 young, ranging from 5 to 5⅝ inches, on August 7, 1933. That the number in a litter may sometimes be greater is indicated by Ruthven

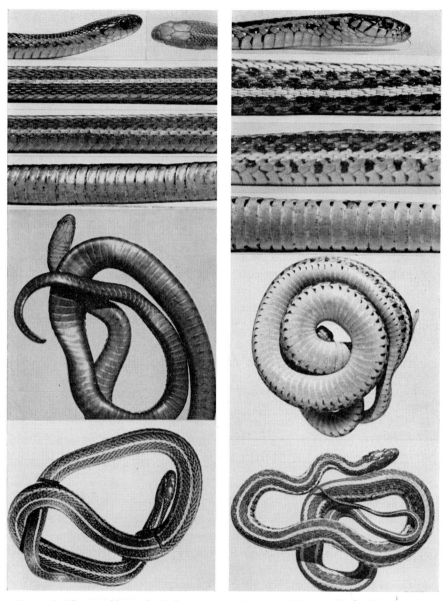

Fig. 236. *Thamnophis r. butleri:* 1,3–7, Toledo, Ohio, R. Conant; 2, Ann Arbor, Mich.

Fig. 237. *Thamnophis r. haydeni,* Colorado Springs, Colo., R. Hegener.

(1908, 90) who states, 'In the specimens examined the number of embryos is about 12 or 15.' " In 1939 Conant and Bridges (Gen.) gave 4 to 15 young 5 to 7 inches in length, two years later Schmidt and Davis (Gen.) gave 4 to 14 young (average 8), 6 inches long.

Food: Earthworms, frogs, insects, field mice, leeches, salamanders. Ruthven (several references), Nash (Ont., 1908), Conant (O., 1938), Minton (Ind., 1944), Goodman (Gen., 1951).

Authorities:

Butler, A. (Ind., 1892)

Clark, H. L. (Mich., 1903a)

Conant, R. (Ohio, 1938; Ill., 1950)

Cope, E. D. (Ind., 1889)

Davis, D. D. (Wis., 1932)

Finneran, L. C. (Mich., 1949)

Hay, O. P. (Ind., 1892)

Logier, E. B. S. (Ont., 1939a)

Reddick, G. (Ind., 1896)

Ruthven, A. G. (Gen., 1908; Ind., 1904; Mich., 1909, 1912)

Schmidt, K. P. (Gen., 1938)

Smith, A. G. (Gen., 1945, 1949)

Stejneger, L. (Ind., 1895)

Whittaker, C. C. (Mich., 1905)

1938, K. P. Schmidt: *"Thamnophis butleri,* for example, might represent the *T. radix* of some interglacial stage, the present contact of *radix* and *bulteri* being of post-Wisconsin date."

1950: R. Conant devoted his paper to proving quite satisfactorily that there are not intergrades between *butleri* and *radix* in the Chicago area, a thesis Smith apparently adopted.

Plains garter snake, Hayden's garter snake

Thamnophis radix haydeni (Kennicott) 1860. Fig. 237; Map 58

Other common names: Twining's garter snake (see also names of *T. r. radix* above).

Range: Great Plains from Manitoba, Can., s. through Minnesota, w. Iowa, Kansas, and Oklahoma panhandle, w. to foothills of the Rockies, n. to Alberta, Can.—U.S.A.: Colo.; Ia.; Kan.; Minn.; Mo.; Mont.; Neb.; N.D.; Okla.; S.D.; Tex.; Wyo.　Can.: Alta.; Man.; Sask. *Elevation*—1,000 to 6,500 feet. To 5,000 feet (Ruthven); to above 6,500 feet (Ellis and Henderson, Colo., 1913).

Size: Adults, 14–42 inches.

Distinctive characteristics: "Head broader and more depressed in front than in *E. radix.* Form stout, compact, and cylindrical, most so of the genus, except *E. radix.* Ground color light olive green, with 3 longitudinal yellow stripes and 6 series of distinct black spots. In life some red coloring visible on the sides. Lateral stripe on 3rd and 4th rows less sharply defined than in *E. radix.* Dorsal rows 21" (Kennicott). Smith's key gives these characters: "Lateral stripe on 3rd and 4th scale rows, at least on the anterior half of the body. Scale rows usually 21 at neck; ventrals generally 155 or more. *Haydenii."* Like *T. radix radix,* upper labials usually 7, occasionally 8.

Color: The larger of 2 snakes from Colorado Springs, Colo., received from Ruth Hegener, Oct. 2, 1935. The background color of the back is deep grape green, pois green, or rainette green. The dorsal stripe is prominent, beginning at the rear end of the suture between the parietals. Here it is cadmium orange or mikado orange, fading on the body to capucine buff or even orange-pink. It extends distinctly to the tip of the tail. The lateral stripe beginning just behind the last upper labial is on the 3rd and 4th rows of scales. For a short distance in front it is primrose yellow, but soon becomes marguerite yellow. Between the dorsal and lateral stripes are 2 very distinct rows of alternating roundish or elliptical black spots. Those of the upper row are less distinct in outline and have their corners stretched out to form a black border for the dorsal stripe. These spots occupy 1½ to 2 rows of scales with the intervening connections covering ½ to 1 scale. The 2nd row is just above the lateral stripe, and the spots are 2 to 2½ scales wide with plenty of lighter space between them. There is a more or less complete row of vertical spots below the lateral stripe and located principally on the 1st scale row and narrowly on the 2nd row. The top of the head is much like the back or may be light cress green. The upper labials and rostral are yellowish glaucous. The oculars are a faded-out primrose yellow; the parietal spot is pale orange-yellow surrounded by black. There is a black stripe extending from the postoculars along the upper border of the upper labials which expands into a prominent spot back of the parietals. The sutures of the upper labials are black. The iris is black in the lower front and rear with a pupil rim of primrose yellow or colonial buff, which expands above the pupil and there becomes cream-buff. The throat is white. The color of the belly is glaucous, corydalis green, or pale olivine, the rear edge of each ventral being white or marguerite yellow. The black spots near the ends of ventrals are prominent. The color of the belly invades the spaces between the vertical spots below the lateral stripe. The whole appearance is very much like that of *Thamnophis cyrtopsis* which has the lateral stripe on the 2nd and 3rd rows. In this species, *T. radix haydeni,* the stripe is on the 3rd and 4th rows.

Habitat: From 1878 when Coues and Yarrow (Mont.) outlined this topic, to Jacobs' work (Minn.) in 1950, we have 20 or more authors who have contributed to our knowledge. Most agree that almost anywhere or "almost every habitat suitable to snakes" is possible. Prairie lands with prairie sloughs, ponds, pools, streams, swamps, rivers, and lakes provide desirable spots. Often herbage, grass, brush, or sparse brush may edge these waters. Authors have taken these snakes under stones on hillsides, in the drier parts of groves, in meadows, dooryards, gardens, and parks. One author found it from a high elevation on a high grass mesa to the pinyon-juniper association.

Period of activity: *Early appearances*—Apr. 15, 1912 (Hankinson, Ill., 1917); Mar. 30, 1929 (Burt, Kan., 1933); Apr. 29, 1906 (Ellis and Henderson, 1913); May 16, 20, 27, 28, June 3, 9, June 11, 17, 18 (Marr); May 4, 13, 1926; Apr. 19, May 23, 1927; May 21, June 4, 1928 (Gloyd). "This garter snake and *Thamnophis parietalis* (Say) are the first snakes to appear in the spring about Boulder" (Ellis and Henderson, Colo., 1915). *Fall disappearance*—(See excerpts from article by Criddle in account of *O. v. blanchardi;*

8 of the 257 snakes taken from an anthill in Manitoba were *T. r. haydeni*.) "The snakes become much less numerous in the latter part of September, but Dr. Coues occasionally saw them abroad on warm days up to the middle of October, even after there had been snow, sleet, and freezing of the more shallow waters" (Coues and Yarrow). Sept. 5, 1900; Aug. 25, 1905; Aug. 31, 1911; Dec. 12, 1911; Oct. 29, 1912 (Ellis and Henderson, Colo., 1913); Aug. 25, 26, 27, 28, 1915; Sept. 14, 1915 (Wheeler, N.D., 1947); Nov. 26, 1926 (Gloyd); Aug. 28, 1932 (Burt); Nov. 5, Nov. 12; Sept. 17, 1939 (Breckenridge).

Breeding: Viviparous. Males 545–853 mm., females 515–1,045 mm. *Sexual dimorphism*—(See under *T. r. radix* above.)

Mating—"Drs. Coues and Yarrow tell us that the females of the closely related species *E. radix* are pregnant in July and August . . . and that they are found *in coitu* in September and October. Can it be that snakes copulate twice in the year, as Agassiz says some turtles do, and as Gage has recently found to be the habit of the newt *Diemyctylus*" (Hay)? Regarding this observation, Ruthven wrote: "This observation is difficult to explain. It is hardly possible that more than one brood is raised each year, and those that appear in October are probably belated first broods. Likewise it is highly improbable that the period of gestation is protracted over the winter, since such is not the case in the other species of the genus in which coition has been observed. The probabilities are that coition takes place in the spring, and that Coues was mistaken in his observation or was viewing abnormal cases." We have seen average adult snakes mating in the fall, wood and other turtles mating in the fall, and *Notophthalmus* male newts laying spermatophores in September and October and females taking them into the cloaca. There are two or more mating periods. There may be general spring mating and a not infrequent post-parturition mating in the fall, but like Ruthven we doubt that any one female snake, turtle, lizard, frog, or salamander lays eggs twice in one season, or has more than 1 brood a season.

Young—Number, 5–92 (Breckenridge). There are records of 5, 13, 15, 17, 18, 19, 20, 21, 25, 27, 30, 35, 37, 40, 60, 92 in a brood. Time of birth, July 1–Oct. 1. Size at birth, 7–9.25 inches. "The greater part of the females observed in July and August will be found pregnant, the young numbering sometimes as many as 30 or 40" (Coues and Yarrow). Ruthven observed: "I have examined pregnant females in July, August, and September in western Iowa that contained 17 to 25 young, and have kept females in captivity that gave birth to young on Aug. 31 and Sept 7, 29 and 30 (1907). By the size of the embryos examined I believe that broods may appear as early as the latter part of July." In 1910(b) he (Ia.) wrote: "It may be added, however, that while as stated in that paper, the pregnant females had a maximum number of 25 embryos, 2 females later kept in captivity each gave birth to 35 young." In 1913 Ellis and Henderson reported it had 15 to 40 young in the latter part of summer, but cited one with 20 well-developed embryos in early July. In 1928 Gloyd observed: "Only 1 gravid female was kept until young were born. . . . Thirteen young were born August 6; 2 were dead when discovered and 1 of these was still coiled within the foetal membranes. At the age of 6 days the remaining 11 averaged 187 mm. in length." Burt (Kan., 1933) reported that a gravid female was crushed in the road Aug. 28, 1932. It had fully formed young. In 1942 Hudson in Nebraska reported that "a female dissected contained 19 embryos, another 21. A captive female gave birth to 27 young, the intervals between the discharge of young averaging about 75 seconds." In 1944 Marr wrote: "Eggs were noted as follows: Ford Co., May 28, 17 eggs; Hamilton Co., June 3, 18 eggs; Wallace Co., June 9, 13 eggs; Rooks Co., June 11, 25 eggs; Sheridan Co., June 17, 37 eggs with the embryos visible; and Perkins Co., Nebr., July 22, 27 embryos 11 to 12 centimeters in total length. A juvenile 9¼ inches in total length (fresh) was taken in Wallace Co., on June 9." Breckenridge summarized thus: "Eleven Minnesota specimens gave birth to young varying in number from 5 to 92, the majority having between 20 and 60. The largest number 92 was reported by Richard Anderson of Minneapolis, who had a female segregated in a cage at the time of the birth. Minnesota records indicate that the young are born in late July and early August."

Food: Frogs, insects, earthworms, mice. Coues and Yarrow, Brons, Taylor, Ruthven, Marr, Ellis and Henderson, Burt and Burt (Ariz., 1929), Over, Gloyd, Burt and Hoyle (Tex., 1935), Hudson (Neb., 1942).

Authorities:

Bragg, A. N., and H. A. Dundee (N.M., 1949)
Branson, E. B. (Kan., 1904)
Breckenridge, W. J. (Minn., 1944a)
Brons, H. A. (Kan., 1882)
Coues, E., and H. C. Yarrow (Mont., 1878)
Criddle, S. (Man., 1937)
Ellis, M. M., and J. Henderson (Colo., 1913, 1915)

Gloyd, H. K. (Kan., 1928)
Hay, O. P. (Gen., 1893)
Kennicott, R. (Gen., 1860)
Marr, J. C. (Gen., 1944)
Over, W. H. (S. D., 1923)
Ruthven, A. G. (Gen., 1908)
Smith, A. G. (Gen., 1949)
Smith, H. M. (Kan., 1950)
Taylor, W. E. (Neb., 1892a)

1878: E. Coues and H. C. Yarrow write that these garter snakes "are themselves preyed upon by hawks, especially the Marsh Harrier (*Circus cyaneus hudsonius*) and Swainson's Buzzard (*Buteo swainsoni*). They are less active than some of the slenderer species, are readily caught, and when captured make little or no resistance. Only the largest individuals assume for the moment a defensive attitude and attempt to bite; most may be at once handled with impunity."

In Minnesota W. J. Breckenridge "on Sept. 17, 1939, . . . found 93 of these snakes on an eleven mile stretch of graveled highway in southern Norman and Mahnomen counties." What a toll!

Ribbon snake (100—Catesby), Riband snake (18—Catesby)

Thamnophis sauritus sauritus (Linné) 1766. Fig. 238; Map 59

Other common names: Eastern ribbon snake (7); (little) garter snake; North American ribbon snake; saurite snake; slender garter snake; slim garter snake; spotted ribbon-snake (Catesby); striped (water) snake; swift (garter) snake; swift streaked snake; water garter snake; yellow-headed garter snake.

Range: In the area bounded by s. Maine across n. New York, s. Ontario, s. peninsula of Michigan to Chicago, down Wabash Valley to Ohio River and e. of Mississippi River to cent. Mississippi; e. to the coast in South Carolina, north to s. Maine.—Ala.; Conn.; D.C.; Del.; Fla.; Ga.; Ill.; Ind.; Ky.; Mass.; Md.; Me.; Mich.; Miss.; N.C.; N.H.; N.J.; N.Y.; O.; Pa.; R.I.; S.C.; Tenn.; Va.; Vt.; W. Va. Can.: Ont.; Que. *Elevation*—Sea level to 2,000 feet.

Size: Adults, 16–36 inches.

Longevity: 4 years (Conant and Hudson, Gen., 1949).

Distinctive characteristics: A medium-sized, 19-rowed, glossy black "graceful and beautiful" snake with 3 striking yellow or buff stripes, all prominent and more or less uniform; lateral stripe on 3rd and 4th row for length of body; upper labials normally 7; tail ⅓ of total length or more. Venter yellowish. Eye over labials 4 and 5.

Color: A snake from Rochester, N.Y., received from E. S. Phillips, Oct. 5, 1929. The background of the back on the 5th to the 8th and the lower half of the 9th scale rows is velvety black. The dorsal stripe is pale chalcedony yellow, seafoam yellow, or cartridge buff with a faint tinge of pale cinnamon-pink. It covers the median scale row and halves of the 2 adjoining rows. The lateral stripe is barium yellow, massicot yellow, or chartreuse yellow slightly edged above and below with pale ochraceous-salmon or light pinkish cinnamon. The lateral stripe is on the 3rd and 4th scale rows, but the upper edge of the 4th and the center of the lower edge of the 3rd rows are black. The top of the head and the face in front of the eye is saccardo's umber or buffy brown. Two closely approximated parietal spots are like the dorsal stripe or less clear in color. The black of the back extends along the side of the head to the eye. The preocular has a white or cartridge buff center, and the lower postocular may have the same color. The upper and lower labials are white, pure or with touches of pale vinaceous-fawn. The iris is orange-cinnamon above, verona brown or warm sepia below and with a pupil rim of pale cinnamon-pink. The chin and lower throat are pure white or pale vinaceous-fawn. Along the ends of the ventrals and penetrating the dark lower border of the lateral stripe there is a band of vinaceous-tawny, orange-cinnamon, kaiser brown, or hay's russet. This makes a striking border to the lateral stripe and to the belly, which is pale chalcedony yellow with reflections of light pinkish cinnamon or pale cinnamon-pink.

Habitat: This snake normally belongs on the ground, although there are some records of climbing. A summary of some 50 or 60 writers shows these habitats: *stream*—near, vicinity of, banks of, edge or margin of, fields near—occurs 26 times; *water*—takes to, about, vicinity of, border of—10; *pond*—border of, bank of—9; *lake*—margin of, shore of—11; *swamp* or *marsh* 12; *woods*—damp wet lowland—5; *meadow* 11; *ditch* 4; *pool* 3; *pasture* 4. Adjectives: *damp*—woods, localities, meadows, thickets, situations—7 times; *wet*—woods, localities, situations, marsh, meadow—6; *low*—grounds, meadows, woods, lands—6; *moist* 1.

Whenever we went to Bergen swamp, N.Y., a sphagnaceous or marly marsh, we hoped to see both the ribbon snake and the little rattler (*Sistrurus*). We therefore note Swanson's 1930 (Pa.) statement, "Their habitat (*Sistrurus c. catenatus*) seems to be identical with that of the ribbon snake." A recent characterization of its habitat is Axtell's paragraph: "Of the 73 that were seen, 33 were at 2 dens and 11 were found dead. It is ordinarily a dweller of the vicinity of ponds and marshes where frogs are abundant. Occasionally, though, one may be found from 1 to 3 miles from the nearest good habitat of that sort."

This subspecies combined with *proximus* and *sackeni* has practically the range of *T. s. sirtalis,* but *T. s. sauritus,* the eastern ribbon snake, has been assigned to various zonal or ecological areas such as Alleghanian and Louisianian (Agassiz, Ecol., 1854), Atlantic district and Illinois (Cooper, Ecol., 1859), Eastern and Louisianian (Cope, Ecol., 1873–81), deciduous forest and northern pine and coast pine (Sargent, Ecol., 1884), Appalachian and Austroriparian (Allen, Ecol., 1893).

Period of activity: First appearance—Mar. 15, 1908 (Fowler, N.J., 1909); May 16, 1900, May 9, 1901 (Evermann, N.Y., 1918a); Mar. 15–Nov. 1 (Wright, N.Y., 1919b); Apr. 22, 1917, Apr. 27, 1918, Apr. 22, 1923, Apr. 8, 1928 (Dunn, N.C., 1930); Apr. 15, 1906 (Fowler, N.J., 1907); Mar. 31 (Axtell). "For 3 years it has been the first species seen in Spring—the dates being Mar. 18, 22, and 23" (Blatchley, Ind., 1891). *Fall disappearance*—Oct., 1905 (Fowler, N.J., 1907); Oct. 30 (Wright and Allen, N.Y., 1913); Nov. 1 (Wright); Jan. 2, 1942 (Lachner, Pa., 1942); Oct. 9, 1929 (A.H.W.); Jan., 1946 (Wilson and Friddle, W.Va., 1950); Oct. 22 (Axtell). *Seasonal catch*—Jan., 3 snakes; Feb., 5; Mar., 10; Apr., 20; May, 12; June, 7; July, 1; Aug., 3; Sept., 1; Oct., 3; Nov., 2; Dec., 1. Total 68 (Brimley, N.C., 1925). *Hibernation*—"We discovered a den near the marsh between Horseheads and Pine Valley at which an April visit in suitable weather always revealed several specimens (up to 8)" (Axtell).

Breeding: Viviparous. Males 400–819 mm., females 451–900 mm. Heyen (N.J., 1937) gives adult males 598–842 mm., adult females 540–932 mm.

Young—Number, 3-20. 3 (Ditmars); 4 (4 authors); 5 (5); 6 (4); 7 (1); 8 (1); 9 (4); 10 (1); 11 (2); 12 (7); 14 (3); 15 (1); 16 (Evans, Wilson and Friddle); 20 (Schmidt and Davis, Fowler); 30? (Herman Strecker). Time of birth, July 15 to Sept. 1. August (Schmidt and Davis, Babcock, Surface); July 23, Aug. 7 (Minton); Aug. 1, 12, 17 (Ditmars); Aug. 1 to Sept. 1 (Wright and Allen); Aug. 6 (Langlois); Aug. 10, 11, Sept. 22 (Axtell); Aug. 10 (Duellman); Aug. 19 (Bishop and Alexander); Aug. 26 (Conant and Bailey); late summer (Brimley). Size, 8–9.2 inches. 8 inches (Conant); 8 inches, 8.6 inches, 8.8 inches, 8.9 inches, 9 inches, 9.1 inches and 9.2 inches (Conant and Bridges, Gen., 1939); 8.5 (Schmidt and Davis, Gen., 1941); 9 (Conant); 9 (Langlois). One of the best early accounts is by Langlois.

Food: Insects, toads, frogs, mice, spiders, salamanders, and fish. Abbott; Babcock; Blatchley; Brimley; Conant; Duellman; Fouquette; Hay; Linsley; Lowe; Macauley; Minton; Nash; Toner; Uhler, Cottam, and Clarke; and Williams.

Authorities:

Axtell, H. (N.Y., 1945)
Conant, R. (O., 1938a)
Conant, R., and R. M. Bailey (N.J., 1936)
DeKay, J. R. (N.Y., 1842)
Holbrook, J. E. (Gen., 1836–42)
Klauber, L. M. (Gen., 1948)

Langlois, T. H. (Mich., 1925)
Putnam, F. W. (Gen., 1868)
Ruthven, A. G. (Gen., 1908)
Say, T. (Gen., 1819)
Shaw, G. (Gen., 1802)
Storer, D. H. (Mass., 1838)
Thompson, Z. (Vt., 1842)

1819, T. Say: "What is the difference between *sirtalis* and *saurita*? They must be very closely allied, if not synonymous."

1838, D. H. Storer: "*C. saurita.* Lin. The riband Snake. Shaw's *Gen. Zoology,* vol. iii, pt. 2, p. 532. Harlan's *Med. and Phys. Res.,* p. 115. This beautiful little snake is not very common; it resembles somewhat the *sirtalis,* but it is smaller, lighter colored, and much more graceful in its figure and proportions. Its form is very slender, tapering to an acute point."

1842, Z. Thompson: "The Ribband Snake, *Coluber saurita,* Linn. *History* —I forwarded a specimen of this snake to my friend Dr. Storer, of Boston, who, in acknowledging its reception, says that it 'is without any question the *sirtalis.*' After so decided an opinion from such high authority, it may be thought presumption in me to introduce it as a different species."

1948, L. M. Klauber: "It is difficult to see how Linnaeus' *Coluber sirtalis* ever became attached to the common garter snake, for the subcaudal scale counts of the type do not fit that snake. Linnaeus gives the number as 114; the common garter snake rarely, if ever, exceeds 95 in any part of the range of its subspecies, and seldom exceeds 85 in the area where the type was collected. But both scale counts and description fit the ribbon snake. . . . Linnaeus' pattern description of *sirtalis* fits either the garter snake or ribbon snake, but his scale counts are applicable only to the ribbon snake. I think

Fig. 238. *Thamnophis sauritus sauritus*, Rochester, N.Y., E. C. Phillips.

Fig. 239. *Thamnophis s. proximus*: 1,3–5, Imboden, Ark., B. C. Marshall; 2, Bayou Bouff, La., P. Viosca, Jr.; 6, San Benito, Tex.; 7, Helotes, Tex.

the conclusion inevitable that the name must be applied to the latter." Never-theless, long-term usage has determined that the ribbon snakes must be called *Thamnophis sauritus.*

Western ribbon snake (25—Ditmars 1907), Long's garter snake (12)

Thamnophis sauritus proximus (Say) 1823. Figs. 239, 240; Map 59

Other common names: Fairie's (Fairey's) garter snake (6); Fairie's (Fairey's) ribbon snake; garter snake; Long's ribbon snake; moccasin; plains ribbon snake; ribbon snake (18—Hay 1893); red-striped garter snake; riband snake; Say's garter snake (Coues and Yarrow 1878); Say's ribbon snake; slender garter snake; spotted garter snake; swift striped snake (Kennicott 1853).

Range: In cent. United States, e. Louisiana w. of Mississippi River to s. Illinois, e. of Wabash Valley to s.w. Michigan; s. Wisconsin across Iowa, e. Nebraska, Kansas to e. New Mexico. Thence s.e. to Mexico.—U.S.A.: Ark.; Colo.; Ia.; Ill.; Ind.; Kan.; La.; Minn.; Miss.; Mo.; Neb.; N.M.; Okla.; S.D.; Tex.; Wis. Mex.: Coahuila; Nuevo León; Puebla; San Luis Potosí; Tamaulipas; Veracruz. *Elevation*—Sea level to 4,000 or more feet. 1,000–8,000 feet (Smith, Kan., 1946).

Size: Adults, 17–50 inches, rarely 45 to 51 inches.

Longevity: 3 years 7 months (Conant and Hudson, Gen., 1949); 6 years (Mann).

Distinctive characteristics: *"Coluber proximus.* Body above black, trilineate, vertebral line ocraceous, lateral one yellowish, a double white spot on each parietal plate" (Say). *"Eutainia Faireyi,* B. and G.—Body above blackish brown, with 3 longitudinal stripes of uniform tint. Abdomen greenish white. Stouter than *E. saurita.* Head large. Tail rather less than ⅓ total length" (Baird and Girard, Gen., 1853). "A remarkable variety of this species comes from Fort Stockton, Texas. A pale shade represents the dorsal stripe, and the generally green colors are metallic in luster" (Cope, Gen., 1900).—Scale rows 19-17; upper labials 8; eye over labials 4 and 5.

Color: A snake from Imboden, Ark., received from B. C. Marshall, Apr. 18, 1929. The dark bands between the light stripes look black, but are mars brown, mummy brown, carob brown, or clove brown. The median dorsal stripe is ochraceous-buff, clay color, or honey yellow. For a short distance on the neck, it is like the lateral stripe, which is seafoam yellow, marguerite yellow, or pale chalcedony yellow. The top of the head is colored like the dark bands and has 2 white parietal spots. The rostral, prenasal, and first upper labial are buff-pink or light vinaceous-cinnamon. The rest of the upper labials and the lower ones are white. The iris is amber brown or argus brown with a patch of xanthine orange or zinc orange in the upper part.

The pupil rim is pale yellow-orange or cream color. The throat and lower neck are white, the rest of the venter being marguerite yellow with a wash of pale cinnamon-pink that is particularly noticeable on the ends of the ventrals.

A young snake from Palo Pinto, Tex., received from Harter, Aug., 1938. This little snake has a white spot on top of the head. Down the midback is a rusty stripe outlined on either side by a black thread, and this in turn by a white one.

Field note: July 22, 1942, Balmorhea, Tex.: A boy wanted to know if I wanted water moccasins (*Thamnophis* and *Natrix*). In the large spring saw *Pseudemys*. Didn't catch it. Farther along outlet, Anna saw a garter. I spotted where it was and without seeing it or it me I grabbed it. Then we saw another garter and later a horned toad. This striped garter I caught is *T. s. proxima*, in appearance unlike the northeast and southeast forms of *proxima*. Cope remarked its difference and called the one at Fort Stockton "a remarkable variety." This *proxima* is very brown and the stripe (dorsal) is not reddish or orange, merely a light dorsal area.

July 23: Returned to Balmorhea. Caught another ribbon snake of the same color in the outflow from the spring.

Habitat: Five accounts before 1911 indicate this snake's aquatic character. There are some 45 to 50 more habitat notices which we will summarize. The areas favored are in, near, in the vicinity of, in proximity to, or by the side of, marshes (10); swamps (2); rivers (6); streams (5); creeks (4); pools (4); ponds (3); lakes (3); tanks (2); springs (2); water courses (1); and sloughs (1). This form likes the grasses, reeds, weeds, and other cover of borders, edges, shores, and margins of bodies of water. Sometimes authors characterize the habitat as river bottoms, creek bottoms, lowlands, and overflow lands. Some unusual habitats are: in mangrove swamps; under logs in dried-up streams; under rocks in a prairie ledge; on drier ground near the top of a bluff; near the ground in small trees; and in gravel pits.

Period of activity: *Early appearances*—Mar. 9, 1927 (Burt, Kan., 1933); Apr. 26, 1927, Mar. 24, 1928, Apr. 6, 1929 (Gloyd, Kan., 1932); Apr. 6, 1924 (Linsdale, Kan., 1927); Apr. 9, 1927; Apr. 18, May 22, 1926 (Gloyd, Kan., 1928); Apr. 9, 30, May 20 (Evermann and Clark); Apr. 8, 14, 16, 22, May 6, 13, 16, 20, 21 (Hurter); Feb. 19, 1930 (Allen, Miss., 1932); Apr. 3, 1916 (Ellis, N.M., 1917); Apr. 19 (Marr, Gen., 1944). *Fall disappearance*—Nov. 10 (Allen); Aug. 31, 1928 (Gloyd, 1932); Nov. 30, 1922 (Linsdale); Sept. 21, 1900 (Evermann and Clark); Sept. 2, 30, Oct. 18, 23 (Hurter); Jan. (Schwardt); Aug. 20 (Marr). *Hibernation*—"On November 30, 1922, one that was about 2 feet long was found in a spring" (Linsdale). In Arkansas, Schwardt wrote this interesting note: "Like many other species in this group, the western ribbon snake often lives in town. The writer's back yard yields 2 or 3 each summer, and the neighborhood cats are frequently seen carrying them about. A plumber who spent more than the usual time digging up a sewer line 20 feet from the house one January explained his delay on the basis that he had been busy 'dodging snakes.' It was found that 6 western ribbon snakes averaging a foot long had been dug out of small chambers in the rocky soil 2 feet below the surface."

Breeding: Viviparous. Males 475–1,119 mm., females 383–1,268 mm. *Mating*—"As to the term of gestation I am not certain, but pairing occurs in March and April, for I have had repeated opportunities to observe it in our swamps and palmetto thickets" (Beyer, La., 1898).

Young—Number, 5–27. 5, 8, 9 (Beyer); 6 (Conant and Bridges, Gloyd; Burt and Hoyle); 6, 12, 17 (Pope); 8 (Gloyd); 9 (Guidry); 9, 12, 20 (Hay); 10, 20 (Schmidt and Davis); 12 (Hudson); 15 (Ditmars); 27 (Klein). In 1941 Hudson and Davis (Neb.) gave 36, but this must have been only an estimate, for the next year Hudson (Neb.) gave 12. Nevertheless, Klein (Tex., 1949) recently recorded 27. Time of birth, July 4–Aug. 31. July 4 (Hay, Gen., 1893); July 7 (Pope); July 27 (Gloyd); July 30; Aug. (Hudson and Davis); Aug. 9 (Guidry, Tex., 1953); Aug. 20 (Marr, Gen., 1944); Aug. 24 (Ditmars, Gen., 1907; Pope); Aug. 31 (Gloyd, Kan., 1932). Size, 5.75–10 inches. Variable. Beyer (La., 1898) records 5¾ inches, but all others give 9 or more inches, such as 9⅞ (Garman, Tex., 1887), 9⅜ (Pope), 9–10 (Gloyd), 9 (Hay, Gen., 1893; Ind., 1892). Marr on Aug. 20 secured three— 226, 243, and 283 mm. long.

Food: Insects, fish, frogs, salamanders, mice, toads.[1] Taylor (Neb., 1892a), Evermann and Clark, Gloyd, Trowbridge (Okla., 1937), Schwardt, Anderson (Mo., 1942), Klein (Tex., 1949).

Field notes: 1925, Helotes and Houston to Brownsville, Tex., 9 notes June 15, 1930, San Benito, Tex.: A mile or more south of town at Highland found a fine blue water-lily pond. Found a riband snake (*T. s. proximus*). When I stepped on it, it regurgitated 3 transformed *Hypopachus cuneus*. Then I made it give up more. Had 9 or 10 of these little narrow-mouthed toads. . . . Saw another riband snake. Made it disgorge.

Authorities:

Baird, S. F., and C. Girard (Gen., 1853; Okla., 1854)

Blatchley, W. S. (Ind., 1900)

Davis, N. S., Jr., and F. L. Rice (Gen., 1883)

Evermann, B. W., and H. L. Clark, (Ind., 1920)

Garman, H. (Ill., 1892)

Gloyd, H. K. (Kan., 1928)

Hay, O. P. (Ind., 1892)

Hudson, G. E. (Neb., 1942)

Hurter, J. (Mo., 1911)

Wied, M. zu (Gen., 1865)

Pope, C. H. (Ill., 1944)

Ruthven, A. G. (Gen., 1908)

Say, T. (in James, Gen., 1922–23)

Schwardt, H. H. (Ark., 1938)

Shannon, F. A., and H. M. Smith (Tex., 1949)

Smith, H. M. (Kan., 1950)

---

[1] In 1955 Fouquette (Tex.) found that its food was chiefly amphibians, 82%.

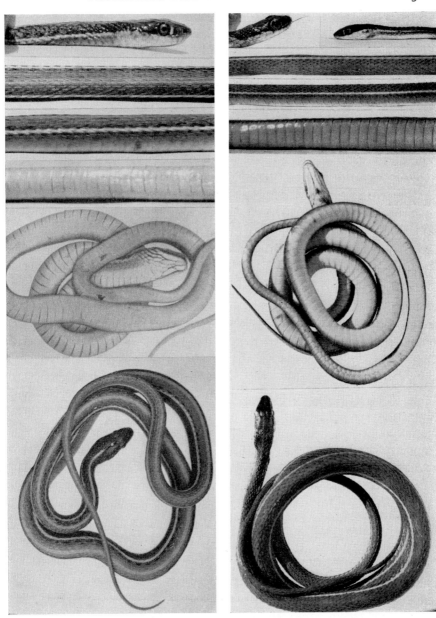

Fig. 240. *Thamnophis s. proximus,* western, Toyahvale, Tex.

Fig. 241. *Thamnophis s. sackeni:* 1, Eureka, Marion Co., Fla., C. C. Tyler; 2–7, Silver Springs, Fla., E. R. Allen.

1892, O. P. Hay: "Prof. Cope, in his most recent publication . . . , unites *faireyi* with *proxima,* and distinguishes these from *saurita* by their having 8 upper labials instead of 7. It is doubtful if this will hold good."

Southern ribbon snake (6—Ditmars 1907),
Florida ribbon snake (4)

Thamnophis sauritus sackeni (Kennicott) 1859. Fig. 241; Map 59

Other common names: Grass snake; (Osten-Sacken's) garter snake; Osten-Sacken's (ribbon) snake; Osten-Sacken's snake; ribbon snake (6); Sacken's garter snake; southeastern ribbon snake.

Range: Coastal s.e. South Carolina across extreme s. Georgia, Alabama, s.e. Mississippi, and all of Florida.—Ala.; Fla.; Ga.; Miss.; S.C. *Elevation*—Sea level to 500 feet.

Size: Adults, 16–30 inches.

Distinctive characteristics: "Body with longitudinal stripes; 2 labials in orbit; body very slender; tail long; lateral stripe on 3rd and 4th rows; all scales keeled, in 19 rows; tail ⅓ of length or more. . . . Scutellation and proportions as in *saurita,* but the upper labials are almost invariably 8, instead of 7. The color is greenish olive, or blackish in old specimens, and the dorsal stripe is usually absent, in such cases showing for a short distance behind the head" (Brown, Gen., 1901).

"Very slender; tail forming ⅓ of the total length. Crown more elevated and convex anteriorly than in *E. saurita.* Nineteen dorsal rows of scales. Color olive black above, not lighter below the lateral stripe. Lateral stripe greenish yellow, very narrow on the 3rd and 4th lateral rows. No dorsal stripe. Abdomen uniform greenish. In form, this closely resembles *E. saurita,* but is at once distinguished by the absence of the dorsal stripe, of which there is no trace, except for about a half inch behind the head. The color of the upper parts is also much darker, and the first 2 rows of scales below the dorsal stripe are not lighter than above it. Florida.—Baron Osten Sacken" (Kennicott). Eye over labials 4 and 5.

Color: A snake caught by Henry Harrison Lee, June 21, 1921, at Billy's Lake, Okefinokee Swamp, Ga. The dorsal color is brussels brown, raw umber, or medal bronze. The dorsal stripe is vetiver green or light olive-gray bordered on either side with black. The skin between the dorsal scales shows as black or white flecks, and sometimes there are black markings on the scales. The lateral stripes are marguerite yellow. The stripes cease on the tail, the dorsum there being light brownish olive to brownish olive to buffy olive. The color below the lateral stripe and on the ends of the ventrals is avellaneous, wood brown, or cinnamon-drab. The top of the head is grayish olive to deep grayish olive or citrine-drab to deep olive. There is a black stripe on the side of the head. The upper labials and lower side of the head are white, pale gull gray, or pallid purplish gray. The belly to the vent is tilleul buff or almost vinaceous-buff. The underside of the tail is olive-buff or deep olive-buff.

A snake from Okefinokee Swamp, Ga., described Apr. 25, 1921. The chin and gulars are satiny and white or bluish white. The ventrals are cream with 3 mm. of the end a light bronzy brown. This is not as intense or as extensive as in our northern *T. s. sirtalis,* nor is this as beautiful a snake. The under surface of the tail is yellowish.

A snake taken at Crosby Pond, May 11, 1921, by A. H. Wright. A light-colored *T. sirtalis sackeni.* Body is brussels brown. Dorsal stripe dull citrine. Side of each belly plate apricot buff, or cinnamon rufous. Lateral stripe pale chalcedony yellow, as is underside of tail.

Habitat: Before Wright and Bishop discussed it at length, there were few notes on its habitat. They found it throughout Okefinokee Swamp, Georgia. The best summary is Carr's: "Marsh-borders and wet meadows; lake, pond and stream shores. Common. Semiaquatic and semi-arboreal; willow thickets in inundated meadows are a favorite habitat; they are al-most as graceful and agile climbers as *Opheodrys aestivus,* and are fre-quently found with the latter in trees and bushes along lake margins."

In the language of 1859, 1862–65, 1873–81, this form was in the Floridian district (Cooper, Binney, Cope, Porter, all in Ecol.); in 1898 in the Gulf strip of the Lower Austral (Merriam, 1898) or in the Sabalian zone of Hebard. It is primarily of Florida, but like others once thought Floridian, it has extended northward along the coast.

Period of activity: *Early appearances*—May 31, 1912; Apr. 25, May 11, May 17, 1921; Mar. 18, 1934; Mar. 31, 1934 (A.H.W.). *Fall disappearance*—Aug. 15, 1911, Aug. 13, 1912 (Deckert, Fla., 1918).

Breeding: Viviparous. *Young*—Number, 5-12. Time of birth, July 12–Aug. 1. Data for this form are meager. All Ditmars says is that it produces small broods of living young. The most extended account is Ruthven's: "During the summer of 1905 I reared 2 broods which were born on July 19. The young resembled those of other forms in habits except for their greater agility. Like the adults they steadily refused earthworms, but at the age of 3 days took to the water and captured and ate live minnows voraciously. Their manner of catching fish was interesting. Dropping or climbing into the basin they would rush around about, mouth open, until they encountered a fish, when they would rush out of the water, lashing their tails energetically, carry the fish to a corner and proceed to devour it. The sense of sight seemed to be depended upon but little in capturing the fish, and dead ones were eaten apparently as frequently as live ones." In 1917 Safford merely recorded that "they bring forth their young alive," but in 1931 Van Hyning (Fla., 1931) gave a definite record: "On July 12, 1928, a southern ribbon-snake, which had been kept in captivity for several weeks, gave birth to 11 living young." Conant and Bridges (Gen., 1939) gave about 5 to 12, and Schmidt and Davis (Gen., 1941) gave 5 to 20 for all 3 subspecies of ribbon snakes. We have seen after July 17 *sackeni* females which we deemed pregnant; hence the date of about Aug. 1.

Food: Frogs, treefrogs, fish, earthworms, toads, salamanders. Wright and Bishop, Safford, Haltom (Ala., 1931), Allen (Miss., 1932a), Carr.

Authorities:

Carr, A. F., Jr. (Fla., 1940a)
Cope, E. D. (Fla., 1889)
Kennicott, R. (Gen., 1860–61)
Loennberg, E. (Fla., 1895)

Ruthven, A. G. (Gen., 1908)
Safford, W. E. (Fla., 1919)
Wright, A. H., and S. C. Bishop (Ga., 1916)

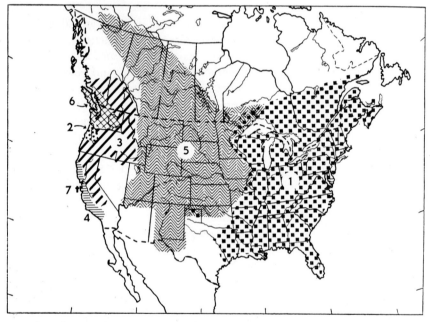

Map. 60. *Thamnophis*—1, *sirtalis*; 2, *s. concinnus*; 3, *s. fitchi*; 4, *s. infernalis*; 5, *s. parietalis*; 6, *s. pickeringi*; 7, *s. tetrataenia*.

Garter snake (127—Taylor 1835), **Common garter snake** (76—Craigin 1881)
Thamnophis sirtalis sirtalis (Linné) 1766. Fig. 242; Map 60

Other common names: Adder; blue spotted snake; broad garter snake; brown snake; Churchill's garter snake; common streaked snake; common striped snake; dusky garter snake; eastern garter snake (3); first and last; garden snake; grass garter snake; green (spotted) garter snake; green spotted snake (Catesby, 1731–43); hooped snake; little brown snake; little green snake (Catesby, 1731–43); North American garter snake; North American striped snake; northeastern garter snake; northern garter snake; ordinary garter snake; ordinary spotted garter snake; plain garter snake; red garter snake; sirtal snake; slow garter; spotted (garter) snake; streaked snake; striped (garter) snake; striped (grass) snake; swamp garter; three-striped adder; water garter; yellow snake.

Range: North America, from Maritime Provinces and mouth of St. Lawrence River, through Quebec and Ontario to w. tip of Lake Superior, e. of Mississippi River to cent. Missouri; thence diagonally across Missouri and s.e. corner of Oklahoma to Brazos River, Tex.—U.S.A.: Ala.; Ark.; Conn.; D.C.; Del.; Fla.; Ga.; Ia.; Ill.; Ind.; Ky.; La.; Mass.; Md.; Me.; Mich.; Miss.; Mo.; N.C.; N.H.; N.J.; N.Y.; O.; Okla.; Pa.; R.I.; S.C.; Tenn.; Tex.; Va.; Vt.; W. Va.; Wis. Can.: N.B.; N.S.; Ont.; P.E.I.; Que. *Elevation*— Sea level to 6,000 feet. Sea level to 1,500 feet (Manville, Me., 1939); 1,000–6,000 feet (King, Tenn.); 3,500 feet (Rhoads, Tenn.); 2,500, 4,000, 4,200 feet (Dunn, N.C., 1917); to 6,400 feet (Brimley, N.C., 1941–42); 900–2,400 feet (Smith, Pa., 1945); 1,400–4,000 feet (Barbour, Ky., 1950).

Size: Adults, 18 or 20–48 inches. We have seen live garters 42 inches and once saw a 4-foot one which one of our embryology students received from Florida.

Distinctive characteristics: "The lateral stripe is always on the 2nd and 3rd scale rows, and the eye is large. The dorsal stripe usually occupies the median and halves of the adjacent rows, is frequently narrower and occasionally wanting. The dorsal scale formula is practically always . . . 19-17; the supralabials nearly always 7, occasionally 8, rarely 6; the infralabials 10, occasionally 9 or 11. The oculars are usually 1–3, often 1–4, rarely 1–2; the subcaudals 54 (female) to 84 (male); the ventrals 137 (female) to 167 (male). Tail length .192 to .262. . . . There are 2 rows of well-defined spots (rarely fused) on the skin between the lateral and dorsal stripes, and these usually cover the involved scales (exclusive of the keels). The spots are not usually distinct upon the scales, however, owing to the darkness of the ground color. . . . Stripes greenish, or bluish, usually tinged with yellow" (Ruthven, Gen., 1908).

Color: A snake from Hagerstown, Md., received from R. H. McCauley, Jr., Aug., 1937. The back is marked with 3 stripes. The middorsal one is straw yellow on the neck, becoming later cream color and then light dull green-yellow. The last-named color is that of the lateral stripes, or they may be light lumiere green or on the neck veronese green. The space from the 4th to 9th scale rows between the dorsal and lateral stripes is traversed by 2 rows of squarish alternating spots of mummy brown to black. Each occupies about 3 rows of scales vertically and 1 to 2 scale rows longitudinally. The interscale space in the intervals between the spots is oural green. Below the light lateral stripe is a buffy olive band located on the 1st scale row and crossing the ends of the ventrals. Within this area and alternating with the lower row of spots above the lateral stripe is a series of small black spots. These spots are principally the vertical sutures between 2 scales of the 1st scale row plus a more or less disjointed horizontal black spot between the 2nd and 3rd scale rows. The top of the head and the temporal scales are black. The face is light cress green. The upper labials, which tend to have dark sutures, are rainette green except for the 5th, 6th and 7th, which have in the lower half a touch of glass green or deep seafoam green. The rostral is like the lower labials. The iris is blackish with a wash of light yellowish olive or mignonette green above the pupil and a slight wash of honey yellow below it or merely on the lower pupil rim. The lower labials may be washed with rainette green, but in general appear seafoam yellow or almost white, as do also the chin shields and gulars. The ventrals are kildare green, becoming deep seafoam green on the 1st neck plate. There is a half-concealed black spot near either end of each ventral on its anterior border. Unlike many garter snakes farther north, this snake has also a slight irregular sprinkling of black spots on the venter between the 2 rows of partly concealed hemispheric spots.

Abnormal coloration—Melanism. Patch of Point Pelee, Ont. (1919), had 3 melano specimens, one of which had 2 black individuals in a litter of 38 young. In the same place Logier (1925) had 1 black specimen all of whose offspring were black. Several normals had some black offspring. Logier (Ont., 1929) later wrote: "It will be seen from the above figures that out of 46 young born of 2 black females, 28 or 60.87% were black; and out of 56 young born of 3 normal females, 29 or 51.78% were black. Out of a total of 102 young born of these 5 females, 57 or 55.88% were black." In 1930(a) he stated: "Out of the total of 276 young born of these 10 females 99 or 35.86% were black, a much lower percentage than in the 1927 broods." In 1941(a) the Blanchards (Gen.) declared: "A 2nd attempt to study the inheritance of melanism with several specimens from Toledo showed that blackness is inherited in simple Mendelian fashion. . . ." They held that the Ontario specimens (not according to the Mendelian ratio) were thus because more than 1 male was involved. Evans and Roecker (1951) reported that of 25 snakes taken at Long Point, Norfolk Co., Ont., 6 or 24% were melanistic.

Axtell of the Buffalo Museum also had snakes from Long Point, Ont. All garter snakes seen on one trip were measured and sexed and their color noted. Ten others, black and of regular pattern, escaped. Of a group of 16 black in color, a large female had 20 young, 14 of which were black, the others typical, hence 70% black. In contrast to the 16 black snakes, were 21 of normal pattern caught.

Albinism—Several albinos have been recorded. Eaton (N.Y., 1945) reported one: "A partial albino, half grown, found about Aug. 1 along Lime-stone Brook. The general color was light buff, with lateral stripes and dorsal spots faintly indicated in orange."

Erythrism—"From reports and from scant literature it would seem that a population of garter snakes does occur in northern Michigan and northern Ontario which shows a peculiar reddish tendency in some specimens. This red color is not limited to the skin, but is the color of the actual scale" (Carpenter, Mich., 1948). Carpenter took a red one on "Bois Blanc Island, Mich., in the northern part of Lake Huron."

Habitat: All early authors called it the most common, abundant, ubiqui-tous, widespread snake of eastern Canada and the United States from James Bay and the Gulf of St. Lawrence to the Gulf of Mexico.

Of the 154 habitat categories we secured, the 20 found most frequently are: everywhere (all sorts of situations) 18; woods 16; near water 13; lakes 12; fields 10; meadows 8; swamps 8; borders of rivers 8; marshes 7; along streams 6; gardens 6; roadsides 6; parks 6; clearings 4; margin of ditches 4; margins of creeks 4; moist situations 4; in water swimming 4; in water (otherwise) 4; low ground 4. Over 110 habitat characterizations occurred only once. Seventeen other habitats are: under logs 3; cultivated fields 3; open fields 3; margins 3; lowlands 3; damp localities 2; moist places 2; high ground 2; forest clearings 2; rocky islets 2; ponds 2; along water courses 2; under or near fences 2; low bushes 2; pastures 2; vacant lots 2; wastelands 2.

In 1898 Mearns said, "It ranges from Hudson River to the highest altitudes in the Highlands." In 1899 he had it "abundant from the margin of Schoharie Creek up to the summit of Hunter Mountain." It inhabits the eastern wooded region of North America. It is not really an aquatic animal (in water 4, swimming 4), but rather semiaquatic, as these adjectives show: *low* 11, *moist* 7, *wet* 7, *marshy* 4, *swampy* 3, *damp* 2. From coniferous forest to open pastures or water, from rocky mountain top to valley city wastelands it dwells—our most common snake.

Period of activity: *Early appearances*—Mar. 22, 1842 (Linsley, Conn.); May 4 (Smith, O.); Mar. 5, 13 (Hurter, Mo.); Mar. 15, April (Englehardt et al., N.Y.); Apr. 28, 1901, Apr. 28, 1903, Apr. 30 (Evermann, N.Y.); Apr. 17, 1917, Mar. 29, Apr. 10, 1918, Apr. 10, 1922 (Dunn, Mass.); Mar. 6 (Minton, Ind.); Mar. 16 (Allen, Mass.); Apr. 9 (Evermann and Clark); Mar. 30 (Wright and Allen, N.Y.); Mar. 15–early April (Englehardt, N.Y.); Mar. 24 (Seiss); Mar. 29 (Wright, N.Y.); Nov. 23 (Breckenridge); Mar. 24 (List, Ind., 1950). The first appearance dates of our journal notes (1903–15) are: Apr. 7, 1903; Apr. 17, 1904; Mar. 29, Apr. 2, 1905; Apr. 6, 28, 1907; Apr. 26, 1908; Apr. 7, 17, 1909; Mar. 31, Apr. 9, 1910; Apr. 18, 1911; Mar. 31, Apr. 20, 1912; May 17, 1914; Apr. 21, 22, 1915. *Fall disappearance*— Oct. 7 (Jones, N.S., 1865); Dec. 10 (Englehardt et al.); Oct. 16, Nov. 13

(Hurter); Nov. 2 (Wright and Allen); Oct. 22 (Dunn, Mass.); Oct. 30 (Wright); October (Axtell). *Seasonal catch* (Raleigh, N.C.)—Jan., 4 snakes; Feb., 1; Mar., 7; Apr., 8; May, 3; June, 8; July, 4; Aug., 2; Sept., 0; Oct., 2; Nov., 4; Dec., 0. Total, 43 (Brimley, N.C., 1925).

Hibernation—"Most commonly seen and found when gathered preceding hibernation, and also in the spring when sunning themselves just after appearance from hibernation" (Wright, N.Y., 1919b).

Mention has been made of snakes associated in hibernation; in 1942 Lachner (Pa., 1942) added newts and Wehrle's salamander. These were unearthed on January 3 from gravel 2½ feet from the surface, not in a mass, but torpid. Besides garters, there were the ring-necked snake, ribbon snake, red-bellied snake, DeKay's snake, milk snake, smooth green snake, and a rattlesnake (*Sistrurus?*). Gilpin (N.S., 1875) found garters wintering in an anthill. Smith (O., 1882) reported them ploughed up in bunches. Hurter (Mo., 1911) found them in a torpid condition in a rotten stump, 30 inches down. Sometimes they reappear from mid-December to mid-February. See Ruthven (1908) and Bishop and Alexander.

In 1949 Bailey, in his studies on temperature toleration of garter snakes in hibernation, found that survival at the 18-inch level each winter demonstrates the ability of garter snakes to withstand a minimum temperature of approximately $-2°C.$ ($-2.2°$ and $-1.5°$ in two years) and to resist subfreezing temperature for a protracted period (28 and 18 continuous days during the 2 years).

In 1944–45 other interesting observations on hibernation appeared, such as those by Pope (Ill., 1944), Breckenridge, and McCauley (Md., 1945).

Breeding: Viviparous. Males 392–764 mm., females 469–1,195 mm. In his long years of observations W. DeW. Miller measured 25 adult males, 469–710 mm., and 40 adult females, 506–925 mm. No discussion can be comprehensive or detailed without attention to the Blanchards and their students who worked on various phases of breeding in this species. See, for example, "Authorities" below.

Sexual dimorphism—In 1933 Harrison stated: "The dorsal keels in the anal region of the garter snake *Thamnophis sirtalis sirtalis* are characteristically knobbed in males of a length greater than 475 mm. In males under this length they are usually absent or very weakly developed. In females of all lengths they are generally absent." In 1928 M. D. Burt stated, "All females below 550 mm. . . . were found to be without embryos." Also, "The right oviduct bears the greater number of embryos" and "over half of the mature females were not bearing young." One of the best local studies is that of Axtell, who handled 1,414 specimens. "It was observed that between 80% and 95% of the adult females were pregnant. In late July and early August, gravid females were usually 20 inches or more in length. We found very few that were smaller. The smallest pregnant individual was 18½ inches. Non-gravid females up to 19¾ inches were common. Since there was a slightly higher percentage of non-gravid females between 20 and 21 inches than at greater lengths, this suggests that a few immature specimens may reach and even slightly exceed the 20-inch mark that typically divides adult females from immature at this season. The earliest that we encountered new young of the year was July 25. . . . The largest of the 1,414 specimens was 33¼ inches, a female. The second largest was 32 inches, and 7 others ranged from 30 to 31. These were all females. The largest male was 28½, the second largest 27½. These were the only 2 males that had attained a length of 27 inches or more. Forty females, however, were as large as this or larger. Only 22 males reached 2 feet. This was a common length for females."

Mating—In the light of recent emphasis on fall mating it is well to recall that as early as 1882 Smith (O., 1882) recorded that "in September and October the sexes have been seen in copulation." Back in 1890 Seiss and Mayer marveled about the sexes finding each other. The former wrote: "The males and the females immediately [after first appearance] seek each other, and may often be found in warm sunny spots, joined in copulation. At this season especially they emit a rank and disagreeable odor, particularly noticeable when captured, and I feel convinced that the sexes follow and find each other entirely by scent."

The most striking case of the sexes finding each other is recounted by Bishop and Alexander. "We have not observed the mating habits of this species in Alleghany State Park, but in John Boyd Thacher Park, Albany County, some observations were made by E. J. Stein and H. H. Cleaves, which are of interest. On May 2, 1926, while crossing a wooded terrace on the Helderberg escarpment several garter snakes were noticed moving restlessly about on the ground. A more careful search revealed the presence of another individual, which subsequently proved to be a female, stretched out on the low branch of a small hemlock. While this individual was under observation, two of the snakes on the ground made their way to the tree and climbing out on the branch attempted to place themselves in contact with her. The struggles of the competing males caused all three to tumble to the ground. The female again climbed into the hemlock and was followed by the two males which covered her track exactly as a dog follows the scent of a rabbit. The first male to reach the female measured his length on her body following all its curves with the chin pressed to her back. Mating followed, with the second male attempting so persistently to join the pair that all three again fell to the ground. The mated pair, maintaining their position, crawled off beneath loose leaves on the ground, the second male in the meantime having disappeared."

Several instances of a female mating successively with two or three males are known. Rarely a simultaneous mating of two males with one female occurs. See Brennan's note (Wis.) of 1924.

Many wild tales have been told and emotional conclusions related concerning marital devotion and retaliatory aggressiveness by the male defending the dead female. He probably follows her scent for mating purposes. Truitt (Md., 1927) wrote: "Moving the bucket (with female in it) to another part of the bog area, some 20 yards distant, and returning at about 4:30 P.M., things were found to be greatly disturbed. . . . There were two dead garter snakes to one of which was attached a living snake in copulation. The second dead snake was a male. . . . To the mutilated body of the female the male remained attached for a period of 11 minutes after first being seen; how much longer he had been attached there was no way of determining."

Noble and Clausen's (Gen., 1936) study of sense organs in *Storeria* and *Thamnophis* influenced several interpretations of trailing, etc. Significant excerpts are: "Snakes in following trails make use of their tongues to carry the odors to the Jacobson's organs as Baumann, 1929, Kahmann, 1932, and others have described. . . . Similarly we find that in both food-seeking and companion-seeking activity, *Storeria* and *Thamnophis* are guided more by stimulations of the olfactory than by those of their Jacobson's organs. . . . Species identification is accomplished chiefly by the olfactory sense while vision enters into the response secondarily. The tongue itself plays no part in species identification. . . . The secretion of the cloacal glands does not attract. The integumental covering of the body is the source of odorous substances which serve in one case as an attraction to other individuals of the same species and in the other case to individuals of the opposite sex. . . . The olfactory organs alone are adequate sensory mechanism for food trailing in *S. dekayi* and *T. sirtalis*. The tongue and Jacobson's organs in combination make trailing possible, but either one of these structures alone is inadequate." In 1946 Breder reported a series of observations on the mating behavior of male garters when the females rested on the edge of a pond. The males had difficulty in locating the females. They swam definitely and carefully around the edge of the pond examining the land for 6 inches in from the edge and flicking the tongue in the explorations.

The courtship behavior discussed above is of the *T. radix* type described by Davis and by Weed. See also a recent paper by List (Ind., 1950) wherein he describes in detail the courtship attitudes of 2 males.

Young—Number, 3–85. 3, 20, 50, 61, 72 (Breckenridge); 7, 11, 21, 42 (Axtell); 8, 21, 24, 35, 41, 42, 44, 45, 48 (McCauley); 8, 11, 16, 27, 28, 31, 34 (Ditmars); 10 (Barbour, Conant); 10, 70 (Funkhouser); 10, 12, 13, 15, 17, 30, 32 (Conant); 12 (Bishop and Alexander); 12, 24, 26, 27, 31, 34, 49 (Logier); 13 (Garman); 13, 80 (Seiss); 13, 15, 16, 17, 18, 30, 32 (Burt); 14, 28, 40 (Fowler); 14, 16, 22, 33, 39 (Conant); 14, 30, 33, 39, 57 (Wood);

17, 27, 39, 45 (Wright and Allen); 18 (List); 19 (Wright and Simpson); 20 (Williams); 21 (Barbour, Meade); 25, 40 (Smith); 30 (Ditmars, Cook, Pope); 31 (Ramsey); 35 (Welter and Carr, Lowe); 35, 39 (Hay); 37 (Breder and Breder); 38 (Patch); 40 (Mayer, Loennberg, Gaines, Evermann and Clark); 42 (Putnam); 50 (Lowe, Babcock, Graf, Jewett and Gordon); 57 (Wood); 64 (Mattlin); 65 (Fowler); 70, 80 (Boulenger); 72 (Reddick); 73 (Wallace); 78 (Schenck); 80 (Morse); 85 (Martof).

Time of birth, June 24–Sept. 20. June 24 (Meade); July–August (Smith); late July–August (Creaser); late July to mid-September (Ruthven, Breckenridge); July 3, Aug. 1 (Conant); July 17 (Reddick); July 21, August (Barbour); August, September (Bishop and Alexander); Aug. 1 (Hay, Wood); Aug. 1, 22, Sept. 15 (Wright and Allen); Aug. 2, Sept. 5 (Mattlin); Aug. 5 (Ramsey); Aug. 6 (Martof); Aug. 9, Sept. 5 (Ditmars); Aug. 11 (Wright and Simpson); Aug. 11, 25 (Garman); Aug. 12, 23, Sept. 21 (Axtell); Aug. 13 (Evermann and Clark); Aug. 15, 21, Sept. 3, 11 (Logier); Aug. 16, Sept. 20 (Wright and Allen); Aug. 25 (Surface); Aug. 28 (McCauley); last of August (Mayer); August and early September (Ditmars, Atkinson); early September (Jones); Sept. 1 (Logier); Sept. 14, 16 (Wallace); Sept. 20, 22 (Conant).

Size, 4–9 inches. 4 inches (Jones); $4\frac{5}{8}$ (Wright and Allen); 5, 7 (Schenck); 5.5 (Putnam, Mayer); 5.6, 6, 6.4, 6.9, 7 (Evermann and Clark); 5.8, 5.9 (Conant); 6.1 (McCauley, Surface); 6, 7 (Hay); 6.25, 6.8, 8.1 (Conant); 6.8, 7, 7.4 (Boyer and Heinze); 6.8, 7.5 (Wood); 7 (Schenck, Reddick); 7.2, 7.8 (Mattlin); 7.5 (Seiss); 7.7 (Yarrow); 8.1 (Fichter). Recently, Martof (Mich., 1954) in one brood of 85 found the males were from 152–197 mm. in total length and the females, 150–191 mm. In newborn garter snakes the large musk glands are easily seen at the base of the tail in females; in males they are not visible externally.

In captivity sometimes a female may give birth to 1 or 2 young, then later several, then a tardy 1 or more a day or several days later. In nature no doubt the brood is usually shed at 1 parturition. Triplehorn had a female which, on Jan. 11, 1952, gave birth to 36 young, 202–225 mm. long. Wood (O., 1945) records that a female gave birth to 57 young in $1\frac{1}{2}$ hours. Boyer (Gen.) observes that it takes 3 hours and $4\frac{1}{2}$ minutes for 27 young to be born, and recounts further details about the newly hatched young.

Food: Frogs, mice, toads, insects, fish, salamanders, mammals, young birds, earthworms, molluscs. Macauley (N.Y., 1829), Storer, Atkinson (Pa., 1901), Lagler and Salyer (Mich., 1945), Uhler, Cottam, and Clarke (Va., 1939), Axtell, Hamilton (Gen., 1951).

Authorities: From the high pile of material on this species that we have assembled, an immense book could be written. Many of the principal references are listed below, but some are necessarily omitted from the discussion, which includes only authors from 1836 to 1954.

Arnold, D. E. (Mass., 1929)
Axtell, H. H. (N.Y., 1947)
Bailey, R. M. (Ia., 1949)
Bishop, S. C., and W. P. Alexander (N.Y., 1927)
Blanchard, F. N. (several)
Blanchard, F. N. and F. C. (Gen., 1941, 1941a)
Boyer, D. A. and A. A. Heinze (Mo., 1934)
Breckenridge, W. J. (Minn., 1944a)
Breder, C. M., Jr. (Gen., 1946)
Burt, C. E. (Mich., 1928)
Burt, M. D. (Mich., 1928a)
Conant, R. (O., 1938a; Pa., 1942)
Davis, D. D. (Gen., 1936)
Eckel, E. C. (N.Y., 1902)
Evans, H. E., and R. E. Roecker (Ont., 1951)

Evermann, B. W., and H. L. Clark (Ind., 1920)
Funkhouser, W. D. (Ky., 1925)
Harrison, M. B. (Gen., 1933)
Hay, O. P. (Ind., 1892)
Holbrook, J. E. (Gen., 1836–42)
Jacobs, D. I. (Minn., 1950)
Logier, E. B. S. (Ont., 1929, 1930a)
McCauley, R. H. (Md., 1945)
Martof, B. (Mich., 1954)
Mayer, A. G. (Gen., 1893)
Putnam, F. W. (Gen., 1862; Mass., 1866)
Ruthven, A. B. (Gen., 1908, 1909)
Seiss, C. F. (Gen., 1890)
Speck, F. G. (Mass., 1916)
Sperry, W. L. (Mich., 1904)
Storer, D. H. (Mass., 1839)
Surface, H. A. (Pa., 1906)
Wallace, G. J. (Mass., 1938)

When Ruthven and one of the present authors entered the herpetologic field (1900–1908), we were confronted with 8 forms: *sirtalis, ordinatus, dorsalis, obscura, melanota, graminea, semifasciata,* and *pallidula.* To New Yorkers, Eckel in 1902 offered 6 forms; to Hoosiers, Cope, Hay, Butler, and Blatchley offered 5 of the above forms; and to Illini, Davis and Rice offered 4. We will not go into an extended account of these forms except to give a summary of a few comments from the many writers opposing Cope.

1890, C. F. Seiss: "Naturalists from time to time have made about 26 distinct species out of this 1 *sirtalis,* and it is extremely perplexing and enough to make the young scientist weary, to study these many long, dry, and useless descriptions, only to find in the end that they describe one common species known to science since 1748."

1904, E. B. Branson (Kan.): "The calling of this variety a subspecies is another example of Cope's readiness to base subspecies on slight, variable, and unimportant color markings."

1900: E. D. Cope (1898) gave a synopsis. Our chronological summary of authors on the 7 so-called forms follows:

I. *ordinatus* Linnaeus phase, 1766. Baird and Girard (1853); Cragin; Hay; Loennberg; Rhoads; Garman; Ditmars; Blatchley; Atkinson; Eckel; Morse; Drowne; Notestein; Surface; Nash; Brimley, 1910.

II. *dorsalis* Baird and Girard, 1853. Yarrow, 1875; Mozley; Smith; Cragin; Davis and Rice; Higley; Hay; Taylor; Blatchley; Beyer; Atkinson Strecker; Eckel; Surface; Nash, 1908.

III. *obscura* Cope, 1875. Cope, 1880; Davis and Rice; Cragin; Townsend; Hay; Taylor; Rhoads; Blatchley; Cope; Eckel; Brown; Morse; Strecker, 1915.

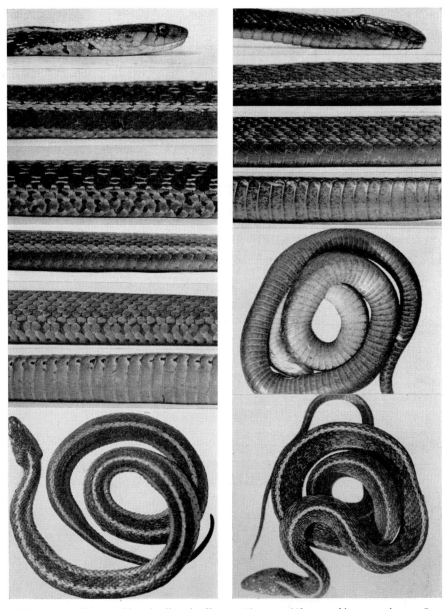

Fig. 242. *Thamnophis sirtalis sirtalis,* Ithaca, N.Y.

Fig. 243. *Thamnophis s. concinnus,* Corvallis, Ore., K. Gordon.

IV. *melanota* Smith, 1882. Smith, W. H., 1882; Higley, 1889.
V. *graminea* Cope, 1888. Cope, 1888; Butler; Hay; Rhoads; Eckel; Morse; Drowne, 1905.
VI. *semifasciata* Cope, 1892. Atkinson, 1901; Branson; A. E. Brown, 1904.
VII. *pallidula* Allen, 1899. Allen, G. M. 1899; Eckel; Henshaw; Ruthven, 1908.

1948, L. M. Klauber (Gen., 1948): "It is difficult to see how Linnaeus' *Coluber sirtalis* ever became attached to the common garter snake, for the subcaudal counts of the type do not fit that snake." Most herpetologists agree, as do we, with Klauber's extended argument in spite of the confusion to the present generation. In 1900–1910 we preferred *ordinatus*, but were offered *sirtalis* and accepted it. Between 1948–1952 we have changed this manuscript three times; we now use *sirtalis sirtalis,* anticipating the International Commission's decision.

Northwestern garter snake (8—Van Denburgh 1897), Pacific red-barred garter snake

Thamnophis sirtalis concinnus (Hallowell) 1852. Fig. 243; Map 60

Other common names: California garter snake; embellished garter snake; one-striped garter snake; Pacific garter snake; Pacific red-sided garter snake; Pickering's garter snake (6—Coues and Yarrow 1878); red-spotted garter snake.

Range: N.w. Oregon coast and Willamette drainage area.—Ore.; Wash. *Elevation*—Sea level to 5,000 feet or more.

Size: Adults, 16 or 17–36 inches.

Distinctive characteristics: "Top of head and face, including supralabials and infralabials, predominantly red; dorsal stripe pale yellow, narrow (1⅔ scale rows wide), with even and sharply defined borders; dorsal ground color jet black; red lateral blotches sharply contrasted with ground color and in a single series; red blotches small, usually not more than ⅓ as long as black areas separating them; lateral stripes narrow, pale milky yellow, with irregular borders, bounded below by jet black areas that set them off, or else partly or entirely absent; ventral surface heavily marked with black, often in extensively continuous areas, superimposed on pale blue background" (Fitch, Gen., 1941).

Color: A snake from Corvallis, Ore., received from Kenneth Gordon, June, 1929. The general color of the upper parts is black, becoming on the lower scale rows and ends of ventrals bluish black. A sulphur yellow dorsal stripe covers the median dorsal scale row, with paired spots of the same color on halves of the 2 adjoining rows. There are vertical bars of scarlet or jasper red on the scales above the 1st row. The forward part of the head is russet or cinnamon-rufous, the rear of the head vinaceous-rufous. The rear labials are scarlet or grenadine red. The iris is black, the pupil rim olive-buff or sulphur yellow. The lower labials and the gulars are marked with considerable scarlet. Otherwise, the lower part of the head is white or cartridge buff. The ventrals on the rear part of neck are pale yellow-green, the next ones oural green, and after passing through a stretch of microcline green, they become bluish black or bluish slate-black except for a narrow caudal border of white on each plate.

Habitat: Information on this species is rare and rather incidental. Fitch (Gen., 1941) wrote: "*T. s. concinnus* is abundant in the upper Willamette Valley and in that region its racial characters are strongly developed. During several years' residence at Eugene, Lane County, Oregon, the writer was familiar with this form and knew it to be distinct from *sirtalis* of southwestern Oregon (a population of fitchi which heretofore has been included with *concinnus*), since living individuals are strikingly different in color and pattern." In 1939 Gordon said: "This is perhaps the commonest snake in western Oregon from the coast to the Cascades and from the Columbia River to California. Because of their red heads, snakes of this and other subspecies of *sirtalis* are locally known as copperheads, and some part of the reputation of the true copperhead is transferred to them. The real copperhead is an eastern form, and these garter snakes are in no way dangerous." In 1942 we saw that it was common in the Corvallis area. When we visited Gordon, we encountered several on our field trips. He let it be known that we wanted some, and several boys soon furnished us plenty of garters from which to pick specimens. Seemingly it is widespread, particularly liking hills, sunny slopes, southern exposures, and almost any cover the region furnished. Under this form Cooper wrote about garter snakes in general.

Period of activity: MVZ dates are Apr. 13 to Oct. 14.

Breeding: Viviparous. *Young*—We know no published information on this subject. SU No. 4504 from Alsea River near Alsea, Benton Co., Ore., taken Aug. 28, 1899, by Allen and Burchon is a young snake only 220 mm. in length. When we saw it we made the note, "This must be beyond newborn size."

Food: Small vertebrates, frogs. Fitch (Calif., 1941a).

Authorities:

Brown, A. E. (Calif., 1903)
Cooper, J. G. (Gen., 1860)
Cope, E. D. (Gen., 1883–84, 1900)
Fitch, H. S. (Gen. 1941; Calif., 1941a)
Gordon, K. (Ore., 1939)
Hallowell, E. (Ore., 1854)

Johnson, M. L. (Wash., 1942)
Ruthven, A. G. (Gen., 1908)
Van Denburgh, J., and J. R. Slevin
   (Gen., 1918)
Yarrow, H. C. (Ariz., 1875)

1944, A. H. and A. A. Wright: Some of the *concinnus* specimens of Corvallis, Ore., are strikingly colored garters. To Hallowell this form is the most beautiful North American serpent, but we still hold *T. cyrtopsis* the most beautiful (*ocellata, aurata, ornata,* etc.) garter west of the Mississippi. Gordon shows that the dorsal stripe is varied and red heads sometimes are white. We confess that when we first saw the McKenzie River specimen we wondered if it was *concinnus;* so with those of the Washington side of the Columbia River. No tyro can evaluate garters without knowing them alive and in the field.

Cascade garter snake, Northwestern garter snake

Thamnophis sirtalis fitchi Fox 1951. Fig. 244; Maps 59, 60

Other common names: California garter snake; Pacific garter snake; red-barred garter snake.

Range: "The great valleys of California between the Coast Range and the Sierras, extending into western Nevada; reaching the coast in northwestern California and southwestern Oregon; eastern Oregon and Washington into Idaho (and extreme western Montana) and British Columbia" (Fox, Gen., 1951).—U.S.A.: Calif.; Ida.; Nev.; Ore.; Wash. Can.: Alta.; B.C. *Elevation*—Sea level to 6,100 feet. 260, 270, 600, 1,000, 4,800, 6,100 feet (Klauber, 1930b); above 2,500 feet (Ferguson, Ore., 1952).

Size: Adults, 17–48 inches.

Distinctive characteristics: "A *Thamnophis sirtalis* in which the top of the head is black or very dark; the red and black colors of the sides of the body are arranged into an upper black stripe and a lower series of regularly spaced blotches which are continuous with the stripe dorsally and which are separated from each other laterally by regularly arranged red blotches; little or no black markings on the belly" (Fox, Gen., 1951).

Color: A snake from Lapine, Ore., taken by the roadside ditch where the frogs, *Rana,* were caught Apr. 5, 1942. The ground color of the back is black with a dorsal stripe 1 scale and 2 half-scales wide of ochraceous-buff, becoming on the tail cream-buff and on the neck buff-yellow. The top of the head is olivaceous black (1) or dark grayish olive. The upper labials are deep olive-buff, each of the rear 2 having a touch of citrine-drab and the last 1 a spot of brazil red. The preoculars, loreals, and postnasal are also deep olive-buff. The lateral stripe of pale green-yellow is on the 2nd and part of 3rd scale rows, broadening on the side of the neck to about 3 rows. Below it on the ventral half of 1st row and on ends of ventrals is a stripe of dresden brown or medal bronze. Above the lateral stripe and within the black ground color are brazil red interspaces ½ plus 2 plus ½ scales deep and no more than 1 scale longitudinally with the centers of the scales in this brazil red area, black. The eye is black below with a pupil rim of ochraceous-buff. Above the pupil is a patch of black bordered behind and in front with cream. The underside of the head is light buff to cream, the belly greenish glaucous-blue to deep bluish glaucous, absolutely clear of black. The subcaudals are the same except for a space back of vent, where each scale bears a patch of black.

A snake from near Fresno, Calif., 1 mile west of Kerman, received from Hadsall, May 15, 1941. The background of the back is fuscous-black to black with a dorsal stripe on mid-row and halves of 2 adjoining ones. It is honey yellow on forward half of body becoming isabella color in the rear. There is a lateral stripe on the 2nd and lower half of 3rd row of deep colonial buff, becoming on tail reed yellow. This expands on the side of the neck. There is no indication of an upper row of square black spots, these having merged into a solid band on either side of the dorsal stripe. The lower row of lateral spots is subsidiary to this band. The interspaces between these lower ones are brazil or morocco red, but are very small and scarcely show unless the skin is stretched in the rear of the body. There are also touches of this red in the interspaces of the lateral 2nd and 3rd scale row yellow stripe and also on the 1st row. The top of the head is black with no touch of red. The upper labials in their upper portions and the facial plates are ecru-olive, the lower portions of 3rd, 4th and 5th upper labials being reed yellow. The rear edges of 4th and 5th upper labials are black. The iris is black and deep colonial buff. The lower labials and underside of head and throat are ivory yellow. The ventral surface of body and tail is glaucous-green. The ends of ventrals and the 1st scale row are deep grayish olive or yellowish olive. Every alternate ventral on the forward half of the body has a little touch of the characteristic dark spot on its end, as in most *sirtalis* patterns.

Unfortunately our photographs of *tetrataenis* with its 2 black and 2 red bands, and of *fitchi* with its black lateral bars or the spots attached to them surrounded by red do not show clearly. See the contrast between *T. s. infernalis* and *T. s. fitchi* in Fox's (Gen., 1951) original Fig. 2 or Stebbins' Fig. 47 of his recent *Amphibians and Reptiles of North America* (1954).

Habitat: This snake lives along streams, lake margins, sloughs, ditches, ponds and in wet meadows and lowland pools. They are in the water as frequently as outside. They may be in mossy tracts of tepid shallow water of lakes, in driftwood into which they retire, or in tin cans and rubbish dumped into ditches or marsh margins. They may be on sunny open borders, in scanty vegetative cover, in tall grass, on bare ground, or in willow or brushy thickets if water is present. Rarely, they are taken on dry ground like a chaparral slope near a lake, or on a road several hundred feet from water.

The area of this form is in zones which 75 or 125 years ago would have been called Californian + Oregon + Central (Binney, Ecol., 1862-65) or Pacific + Central (Cope, Ecol., 1873-81) or Pacific southern + northern

848 HANDBOOK OF SNAKES

+ Rocky Mt. western (Porter, Ecol., 1873-81) or Californian + Montana (Drude, Ecol., 1883-84) or Coast Pacific + Interior Pacific (Sargent, Ecol., 1884).

Period of activity: *Early appearances*—May, 1925 (Logier); Apr. 12, 1928 (Klauber, Gen., 1930b); Mar. 21, 1894 (J. M. Stowell); Mar. 31, Apr. 5, 6, 7, 8, 11, 19, 1942 (A.H.W.); Mar., 1939, Mar., 1941 (Fitch, Calif., 1947). *Fall disappearance*—Sept., 1930 (Logier); Aug. 6-11, 1918 (Van Denburgh and Slevin); Sept., 1892 (Van Denburgh, Ida., 1895). MVZ dates are Feb. 23 to Dec. 16.

Breeding: Viviparous. *Young*—In 1928(a) Fisher wrote, "So far as can be ascertained from the literature at hand, nothing is known of the young of any of the garter snakes of the southern Pacific Coast district." In a large measure the comment still stands. In 1908 Ruthven recorded "a female from Pullman, Washington, which . . . gave birth to 11 young." We assume it to be *fitchi,* not *pickeringi.* In 1922 Patch recorded that "enroute to Ottawa a 38-inch individual shipped from Bella Coola, Aug. 21, gave birth to 18 young which averaged 9.50 inches. They were marked with pale orange instead of the red of the adult."

As there are few detailed accounts of western snakes, we will give extended excerpts from Fisher: "A Pacific Garter snake, *Thamnophis sirtalis infernalis* (Blainville) [*fitchi*] was brought to the Museum laboratory on June 19, 1926. . . . About 9 o'clock on the morning of August 5, 1926, a young garter snake was discovered in the cage, and others appeared in rapid succession to the number of 52, the last being born a little before noon. The young snakes were so active and numerous that despite the writer's efforts there was danger of their escaping. The mother garter snake crawled slowly about the cage and at irregular intervals, with slightly raised tail, left behind her a young snake. . . . The period of gestation can be estimated as covering approximately 3 months, namely May, June, and July. Even a longer period than this was possible, since fertilization would have had to occur before the capture in April or the first of May. . . . The average length of all the snakes measured is 19.77 cm., but they range in length from 15.45 to 21.6. Ignoring decimals, we have one 15 cm. long, one 16, three 17, four 18, twelve 19, fifteen 20, and eight 21 cm. Of this particular brood more individuals fall into the length groups 19 and 20 than any other, and there are 6 snakes that measure 20.5 cm."

We have heard of broods of 10, 13, and 15 young. The smallest young we ever saw was 202 mm. long. We examined in western museums: (1) CAS 28835, Carlotta, Calif., May 11, 1911, Slevin, 228 mm. (2) SU 4484, Smith Fork, Coos Co., Ore., Aug. 10, 1899, Allen and Robinson, 192 mm. (tail 55). It looks newly born. (3) SU 4423, Takeneitch Cr., Douglas Co., Ore., Aug. 17, 1897, Allen and Robinson. Foetal snake 152 mm. Pattern, dorsal stripe and 1 row of spots on either lower side.

Food: Frogs, toads, salamanders, fish. Smith (B.C., 1920), Grinnell, Dixon, and Linsdale, Fitch (Gen., 1941, Calif., 1947), Compton (Calif., 1933).

Authorities:

Brown, A. E. (Gen., 1901; Calif., 1903)

Fisher, E. M. (Calif., 1928a)

Fitch, H. S. (Gen., 1941; Calif., 1941a, 1949)

Fox, W. C. (Gen., 1951)

Grinnell, J., J. Dixon, and J. M. Linsdale (Calif., 1930)

Hebard, W. B. (Wash., 1951)

Johnson, M. L. (Wash., 1942)

Logier, E. B. S. (B.C., 1932)

Lord, J. K. (B.C., 1866)

Patch, C. L. (B.C., 1922)

Richardson, C. H. (Nev., 1915)

Ruthven, A. G. (Gen., 1908)

Stejneger, L. (Calif., 1893)

Townsend, C. H. (Calif., 1888)

Van Denburgh, J., and J. R. Slevin (Calif., 1918)

Yarrow, H. C. (Ariz., 1875)

Yarrow, H. C., and H. W. Henshaw (Ariz., 1878)

1875, H. C. Yarrow: "Dorsal band. . . . Spots minute; a black band on each side dorsal and black band on 4th and 5th lateral rows . . . subsp. *tetrataenia.*"

1903, A. E. Brown (Calif., 1903): "The red has spread longitudinally, forming a red stripe between the 2 black ones (*E. s. tetrataenia*). . . . Of the 3 *tetrataenia* which Cope is able to name, 2, in the U.S. National Museum, came from Pitt River, Calif., while the 3rd, No. 6085 in the Academy's collection, from Puget Sound, originally entered as *concinna,* has the lower black stripe broken up into spots anteriorly. A smaller snake in the same jar as this specimen, and apparently collected with it, is an ordinary *parietalis.* Hallowell's type of *Tropidonotus concinnus* (No. 6,324, Academy collection) is also marked on the label '*tetrataenia*' by Cope. All these specimens have now been 50 years in spirits."

1941, H. S. Fitch: "These and other predation records as summarized at the end of this paper show a general trend of food preferences in this kind of snake. In keeping with its marshland habitat it seems to be mainly an amphibian feeder."

1944, A. H. and A. A. Wright: If there are "significant differences" between western Pacific forms of *sirtalis* (*ordinatus*) and *T. s. parietalis,* it is regrettable that Johnson did not include them in his synoptic key. Fitch in his 5 pages on "Diagnosis . . . lectotype" did not even mention the big scrap basket form, *T. s. parietalis,* from which he pulled *T. s. fitchi* (old *tetrataenia*). That comparison remains to be made, and the east boundary of *fitchi* and the west boundary of *parietalis* are still nebulous. It is not advisable to trust our range outlines in this regard. We were never able to satisfy ourselves with the western Pacific *T. s. parietalis* of the period before Fitch. We are now following Fitch and think we can recognize *fitchi* specimens when we see them in the field and are glad we have a scrap basket into

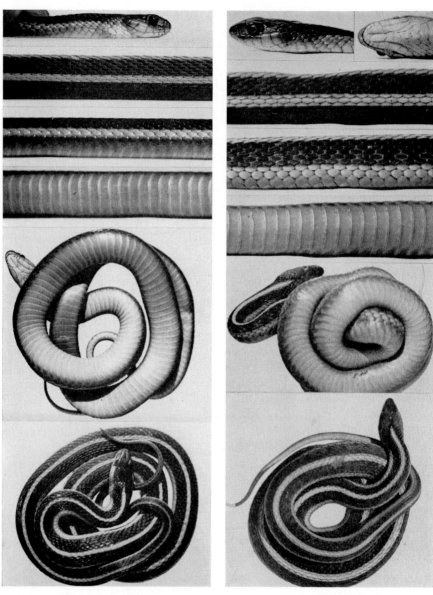

Fig. 244. *Thamnophis s. fitchi,* Buena Vista, Harney Co., Ore., I. Donaldson through S. Jewett, Jr.

Fig. 245. *Thamnophis s. infernalis,* Carmel Valley near Hastings Reservation, Calif.

which to throw troublesome *T. sirtalis* of the extreme western states. Let some alert younger worker view this widespread form with suspicious eyes, and let him work on it in the field of its distribution.

Pacific garter snake (18—Van Denburgh 1922), California red-barred garter snake

Thamnophis sirtalis infernalis (Blainville) 1835. Fig. 245; Map 60

Other common names: One-striped garter snake; single-striped garter snake; western garter snake (2—Ruthling 1915).

Range: Coastal California from n. San Diego County to Humboldt County. *Elevation*—Sea level to 3,000 feet or more. Coast and valley areas (Klauber, Calif., 1931a).

Size: Adults, 17–51 inches.

Distinctive characteristics: "Diagnosis—Top of head, and face including supralabials and infralabials, predominantly reddish; dorsal stripe bright yellow, broad (more than 1⅔ scale rows wide), with even and sharply defined borders; dorsal ground color black in area adjacent to lateral stripe, but paling to gray or brownish farther down on sides; red markings on sides extensive and conspicuous, usually as long as interspaces, extending dorsally to within 1 or 2 rows of dorsal stripe, tending to suffuse and blend into adjacent pale ground color; lateral stripes well developed, bordered below by black or dusky area on 1st scale row and edges of gastrosteges; ventral surface mainly pale, immaculate or sparingly marked with black posteriorly" (Fitch).

Color: A snake from Carmel Valley, found 10 miles north of Jean Linsdale's station (also known as R. Hasting's reservation) Apr. 18, 1942. It has a prominent middorsal stripe, glass green on the neck, but soon becoming light fluorite green. It has very straight edges with a narrow edge of each outer scale row black, and is on 3 scale rows. In the rear it is bordered by a very narrow black band which becomes broader toward the head, where the stripe forms a triangle back of the parietals and between the burnt sienna areas. On the sides, mahogany red intervals predominate with black areas only 1 scale long or only the centers of scales black. Some of the scale edges and interstices are brazil red or scarlet. The first rows of scales and rear ends of ventrals are lincoln green. The lateral stripe on the 3rd and fourth rows is glaucous-green. The parietals and back of head are burnt sienna, as are the postoculars, temporals, top of next to last upper labial, and the entire last one. This color does not extend back of parietals on the meson, but fans out over 3 series of temporals and an additional scale row. On the parietals is an orange chrome spot outlined with black. The supraoculars, frontals, prefrontals, and top of rostral are raw umber. The upper labials are niagara green. The iris is raw umber and burnt sienna with a cream-buff pupil rim. The underside of head is pure white involving the lower labials; the underside of neck is pale niagara green, the belly niagara green.

Habitat: This is a water snake of the sluggish fresh-water sloughs of the lowlands; of ponds, marshes, or creeks. Klauber (Calif., 1931a) gave places such as creek (3), marsh (3), orchard (1), garden (1), cultivated field (2), grass (5), chaparral (1).

This Pacific coast (Sargent, Ecol., 1884), California Coast Range (Harshberger, Ecol., 1911; Fenneman, Ecol., 1931) form occurs "in the neighborhood of San Francisco where the actual rainfall does not exceed 25 inches, but where much moisture is carried over the Coast belt and up the river valleys by the persistent fogs which sweep in from the Pacific Ocean" (Brown, Calif., 1903).

Some think of this as a water snake, but J. L. Hawken (Calif., 1951) took in the concrete tower at the end of the San Francisco Co. water supply only 3 of *T. s. infernalis* in contrast to 149 *C. c. mormon.*

Period of activity: *First appearance*—Feb. 22, 1926 (J. A. Campbell); Apr. 21, 1911 (A. J. Carlson); Apr. 7, 1911 (J. R. Slevin); Mar. 27, 1927 (Klauber, Calif., 1929). "Sixteen Year Census"—Feb., 1 snake; Mar., 5; Apr., 1; May, 10; June, 1; Aug., 2, Total 20. Rank 24 (Klauber, Gen., 1939a). MVZ dates are Mar. 21 to Sept. 10. *Fall disappearance*—Sept. 4, 1928 (Fisher).

Breeding: Viviparous. *Young*—In 1907 Ditmars reported 15 born in one brood on Aug. 20; 8 in another on Aug. 23, and 7 in a third on Sept. 5. I firmly believe he had *infernalis* material (see his Plate LXIX). In 1928 Fisher (Calif., 1928) wrote: "A young garter snake, *Thamnophis sirtalis infernalis,* having two heads, was sent to the Museum of Vertebrate Zoology, University of California, in September of 1926. This specimen (MVZ No. 10469) was found dead on September 4, 1926, near Santa Rosa, Sonoma County, California. The young snake was possibly not more than 2 or 3 days old when it was killed. By what means it met its death is not known. The total length of the snake is 17 cm., the tail equalling 4.8 cm. Each head and neck to the point of union measures 1.5 cm." Two years later Bogert reported: "An average-sized specimen collected in a slough on the outskirts of Los Angeles gave birth to 13 young on July 2, 1928." In 1938 Perkins recorded that "the young are born alive." In 1942, we found in Stanford University Museum an embryo from Pacific Grove taken July 1, 1907, by Snyder. It measured 175 mm. In the California Academy of Science we found 4 specimens which we interpreted as hatched the preceding summer. They measured 247, 257, 285, 310 mm.

Food: Fish, insects, frogs, earthworms. Grinnell and Grinnell (Calif., 1907), Klauber, Perkins, Von Bloecker (Calif., 1942).

Authorities:

Blainville, H. D. de (Baja Calif., 1835)

Bocourt, F. (Calif., 1892)

Brown, A. E. (Gen., 1901, Calif., 1903)

Coues, E., and H. C. Yarrow (Mont., 1878)

Fitch, H. S. (Gen., 1941)

Klauber, L. M. (Calif., 1934a)

Perkins, C. B. (Calif., 1938)   Van Denburgh, J., and J. R. Slevin
Ruthven, A. G. (Gen., 1908)   (Gen., 1918)
Van Denburgh, J. (Gen., 1897, 1922)   Yarrow, H. C. (Ariz., 1875)

1901, A. E. Brown: "Whatever may or may not have been *infernalis* Blainville, I have never seen a living specimen which could be referred with certainty to *infernalis* B. and G. or Cope, and I am persuaded that those so called belong in part to the present form (*E. s. parietalis*) and in part to *E. elegans.*" We do not blame him; there certainly was confusion.

1903, A. E. Brown: "*E. infernalis infernalis* Cope has been shown to be *E. e. elegans,* but *Coluber infernalis* Blain. occupies a doubtful position through the insufficiency of the original description and plate."

1908, A. G. Ruthven: "I am not certain of the identity of *Coluber infernalis* Blainville." Like Brown, he is honest. We grew up in the same period that Ruthven grew up in and experienced the same confusion.

1918: J. Van Denburgh and J. R. Slevin properly made it a *sirtalis.* They gave from life a figure of an *infernalis* as we know it today, but unfortunately they sent the form to Yosemite, the Sierras, and the Klamath Lakes, Ore. Furthermore, their photographs of live western garters were a distinct contribution.

1941, H. S. Fitch: "The type of *infernalis* was collected by Dr. Paolo Emilo Botta along with other California reptiles, including the types of *Phrynosoma coronatum, Gerrhonotus multi-carinatus, Charina bottae, Pituophis catenifer, Lampropeltis getulus californiae.* Botta was surgeon on the French ship 'Le Heros.' Palmer (1917) has published a brief account of Botta's visit to California, showing that he stopped at many places along the California coast from Bodega and Ross to San Diego, and including Solano, San Francisco, Santa Clara, San Jose, Santa Cruz, Monterey, Santa Barbara, San Gabriel, Los Angeles and San Pedro. The type of *infernalis* might have been collected at almost any one of these places."

1944, A. H. and A. A. Wright: We were of the olden days when it was difficult to separate *elegans* and *infernalis; elegans* has resided in *ordinoides, vagrans,* and *infernalis* and has been *sui generis.* Then we had great difficulty justifying our separations of some Yosemite material (*elegans* and *infernalis*). Today we believe we can readily tell a mountain garter, *T. e. elegans,* of the Sierras. Equally well would we distinguish a naples yellow to green yellow dorsal-striped coastal *T. s. infernalis,* as Fitch now restricts it. After our 1942 trip from Carmel to San Luis del Rey we were certain it was as good as any California form. Even the very useful 1922 Van Denburgh volume had no figure of *T. e. elegans,* the mountain garter. And the earlier very useful Ditmars book (1907) was too mixed on the w. and s.w. garters. Some of his figures were unmistakably preserved specimens posed, as palpably so as his *Natrix compressicauda.*

Red-barred garter snake (21—Bailey 1913),
Red-sided garter snake (17—Hay 1887)

Thamnophis sirtalis parietalis (Say) 1823. Fig. 246; Map 60

Common names: (Common) garter snake; green-striped garter snake; northern garter snake; ornate garter snake; Pacific garter snake; parietal garter snake (Coues and Yarrow 1872); prairie garter snake (11); red-backed garter snake; red(-spotted) garter snake; Rocky Mountain garter snake; Say's garter snake; western garter snake.

Range: From Chihuahua, Mex., to Yukon Territory, Can., thence s.e. to Lat. 50°, Long. 86°, n. of Lake Superior, west of Mississippi River to n.e. Missouri, thence s.w. to Big Bend region of Texas.—U.S.A.: Alaska; Ariz.; Ark.; Colo.; Ia.; Ida.; Ill.; Kan.; Minn.; Mo.; Mont.; Neb.; Nev.; N.D.; N.M.; Okla.; S.D.; Ut.; Wis.; Wyo. Can.: B.C.; Mack. Dist.; Man.; Ont.; Sask.; Yukon. Mex.: Chihuahua. *Elevation*—500 to 8,000 feet. 4,000 to 8,000 feet (Bailey, N.M., 1913).

Size: Adults, 17–46 inches.

Distinctive characteristics: "Above blackish with 3 yellowish fillets and about 80 red concealed spots beneath bluish, a series of black dots each side" (Say). "The coloration as observed in life in the Rocky Mountain specimens in August is as follows: The dorsal band, which is 1 scale and 2 half-scales broad, firm and perfectly continuous from head to end of tail, without indentation for the dark body-color, is pure yellow, fading to pale naples-yellow in alcohol. The tint is clearer than that of the lateral bands, which are rather of a heavier golden-yellow from some suffusion with the red that beautifully mottles the sides. The lateral stripe is as firm and continuous as the dorsal one, and broader, occupying 2 whole scales (of the 2nd and 3rd rows). The body-color is black, without obvious shade of brown or olivaceous, speckled between the scales with rich vermilion-red, which is very conspicuous on stretching the skin, forming an incomplete zigzag annulation" (Coues and Yarrow, Mont., 1878). Scale rows 19; upper labials 7 (8); eye over labials 3, 4, (5).

Color: A snake from Cedar Falls, Ia., received from H. G. M. Jopson, June 1, 1936. The dorsal stripe, covering the middorsal scale row and halves of the 2 adjoining rows, is glass green or reed yellow. The lateral stripe is more yellow, being colonial buff. Between the dorsal and lateral stripes the spots of the lower row, 3 scales deep and 1½ scales longitudinally, are very distinct, being black clearly outlined by the english red or scarlet interspace. The spots of the upper row, covering 2 scales transversely, are merged, forming a continuous black edge or border to the middorsal stripe. The lowest lateral scale row and the ends of the ventrals are buffy olive or light brownish olive. On the tip of each alternate or every 3rd scale of this row is a black spot which alternates with the spots of the lower of the 2 series between the lateral stripe and the dorsal stripe. This spot has a black extension to the ventral black spot. The top of the head is ivy green with 2 chartreuse yellow parietal spots. The upper labials are glass green, becoming on the last 2 chrysolite green, the 3rd, 4th, and 5th having black borders which are not complete in the first 2. There is a touch of black between the 1st and 2nd postoculars. The pupil rim is chartreuse yellow or colonial buff, the rest of the pupil being mainly light brownish olive, verona brown, or warm sepia. There is a black spot toward either end of each ventral where the buffy olive of their tips meets the corydalis green or water green of the remaining portions of the ventral plates. Toward the head, these plates are light turtle green or glass green, becoming on the scales just back of the head chartreuse yellow. The underside of the head except for the mental plate is white or tilleul buff.

On a visit May 9, 1951, to the Buffalo (N.Y.) Natural History Museum Axtell showed Mrs. Wright his strikingly beautiful, live, red-sided garter. It came from near the Trans-Canada Highway, 35 miles east of Longlac and 97 miles west of Hearst, Ont. This is about Long. 86° and just below Lat. 50°, on the border of the James Bay and Lake Superior drainages. A note by Axtell says: "Garter snakes that we found in and north of Riding Mt. Nat. Park seemed indistinguishable from typical *parietalis* that we found in the other prairie provinces and in Montana and the Dakotas."

Habitat: A summary of its habitats as expressed by a poll of authors shows it is distinctly an aquatic (10), lives not far from water (8), is a marginal (margin, border, or edge) inhabitant of streams (10), lakes (8), rivers (6), ponds (4), creeks (4), springs (3). It is also a frequenter of marshes (3), marshy spots (2), marshy areas (1), swampy places (1), swamps (1), plains (1), low levels (1), lowlands (1), stagnant pools (1), low wet places (1).

There are a few records of it away from water such as dry fields (1), open woods (1), upland prairie (1), high grassy stubble field (1), rocky slopes (1), hayfield (1). There are also a few records of it under cover (boards 1, rocks 2, limestone 1). Unusual places for it are: on city pavement (1), climbing on bushes (1), in fissures of stone quarry (1), around salt lakes (1).

Period of activity: *Early appearances*—May 10, 1903 (Preble, Alta., 1908); Feb. 23, 1924, Jan. 31, 1924 (Linsdale, Kan., 1927); May 20, 1905, May 2, 1906; Apr. 30, 1892 (Ellis and Henderson, Colo., 1913); Apr. 15, May 10, 17, 1914 (Ellis and Henderson, Colo., 1915); Apr. 21, 1928, Apr. 6, 1929 (Gloyd, Kan., 1932); Apr. 25, May 3, 1927 (Grant, Kan., 1937); Apr. 21, 1932, Feb. 28, 1933 (Burt, Kan., 1933). *Fall disappearance*—Aug. 3 (Test, Mont., 1893); Aug. 6, 24, 1894 (Van Denburgh, Ida., 1912b); Oct. 21, 1925 (Burt, Kan., 1927); Aug. 29, 1926, Nov. 26, 1926 (Grant); Nov. 3, 1922, Oct. 3, 1926, Oct. 1, 2, 16, 1932 (Burt, 1933). *Season*—Early February to late October

(Force, Okla., 1930). *Hibernation*—From a stone quarry Say (Gen., I: 186) took 3 species, including this, of which he wrote: "The stone quarry, which supplied limestone for building chimnies at camp Missouri, was situated at the distance of 100 yards below our cantonment. The labourers that were employed in this quarry opened upon many large fissures, in which were found a number of serpents that had entered there for the purpose of hybernating. Of these, 3 species appear to be new." See Seton (Man., 1918), Linsdale, and Anderson (Mo., 1942).

Breeding: Viviparous. Males 424–685 mm., females 459–1,138 mm. *Fall copulation*—When two of our students, Rahn (on *T. s. sirtalis*) and Trapido (on *Storeria*), discussed fall mating and sperm viability, the former sent us a note on *T. s. parietalis* by Dr. P. L. Risley of the State University of Iowa. The note reads: "The specimen was collected at Fairfield, Iowa, on October 28, 1939, and was autopsied December 9, 1939, after being kept in the laboratory in isolation for that period. Numerous motile spermatozoa were present in the middle and upper thirds of both right and left uteri. None were found in the upper membranous funnel regions and none in the posterior ends of the cloaca." Rahn added: "In view of further evidence it would seem that in this specimen a fall copulation was responsible for the presence of sperm at this time of the year."

Mating behavior—In a detailed study of 1 female, Munro has presented considerable evidence on the nonpassive role of the female. This female mated in the wild in 1945 and in captivity in 1947 and 1948. In March of each year she became restless and active and voided a cloacal discharge. He concluded: "It is evident that at least for the garter snakes the view is erroneous that the role of female is one of complete passivity in the act of mating; it appears also that the female may even definitely be active in the sexes finding each other for mating purposes in the spring."

Young—Number, 6–73; 6, 7, 10 (Tanner, Ut., 1949); 14 (Gloyd); 16 (Tanner, Munro); 24 (Munro); 26 (Hart, B.C., 1934); 28 (Gadow, Gen., 1910); 29 (Hudson); 35, 54 (Over, S.D., 1923); 42 (Anderson, Mo., 1942); 50 (Hudson and Davis, Neb., 1941); 73 (Ruthven). Time of birth, July 26 to Sept. 30. July 26, latter part of July, middle of August (Munro); July 28 (Anderson); July 30 (Langbartel, Ill., 1947); Aug. 2, Aug. 3, Aug. 7 (Tanner); Aug. 8 (Gloyd); Aug. 24 (Burt); August (Coues and Yarrow, Mont., 1878, Hudson and Davis); late summer or fall (Guthrie); Sept. 2 (Burt and Burt, Ariz., 1929); Sept. 30 (Ruthven). Size at birth, 6–9.8 inches. In 1878 Coues and Yarrow gave the newborn as 6 inches. In 1926 Guthrie said the size was 6–7½ inches. In 1928 Gloyd gave a range of 185–203 mm. (7.4–8.1 inches). In 1947 Langebartel's smallest, 183 mm., was taken July 30, while Burt's supposed newborn, taken Aug. 24, was 183 mm. The best study of this topic comes from our good friend, V. M. Tanner, who in 1944 measured and weighed 3 broods. A brood of 16 young born Aug. 2

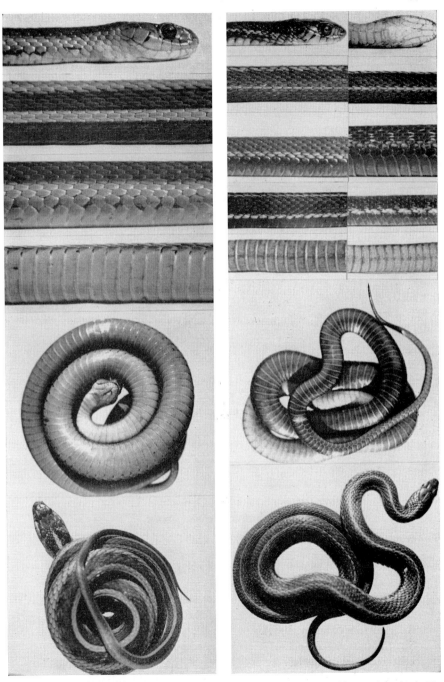

Fig. 246. *Thamnophis s. parietalis,* Albuquerque, N.M., R. Hegener.

Fig. 247. *Thamnophis s. pickeringi,* Tacoma, Wash., J. R. Slater.

ranged from 170 to 246 mm. in length and 1.6 to 2.5 grams in weight. A brood of 10 born Aug. 2 were 197–230 mm. and 1.8–2.8 grs. A brood of 5 young averaged 184–230 mm. and 2.2–2.5 grams.

Food: Insects, frogs, toads, small mammals, earthworms, spiders. Hay (Ind., 1892), Taylor (Neb., 1892a), Branson, Cockerell (Colo., 1910), Ellis and Henderson (Colo., 1913), Seton (Man., 1918), Guthrie, Gloyd, Force (Okla., 1930), Anderson (Mo., 1942), Hudson, W. W. Tanner (Ut., 1949), Owens (Mo., 1949).

Authorities:

Branson, E. B. (Kan., 1904)
Breckenridge, W. J. (Minn., 1944a)
Brown, A. E. (Gen., 1901, Calif., 1903)
Burt, C. E. (Kan., 1949)
Ellis, M. M., and J. Henderson (Colo., 1913)
Gloyd, H. K. (Kan., 1928)
Guthrie, J. E. (Ia., 1926)
Hudson, G. E. (Neb., 1942)
Munro, D. F. (Ark., 1948)
Over, W. H. (S.D., 1923)
Pack, H. J. (Ut., 1930)
Ruthven, A. G. (Gen., 1908)
Say, T. (Gen., 1822–23)
Tanner, V. M. (Ut., 1949)
Van Denburgh, J. (Gen., 1922)
Woodbury, A. M. (Ut., 1931)

1944, A. H. and A. A. Wright: The boundaries of the wide range of this beautiful snake are rather nebulous in places. On the west, when Fitch made most of Ruthven's *T. s. parietalis* west of Nevada to be *T. s. tetrataenia* (now *fitchi*), he left the eastern limit of *T. s. tetrataenia* (now *fitchi*) with no confines at all, nor compared it with *T. s. parietalis*. He was dealing solely with Pacific *sirtalis* subspecies.

1951, A. H. and A. A. Wright: In 1908 Ruthven hesitated about extending the range of *parietalis* to Isle Royale, Mich., on the basis of specimens taken there earlier by him. The *parietalis* that Dr. and Mrs. Harold Axtell showed Mrs. Wright, as recounted under "Color" above, came from well east of the middle longitude of Lake Superior.

Pickering's garter snake (5—Coues and Yarrow 1878), Washington garter snake

Thamnophis sirtalis pickeringi (Baird and Girard) 1853. Fig. 247; Map 60

Other common names: Nisqually garter snake (2); northwestern garter snake (2).

Range: State of Washington and s.w. British Columbia including Vancouver Island.—U.S.A.: Wash. Can.: B.C. *Elevation*—Sea level to 5,000 feet. 4,000 feet (Maslin, B.C.).

Size: Adults, 18–42 inches.

Distinctive characteristics: "Top of head dark brown, sometimes black or nearly black in parietal region, paler on rostrum and temporals; dorsal stripe narrow, less than 1⅔ scale rows wide and often confined to middorsal row, its borders irregular; dorsal ground color jet black; red lateral blotches small, inconspicuous, mainly confined to skin between scales; lateral stripe pale, whitish, conspicuous because bordered above and below by areas of solid black, its borders irregular, and skin between its scales black; ventral surface heavily marked with black or solidly black posteriorly; supralabials pale with well-developed black wedge-marks along their posterior borders" (Fitch). Scale rows 19; upper labials 7; eye over labials 3 + 4.

Color: Five snakes from Tacoma, Wash., received from J. R. Slater, described Oct. 24, 1940. These snakes are jet black on top of head and dorsum, with a light middorsal and lateral stripe. On the largest snake, the dorsal stripe is deep lichen green and soon becomes but 1 scale wide. The lateral stripe, which is mostly on the 2nd scale row, is glaucous-green. The black of the 1st scale row entirely engulfs the characteristic "sirtalis spot" of the end of the ventrals, thus making a black band crossing the ends of the ventral plates. The face plates are light terre verte with black sutures between 4th and 5th, 5th and 6th, 6th and 7th upper labials. The upper edges of the 2nd and 3rd upper labials are black. The iris is black except for a wash of terre verte across its top and a pupil rim of the same. The underside of the head is white. The throat and side of the neck are light terre verte. Passing through glaucous-blue to dusky green-blue (2), the venter becomes bluish slate-black and then black back of the vent.

On a smaller, more brightly colored snake, the dorsal stripe on the neck is light turtle green, soon becoming light fluorite green. The lateral stripe is tiber green. It is principally on the 2nd scale row, but may extend across the 3rd row, and the light color may extend upward on interscale spaces for 3 rows as flecks of etain blue, thus outlining, in inflated condition, a lower row of black spots. The scales of the 1st row are black, and the black marginal "sirtalis spots" on the forward ends of ventrals are rather prominent and unite with the black of 1st scale row. The facials and upper labials are olivine or pale olivine. The 4th, 5th and 6th upper labials have dark margins. The iris is black with a touch of reddish and with a pupil rim of pale olivine. The underside of the head is white, the throat deep lichen green or glaucous-green, shading into deep glaucous-green and soon becoming light terre verte. Where this color appears, the black rear edges of ventrals become prominent and are soon accompanied by black punctae through centers of the plates. The subcaudals are black.

Habitat: Two of our best accounts were published nearly a century ago. In 1860 Cooper and Suckley (Gen.) recorded one of our few characterizations: "In midsummer the colors remain the same, except that they are darker (deeper). This species exists in great abundance near Steilacoom and Nisqually. They are found on the gravelly prairies and in the vicinity of the numerous small lakes of this section of country. About the first of April they begin to come out of winter quarters, and can be seen at mid-day sunning themselves near small clumps of scruboak bushes, to which they retreat when alarmed. A little later they are found in couples or in small companies. Although they are rarely ever found more than ⅛ of a mile from water, they are, nevertheless, still more anxious to be close to it as the season advances. They will then (in May and June) be found lying close to the water, on the lake shores in the grass, and among the sedges of the marshes, and even upon small bog islands, as much as 50 yards from the shore. In summer, like other members of this genus, they are found lying in small pools, and in the water at the edges of the lakes, during the heat of the day. They appear to be a harmless lazy species, and as above stated, exceedingly fond of water. They rarely exceed 25 inches.—S."

Period of activity: The MVZ dates are May 13 to Sept. 10.

Breeding: Viviparous. Males 531–727 mm., females 617–1,037 mm. (Hebard, 1950a). *Young*—The smallest we have seen measured 192 mm. It was taken July 22, 1930, by Edson, near the Cascade River in Washington. "It is worth recording here that a female from Pullman, Washington, which the writer kept in captivity, and which had a labial formulae of ⅞₀, gave birth to 11 young" (Ruthven, Gen., 1908). Is this of *T. s. pickeringi?* In 1950 Hebard recorded male juveniles at birth as 198–228 mm. long and females 194–221 mm.

Food: Batrachians, insects, slugs, frogs. Lord, Schonberger (Ore., 1945).

Field notes: Mar. 30, 1942: Went on a short trip with Slater to Sparaway Lake. . . . Then went to the head of the lake. Here on a stone pile beside the road—the stones for fill—where it enters a swampy pond, Slater turned over a tar paper. Some 4–6 snakes under it. Caught in these stones some 6 or more snakes, mainly *T. s. pickeringi* and 1 or 2 *T. o. ordinoides.* . . . Went to drainage ditches for *R. p. pretiosa.* Along these ditches saw more snakes. Took one large *T. s. pickeringi.*

Authorities:

Baird, S. F., and C. Girard (Gen., 1853)
Brown, A. E. (Gen., 1901; Calif., 1905)
Cooper, J. G. (Gen., 1860)
Fitch, H. S. (Gen., 1941)
Hebard, W. B. (Wash., 1950a, 1951, 1951a)
Johnson, M. L. (Wash., 1942)
Lord, J. K. (B.C., 1866)
Svihla, A. and R. D. (Wash., 1933)
Van Denburgh, J. (Gen., 1922)
Van Denburgh, J., and J. R. Slevin (Gen., 1918)
Yarrow, H. C. (Ariz., 1875)

1903, A. E. Brown (Calif.): "*E. s. pickeringi* seems to be entitled to rank as a well-marked geographical form, always so dark as to obscure the spots, stripes usually narrow, very distinct and variable in color, occasionally a little red on the sides, and the ventral surface always more or less dark, sometimes entirely black. The region of great moisture, with a rainfall of from 50 to over 100 inches, occupies not more than 100,000 square miles, extending from latitude 40° in northern California to British Columbia."

1942, M. L. Johnson: "Strictly a subspecies of western Washington, confined to the Puget Sound country. Fitch has independently arrived at the conclusion that *pickeringi* is a recognizable race."

1950(a): W. B. Hebard gives body dimensions of 32 males and 36 females at birth and 21 males and 32 females sexually mature.

1944, A. H. and A. A. Wright: When one collects in the area of the old Wilkes U.S. Exploring Expedition, he is well satisfied that the melanistic *T. s. pickeringi* is a very distinct form. We have found considerable variance on the part of Washington herpetologists concerning Fitch's ranges and allocations of the *sirtalis* forms. They follow to a certain extent, and it is hard for us to reconcile all the allocations. Years ago we struggled with Pullman specimens that our old student D. J. Leffingwell sent us, and we are not entirely reconciled to some of them being adjudged *T. s. pickeringi*. Still that's a better category for them than *tetrataenia* (now *fitchi*) or *parietalis*. Neither are we sure that the old *T. s. concinnus* of Ruthven, Van Denburgh, and others is judged rightly, but we are following Fitch, for his is a field study. We followed his *ordinoides* (now *elegans*) field trail. *T. sirtalis* deserves as careful a field and laboratory study as he gave *elegans*. At Tacoma, on live specimens, we wrote: "*T. s. pickeringi* are darker underneath than *T. o. ordinoides*. Dorsum black. Dorsal stripe is thin and greenish blue. The lateral stripe is broken." The largest specimen we found in Slater's collection was taken in S. Tacoma Swamp. It had the notation "Nearly black—very tiny stripes. Those on sides are bluish green." This specimen is 1,000 mm. in length (39⅓ inches) and is 3½ inches in circumference. Its head is massive.

South San Francisco peninsula garter snake

Thamnophis sirtalis tetrataenia (Cope in Yarrow). Fig. 248; Maps 59, 60

(Since we had no personal experience with this form before Oct. 23, 1953, we quote from Fox's description of 1951.)

"**Type locality**—'Banks of Pit River, California' in error. Type specimen undoubtedly came from the San Francisco peninsula.

"**Range**—Occupies the western portion of the San Francisco peninsula from about the San Francisco County line south along the crest of the peninsula hills at least to Crystal Lake, and along the Coast west of this region south to Point Ano Nuevo, San Mateo County, California."

Distinctive characteristics: "A *Thamnophis sirtalis* in which the top of the head is red; the red and black colors of the side of the body are arranged into 1 red between 2 black longitudinal stripes. These stripes extend from the neck to the anus and are uninterrupted except in the neck region of an occasional individual. Many specimens have a thin stripe of red below the lower black stripe. The sides of the tail are marked with alternating black and red bars. The dorsal stripe occupies ½ + 1 + ½ scale rows and is pale green or blue green. The typical lateral stripe, common to most gartersnakes, occupies the 2nd and 3rd scale rows. It is a pale blue-green and not strongly differentiated from the 1st scale row. The belly is also blue-green. The top of the head is red, the red extending down over the superior margin of the supralabials and over both supra- and infra-labials posteriorly. Aside from this the labials are pale blue and the throat becomes even paler, almost white. The iris is cinnamon. There are usually 7 upper labials, 10 lower labials, 1 preocular and 3 postoculars on each side. The scale rows are 19-19-17. Ventral scutes range from 156 to 172 in males and 153 to 169 in females. Caudal scutes range from 80 to 95 in males and 71 to 87 in females.

"The following is a description of a freshly killed specimen, M.V.Z. No. 47716, female. Two uninterrupted dorsolateral black stripes run the entire length of the body and are separated from each other by a red stripe. Anteriorly, the lower black stripe occupies the upper half of the 3rd scale row, all of the 4th, ¾ of all of the 5th and frequently encroaches on the 6th scale row. Posteriorly, it occupies ½ + 1 + ½ scale rows, the 3rd, 4th and 5th respectively. The upper black stripe occupies ½ + 1 + ½ scale rows which are the 7th, 8th and 9th anteriorly and the 6th, 7th and 8th posteriorly. At the end of the body it touches the 6th row only slightly. The red stripe varies from Scarlet (Ridgway nomenclature) on the anterior part of the scales to Brazil Red on the posterior part. It irregularly occupies ⅓ + 1 + ½ scale rows anteriorly and is limited posteriorly to the adjacent halves of the 5th and 6th scale rows. The middorsal stripe is Light Fluorite Green at the nape and Glaucous-Green posteriorly, and occupies ½ + 1 + ½ scale rows. The lateral stripe occupies nearly all of the 2nd and over half of the 3rd scale row; it is Light Glaucous-Blue throughout, but has many conspicuous Grenadine Red flecks in the neck region. Although the 1st scale row is Glaucous-Blue, it is heavily marked with fine black punctations that also cover the lateral edges of the ventral scutes. Medially, the ventral scutes are Light Dull Glaucous-Blue. The black and red stripes of the body do not extend onto the tail which is marked by alternating black and red bars that become indistinct towards the tip. The top of the head is Burnt Sienna from the snout through the temporals and over most of the 6th and 7th upper labials. The upper margin of the anterior labials is also reddish, but they are primarily Pale Glaucous-Blue. The lower labials are pale and grade into the Pale Dull Glaucous-Blue of the throat" (Fox).

Color: A snake collected 2½ miles west of San Bruno, San Mateo Co., Calif., Sept. 18, 1953, by William Reimer and Peter Thorngreen, and loaned by Wade Fox, Oct. 19, 1953. The middorsal stripe ½ + 1 + ½ scales wide is corydalis green, becoming on the tail pois green. It is bordered on either side by a prominent black stripe ½ + 1 + ½ scales wide. Above the lateral stripe is a much broader black stripe. The 2 black stripes are separated by a stripe of scarlet to nopal red. This striped pattern is abruptly broken back of the vent, where bars of black and red alternate, the *infernalis* type of pattern. The lateral stripe on the 2nd and 3rd scale rows is greenish glaucous-blue to dark bluish glaucous. It has a prominent black margin bordering it below which crosses also the ends of the ventrals. The top of the head ahead of the eyes is auburn followed caudad by burnt sienna with temporals and last 2 upper labials orange-rufous. The iris is suffused with auburn and has a light pupil rim.

Habitat: "This snake is most abundant in the vicinity of ponds and lakes; large creeks and streams are not numerous in the area. The animals are frequently found in the water or on the edge of a bank. If approached in either of these situations, they attempt to dive under water and hide among the water plants or occasionally they swim out of reach with only their heads out of water. Most specimens were found anywhere from a few feet to several yards from water on higher, well-drained banks or hillocks covered with grass or open brush. They habitually bask in the morning sun just out of the shadow of a small bush and when disturbed attempt to escape into holes opening among the roots of the bush. They are abundant in the marshy regions surrounding ponds and lakes. Other races of the species feed on a large variety of food and I do not doubt this race can do likewise. Nevertheless, all of the numerous food samples I have found in their stomachs have been either metamorphosed or unmetamorphosed frogs (*Rana aurora*). I believe this to be due largely to the abundance of frogs in the areas where most of the specimens were collected" (Fox).

Authorities:

Fox, W. (Gen., 1951)   Wright, A. H. and A. A.

In 1942 we traveled from extreme s. California to extreme n. Washington with Fitch's "A biogeographical study" (1940) in hand, saw every one of his forms, and returned with admiration for his analysis of the garters of the *elegans* (or *ordinoides*) group. Because they are endorsed by Fitch, Fox's revisions are included here.

1953, A. H. and A. A. Wright: On Oct. 19, 1953, Fox (Dept. of Anatomy, Louisiana State University School of Medicine, New Orleans) sent us live representatives of his new *T. sirtalis tetrataenia* and *T. elegans terrestris* and his revised *T. elegans atratus*. From our experience with *T. sirtalis infernalis*, alive and alcoholic, we can readily see how Van Denburgh and Slevin in 1918 and Fitch in 1941 could have considered *T. sirtalis tetrataenia* a part of it. The instant we saw it we thought it a derivative of *T. s. infernalis*, but the red stripe and lack of lateral bars at once set it apart. Pure *T. s. tetrataenia* is very distinct and is one of the 5 most beautiful garters of the U.S. The other 4 are *T. c. cyrtopsis*, *T. s. infernalis*, *T. s. sauritus*, and *T. e. elegans*.

PROBLEMATICAL FORMS

Thamnophis elegans nigrescens Johnson 1947

Range: West of the Cascades in w. Washington and British Columbia.

Distinctive characteristics: "This species closely resembles *Thamnophis elegans vagrans,* differing mainly in being darker in general coloration and in having a lower number of gastrosteges and urosteges. It attains a medium size. The head is distinct from the neck. Dorsal scales number 21. Supralabials 8 (occasionally 7 or 9); infralabials 10; preoculars frequently divided; gastrosteges vary from 155 to 173; urosteges from 60 to 95. . . . In *T. e. nigrescens* this pattern is a gray to gray-brown base color, a straw-colored dorsal line, a light gray to straw-colored ill-defined pair of lateral lines, and well-defined temporal bars. Gastrosteges are freely marked with black over the grey ground color. There are 2 alternate rows of black spots between the dorsal and lateral lines, of which the dorsal row invades the dorsal line and is much more prominent than the lateral row. (The converse is true of *T. o. ordinoides*)" (Johnson). The describer's type is a female 720 mm. (28.8 inches) long.

Authorities:

Fitch, H. S. (Gen., 1948)

Johnson, M. L. (Wash., 1947)

Johnson, M. L., and J. R. Slater (Wash., 1949)

Logier, E. B. S. (B.C., 1932)

1947, M. L. Johnson: "Working with Professor James R. Slater at the College of Puget Sound, I have received available material and have been forced to change my previously held opinion that there was no difference in the *elegans* populations of the eastern and western portions of the state. Though closely related to the wide ranging *Thamnophis elegans vagrans* which occurs in typical form in the eastern part of the state, the population of Western Washington is subspecifically distinct."

1947: M. L. Johnson in a letter of July 18 said: "Enclosed is a separate of my paper dealing with the *elegans* of *Thamnophis,* including the type description of *Thamnophis elegans nigrescens.* Under separate cover we are sending a couple of topotypes of *T. e. nigrescens* for your use. . . . I'm also sending a couple of *Thamnophis sirtalis pickeringii* from Tacoma."

1948, H. S. Fitch: "However, the incipient racial differentiation does not seem to me great enough to warrant its separation as a subspecies distinct from *vagrans."*

1948, A. H. and A. A. Wright: Since we can have in California a southern coastal garter (*T. e. hammondi*) and a northern coastal garter (*T. ordinoides*), why not one (*T. e. nigrescens*) in western Washington and British Columbia? If an author will accept *T. s. pickeringi* or *T. o. concinnus,* why not *T. e. nigrescens* for a similarly restricted region? Before 1942 we were brought up on a widespread *biscutatus* (not just that of the Klamath Lake area) and on *couchi* not split into *gigas* and *couchi,* and we had not yet been introduced to another limited coastal form, *hydrophila*. We then felt the western Pacific garters were minutely separated. From 1917–48, having seen in life and *in situ* that *T. e. vagrans* from New Mexico to the Pacific coast varied considerably in color, we dreaded to have anyone go to work on it. (See color descriptions of *T. e. vagrans*.) However, in 1942 we traversed the area of *T. elegans* subspecies from New Mexico and s. California to Washington and Wyoming and came to have more admiration for Fitch's thesis than for almost any other in recent times. We have seen his forms in the field, and we accept them. But we are not too pleased with *biscutatus* in s.e. Oregon, are not certain we can always tell *gigas* from *couchi or* Kings River large female, and young *couchi* from *hydrophila*. If Fitch accepts Fox's study, possibly Johnson and Slater may present more evidence for the acceptance of *T. e. nigrescens*. With admiration for Fitch's past studies and with appreciation of the Slater group's field work, we hold ourselves unresolved concerning this whole matter. Through the years our puzzles involving *T. e. vagrans* in e. Washington, Oregon, and w. Idaho prompt such hesitation.

1949, M. L. Johnson and J. R. Slater: "Continued field work has verified the opinion that the differentiation of *T. e. nigrescens* is sufficient to satisfy present exacting herpetological as well as genetic criteria. Granted that such criteria may be matters of personal opinion, we believe that opinions based on actual field experience coupled with adequate laboratory analysis should not be disregarded."

1950, A. H. and A. A. Wright: We await more evidence to determine whether this Northwest (Hinds, Ecol., 1843, Sargent, Ecol., 1905), Northwest coniferous (Shelford, Ecol., 1926), Puget Sound + edge of Cascades (Mulford, Ecol., 1937–38) form is as acceptable as *T. s. pickeringi* or *T. s. concinnus* from the same regions.

1950: W. B. Hebard (Wash., 1950) implied that he considered *T. e. nigrescens* not a valid subspecies.

Vancouver garter snake

Thamnophis sirtalis trilineata (Cope, 1892)

In our synonymy of *T. s. pickeringi* we united *T. s. trilineata* Cope with *T. s. pickeringi*. In 1901, when the material was fresher, Brown said that *E. s. trilineata* Cope is simply *pickeringi* "with the stripes inconsiderably wider." In 1903 (Calif.) he mentioned *"E. s. pickeringi* B. and G. and *E. s. trilineata* Cope, the differences between which are trivial." Even Cope in

1900 held that it was not unlikely that the two subspecies, *E. s. pickeringi* and *E. s. trilineata*, might have to be united. Schmidt's *Check List* of 1953 therefore poses the problem of its true status.[1]

LYRE SNAKES

Genus *TRIMORPHODON* Cope (Fig. 25)

"The group of back-fanged snakes belonging to this genus is characterized by greatly enlarged anterior maxillary teeth followed by smaller teeth which decrease somewhat posteriorly, and are followed after an interspace by a pair of enlarged, grooved fangs; anterior mandibular teeth and to a lesser extent, the anterior palatine teeth enlarged; head distinct from neck; 2 pairs of chin shields, the anterior largest; 7 or 8 scale rows between 1st ventrals and posterior lower labial; 2 loreals present, and frequently a 3rd, which is situated below the posterior; nasal divided, the nostril vertically elongate; eye moderate, less than the distance from nostril; usually 3 preoculars (2 preoculars '1 subocular') and 3 postoculars; scales smooth (or bluntly keeled in males), slightly oblique, with paired apical pits, in 22–27 rows. Ventrals obtusely angulate; subcaudals divided; anal divided usually (single in *vandenburghi*). Body compressed" (Taylor, Gen., 1938). Hemipenis (in *lambda*)—"22 caudals long, 3 large flounces extending to the 13th caudal from base, passing *through* an area of enlarged spines covering the length of 3 caudals; remainder ridged, with tiny spicules" (Smith, Gen., 1941). In *lyrophanes* and *vandenburghi*, shorter and spineless. Synonyms: *Eteirodipsas, Lycodon.*

---

[1] *Thamnophis sirtalis* sp. (In British Columbia.) In 1955, Logier and Toner's (*Check List*, 63) statement strikes a responsive chord with us. "This complex includes within the borders of British Columbia forms that have been assigned by various authors, at various times, to one or more of the following races of *Thamnophis sirtalis: Concinnus fitchi, infernalis, parietalis, pickeringi, tetrataenia* and *trilineata.* . . . The application of race names can mean nothing, until geographic ranges can be defined with some degree of consistency for some or all of them (in British Columbia) and it can be shown any two or more alleged races do not intergrade throughout their ranges within that province.

"In the past history of this group a number of race names have been erected upon individual variations and later discarded. We should learn from experience in dealing with such a highly variable species as *sirtalis*, that the naming of supposed races should not be lightly undertaken. . . . Until zoologists who are studying (and naming) the races can find less fluid ground of common agreement, the writers prefer not to commit themselves."

Fig. 248. *Thamnophis s. tetrataenia,* San Bruno, Calif., W. Fox.

Fig. 249. *Trimorphodon lambda:* 1–5, young, Menlo Park, Tucson, Ariz., S. C. Bishop; 6–12, San Diego, Calif., L. M. Klauber.

KEY TO THE GENUS *TRIMORPHODON*

a. With prominent dark-bordered light V-shaped mark on head, with apex forward. Ventrals 244 or less.

    b. Anal entire. Angle of light head V has tail cutting across anterior dark bordering band. Dorsal saddles have a light central core of interval color 1 scale wide; saddle crosses 6–7 middorsal rows, component bars unite on side and may extend to venter or be broken and succeeded by supplementary spot from 3d or 4th row to venter; alternating intermediate lateral spots are barlike extending from end of ventral to 6th or 7th scale row. Interval on dorsum 2 scales, at venter 5 scales. Hemipenis 14 caudals long and flounces relatively small as in *lyrophanes*. (Coastal and desert southern California from Los Angeles Co. and Argus Mts., Inyo Co., to the Mexican border.)

T. vandenburghi

    bb. Anal divided.

        c. Angle of light V-shaped head mark entirely bordered with dark on frontal region; the light V merges at divergent ends into the light ventral area, and the dark V anterior to it terminates a little posterior to the labials. Dorsal saddles have conspicuous light margins, the light central core lighter than interval color and more than 1 scale wide, and this core may cross 13–14 scale rows transversely and the dark enclosing bands unite below this as lateral bar crossing 5 or 6 scale rows to the venter; intermediate spots relatively small and most conspicuous on lowest scale row and on ends of ventrals. Each of the dark paired bands of each composite saddle is sometimes split transversely across 7 or 8 middorsal rows by a secondary light line. Saddles may be 7–9 scales long and extend 10 scale rows stopping only 1 or 2 scales short of the ventral plates. Intervals on dorsum may be 2 scales long and at venter 8 scales. Hemipenis 22 caudals long, 3 large flounces with middle belt of spines. (Sonora, Mex., n. to s. Nevada, n. California, and s.w. Utah.)   *T. lambda*

        cc. Angle of light V-shaped head mark has extension on frontal area cutting across the dark bordering band completely or partially to the light interocular area, thus turning the V into a lyre, with diverging ends extending onto neck, but cut off from ventral area by the dark V which margins it anteriorly and which cuts across below it to terminate also on the neck. Dorsal saddles longer and narrower than in *lambda* and their lateral extensions frequently separated from them. Intermediate bars conspicuous. Smaller number of spots on tail. Hemipenis relatively short without mid-belt of spines. (S. half of Baja California.)   *T. lyrophanes* aa. Without prominent light V-shaped mark on head with apex forward. Ventrals 232 or less.

b. Body blotches narrow, ⅓ to ¼ of the interval length, few 17–22; 7–10 on tail; dark on head diffuse or forming 3 black spots in young. (Chihuahua, Mex., to extreme western Texas, El Paso region.)

T. vilkinsoni

bb. Body blotches wider, greater than intervals, 23–32 on body; 11–15 on tail; narrow light Y-shaped mark on head, tail of Y caudad on parietal sutures. (S. Chihuahua, Mex., southward and eastward.)

T. upsilon

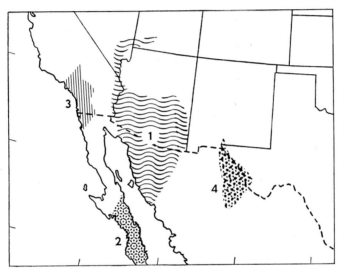

Map 61. *Trimorphodon*—1, *lambda;* 2, *lyrophanes;* 3, *vandenburghi;* 4, *vilkinsoni.*

Sonoran lyre snake

Trimorphodon lambda Cope 1886. Fig. 249; Map 61

Range: From Sonora, Mex., n. through s. and cent. Arizona and up Colorado River drainage area in California, Nevada, and southwestern Utah.—U.S.A.: Ariz.; Calif.; Nev.; Ut. Mex.: Sonora. *Elevation*—Sea-coast or 500 feet to 5,000 or more feet.

Size: Adults, 24–41 inches.

Distinctive characteristics: "Head with brown chevrons above; back with diamond-shaped spots" in contrast to *lyrophanes* which has "head with lyre-shaped pattern above; dorsal spots in pairs" (Cope). "Large V-shaped marks on head, these not continued on neck, but disappearing laterally just behind head; hemipenis long, with a middle belt of spines; ventrals 243 or less, caudals 86 or less; anal entire; spots on body 34 or less" (Smith).

Pattern: A young snake from Menlo Park, Tucson, Ariz., received through Sherman C. Bishop, Apr. 14, 1936, had 38 saddles to the tip of the tail, 12 of which were on the tail.

Color: A snake from the vicinity of Tucson, Ariz. (probably Catalinas), loaned to us by C. M. Bogert and described Mar. 10, 1943. This pale-colored *Trimorphodon* is without black in its markings. The dorsum of the body is crossed by 34 bars which in the middle descend in pairs on the side to focal points, thus forming composite saddles. There are 12 or 13 bars on the tail. Various authors doubtless have counted each of the saddles in rear and on neck as 1 unit, but each composite saddle of middle portion as 2. Each composite saddle is formed of 4 bands of tawny-olive, the edge of the forward one tipped with sepia for 7, 8, or more transverse scales, and the rear edge of caudal 4th band of the group similarly tipped on 4 to 6 scales. In each group of 2 bands, the bands are separated by a thread of pale pinkish buff, which crosses 7 or 8 scales transversely. The same color exists as a light core of the composite saddle between the 2nd and 3rd bands of the group, crossing 13 or 14 scale rows and often bearing 1 or 2 prominent spots of sepia. The background of the back between the saddles is buffy brown 2 scales long on the back and 8 scales at the ventral plates, with a triangular spot in the middle of its side 4 scales long at its base next the ventral plates and 5 scales deep at its apex. This has the color of the venter with the apex bearing the dark colors of the dorsal saddles. On the forward half of the body the complex saddles are 6½ or 7½ scales long on the meson and extend down the sides 10 scale rows, the lower point stopping 1 or 2 scales short of the ends of the ventral plates. The top of the head is marked by several light and dark intervals, the light ones drab-gray with very minute punctae, the dark ones tawny-olive. The first light interval is an angle with its point at the rear of the frontal, the diverging bars crossing the middle of the parietals as they extend distinctly or nebulously downward across the temporal region to the ventral surface. Certainly no black bar from the eye separates them from the venter. This interval is sharply marked off ahead by a tawny-olive bar which covers the rear half of the frontal and much of the forward half of the parietal and becomes 2 or 3 scales wide on the temporals. The next light interval starts from the rear of the eye and crosses the forward half of the frontal to a corresponding point on the other side. This in turn is outlined ahead by a tawny-olive bar extending from front of eye on edge of supraocular across edge of frontal and prefrontal to other eye. Ahead of this tawny-olive bar, the head is cinnamon-buff. The underside of the head is white or pale pinkish cinnamon, as are the lower edges of the upper labials back of the eye. The upper labials ahead of the eye and most of the other facial plates are clear white or pale pinkish cinnamon. The iris is clay color, the pupil vertical. The ventral color is white or pale pinkish buff on the caudal 3rd of each plate, the rest pinkish cinnamon. About every 3rd ventral and often extending onto the 1st scale row is a square spot of tawny-olive with a touch of sepia on its end.

Habitat: In 1922 Van Denburgh wrote, "Nothing is known of the habits of this snake." In 1934 Campbell noted the vibrating of its tail. In 1936 at Guaymas, Taylor took three near the sea, two at night and one at 10 in the morning. The last was tightly coiled in a niche in a low rock cliff. In 1941(a) in Utah, W. W. Tanner considered it of the Lower Sonoran areas and found that "since 1935, several specimens have been collected within Washington County." Others who have contributed to our knowledge of this nocturnal snake hidden in rocky crevices by day are Woodbury (Ut., 1931, 1934), Gloyd, and V. M. Tanner. Ditmars held that it fed on lizards, young snakes, and batrachians.

Period of activity: *First appearance*—May 20, 1936, Apr., 1938 (Tanner, 1940); May 6 (Slevin, 1940, Calif.). *Fall disappearance*—Oct., 1874 (Stejneger); Aug. 1, Aug. 17, 1933 (Campbell, Ariz., 1934); Sept. 9 (Woodbury, Ut., 1931).

Breeding: Oviparous. Males 296–788 mm., females 359–1,026 mm. "Van Denburgh reports a female taken on March 16, containing eggs, 9 by 21 mm. The female taken in Zion Canyon September 9, contained no eggs and the ovaries were not active" Woodbury (Ut., 1931).

Field notes: June 9–13, 1934, Ramsey Canyon, Huachaca Mts., Ariz.: Mrs. Holbert secured a Jews' harp snake (*Trimorphodon*) in her yard. She found this individual because the jays made a fuss. They followed the snake.

Aug. 17, 1930: In tin box, it will shake its tail and this often sounds like a hiss when it hits the box. It vibrates so fast it looks a blur.

July 9, 1942, Globe to Show Low, Ariz.: At 4,650-foot altitude beyond Seven Mile Wash saw *Cnemidophorus* and several *Holbrookia*. . . . A mile farther found DOR *Trimorphodon lyrophanes* (*lambda*). . . . Water in a little stream beside road for area from *Trimorphodon* on to *Holbrookia*. This point is just south of 66 miles from Show Low.

Authorities:

Bogert, C. M., and J. A. Oliver (Ariz., 1945)

Campbell, B. (Ariz., 1934)

Cope, E. D. (Gen., 1886)

Cowles, R. B., and C. M. Bogert (Calif., 1935)

Gloyd, H. K. (Ariz., 1937a, 1937)

Klauber, L. M. (Calif., 1928, Gen., 1940b)

Smith, H. M. (Gen., 1941)

Smith, H. M., and E. H. Taylor (Gen., 1945)

Stejneger, L. (Ariz., 1903)

Tanner, V. M. (Ut., 1935)

Tanner, W. W. (Ut., 1940, 1941a)

Taylor, E. H. (Gen., 1936, 1938)

Van Denburgh, J. (Gen., 1922)

Van Denburgh, J., and J. R. Slevin (Ariz., 1913)

Woodbury, A. M. (Ut., 1934)

1938, E. H. Taylor: "The relationship of this form is with *Trimorphodon lyrophanes* (Cope). There are apparent differences in dentition and it is likely that 2 is the normal number of loreals. Known only from southern Sinaloa, Mexico. *I suspect the species occurs also in Arizona, where it has probably been confused with T. lyrophanes.*" Italics ours.

1940(b), L. M. Klauber: "Is *lambda* specifically different from *lyrophanes,* and to which of these species should the snakes of Arizona, southern Nevada, and southwestern Utah be referred? . . . With respect to the second problem, namely the relationships between *lyrophanes* and *lambda,* and the validity of the latter, I find the material still insufficient to permit a decision with any claim to finality. Tentatively, I conclude that *lambda* is not a valid species; additional specimens may warrant its retention as a subspecies of *lyrophanes,* but I do not so recognize it at this time. . . . So I think it best to consider *lambda* a synonym of *lyrophanes* until more specimens become available and the dispersion of these two characters within each subspecies can be better defined or until other differences are discovered."

1945, C. M. Bogert and J. Oliver: "Smith points out that penial characters serve to separate the mainland form from *lyrophanes* of the peninsula of Baja California. This character may indeed prove to be valid, but on the other hand there may prove to be sufficient variation in penial characters to make it necessary to reduce *lambda* to subspecific status under *lyrophanes.* Geographic isolation does not, of necessity, indicate complete differentiation, nor is it safe to assume that penial characters are any more stable than external characters."

California lyre snake (12—Klauber 1928), Van Denburgh's lyre snake (Ditmars 1936)

Trimorphodon vandenburghi Klauber 1924. Fig. 250; Map 61

Another common name: Lyre snake.

Range: Coastal and desert s. California from Los Angeles County and Argus Mountains, Inyo County, s. into n.w. Baja California, Mex.—U.S.A.: Calif. Mex.: Baja Calif. *Elevation*—Ocean to 1,500 to 3,000 feet. 1,520 feet (Linsdale, Nev., 1938–40); coast to the westerly fringe of the desert, but excluding the mountains (Klauber, Calif., 1931a); ocean to desert foothills (Perkins); 60–2,900 feet (Klauber, Calif., 1928); not above 3,000 feet coast side; not above 2,800 feet desert side (Klauber, Gen., 1940b).

Size: Adults, 24–43 inches. Klauber (Gen., 1943b), observing 22 males and 16 females, gives the following: Mean length over all—males 555.23 mm., females 556 mm.; over-all maxima—males 738 mm. (tail 114); females 1,054 mm. (tail 137).

Distinctive characteristics: "A species of *Trimorphodon* characterized by an entire anal plate, and a relatively high number of body blotches. . . .

Summarizing, the most characteristic items of the *T. vandenburghi* pattern, and in fact of several other species, are the lyre-shaped marks or chevrons on the head, and the light crossmarks splitting the body blotches. In *vandenburghi* the body blotches vary from 28 to 43, interquartile range 32.6 to 37.3, mean 34.92 ∓ 0.49, coefficient of variation 10.02 per cent. The tail spots vary in number from 11 to 19, interquartile range 13.4 to 15.8, mean 14.62 ∓ 0.26 coefficient of variation 12.07 per cent. Sexual dimorphism is evident in the *Trimorphodon* pattern. The males average 34.27 ∓ 0.59 body blotches and the females 36.74 ∓ 0.72. In tail spots, the males average 14.54 ∓ 0.29, and the females 14.35 ∓ 0.41. The body blotches are significantly different in the sexes; but the tail spots are not" (Klauber, Gen., 1940b).

Color: A snake from San Diego, Calif., loaned by L. M. Klauber, June 13, 1929. The background is tilleul buff, ecru-drab, pallid brownish drab, or even pale cinnamon-pink in the intervals within the paired spots as well as the dorsal intervals in general. On the 6 or 7 middorsal scale rows are 32 pairs of transverse spots, which are buckthorn brown or buffy brown, excepting the rear ones, which are olive-brown, all edged with black or mummy brown. There are 17 similarly colored spots on the tail, but not in pairs. Each pair of dorsal spots unites on the sides in a similarly colored lateral spot. Below these united lateral spots is a series extending from the 3rd or 4th row of scales to the ends of the ventrals. Alternating with these lateral spots is another series extending from the ends of the ventrals to the 6th or 7th scale row. On top of the head is an irregular band in the eye region, broadest at the eyes and tapering to a common median point. This band is isabella color or like the dorsal saddles and is also dark-bordered. A similar band, a broad one, starts at the upper rear of the eye and extends obliquely backward to the angle of the mouth. Back of this is a median dorsal spot which is followed by a Y-shaped spot on the neck, the 2 points forward. The interstices of the head are like the background of the body. The rostral, nasals, and internasals are grayish olive. The upper labials back of the eye have upper borders of buffy olive. The lower part of the upper labials is white. The eye is dark olive-buff, chamois, deep colonial buff, or olive-ocher with a sprinkling of body background color on the outer part. The pupil is perfectly vertical and slitlike. The underside of the head is white. The whole under surface is a glistening white like the lining of many bivalve shells, except occasionally the base of each ventral may be marked with a narrow band of warm buff.

Habitat: Before 1940 this night-roving snake was characterized as a dweller among rocks and rarely in the open by day. In 1940(b) Klauber discussed *Trimorphodon* hunting at length: "Most of the specimens which have been taken alive have been found in one of two ways: either by prying off chunks from parent boulders, or by driving along paved roads at night. The first scheme is best for daylight collecting on the coastal slope, and the other for night collecting in the transmontane area. In the first type of hunting it has been my experience that the lyre snakes do not take refuge under the thin rock flakes which so often harbor *Xantusia henshawi* and other lizards, and *Hypsiglena ochrorhynchus* amongst the snakes. Rather, they seem to prefer deeper and safer crevices, and thus more strenuous work is required to find them than by stripping off exfoliating sheets. Although some years ago I did extensive collecting of this kind, and must have pried off a good many thousand flakes, I never found a *Trimorphodon* under one; but no less than 5 were found under chunks, although decidedly fewer of the latter were the subject of an investigating pinch bar. In this manner the type specimen was collected on May 4, 1924. It was found under a large and thick fragment which had pulled away from a granite boulder. On May 1, 1926, at Viejas, one large and one medium specimen were found together in a crack between two boulders, from which they were extracted with difficulty. These snakes were discovered because a section of the body of one was visible from the surface. It was a cold, dark, and foggy day. On April 8, 1927, at Shady Dell, a specimen was disclosed under one large rock resting on another; and on April 20th of the same year at San Pasqual, one was discovered under a large cap rock, level and closely fitting to the top of a boulder. All of these points are in San Diego County.

"Other collectors have had similar experiences. James Deuel found 2 young specimens under cap rocks a few hundred feet apart at the foot of El Capitan Mountain, on March 31, 1939. The San Diego Reptile Club collected 3 specimens in Moosa Canyon on its field trip April 24, 1938. Two were found in deep rock crevices as usual, but the other was lying coiled under a bush near a pile of granite boulders, at 3:15 in the afternoon. It was a partly cloudy day. Of the other type of collecting, that is, by driving on desert roads and picking up the snakes found crossing the highway, as discussed elsewhere (1939) I have records of specimens collected at 7:25, 8:10, 9:00, 9:15, 9:55 P.M. and 12:30 A.M. On 2 of these occasions snakes were found abroad on unusually cold and windy nights. On the first evening, May 22, 1937, a lyre snake was crossing the road at 9:15 P.M. This was in upper Sentenac Canyon, air temperature 66°F., and a strong wind blowing."

Period of activity: *First appearance*—January, March, April, May, July (Klauber, Calif., 1928); Jan. 2, 1927 (Silver-Atsatt in Klauber); May 23, 1934 (Cowles and Bogert, Calif., 1935). "Sixteen-Year Census"—Jan., 1 snake; Feb., 1; Mar., 5; Apr., 10; May, 13; June, 3; July, 3; Aug., 3; Sept., 2; Oct., 2; Dec., 1. Total 44. Rank 23. Per cent 0.34 (Klauber, Gen., 1939a). *Fall disappearance*—Sept. (Klauber, Grinnell, in Klauber); Oct. 1, 1934 (Cowles and Bogert, Calif., 1935).

Breeding: Oviparous. Males 555–738 mm., females 556–1,054 mm. *Eggs*— "R. B. Cowles has advised me that a large *vandenburghi* (length 1,055 mm.) deposited 12 eggs in September" (Klauber, Calif., 1940b). *Young*—"What apparently is the first record from the coastal region of Los Angeles County is a specimen from the Santa Monica Mountains a few miles northwest of Beverly Hills, brought to the University of California at Los Angeles by Mr. J. S. Martin, who had discovered '3 or 4' small snakes on October 1, 1934, under a boulder which he turned over while on a picnic. Apparently he discovered a brood of young lyre snakes, for the others were similar to the 1 captured and the specimen brought to us has only recently emerged from the egg as the umbilical groove was still present. This individual measures 205 mm. and is marked with 32 blotches on the body and 13 on the tail. The blotches are dark brown on a grey ground color" (Cowles and Bogert). "The young are hatched from eggs" (Perkins). Klauber's (Gen., 1943b) minimum lengths over all are 264 mm. (tail 45) for males and 234 mm. (tail 35) for females.

Food: Lizards, mice. Klauber (Calif., 1928), Perkins (1938), Cowles and Bogert (1935), Rodman (1939).

Venom: "In captivity, *Trimorphodon vandenburghi* is rather vicious, particularly if cornered. While practically helpless in the light, it strikes with fair accuracy in the dark. The tail is rapidly vibrated when the snake is annoyed. When frightened, it progresses with the anterior part of the body raised well off the ground. I was bitten by 1 specimen without noting a result differing from the bite of any harmless snake. However, the posterior teeth probably did not take effect and the snake was given no opportunity to chew" (Klauber, Calif. 1928). "It is harmless to man, as a bite from its small teeth probably would not break the skin and should this occur, the poison might cause as much inconvenience as a mosquito bite, as it is too weak to kill a mouse. It is hard to believe that a person bitten would permit the snake to advance its jaws, with their characteristic chewing motion, far enough to imbed its fangs" (Perkins).

Cowles and Bogert made a study of the fang of *Trimorphodon vandenburghi,* its venom, and the effect on reptiles and mammals. They concluded: "On each occasion when *Trimorphodon* was induced to bite, chewing movements were apparently necessary in order for the small rear fangs to be brought into action. Possibly these chewing motions also serve to stimulate the flow of the venom. While experiments made with the single live specimen are too meagre to draw certain conclusions, the effect of the venom on the rodents bitten by *Trimorphodon* would suggest that the action of the venom is chiefly hemorrhagic as indicated by the severe local edema produced, which was unaccompanied by any marked evidence of nervous symptoms."

Authorities:

Bogert, C. M. (Calif., 1930)

Cowles, R. B., and C. M. Bogert (Calif., 1935)

Klauber, L. M. (Gen., 1940b; Calif., 1928, 1929)

Perkins, C. B. (Calif., 1938)

Rodman, G. B., Jr. (Calif., 1939)

Taylor, E. H. (Gen., 1938)

1940, L. M. Klauber: "So adverse were conditions that night that, although this is in the best area for the night collecting of desert reptiles of which I have knowledge, not another snake was found in 2 hours and a half of travel. Again, May 6, 1939, on the aqueduct road along the base of the Little San Bernardino Mountains, Riverside County, near the Pushawalla branch, a specimen was crossing the road at 7:25 P.M., the temperature 64° and a gale blowing. Only 3 other snakes were found abroad that night, all sidewinders, 2 of them a mating pair. But the sidewinders were in a partially protected canyon, while the *Trimorphodon* was out in the open wash. These two experiences indicate that lyre snakes can probably withstand as unfavorable nocturnal weather conditions as any of our desert snakes."

Wilkinson's lyre snake (2—Ditmars 1936), Texas lyre snake (3)

Trimorphodon vilkinsoni Cope 1885. Fig. 251; Map 61

Another common name: Wilkinson's snake.
Range: From Franklin Mts., Tex., into Chihuahua, Mex.—U.S.A.: Tex. Mex.: Chihuahua. *Elevation*—4,000 to 5,000 feet. 5,000 feet (Crimmins).
Size: Adults, presumably 24-40 inches.
Distinctive characteristics and color: "Scales in 23 (24) rows; superior labials 9. Top of head white, with 3 round black spots; dorsal spot; few transverse undivided black rhombs, with pale edges" (Cope, Gen., 1900). "A broad, light area on neck, between dark areas on head and first body blotch; bands ⅓ length of interspaces; dark head area [is] only 3 spots in young" (Smith).

Authorities:

Cope, E. D. (Gen., 1886, 1900)
Crimmins, M. L. (Tex., 1925)
Jameson, D. L., and A. G. Flury (Tex., 1949)

Klauber, L. M. (Gen., 1940b)
Smith, H. M. (Gen., 1941)
Smith, H. M., and E. H. Taylor (Gen., 1945)
Taylor, E. H. (Gen., 1938)

1886, E. D. Cope: "One specimen; No. 14268. This species is nearest the *T. biscutatus* D. and B. in squamation, but differs greatly in coloration from this or any other species of the genus."

1925, M. L. Crimmins: "On October 26, 1924, on the east slope of Mt. Franklin, about 5 miles north of El Paso, Texas, Staff Sergeant J. C. Owens, Q.M.C., found a small snake which on further examination has proved to be *Trimorphodon vilkinsonii* Cope. The locality where the snake was found lies within the Pennsylvania series of limestone at an elevation of about 5,000 feet."

1938, E. H. Taylor: "A 2nd specimen which I have been privileged to examine is one in the Blanchard collection, collected 3 miles northwest of El Paso close to the Rio Grande on the road to Las Cruces, June, 1935. It presents the following characters: Rostral very much wider than high, fold-

Fig. 250. *Trimorphodon vandenburghi,* San Diego, Calif., L. M. Klauber.

Fig. 251. *Trimorphodon vilkinsoni,* El Paso, Tex., F. N. Blanchard, after Taylor.

ing back on the snout so that part visible above is less than ⅓ its distance from frontal, its length about equal to the suture between the supranasals; greatest length of the supranasal ⅗ to ¾ the length of prefrontals; suture between the internasals less than ½ the prefrontal suture; frontal width, 3.7 mm.; length, 5.1 mm., slightly shorter than its distance to tip of snout (5.4 mm.); length of parietal, 7 mm.; parietals to tip of snout, 10 mm.; nasal distinctly divided; 3 loreal scales; 3 preoculars; 3 postoculars; upper labials 9–9, the 7th divided transversely on left side; lower labials 13–13; temporals, 3 + 4 + 6; 3 + 5 + 5; 5 labials touch chin shields; 2nd pair of chin shields completely separated; about 4 pairs of scales between 2nd chin shields and 1st widened ventrals scale; scales with double apical pits; scale formula: 34, 22, 22, 23, 18, 16; ventrals, 228; subcaudals, 79; anal undivided.

"*Color*. Brownish-gray with a series of somewhat irregularly-shaped blackish transverse blotches; first, 9 or 10 scales back of the parietals, somewhat narrowed on the median line, its greatest length equal to 7 scales, not reaching 3rd scale row laterally; this blotch followed by 27 blotches on body and tail; each blotch is grayish in the middle, and is bordered by creamy gray; 9 blotches on tail; 45 pairs of ventrolateral spots touching outer scale row, but for the most part on the ventrals, occasionally confluent with the dorsal blotches, which terminate on 2nd scale row (except 1st blotch which is narrowest of all). The markings on the head are diffuse, but there is evidence of a pattern with darker areas on the prefrontals, frontals and parietals." Taylor furnishes the only photographs of this form.

1941, H. M. Smith: "The body pattern of *vilkinsonii* is highly suggestive of the pattern of *Lampropeltis leonis,* which is fairly certainly known to have been derived by suppression of alternate blotches. This similarity at least suggests the possibility that *vilkinsonii's* pattern was produced in the same manner."

1949, D. L. Jameson and A. G. Flury: "A specimen was found active and apparently foraging at the junction of the stream beds of Fox Hollow and Box Canyon, about 9 P.M., on a clear, calm night. The surrounding area was extremely rocky, a habitat of many other members of the genus. . . . Our specimen is 625 mm. long. There are 229 ventrals and 84 subcaudals. The scale row count is 21-22-17. . . .

"The color pattern, with exceptions, matches that of Klauber's description. The head has 3 dark brown spots on a grey background. One spot is on the posterior part of the frontal, and there is 1 on the anterior part of each parietal. The spots on the parietals are connected to the one on the frontal by light brown marks. There are 20 dark brown body bands on a gray background. The first 11 spots are constricted at the median line. The area lateral to these constrictions is 4 to 5 scales wide in the first 7 bands and 3 scales wide in the others. There are 12 tail bands, each 2 to 3 scales wide except for the most posterior one, which is 1 scale wide. Each back and tail band is bordered both posteriorly and anteriorly by a very light band, which is 1 scale wide. The lateral edges of the body bands are 1 scale wide. All but the last 4 bands reach the ventrals. All but the 1st are 2 scales wide at the lateral edges. There are 1 to 3 lateral spots of dark brown between each of the body bands. Each lateral spot covers 1 to 3 scales, and several of them overlap into the ventral surface. This gives the ventral surface a rather broken-edged effect. The interspaces are 4 to 9 scales wide. This is a marked difference from the specimens examined and described by Klauber (1941b). Klauber describes the interspaces as 8 to 12 scales wide and the bands as 4 to 5 scales wide. The bands in our specimen are 3 scales wide except for the first 7. Our specimen differs from the other known specimens in the number of tail spots or bands. In our specimen there are 12 spots while in the others there are 7 to 10. Our specimen has 84 subcaudals as opposed to 77–79 in the other specimens."

LINED SNAKES

Genus *TROPIDOCLONION* Cope (Fig. 20)

Size small, 9–21 inches; head small, not distinct from body; tail very short; anal entire; caudals paired; scales keeled, without pits, in 17-19-17 rows; maxillary teeth 15 gradually increasing in size posteriorly; upper labials 5–7; lower 6 or 7; nasal 1 (semidivided); oculars 1–2; internasals 2; temporals 2 (1) + 2 (1); loreal 1; ventrals 138–150; very few caudals 32–45 (while *Thamnophis* has 49$^+$); middle of venter has 2 rows of spots; hemipenis—slightly bilobed, each lobe with a solid apical awn, sulcus undivided. Synonyms: *Ischnognathus, Microps, Storeria, Tropidoclonium.*

Lined snake (31—Yarrow 1882), **Striped swamp snake** (9—Ditmars 1907)

Tropidoclonion lineatum lineatum (Hallowell) 1856. Fig. 252; Map 62

Other common names: Common snake; dwarf garter snake; grass snake; line snake; ribbon snake; streaked snake; striped snake (3); swamp snake.

Range: From extreme s.e. South Dakota and s.w. Minnesota to w. Illinois, s. across Missouri and n.w. Arkansas to s. cent. Texas, northward e. of 98° Long.—Ark.; Colo.; Ia.; Ill.; Kan.; Minn.; Mo.; Neb.; N.M. (Koster); Okla.; S.D.; Tex. *Elevation*—Sea level to 1,500, possibly 2,000 feet.

Size: Adults, 9–21 inches.

Distinctive characteristics: See generic characterization above. "A yellow dorsal stripe, covering 1 and 2 half rows of scales, extends from the nape to the tip of the tail. A lateral stripe is present on the 2nd and lower half of the

3rd row of scales. This stripe is yellowish and mottled with brown. A row of black dots on each side of the dorsal stripe and another row near the lateral stripe. Color above light brown to dark brown. Inferior row of scales brownish. Belly greenish, with 2 rows of triangular black spots down the middle. Upper part of the head mottled with black and brown. Superior labials and lower part of temporals drab. Under part of head whitish, often maculated with small black spots" (Hurter). Ventrals 135–150; caudals 32–46.

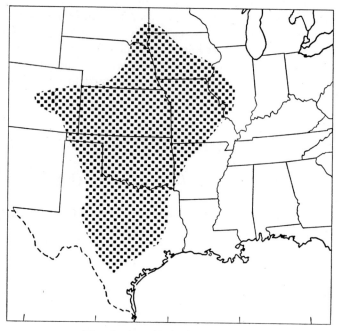

Map 62. *Tropidoclonion lineatum.*

Color: A snake from St. Louis, Mo., received from R. M. Perkins, Apr. 11, 1929. The general background of the back is grayish olive or deep olive. There is a median dorsal stripe and a lateral stripe on the 1st 3 scale rows of pale drab-gray or pallid brownish drab. There is a border of minute black spots along either side of the middorsal stripe. Bordering the light lateral stripe above is a row of black spots, each covering 2 or 3 scales, and separated from each other by 1 scale. The top of the head is citrine-drab, grayish olive, or light grayish olive. The plates back of the eye are heavily spotted with black. The iris is olive-brown spotted with wood brown, and with a very narrow pupil rim of colonial buff. The underside of the head is pale drab-gray or pale vinaceous-fawn. The ends of the ventrals are pale smoke gray or almost white merging into the color of the 1st 3 scale rows. The general color of the belly is glass green, pale lumiere green, or pale dull green-yellow. Beginning on the neck is a central row of black spots. These soon divide and extend as 2 rows to the tip of the tail. From these central rows, a narrow front edge of black extends across each ventral to the 1st scale row, where it occurs on the forward basal end of each scale.

Habitat: In 1885 Cragin wrote entertainingly of this form: *"Storeria lineata,* Hallowell: Line Snake—This is the *Tropidoclonium lineatum* of my preliminary catalogue. It proves to be one of the commonest serpents of Kansas. Every state has its 'Schoolboy's Snake,' a snake of small size and meek demeanor, though a horror to the uninitiated, which the untamed urchin of school and field carries about in his pocket or fist for purposes of terrorism. This 'School-boy's Snake' of Kansas is the Line Snake."

In 1893 Hurter gave an equally extended account:"A plain-looking snake resembling a garter snake; found along the river front in an abandoned quarry near the Arsenal grounds, in city of St. Louis. They are found under rocks and under sods. In 1892 during the big inundations, I have found hundreds of them drowned and washed against the settling basins of the St. Louis water-works, at Bissel's Point. They came all from a tract of lowland above the water-works, about 1½ miles long by about 600 feet wide. This place is covered with rank grass, and in dry weather the ground which is of a boggy kind of black earth, cracks in all directions, thereby forming hiding places for these snakes."

This snake has been found living under rocks, in clay banks, in prairie

Fig. 252. *Tropidoclonion lineatum:* 1,3, Imboden, Ark., B. C. Marshall; 2,7, St. Louis, Mo., R. M. Perkins; 4–6, San Antonio Reptile Garden, Tex., J. Hindman.

ledges near the bottom of a rocky hill, beneath stones in a shallow ravine above a pasture, in flood plains, and in many diverse places. This small retiring form lives in civilized parts also: in waste places, under sidewalks, trash piles, woodpiles, old buildings, storehouses, warehouses, tar paper, cement blocks, broken tile, and even in a crevice of a post.

Period of activity: *Early appearances*—Feb. 25, 1925 (Gloyd); Feb. 28, 1905 (Bailey, Tex., 1905); Apr., 1889 (Garman); Apr. 9, 1934 (Burt, Gen., 1935); Apr. 21, 1948, Apr. 30, 1949 (Maslin, Colo., 1950); Apr. 9, 1933, Apr. 11, 30, 1932, Apr. 22, 29, 1933, May 4, 1932, May 9, 1888, May 13, 14, 1933 (Burt and Hoyle, Gen., 1935); May 6, 1934 (Burt, Gen., 1935); May 29, 1942 (Loomis, Ia., 1948). Blanchard and Force reported them emerging from hibernation from the middle of March to April 1. *Fall disappearance* —Oct. 21, Nov. 5, 11, 1925; Oct. 27, Nov. 7, 15, 1926 (Gloyd); Nov. 13, 1932 (Burt); Oct., 1933 (Burt and Hoyle, Gen., 1935); Aug. 27, 1947, Sept. 15, 1949 (Maslin). Blanchard and Force reported their going into hibernation from the middle of October to Nov. 1, giving a season of activity of 7 months. *Hibernation*—our associate, W. J. Hamilton, Jr. (Tex., 1947), has written: "In January, 1943, I lived in a suburb of Dallas, Texas. During the mild weather of the first 2 weeks, my family and I dug a small garden patch of black gumbo, a sticky clay, thickly grown to Johnson grass, *Sorghum halepense*. At a depth of 6 to 8 inches, we uncovered 7 hibernating lined snakes (*Tropidoclonion lineatum*) in a plot of 1,200 square feet. Four of the snakes were in an area the size of a dinner table. The snakes were coiled, one ring upon another, similar to preserved specimens coiled to fit into a small jar. The heads of the snakes inclined slightly into the center of the circle formed by the coils. On exposure to bright sunlight for an hour, at a temperature of 76° F., the snakes showed little movement, retaining their hibernating pose. On January 19 an unprecedented cold spell occurred with temperatures of 7° F. This observation suggests that the species is somewhat communal in its hibernating behavior. Similar habitat encompassed more than 2 acres."

Breeding: Viviparous. Males 230–390 mm., females 210–510 mm. *Mating*— In 1928 Gloyd posed the possibility of fall mating. Force (1931) and Ramsey added evidence of the same sort.

Young—Number, 2–12. 2, 7, 8, 9, 11, 12 (Force); 4, 9 (Hamilton); 6 (Stejneger, Hurter); 6, 8, 9, 10 (Strecker). Time of birth, Aug. 1–31. Size, 2.6–5.4 inches. Blanchard and Force had few from 65–90 mm., but many from 95–135 mm., the mean being 111 mm. We have seen young from Iowa, Kansas, Oklahoma, and Texas. From 5 diverse collections we chose specimens 110 mm., 119 mm., 126 mm., 128 mm., and 156 mm. long, the last not being newborn. Blanchard and Force's study of sexual maturity in the lined snake indicates that "the period of adolescence in this species is only a year and 9 months. This means that these snakes reach sexual maturity in the 2nd spring after birth." With her abundant material, Force brought out two papers in 1930 and 1931 on breeding in the lined snake. Her first paper yields these data: "Females under observation brought forth living young between August 9 and 31. They ranged in number from 2 to 11, usually 7 to 9, averaging 120 mm. in length. They shed frequently and took earthworms the third day. The largest example the writer has recorded is 510 mm. long, but the usual size of the adults is 240 to 350 mm." Her second paper, on habits and birth of young, developed the topic more in detail. Stejneger (Tex., 1891) gave 90 mm. at birth. Strecker (Tex., 1926c) held them to be nearly 4 inches and born Aug. 1–15.

In 1946 Ramsey observed 2 pregnant females. One taken in November was provided with males in the spring; during Aug. 1–14 its voracious appetite ceased; and on Aug. 14 it gave birth to 4 young. It shed for the 4th time that year on Aug. 27. It mated again on Sept. 1. The other female, caught May 27, "when threatened with capture . . . flattened her entire body, including part of her tail, and spread her head, coiled, and struck at me. . . . She gave birth to a litter of 9 on Aug. 14. . . . Five of them shed their skins soon after their birth."

Food: Insects, earthworms, sowbugs. Stejneger (Tex., 1947a), Over (S.D., 1923), Gloyd, Force, Pinkus (Mo., 1932), Ramsey (Tex., 1947a).

Field notes: Apr. 26, 1934, Witte Museum, Brackenridge Park, San Antonio, Tex.: Had an excellent session with specimens and noted a fine *Tropidoclonion lineatum*. A few days ago as we went around the reptile exhibit we saw *Tropidoclonion lineatum* in the various cages. We asked why one of these in each cage and found they were used as food. A young boy supplied them and had a monopoly on the business. Soon made the acquaintance of an alert lad, Joe Hindman, who discovered these snakes in February and March while they were hibernating under boards and similar cover. (The area was within the park and partially in the old stone quarry where the excellent San Antonio Zoo now is.)

Inasmuch as John Henry Comstock, American entomologist and author of *The Spider Book,* founded the company which is now Comstock Publishing Associates, a division of Cornell University Press, we add this amazing note. In 1932 Pinkus (Mo., 1932) wrote in *Popular Science Monthly* an interesting article on "How a spider caught and dined upon a six-inch snake." The spider was identified "according to *Anthony* Comstock's Spider Book." What a crime! So far removed from the crimes in which the reformer specialized.

Authorities:

Blanchard, F. N., and E. R. Force (Okla., 1930)

Branson, E. B. (Kan., 1904)

Burt, C. E. (Kan., 1913)

Call, R. E. (Ia., 1891)

Cragin, F. W. (Kan., 1885)

Dunn, E. R. (Gen., 1932)

Force, E. R. (Okla., 1930, 1931)

Garman, H. (Ill., 1892)
Gloyd, H. K. (Kan., 1928)
Hallowell, E. (Kan., 1857)
Hamilton, W. J., Jr. (Tex., 1947)
Hay, O. P. (Ind., 1892)

Hurter, J. (Mo., 1911)
Maslin, T. P. (Colo., 1950)
Ramsey, L. W. (Tex., 1946, 1947a)
Strecker, J. K., Jr. (Tex., 1915, 1926c)
Stejneger, L. (Tex., 1891)

1932, E. R. Dunn: "The snake known as *Tropidoclonion lineatum* is generally conceded to be a degenerate ally of the genus *Thamnophis*. . . . The relationship of *lineatum* to the *Thamnophis elegans* group is indisputable." For several years after this statement appeared, *Thamnophis* was widely used.

1950, A. H. and A. A. Wright: In 1932 when Dunn wrote that it was related to *Thamnophis elegans,* the western limit of *Tropidoclonion lineatum* was only known to extend from e. Nebraska and Kansas through e. and cent. Oklahoma to cent. Texas. But today, with the w. limit known to extend from Denver to the extreme end of the Oklahoma panhandle to Mertzon, Tex., the limit is practically the same as the e. limit of *Thamnophis elegans vagrans*—a fine topic for study in this contiguous area.

1953: L. W. Ramsey (*Herpetologica,* 9: 7–24) subdivides this species as follows:

"KEY TO THE SUBSPECIES OF *TROPIDOCLONION*

"1. Caudals in females fewer than 34; in males fewer than 41. Ventrals in females fewer than 145; in males fewer than 144. Ventrals plus caudals fewer than 178 for females; fewer than 185 for males. Range Texas. *l. texanum*

Caudals in females 34 or more; in males 41 or more. Ventrals and ventrals plus caudals may or may not be as above. Range north Texas to Illinois . . . 2.

"2. Ventrals fewer than 144 in females, fewer than 143 in males. Range Colorado, northeastern Kansas, Missouri, Iowa, Illinois, eastern Nebraska, and southeastern South Dakota. *l. lineatum*

Ventrals 144 or more in females, 143 or more in males. Ventrals plus caudals 178 or more in females, 185 or more in males. Range north Texas, Oklahoma, southern Kansas. *l. annectens.*"

CORAL SNAKES

FAMILY ELAPIDAE Boie

Has pair of large, permanently erect fangs near front (proteroglyph) of upper jaw and is thus allied with the sea snakes; facial bones not movable; maxillary bone horizontal, elongated posteriorly, abbreviated and supporting the fangs; fang groove not perfectly consolidated over the canal; scales smooth, rows 15 on mid-body; caudal vertebrate normal, without greatly developed processes; eye small, pupil elliptic or subelliptic; tympanic bone shortened, causing head to be but little distinct from body; occipital region has plates; size, small medium (280 mm.) to medium (1,000 mm.) to large (some South American forms 1,300-1,900 mm.); hemipenis—"bifurcate with each half with a spinous apex" (Cope); coloration in United States forms in rings, red separated from black by yellow (i.e., 2 yellows to each black or red, not 2 blacks to each yellow or red).

KEY TO THE GENERA (Fig. 253)

Representatives in U.S. are *Micrurus* and *Micruroides* with the following characters in common: size, small medium to medium, 15–43 inches; slender; head small; anal divided; rostral normal; scales smooth; no loreal; ventral plates more than 200; grooved fangs in anterior part of upper jaw; pattern of red and black rings separated by narrower yellow ones, all crossing the belly; eye small.

a. Tip of head to *angle of mouth* black, then yellow or pale lumiere green behind and *barely tipping* the parietals, followed by a *broad red band;* 1 pair of chin shields; caudals 21–29; 2 fangs in front and a solid tooth posteriorly.   *Micruroides*

aa. Tip of head to *back of eye* black, yellow bands across *frontal* between eyes and angle of mouth, then *broad black band;* 2 pairs of chin shields; caudals 28–45; maxilla with 1 fang.   *Micrurus fulvius*

ARIZONA CORAL SNAKES

Genus *MICRUROIDES* Schmidt

Size small, 15–20 inches; cylindrical and appears slenderer than *Micrurus;* head to angle of mouth black, succeeding yellow barely tipping parietals, followed by *broad red band;* red dorsal areas unmarked with black; 2 black rings on tail; long ventral suture between 1st lower labials; 1 pair chin shields with many gulars between them and ventrals; caudals 21–29; maxilla with 2 fangs; maxillary bone bears 1 or 2 small posterior solid teeth in addition to the anterior fang; small scales on neck in 17 rows; temporals 1–2; last upper labial small; range: s. New Mexico and Arizona, n. Mexico and Tiburón Island, and Swan Falls, s.w. Idaho on the Snake River. Synonyms: *Elaps, Micrurus.*

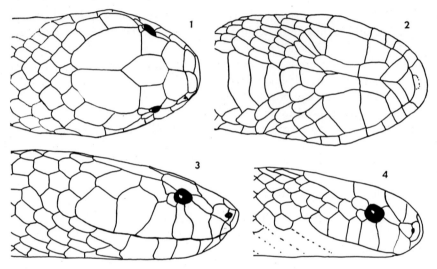

Fig. 253. 1–3, *Micrurus f. barbouri;* 4, *Micruroides euryxanthus.*

Sonoran coral snake (22—Stejneger), Arizona coral snake (5—Schmidt 1928)

Micruroides euryxanthus (Kennicott) 1860. Figs. 254, 255; Map 63

Other common names: Coral snake (Dall 1869); king snake; "ring" snake; Sonora coral snake; Sonora harlequin snake; western coral snake.

Range: From cent. and s.e. Arizona and s.w. New Mexico to Mexico (Chihuahua, Sonora, and Tiburón Island). One record each for s. Utah and Snake River, Ida.—U.S.A.: Ariz.; Ida.; N.M.; Tex.; Ut. Mex.: Baja Calif.; Chihuahua; Sonora. *Elevation*—Mainly 3,000 to 4,000 feet, possibly from 500 to 5,000 feet. 3,500 feet (Little, Ariz., 1940); 5,000 feet (Stejneger, Gen., 1895), 5,750 feet (Woodin, Ariz., 1953).

Size: Adults, 15–20 inches.

Distinctive characteristics: See generic characterization above.

Color: A snake from the W. B. Trowbridge ranch, Oracle, Ariz., described June 13, 1934. The body is ringed with red, pale lumiere green,

Fig. 254. *Micruroides euryxanthus:* 1–5,
Oracle, Ariz., C. Vorhies; 6,7 (dead), Naco-
zari, northern Sonora, Mex., Mrs. R. B. Alves.

Fig. 255. *Micruroides euryxanthus,* Swisshelm Mts., Ariz., R. I. Hewlett.

and black. On the body are 24 light rings of pale lumiere green which
are 2½ to 3 scales longitudinally. The black or blue-violet black bands
of the body are usually 7 to 7½ scales long. On the belly these become dark
plumbago slate. The scarlet or brazil red bands are usually 6 to 7 scales
long.

A snake from Bisbee, Ariz., received from R. I. Hewlett, Aug. 14, 1950.
It is ringed across back and belly with black, yellow, and red bands; 12
red bands on body; 12 black on body, not counting head + 2 on tail. The
head is black except for the rear tips of the parietals, where the 1st light
band begins, it being 6 scales wide longitudinally, the others 3, counted
on middorsum. The first 3 or 4 bands are maize yellow, the subsequent
ones sulphur yellow. The first 2 rings and the 2 tail rings are clear in
color, but the scales of the other light rings have each a medal bronze
thread just within the edge outlining the scale. On the forward part of
the body each yellow band occupies 2 ventrals, but one of these may often
have a small median encroachment of rose doree. The 1st red band is 9
scales longitudinally, but thereafter the red bands are 5½ to 6 scales on
middorsum. The color on the dorsum is ox-blood red or vandyke red, being
darker than the belly because the scales have dark edges. The bands on the
belly have no dark edges, being clear rose doree, crossing 6 plates, and
extending up the side across scale row 1. There are no dorsal or ventral
red bands on the tail, but a slight touch of rose doree on the anal plates.
The middle of the 1st reddish ring has on the venter a spot of slate-blue.
The black bands are like the reds, but the 1st is 8 scales longitudinally, the
others 6 or 7. These black or dusky slate-violet rings are glistening black on
middorsum, becoming on scale rows 1–3 deep slate-blue and slate-blue
on the venter, where this color covers 7 plates. The black of the head
covers 1 scale row back of the angle of the mouth and on the venter extends
medially to the 1st rose doree band, thus interrupting the 1st yellow neck
ring. *Structure*—One pair of chin shields. Many gulars between shields and
ventrals.

Habitat and habits: Except for food habits, we know little of its habitat,
habits, or breeding. Because of its amiability, many in Arizona consider it
not venomous (see Ruthven). In 1929 Vorhies gave a graphic account of
the struggle of a coral snake with a Tantilla which was finally swallowed
after 65 minutes. He also said the worm snake, *Leptotyphlops humilis,* was
a probable food species. In 1940 Little (Ariz.) reported "one was caught in
a run off tank near the upper border of the semi-desert zone." "One specimen measuring 443 mm. in total length was brought from Dos Cabezas
by Mr. Holland. It was found July 13 in an empty swimming pool near
an abandoned mine at an elevation of 5,750 feet, apparently an altitudinal
record for the species. . . . Only one, a DOR, has been obtained in over
3,600 miles of night collecting near Tucson. . . . Many of these are either

dug up or else found trapped in swimming pools, cattle guards, and the like; others are found crawling about, generally after dark, sometimes inside houses" (Woodin).

Food: Tantillas, worm snakes, lizards. Vorhies, Lowe, and Woodin.

Field notes: Aug. 12–Sept. 14, 1950: R. I. Hewlett, Bisbee, Ariz., first writes, "I have a coral snake about 16 or 18 inches long. Would you be interested in such a pet?" Later, "I think you will be surprised where the little snake was caught. I caught it in our kitchen one night about 9 o'clock. We have a rock house with concrete floors. It must have crawled through a screen door as the house is snake proof everywhere else. We live in the edge of the Swisshelm Mts., 20 miles north of Douglas, Ariz. I killed one in our yard two years ago. It was just crawling in the grass when I saw it." This brought the climax to our 33 years of wishing to possess a live Arizona coral snake.

Authorities:

Amaral, A. do (Gen., 1927c)
Bogert, C. M., and J. A. Oliver (Ariz., 1945)
Cope, E. D. (Baja Calif., 1862)
Gloyd, H. K. (Ariz., 1937a)
Hensley, M. M. (Ariz., 1950)

Lowe, C. H., Jr. (Ariz., 1948a)
Pack, H. J. (Ut., 1930)
Ruthven, A. G. (Ariz., 1907)
Schmidt, K. P. (Gen., 1928)
Terron, C. C. (Gen., 1932)
Vorhies, C. T. (Ariz., 1929)
Woodin, W. H. (Ariz., 1953)

1927, A. do Amaral: Unfortunately he writes thus: "Head all black; nape with a yellow ring followed by a black one—*M. euryxanthus* (Sonoran Coral Snake)." It should read "nape with a yellow ring followed by a *red* one." We make this correction with a live one before us.

1928, K. P. Schmidt: "Other herpetologists, and especially Cope, have commented on the isolated position in the genus *Micrurus* occupied by the Arizona coral snake, *Micrurus euryxanthus* (Kennicott). The form of the head shields, the small size of the last upper labial, and the color pattern, differ conspicuously from other species of the genus. The dorsal scales are small anteriorly and form 17 rows for some distance on the neck. This count is rarely to be observed in other species of *Micrurus*. The temporals are always 1–2. . . . The elongate maxillary bone bears a small posterior solid tooth in addition to the anterior fang. . . . With this dental character to support its other peculiarities, I have no hesitation in separating *euryxanthus* as the type of a distinct monotype genus, proposing for it the name *Micruroides,* type *Elaps euryxanthus* Kennicott."

1945, C. M. Bogert and J. R. Oliver: "It is possible that it represents a fragment of an old northern element that remained in North America when other New World elapids were cut off in South America in early Tertiary times; its supposedly more primitive characters do not necessarily belie this hypothesis."

1953, W. H. Woodin: Too late for inclusion under each species appeared this paper, one of the most important of the year. Woodin camped for 6 weeks in Carr Canyon at 5,500-feet elevation and above Major and Mrs. J. H. Healy. Like us he confirms the presence of *Sistrurus c. tergeminus* in s.e. Arizona. Among the rare forms recorded are *Gyalopion canum, Trimorphodon lambda, Tantilla w. wilcoxi, Crotalus p. pricei, Crotalus w. willardi,* and *Micruoides euryxanthus.* "Preferring open dry areas under 6,000 feet in elevation, *Micruroides* in the United States appears to range from southwestern New Mexico, possibly including the extreme western corner of Texas, northwestward to at least as far as the Prescott–Camp Verde area of central Arizona and as far west in that state as southeastern Mojave and extreme western Pima Counties."

CORAL SNAKES

Genus *MICRURUS* Wagler (Fig. 253)

Size, 17–43 inches; tip of head to back of eye black, then yellow band, then *broad black band;* 3 or 4 black rings on tail; 2 pairs of chin shields with few or no gulars between them and ventrals; caudals 28–45; maxilla with 1 fang; temporals 1–1. Synonyms: *Coluber, Elaps, Vipera, Vulpia.*

KEY TO THE GENUS *MICRURUS*
a. Black spots present in red bands.
  b. Black spotting of red bands usually in 2 or more relatively large spots. (Cent. Florida n. and e. to North Carolina and w. to Mississippi River.)   *M. fulvius fulvius*
  bb. Black spots in red bands are small, profuse, and very irregularly arranged. (S.w. Arkansas to s. and s. cent. Texas to n.e. Mexico.)
                                                                        M. f. tenere
aa. Black spots absent from red bands or much reduced; no trace of supra-anal keels in males. (S. part of Florida peninsula.)   *M. f. barbouri*

Coral snake (47—True 1883), **Harlequin snake** (26— Duncan 1880), **Bead snake** (11)
Micrurus fulvius fulvius (Linné) 1766. Fig. 256; Map 63

Other common names: American cobra; candy-stick; common coral snake; coral adder; eastern coral snake; Elaps harlequin snake; Florida coral snake; Florida harlequin snake (*distans* Yarrow 1882–1888); garter snake; harlequin coral snake; king snake; North American coral snake; red bead snake; thunder-and-lightning snake; viper (11).
Range: From n. Dade Co., Fla., to s.e. North Carolina and southwestward

in coastal South Carolina, s. Georgia, s. Alabama to Mississippi River. Indefinite records in e. Kentucky, s.w. Ohio, s.e. Indiana, s.e. and w. Missouri.— Ala.; Fla.; Ga.; Ill.?; Ind.?; Ky.?; La.; Miss.; Mo.?; N.C.; O.?; S.C. *Elevation*—Seacoast to 1,000 feet. Most records below 500 feet.

Size: Adults, 22–45 inches.

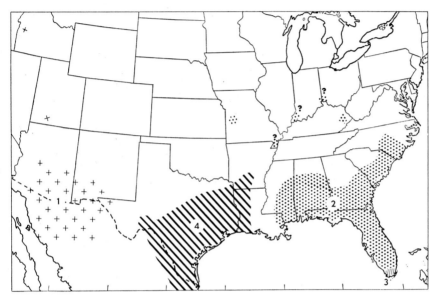

Map 63. *Micruroides* and *Micrurus*—1, *Micruroides euryxanthus;* 2, *Micrurus f. fulvius;* 3, *f. barbouri;* 4, *f. tenere.*

Distinctive characteristics: "The head is black in front, with a bright yellow band at the occiput, running forwards and downwards under the lower jaw, narrower above and broader below. The ground-colour of the body above, as well as below, is jet black surrounded by about 17 crimson rings, each with a yellow border both anteriorly and posteriorly and each with 2 or 3 black spots on the abdomen. The tail is black, with 3 or 4 yellow rings; the tip is yellow" (Holbrook, Gen., 1836–42). "The scales of the red zone are more or less marked with black, and this black pigment in the red zones is often grouped into a pair of black spots" (Schmidt and Davis, Gen., 1941). The alternating black and red rings or bands are separated by narrow yellow rings. Snout black, a broad yellow band across posterior portion of the head. A beautiful, very venomous, but inoffensive, nonaggressive snake.

Color: A snake from Gainesville, Fla., furnished by G. W. Van Hyning, Apr. 10, 1935. The red and black areas are relatively even bands while the yellow rings outlining each color are narrow. The red rings on the dorsum are pompeian red, carmine, or dragons-blood red and are usually marked with 2 elongate black spots 3 to 4 scales long and 3 scales wide. Some of the lower red scales near the yellow ring have black tips. The ventral side of the red ring is lighter than the dorsal, being scarlet-red, nopal red, or jasper red and covering 7 to eight ventrals. In its middle is a blotch of black covering 2 complete plates and parts of the adjoining ones, or sometimes covering 3 or 4 ventrals completely to their ends. The black ring covers 6 to 8 scales longitudinally on the back and 6 to 8 ventrals. The black of the venter is blue-violet black or dull violet-black. The light cadmium or cadmium yellow rings outlining the red and black annuli cover 2 half scales on the body, thus being 1 scale wide, while on the tail they are 2½ to 3½ scales wide. On the body, these rings usually cross the venter as ½ the width of a ventral plate or as a mere edge. Rarely are they not present on that surface. On the tail, the yellow covers 2 to 3 subcaudals. The tip of the head to behind the eyes is solid black, as are the eyes themselves. This black includes 4 upper labials and lower labials. This is followed by an orange or cadmium yellow band of 2½ labials' width covering the parietals except the front edges and corresponding parts of lower side of the head including the chin shields; this in turn is followed by a black ring.

Habitat: Surprisingly, we have few definite notes on the habitat of this snake. We have heard much about its poison, but little about its place or life in nature. It has been assigned to the coast pine belt, coastal plain, s.e. mesophytic evergreen forest, s.e. coniferous area, upper and swampy coastal plain. Hence now and in the past, records from s. Missouri, s. Indiana, s. Ohio, and e. Kentucky are and have been viewed somewhat askance. Nevertheless they may be finally confirmed for this secretive snake.

The states of their greatest abundance are the Carolinas, Georgia, and Florida. This mainly underground snake lives in the sweet potato and other fields. Several report it plowed up. Corrington (S.C., 1929) received all his specimens from planters and engineers. According to several authors it is a dry land form, but Carr (Fla., 1940a) has seen several in or near water and one on a mat of floating vegetation in a shallow pond. He also recounted two instances of their striking him and George Van Hyning in the leg or on the boot.

Neill (Gen., 1951) holds that two specialized uses of the tail obtain in this form. The active "balled tail" may be like the "tail curling" of *Diadophis* or "flash display" of *Farancia*. The tail may also be a constant prober among leaves, etc.

Period of activity: Mainly crepuscular—a burrower. *First appearance*—Many of our records come from spring or fall plowing. April (Brimley, N.C., 1923). "I saw none of these poisonous snakes about Ormond. . . . The *Elaps* is said to be common there in mid-April until late autumn, being often plowed or dug up in the gardens, or disclosed to view when overturning logs or rubbish" (Blatchley, Fla., 1902). *Fall disappearance*—July 29 (Brimley, N.C., 1922); Aug. (Brimley, N.C., 1923); Sept. 29 (Neill, Fla., 1949); Oct. 21 (Obrecht, S.C., 1946). *Hibernation*—Deckert recorded this snake abroad in January. "Seven examples were taken on sunny days in January, on sandy knolls surrounded by swampy country. Temperature 58°F. (shade). The previous night had been 28°F., but the heat of the sun had induced these reptiles to come forth and take a sun bath" (Deckert, Fla., 1918). Neill at Augusta wrote, "No winter records for this snake, only 8 specimens having been collected since 1932."

Breeding: Oviparous. Strangely, we know practically nothing about the life history and, particularly, the breeding habits. Schmidt and Davis (Gen., 1941) mentioned 2–4 eggs; Conant and Bridges (Gen., 1939) gave 3–12 eggs and young 7–9 inches. Other than Davis and Brimley (Gen., 1944) we find scanty literature on this topic. They wrote: "Eggs 3–12 in loamy soil or vegetation. With proper heat and moisture, these hatch in about 3 months, 7 to 9 inches long." Hurter, following Ditmars, said, "The snake lays about 7 eggs at the end of June, which hatch at or about the 27th of September." Ditmars recorded 7 eggs laid June 29, hatching Sept. 26–28. The young were 7 inches long.

Food: Small snakes, lizards. Ditmars, Schmidt (Gen., 1932, 1941), Loveridge (Fla., 1928).

Venom: Reams have been written about the venom and bite of this form. Schmidt (Gen., 1941), the best living author on *Micrurus,* stated: "They are entirely inoffensive in behavior and rarely bite when handled. They are consequently often handled with impunity by reckless persons. In view of the potency of their venom and of the fact that no one knows why or when they *will* bite, they should *never* be handled with bare hands" (Schmidt and Davis, Gen., 1941).

Authorities:

Behre, E. H. (La., 1925)	Loennberg, E. (Fla., 1895)
Ditmars, R. L. (Gen., 1904–05)	Noguchi, H. (Gen., 1909)
Dunn, E. R. (Gen., 1925)	Say, T. (Gen., 1819)
Halter, C. R. (Gen., 1923)	Schmidt, K. P. (Gen., 1928, 1932)
Harlan R. (Gen., 1827a)	Stejneger, L. (Gen., 1895)
Holbrook, J. E. (Gen., 1836–42)	True, F. W. (Gen., 1883)

There are many more. See the catalogue of the Surgeon General's Library, especially bibliographies of poisonous snakes.

1883: F. W. True discussed the bites very extensively: "That coral snake bites are of quite rare occurrence seems due (1) to the lack of abundance of these serpents, especially about towns; (2) to their sluggish disposition, and (3) as Duméril remarked, to the small size of the mouth, which prevents them from fastening upon any but a sharply curved surface."

1893, L. Stejneger: "Such adjectives as 'harmless' or 'innocuous to man' (cannot be applied) to a snake of which it is positively known that its bite is dangerous. . . . It has been repeatedly asserted that the mouth of the *Elaps* is so small it can not bite as well as other poisonous snakes. This, however, is somewhat of a mistake."

1925: E. R. Dunn wrote very pointedly and rightly on this matter in his "The 'harmless' coral snake."

South Florida coral snake, Barbour's coral snake (3—Ditmars 1936)

Micrurus fulvius barbouri Schmidt 1928. Fig. 257; Map 63

Another common name: Harlequin coral snake.

Range: Everglade hammocks of Dade Co., Fla. *Elevation*—Seacost to 50 feet.

Size: Adults, 24–36 inches. We have seen several specimens 20–30 inches long.

Distinctive characteristics: "Distinguished from the typical *Micrurus fulvius fulvius* by the complete absence or relative reduction of black pigment on the dorsal scales of the red interspaces. Ventrals averaging 204 in males, 222 in females; caudals 42–44 in males, 33–34 in females. No trace of supraanal keels in the male" (Schmidt).

Color: A snake from Miami, Fla. (died en route), received Nov. 23, 1937, from G. F. Sirman of the North Miami Zoo. The body is marked with red and black bands separated by yellow rings. The succession of colors is black snout, yellow on rear of head, followed by broad black band, then red, yellow, black, yellow, red, yellow, black, etc. There are 11 red bands, the 1st covering 12 scale rows longitudinally and the others 11 scale rows dorsally and 11 plates ventrally. On the back, the red ring is garnet brown or brick red, while on the venter and 1st scale row it is nopal red or dragons-blood red. The darker color of the back is due to the black tips on the cephalic 3 or 4 scale rows and a few scattered black tips throughout the red band. There are no distinct black spots in the dorsal red areas, but each of the red bands on the belly bears in the center a bluish black spot which may occupy parts of 2 ventrals or may be on 7 to 9 plates. Usually the sides of these spots are far removed from the 1st dorsal scale row, but in 1 case a spot extends up onto the 3rd row of scales. Counting the black band across the snout, there are 13 black rings on head and body and three on the tail. They are black on the dorsum and bluish black on the venter. They cover 8 to 9 scale rows dorsally and 8 to 9 nine plates ventrally. Counting the yellow band on the head and the one involving the anal plate, there are 24 yellow rings on the head and body and 2 on the tail. Dorsally the rings on the body proper cover 2 scale rows longitudinally, the one around the

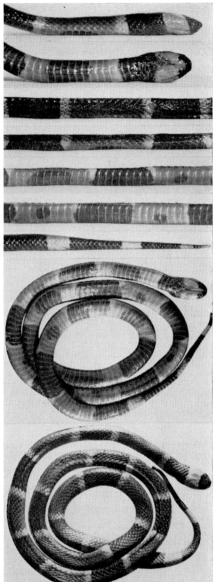

Fig. 256. *Micrurus fulvius fulvius,* Gainesville, Fla., G. Van Hyning.

Fig. 257. *Micrurus f. barbouri,* North Miami, Fla., G. F. Sirman.

anal plate 5 or 6 scale rows, and those on the tail 3 to 4 scale rows. On the venter, the yellow rings become narrow or almost absent, usually occupying about half a ventral. The yellow rings on the head and body are cadmium yellow; the anal ring and tail rings are orange. The yellow headband involves 1½ scale rows and almost the whole of the parietal plates. This color extends diagonally back of the eye involving the lower postocular and the 5th lower labial. It crosses the center of the 3rd lower labial, extends along the chin shield–lower labial sutures, crosses the middle of the 1st lower labial, and involves the tip of the mental. In fact, most of the lower side of the head is yellow except for the mental and 1 or 2 lower labials which are black. The iris is black.

Habitat: This form occurs in a region variously dubbed semitropical forest, tropical Florida, tropical rain forest climax plus grass swamp, tree islands, hammock forests, southern mesophytic evergreen forest, and subtropical Florida. One of the few characterizations of its habitat is from Carr: "Habitat—Tropical hammock; glade land. Abundance—Fairly common in some of the Everglades hammocks. Habits—Apparently those of *fulvius*. Occasionally ploughed up on muckland farms."

Field notes: Mar. 17, 1934, Opalocka Zoo, Fla.: G. F. Sirman and Quimby Sirman have one *M. f. barbouri* preserved. May have to photograph it. It laid some eggs, and Deckert hatched some of them.

Came to Royal Palm Park. Mr. Atkinson's son told us they found 3 coral snakes about the same time. When the boys were digging the big pit for a pool they found one. On the picnic grounds they discovered a little girl playing with a pretty snake she had found. It was *M. f. barbouri*. Mr. McCracken with 3 students sought for the coral snake. The next day after he sought it a picnicker killed one in the early morning near the door of his traveling camping house.

Went to the Florida Tropical Reptile Society's exhibit on a boat where many sea turtles and fishes were exhibited. Met Mrs. Frampton, wife of a newspaperman. She volunteered her services. They have a fine collection. She had several coral snakes from the Miami region. Didn't examine them closely because I was startled at the calm way she handled them barehandedly. I asked if she were not taking chances, but she thought not. At times earlier she had handled them with gloves.

Mar. 18, 1934: Went to Homestead. Saw Capt. Finney in command of C.C.C. camp which is working at Royal Palm Hammock. He said the group of Coast and Geodetic people who are working east of Florida City found some coral snakes in some hammocks. Mr. Sirman came down to talk to the boys. The very next day they found 2 coral snakes on Royal Palm Hammock.

Authorities:

Carr, A. F., Jr. (Fla., 1940a)   Schmidt, K. P. (Gen., 1928)

1928, K. P. Schmidt: "Much the most distinct of the color forms of *fulvius* is found in extreme southern Florida, where the black pigment of the dorsal portion of the red bands is reduced or absent. This form falls into line, both in this character and in its range, with *Lampropeltis getulus brooksi* and *Kinosternon bauri palmarum*. It may be called: *Micrurus fulvius barbouri*, subsp. nov. Type—M.C.Z. No. 13658, from Paradise Key, Dade County, Florida; collected by Thomas Barbour, 1920."

Coral snake (27—Strecker 1902), Harlequin snake (15), Texas coral snake (2)
Micrurus fulvius tenere (Baird and Girard) 1853. Fig. 258; Map 63

Other common names: Barber-pole snake; bead snake; candy-stick garter snake; corn snake; harlequin; tawny harlequin snake (*tristis*); Texas harlequin snake (2); thunder-and-lightning snake; thunder snake.

Range: S.w. Arkansas, extreme w. Louisiana, through e. Texas to Tamaulipas, Mex., and cent. Coahuila, Mex.—U.S.A.: Ark.; La.; Tex. Mex.: Coahuila; Tamaulipas. *Elevation*—Seacoast to 3,000 feet, mainly below 2,000 feet.

Size: Adults, 17–42 inches.

Distinctive characteristics: "Very irregular distribution of the more profuse black spotting of the red zones. In typical *fulvius* the black spots in the red zones are usually concentrated into a pair of good-sized black spots" (Schmidt, Gen., 1933).

Color: A snake from Helotes, Tex., described May 7, 1925. It is ringed with black, yellow, and red. The yellow rings are primuline yellow or light cadmium on the body and light orange-yellow on the tail. The head-band is light orange-yellow with its top deep chrome. These light cadmium rings enclose bands of bluish slate-black, which become on the sides dark green-blue slate and on the belly green-blue slate or deep green-blue gray. These yellow rings enclose alternately red and black bands. The red bands are dragons-blood red or light jasper red on the back, grading to coral pink or light coral red on the belly. The center of this red ventral area is marked with a large spot of green-blue slate. In the red near the light cadmium rings are some bluish slate-black scales and other scales with black tips. The iris is bluish slate-black.

A snake from New Orleans, La., furnished by P. Viosca, Jr., June 15, 1936. Red, yellow, and black rings extend completely around the body. The red of the underside is brazil red and covers 7 or 8 ventrals and is encircled on either end by light orange-yellow or deep chrome rings. There are no red rings on the tail. The dorsal portion of the red rings is heavily marked with black so that it appears morocco red, and the ventral portion bears a prominent black spot in the middle with 2 or 3 smaller ones scattered around. In the black rings the ventral portion is plumbeous-black or blackish violet-gray. There is a prominent band of cadmium yellow across the rear of the head. The iris is black, as is the head from the eye forward.

Abnormal coloration—Albino: "This is the second interesting albino snake captured near Houston within the past few months, an albino Harlequin or Coral snake (*Micrurus fulvius* Linné) having been caught some time ago. The latter specimen was mentioned in the newspapers of Houston and other places in South Texas." J. M. Heiser, Jr., quoted by Strecker (Tex., 1935).

Black (melanistic): "The [black] snake was taken to the Witte Museum in San Antonio and through the kindness of the director, Mrs. Ellen Schulz Quillin, was sent alive to me to study.[1] From information kindly supplied by Mr. and Mrs. J. J. Sanders of New Braunfels and Dr. F. B. Shields, the attending physician of Victoria, I have compiled the following history of the case. . . .

"[Footnote] 1. In so far as I am aware no decidedly melanistic specimens of *Micrurus fulvius tenere* (Baird and Girard) have been recorded in herpetological literature. This one is entirely black except for a slight trace of the yellow band across the parietals, temporal region and throat" (Gloyd).

Habitat: From Cope (Tex.) in 1880 to Ruick in 1948, considerable material has accumulated about this quiet, retiring snake. It is said to dislike sunshine and was once called wholly nocturnal, but has been found several times in open daylight. It lives in holes in the ground, in or under rotten logs and stumps, in well-drained ground, under the steps of buildings, in clumps of weeds, in open grasslands once pine woods, in shady nooks, or in thickly shaded localities. It is not wholly limited to dry places. Specimens have been taken in hummock lands; in woods in the vicinity of ponds, springs, or streams; in swampy bottomlands; on the steep slopes of a river, and once swimming across a slough into a marsh. For more notes see True, Beyer, Mitchell, Strecker (Tex., 1927b), Engelhardt (Tex., 1932), Fitch (La., 1949), and Ruick.

Using the method of the San Diego group, Ruick made 4 trips over a 10-mile stretch, secured 7 living and 3 dead specimens on the Chapman and King ranches in Texas, and wrote: "The coral snake appears to be much more common than formerly supposed, at least in the area around Corpus Christi, as 10 specimens in 4 trips cannot be considered rare, particularly when it is recalled that all 10 were caught in the same 10-mile stretch of road. In each case, the specimen when first observed was travelling down the center of the road in a slow, lateral undulating movement. When first touched with the snake-hook the snake would start for the side of the road."

Breeding: "I have never found a female bearing eggs or young, and I know nothing of their breeding habits and have found no literature throwing light on this subject" (Mitchell). More than fifty years after Mitchell wrote, his statement still holds true except for Werler's (Gen., 1951) record of a mating May 18, the female dying later with 9 thin soft-shelled eggs revealed upon dissection.

Food: Lizards, young and small snakes. Mitchell, Strecker (1908c), Hurter (Mo., 1911), Schmidt, Ruick, Minton (Tex., 1949).

Venom: Specific data on coral-snake-bite cases and treatment are scarce. In a recent case, the patient, bitten at the base of the index finger, suffered severe pain of the palm and arm, but no swelling. He was given morphine for the pain. Tourniquet treatment, suction incisions, whole-blood administration, and hot packs brought him out with "no residuals or sequelae." "There is still much doubt in some quarters, despite recorded fatalities, that the bite of *Micrurus fulvius* is, in most cases, very serious. . . . This is demonstrated by the careless disregard with which a number of amateur herpetologists and snake handlers in the state fondle these snakes" (J. E. Werler and D. M. Darling, Tex., 1950).

Field notes: May 15, 1925, Gutzeit Ranch, Helotes, Tex.: Tonight when we came home, as Anna opened the gate she noticed a snake keeping on the opposite side of the opening gate. With a flashlight she discerned it was a coral snake. It went into the road. With Anna's stick I would pin it down, try to roll the stick to the head, and almost every time it would snap out. Its tail tip curls up and keeps moving. With only a flashlight it is hard to determine which is head end, it moves so quickly. In the daytime it is thus active with head and tail.

Authorities:

Bailey, V. (Tex., 1905)
Beyer, G. E. (La., 1900)
Gloyd, H. K. (Tex., 1938a)
Hurter, J., Sr. (Mo., 1911)
Mitchell, J. D. (Tex., 1903)

Ruick, J. D., Jr. (Tex., 1948)
Schmidt, K. P. (Gen., 1932)
Strecker, J. K., Jr. (Tex., 1908c, 1926d,
    1927b, 1928c, 1935)
True, F. W. (Gen., 1883)
Wright, A. H. (Tex., 1926)

Fig. 258. *Micrurus f. tenere:* 1–5, San Antonio Reptile Garden, Tex.; 6,8, Gutzeit Gate, Helotes, Tex.; 7, San Antonio, Tex., Mrs. W. O. Learn.

Fig. 259. *Ancistrodon contortrix contortrix:* 1–5, Dougherty Co., Ga., through E. R. Allen; 6, Louisiana, photo by S. C. Bishop.

PIT VIPERS

FAMILY CROTALIDAE Gray

With pit on either side of head behind nostril, occupying partly the excavated superior maxillary bone; movable sheathed fangs without external groove, the vertical superior maxillary bone by excessive abbreviation anteriorly and posteriorly supporting venom fangs alone; facial bones movable; head very distinct and triangular, tympanic bone much elongated, giving great breadth to head posteriorly; caudals undivided, occasionally divided toward tip; anal normally entire; eye with vertical pupil; caudal vertebrae normal, without greatly developed processes; at least part of scales keeled, usually with apical pits; scale rows in mid-body 13–37 in world forms; 21–31 in U.S., mainly 23–27.

KEY TO THE GENERA (Fig. 260)

a. Rattle on end of tail.
  b. 9 large symmetrical head plates; tail sharply tapering with a small rattle; upper labials mostly 9–14; 1–2 rows of suboculars between eye and labials; 1 loreal.   *Sistrurus*
  bb. Small plates or scales arranged unsymmetrically on top of head; upper labials normally 9–20; rattle large, conspicuous; 2–4 rows of suboculars between eye and labials; loreals 1–8, usually 2 or 1.
                                                                      Crotalus
aa. Without rattle, tail ending in a point; with 9 large symmetrical head plates; upper labials 7–8; 0–1 row suboculars; loreal present or absent.
                                                                   Ancistrodon

COPPERHEADS, MOCCASINS

Genus *ANCISTRODON* Beauvois (Fig. 260)

Size, large medium to large, 34–72 inches; tail without a rattle and ending in a point; subcaudals mostly entire, some irregularly divided toward tip; with 9 large head plates; scales keeled 17–27 rows, usually in 23 or 25 rows in U.S. forms; upper labials 7–8, lower average 10–11; eye in vertical of upper labials 3–4; hemipenis flounced. Range: Asia, N. and S. America with loreal in *A. mokeson;* no loreal in *A. piscivorus.* Synonyms: *Acontias, Agkishodon, Agkistrodon, Ankistrodon, Cenchris, Coluber, Natrix, Pelias, Scytale, Scytalus, Tisiphone, Toxicophis, Trigonocephalus, Vipera.*

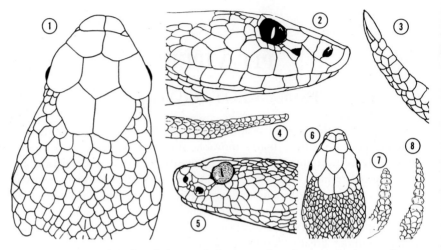

Fig. 260. 1–3, *Ancistrodon piscivorus piscivorus;* 4, *A. mokeson mokeson;* 5,7, *Sistrurus miliarius barbouri;* 6, *S. catenatus catenatus;* 8, *S. miliarius miliarius.*

KEY TO THE GENUS *ANCISTRODON*

a. More slender than aa; with loreal; orbit separated from upper labials by scales; usually 23 rows; scales on neck and side smaller; no post-parietals; color: back orange browns with chocolate- to claret-bordered saddles (about 13 on body); venter background vinaceous-pink to ochraceous-tawny; lower light and dark borders of face vitta on lower labials.

   b. Dark saddles longest on scale row 1 and tapering evenly to mid-dorsum with dark borders united with dark ventral markings so that there is no conspicuous row of dark spots along row 1 and on ends of ventrals opposite the light areas.

      c. Belly terra cotta with irregular extensions of both light and dark areas onto ends of ventrals; caudals less than 54 in males, 52 or less in females. (Southern Kansas to Gulf at Corpus Christi, Tex.)
                                                          A. c. laticinctus

     cc. Belly almost uniformly dark; lower portion of light center of saddle lighter and with dark spot separating its end into 2 prongs, making the lower ends of this core of the saddle appear as an inverted U. (Brewster Co., Tex.)   *A. c. pictigaster*

  bb. Dark dorsal saddles spool-shaped or dumbbell-shaped, the dark borders curving inward on lower side and terminating on or above scale row 1, and thus not continuous with dark markings on ends of ventrals.

     c. Dorsal markings strongly constricted at mid-dorsum (often 2–3 scales in length), often divided and irregular; general color pale; snuff brown to buffy brown and chocolate- or claret-bordered bars, and lateral centers of bars conspicuously lighter. (E. North Carolina to e. Texas, up Mississippi River to St. Louis, Mo.)

A. contortrix contortrix

cc. Dorsal markings not strongly constricted at mid-dorsum (commonly 3–5 scales in length); seldom divided; color pecan brown and mars brown; spots along scale row 1 and ends of ventrals opposite light areas large and conspicuous. (Massachusetts south to n. Georgia and Alabama and westward to e. Kansas and n.e. corner of Texas.) *A. c. mokeson*

aa. Stocky in build; no loreal; upper labials enter orbit; usually 25 scale rows; all scales large and well developed, those on sides and back of head conspicuously so; with postparietals. Color: back brownish olive to olive-brown with pattern frequently indistinct; sometimes appearing as 28 partial dark bars or on old specimens entirely black; vitta from preoculars to back of angle of mouth with its lower light border on the upper labials (subspecies on coloration distinctions only).

b. Color of back light brownish olive, buffy olive to black in adults, clove brown or medal bronze in young; cross bands dark olive with distinct borders olivaceous black in adults, bone brown in young; bands invaded by ground color; rostral and nasal region light with dusky vertical stripe of bone brown or warm sepia between rostral and 1st upper labial and extending onto first 3 lower labials; young with strongly contrasting pattern. (S.e. Alabama to s.e. Virginia.)

A. piscivorus piscivorus

bb. Dark brown or black above in both adults and young; cross bands broad with dusky centers little invaded by ground color, i.e., more or less uniform; rostral and nasal region dark without distinct vertical stripe; young dark without strongly contrasting pattern, looks like copperhead. (S. Illinois to the Rio Grande.) *A. p. leucostoma*

Southern copperhead (4—Conant and Bridges 1939), Highland moccasin (7)

Ancistrodon contortrix contortrix (Linné) 1766. Fig. 259; Map 64

Other common names: Copperhead (33); chunk head; copperhead snake; death adder; (dry-land) moccasin; narrow-banded copperhead; northern copperhead; pilot snake; poplar leaf; red oak; red snake; southeastern copperhead; white oak snake.

Range: Atlantic lower and upper coastal plains from s.e. Virginia to Apalachicola River, Fla.; Gulf coast to Matagorda Bay, Tex.; n.e. in Mississippi embayment to above St. Louis, Mo.—Ala.; Ark.; Fla.; Ga.; Ill.; Ky.; La.; Miss.; Mo.; N.C.; S.C.; Tenn.; Tex.; Va. *Elevation*—Sea level to 1,000 feet, mostly below 700 feet.

Size: Adults, 20–52 inches. C. L. Love took a 4-foot, 4-inch specimen at Apopka, Fla., Dec. 13, 1928.

Longevity: 3 to 9 years; 2 to 4[+] years (Perkins, Gen., 1951).

Distinctive characteristics: "Coloration generally pale and usually with a noticeable pinkish tinge in life. Viewed from above, the pattern consists of a series of hour-glass-shaped crossbands, conspicuously narrow at the

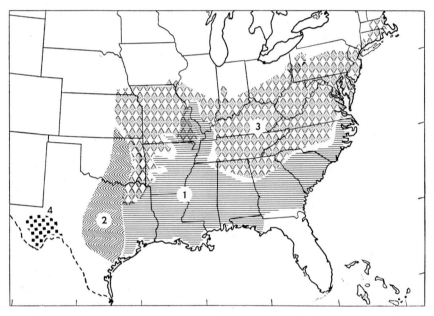

Map 64. *Ancistrodon*—1, *contortrix;* 2, *c. laticinctus;* 3, *c. mokeson;* 4, *c. pictigaster.*

mid-line (rarely more than 2 or 3 scales wide); viewed from the side, the crossbands resemble triangles, roughly equilateral, with acute basal angles rounded off on the 2nd or 3rd row of scales, and bearing an upward extension at the apex which, in this subspecies, often fails to meet the similar extension from the opposite side. Belly pale, not heavily marked. A distinct series of ventro-lateral blotches, the more conspicuous of which alternate with the bases of the triangles" (Gloyd and Conant).

Color: A snake from New Orleans, La., received from P. Viosca, Jr., described June 15, 1936. The background color of the back is snuff brown to mikado brown. This lighter color is in the form of irregular diamonds which are 10 to 11 scales long in the middle of the body. The back is marked with 13 dark saddles on the body and 4 on the tail. On the body, these dark crossbands are about 2 to 2½ scales longitudinally on the dorsum, and 8 to 9 scales long on the lower side. In mid-back, the saddle is chocolate, as is a border 1 or 2 scales wide along the cephalic and caudal edges of the expanded lateral portions of the saddle. The center of the expanded area is pecan brown, terra cotta, or vinaceous-russet. On the end of the ventral directly below this dark saddle is a squarish testaceous or terra cotta spot. Alternating with this and below the light interspace is a similar spot covering the ends of 2 or 3 ventrals. The big plates on top of the head are tawny-olive, the rear portion of the head changing from sayal brown or cinnamon to mikado brown rearward. The face has more or less of the color of the top of the head. There is a narrow chocolate postocular band not quite reaching the eye and extending to the rear of the last upper labial which separates the darker dorsal color of the head from the lighter color of the lower face. The lower portion of the forward upper labials and all the area back of the eye is pale pinkish buff with flecks of tawny-olive. The color of the iris is tawny-olive or cinnamon. The under parts are light pinkish cinnamon approaching vinaceous-pink on the tail, because of the terra cotta flecks on the background. Besides the spots on the ends of the ventrals, the belly is marked with a few other irregular spots of testaceous or terra cotta. The underside of the head and neck is pale cinnamon-pink or shell pink. The rear lower labials, gular, and first 3 or 4 ventrals are reed yellow. *Abnormal coloration*—Livezey (Tex., 1949) finds an aberrant pattern in a specimen from Huntsville, Walker Co., Tex. Of the 17 bands present, 11 fail to meet at the middorsal line.

Habitat: This is a coastal-plain form. It occurs below the fall line and up the Mississippi embayment—in Harshberger's Atlantic-Gulf Coastal Region, pine barrens-strand vegetation area. Like the northern form, this is reported from dry upland woods, in open pine regions, near rock piles, and in wood lots. In fact some writers hold that it is never in lowlands, river bottoms, or marshy situations, although two have seen specimens swimming in water. The reports make it a dweller of stony hillsides, mountains, and heavily wooded areas. Several authors have placed it in hummocks and canebrakes even at times entering swamps.

Period of activity: *Early appearances*—May, 1906 (Brimley, N.C., 1909); Apr. 18, 19, 1932 (Perkins and Lentz); Apr. 12, 1895 (Beyer, La., 1898); Apr. 11, 1894 (Brimley, N.C., 1923b); Mar. 23, 29, 1950 (Hamilton and Pollack). *Fall disappearance*—Oct. 6, 1937 (Allen); Dec. 1, 1914 (Brimley, N.C., 1923b). *Hibernation*—In Arkansas, Perkins and Lentz found this form near the *Crotalus atrox* den. In 1921 Rutledge wrote: "It hibernates in deep crevices in rocks, and in milder climates, in hollow logs and under drifts of leaves. Both rattlesnakes and copperheads are frequently found in pairs; and for the winter, they sometimes gather in considerable number in their dens."

Breeding: Viviparous. *Young*—Number, 2–11. The few records we have specify broods of 2, 4, 5, 7, 9, 10, and 11. Neill recorded 11 young Sept. 10, 1939. In 1923b Brimley gave 4, 6, and 8 in 3 broods he had observed. See also J. D. Mitchell (Tex., 1903) under "Breeding" in the account of *A. c. laticinctus* below. Length, 8–9 inches. Time of birth, late August and early September.

An excerpt from Chenoweth's "Birth and behavior of young copperheads" is apropos: "At 6 P.M. on September 4, 3 small hatchlings were found crawling about in her pen, and a 4th one was being born. The mother was lying in a half-moon position, with her tail twisted to one side but not raised. The snake extruded by a series of muscular contractions in the posterior part of the mother's abdomen. Enclosed in its elliptical, membraneous, semi-transparent sac, which was about 48 mm. by 35 mm., the 4th little snake did not move at all for about 35 minutes. Then it started to break out, struggling 5 minutes before it was free. Meanwhile the 5th and final one was being ejected. This took approximately 10 minutes. When the 5th wriggled free from its sac, all 5 juveniles were very lively and struck often when annoyed, vibrating their tails rapidly. . . . The tips of the tails were lettuce green. Their lengths were 219 mm., 222 mm., 224 mm., 200 mm., and 215 mm. . . . When the young were observed at 8 o'clock on the morning of September 10, two had shed, and by noon the other three had followed suit."

Food: Small rodents, small birds, frogs. Rhoads, Brimley (N.C., 1923b), Corrington, Metcalf, Rutledge (S.C., 1936), Chenoweth.[1]

Venom: Few adults die from the bite of copperheads, though many have been bitten with severe consequences. Schwardt discussed this: "The copperhead frequently wanders into towns, and often lives close to suburban and rural homes, where it is a particular menace to children. Adults are seldom dangerously affected by its bite, and few fatal bites are on record, but it is reasonable to believe that a 30-inch copperhead might inflict a rapidly fatal bite on a child 8 years or younger."

Another observation we wish to make. Because copperheads are usually mild, do not become careless or foolhardy with them. Observe the cautiousness of the veteran herpetologist, Brimley (N.C., 1941–42): "It seems to be of an inoffensive disposition and little likely to bite anyone who does not actually interfere with it. Once in moving some rushes to set a mouse trap, I inadvertently put my hand within 6 inches of one, but it made no effort to strike; and once I knew of one that was lying in a path and a boy stepped right over it, but the snake did not move. Specimens that I have had in captivity have seemed so tame that it appeared that I could have

---

[1] In 1955 Hamilton and Pollack found that the copperhead's diet consisted principally of mammals (mice and rats), 46.1%.

handled them with impunity, *if I had been fool enough to take the risk."*

In 1941, Allen and Maier announced that medical science had found that "venom from the coral snake (*Micrurus fulvius*) and copperhead (*Agkistrodon mokasen*) has been effective as a local coagulent, and in the treatment of epilepsy, neurasthenia, chorea, and shell-shock."

Authorities:

Allen, E. R. (Fla., 1938)
Allen, E. R., and E. Maier (Gen., 1941)
Beyer, G. E. (La., 1898, 1900)
Brimley, C. S. (N.C., 1923b, 1941–42)
Carr, A. F., Jr. (Fla., 1940a)
Chenoweth, W. L. (Okla., 1948)
Corrington, J. D. (S.C., 1929)
Dolley, J. S. (Miss., 1939)
Gloyd, H. K., and R. Conant (Gen., 1943)
Livezey, R. L. (Tex., 1949)
Metcalf, Z. P. (Gen., 1930)

Neill, W. T. (Ga., 1948a)
Obrecht, C. B. (S.C., 1946)
Perkins, R. M., and M. J. R. Lentz (Ark., 1934)
Rhoads, S. N. (Tenn., 1896)
Rutledge, A. (S.C., 1921, 1936)
Schwardt, H. H. (Ark., 1938)
Strecker, J. K., Jr. (La., 1925)
Strecker, J. K., Jr., and L. S. Frierson (La., 1926)
Werler, J. E. (Tex., 1950)

G. E. Beyer (La., 1900) secured mated pairs Apr. 12 and Sept. 16 and gave 7 as the number of young. R. M. Perkins and M. J. R. Lentz, in their rattlesnake hunt, found pairs of copperheads Apr. 18 and Apr. 19. Finally, J. S. Dolley found an embryo "attached to the mesentery and apparently developing ectopically within the body cavity."

1948, W. T. Neill: For a long time naturalists have noted the sulphur yellow, green yellow, or yellow tails of juvenile *ancistrodons* and some crotalids, and several observers have called them lures. Neill suggested that young copperheads wave their tails to lure small frogs. The "lure" theory is not wholly confirmed, and W. L. Burger and P. W. Smith (Gen., 1950) recently found that newly born male fer-de-lances had bright yellow tails and the females usually dull ones.

Broad-banded copperhead (5—Gloyd and Conant 1934), Copperhead (20)

Ancistrodon contortrix laticinctus Gloyd and Conant 1934. Fig. 261; Map 64

Other common names: Copperhead moccasin; copperhead snake; dry-land moccasin; (highland) moccasin; moccasin; ratlesnake pilot; red eye; Texas copperhead; thunder snake.

Range: A vertical band from cent. Texas, between 97° and 99° longitude, across cent. Oklahoma to a point in Cowley Co., Kan., near its s. border.— Kan.; Okla.; Tex. *Elevation*—100 to 1,500 feet.

Size: Adults, 16–36 inches.

Longevity: 6 years 6 months (Conant and Hudson, Gen., 1949); 10 years

7 months (Perkins, Gen., 1951); 2 years 3 months (Kauffeld, Gen., 1951); 13 years 7 months (Perkins, Gen., 1954).

Distinctive characteristics: "Coloration usually bright chestnut or hazel brown, with marked contrast between pattern and ground color; crossbands strikingly broad (7 to 14 scales wide on sides at 1st row of scales, 4 to 8 scales wide at the middorsal line), and extending downward laterally to the ventrals, where they blend with the ventro-lateral pattern of 3 more or less conspicuous spots to each crossband" (Gloyd and Conant, 1943).

Color: A snake from San Antonio, Tex., May 5, 1925. The back is marked by light and dark tapering crossbands; the light bands are broadest at mid-back and may taper to 1 to 3 scales on the lower sides. The dark bands are broadest at the venter, covering possibly 10 or more scales at that line, and often meet irregularly on the mid-back. The light areas are orange cinnamon or wood brown, becoming on the sides and ends of the ventrals vinaceous-fawn or vinaceous-cinnamon. The light areas are margined for the 1st 6 scale rows with pale pinkish cinnamon or cartridge buff. The dark reddish crossbands are kaiser brown, cacao brown, or testaceous (close to terra cotta), with madder brown, hessian brown, or claret brown margins.

The top of the head is sayal brown or cinnamon, the upper labial vinaceous-pink. The iris is sayal brown or cinnamon and vinaceous-pink.

The chin and throat are like the light areas of the back. The venter is largely testaceous, interrupted by irregular extensions of the vinaceous-fawn or vinaceous-cinnamon of the light areas to the ends of the ventrals. The madder brown, hessian brown, or claret brown margins of each dark area also extend onto 2 or 3 ventrals.

Habitat: Customarily called dry-land moccasins, they live in rocky ledges, stretches of dry woods, rocky wooded bluffs, ridges, or wooded river banks. They hide under logs, in decaying stumps, in rock piles, and in crevices. Usually they are scarce in cultivated districts and they seldom climb bushes. Occasionally they occur among piles of driftwood, in wooded river bottoms, and rarely in water.

Breeding: Viviparous. *Young*—Number, 3–11. Time of birth, August and September. For a long period the only note we had was Mitchell's, which may apply to *A. c. contortrix* also: "They gestate their young, and they are born ready for the duties of life. The most I ever found in a female was 11, 7 in one horn of the uterus and 4 in the other horn. I have found as small a number as 3, all in one horn of the uterus." In 1948 Barton wrote: "A Kansas specimen produced 6 young on Sept. 6. A second Kansas female gave birth to 9 snakelings on Sept. 9." In Werler's "Poisonous snakes of Texas" we read: "The young probably average about 4 or 5 to a litter, but little else is known about the breeding habits of this form." In 1951 Werler recorded a female passing 4 young 225–230 mm. long.

Mating: Of the combat dance Shaw (Gen., 1948) wrote that in this form

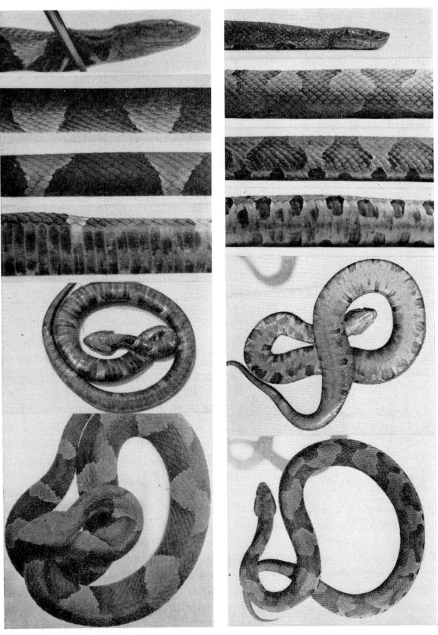

Fig. 261. *Ancistrodon c. laticinctus:* 1,2,3,4,6, Witte Museum Reptile Garden, San Antonio, Tex.; 5, Poteet, Tex., Mrs. W. O. Learn.

Fig. 262. *Ancistrodon c. mokeson,* Ramsey, N.J., L. Hook.

it "is similar to that of *Crotalus* but differs quite markedly, insofar as our observations are concerned, in that one of the males acts as though he were afraid of being bitten on the head."

Food: Small rodents, lizards, frogs, toads. Mitchell, Strecker and Williams, Kirn.

Authorities:

Barton, A. J. (Tex., 1948)

Gloyd, H. K., and R. Conant (Gen., 1943; Tex., 1934)

Mitchell, J. D. (Tex., 1903)

Strecker, J. K., Jr. (8 references)

Strecker, J. K., Jr., and W. J. Williams (Tex., 1928)

Werler, J. E. (Tex., 1950)

1934, H. K. Gloyd and R. Conant: "That copperheads from the extreme southwestern portion of the range of the species differ considerably in color pattern from eastern specimens has been known to herpetologists for some time. . . . In connection with a proposed study of the American forms of *Agkistrodon,* the present authors have examined 88 specimens of the copperhead from Texas and Oklahoma as well as numerous other examples from localities east of this region. From material it is evident that the broad-banded form is a distinct geographic race, and we therefore propose for it the name *Agkistrodon mokasen laticinctus,* new subspecies."

Copperhead (150—Say and Rafinesque 1819), Highland moccasin (20)

Ancistrodon contortrix mokeson (Daudin) 1803. Fig. 262; Map 64

Other common names: Beech-leaf snake; chunk head; copper (adder); copper-bell; copper belly; copperhead moccasin; copperhead viper; copper snake; copper-viper; cottonmouth; deaf adder; deaf snake; dumb rattlesnake; harlequin snake; hazel head; hognose snake; moccasin; North American copperhead snake; northern copperhead; pilot; poplar leaf; rattlesnake pilot; rattlesnake's mate; red adder; red eye; red snake; red viper; thunder snake; upland moccasin; viper; white oak snake.

Range: From s.e. Nebraska e. across lower Hudson valley and Massachusetts, s. in Appalachian and Piedmont regions to n. Georgia and Alabama. West of Appalachian region, it occupies roughly the Ozark, Ohio, and Tennessee River valleys of Van Dersal. West of Mississippi River, from s.e. Nebraska to extreme n.e. Texas, thence diagonally across Arkansas and most of Missouri to s.e. tip of Iowa.—Ala.; Ark.; Conn.; D.C.; Del.; Ga.; Ia.; Ill.; Ind.; Kan.; Ky.; Mass.; Md.; Miss.; Mo.; N.C.; Neb.; N.J.; N.Y.; O.; Okla.; Pa.; S.C.; Tenn.; Tex.; Va.; W. Va. *Elevation*—Sea level or better, 500 feet to 2,500 feet. 1,000–2,500 feet (King, Tenn., 1939); 3,800 feet (Dunn, N.C., 1917); 1,800–3,200 feet (Barbour, Ky., 1950).

Size: Adults, 16–53 inches.

A copperhead over 4 feet long would be a big one, and we question Higgins' estimate of 5 feet. Klauber's (Gen., 1943b) standard body length is 541.31 mm. for males and 498.20 mm. for females, with maxima of 840 mm. for males and 951 mm. for females.

Longevity: 12 years 7 months (Perkins, Gen., 1949); 13 years 6 months (Perkins, Gen., 1950); 10 years (Boulenger, Gen., 1914); 14 years 6 months (Perkins, Gen., 1951); 17 years 6 months (Perkins, Gen., 1954).

Distinctive characteristics: "Coloration reddish brown or chestnut, sometimes with little contrast between pattern and ground color; specimens from some localities finely stippled with gray or brown, and occasionally marked with small round or irregular spots between the crossbands. Pattern of broad, dark crossbands, variously described as 'spool-shaped' or 'dumb-bell-shaped' constricted middorsally (3 to 5 scale lengths in width), and rounded off at the ends above the ventrals . . . ; a ventro-lateral pattern of more or less distinct subcircular blotches. Belly usually dark, mottled with gray or black" (Gloyd and Conant, Gen., 1943).

Color: A snake from N.J. received from Luther Hook, Oct. 7, 1936. The back is crossed with 16–18 spool-shaped saddles. The central bar is 2½ scales longitudinally, and then widens on the sides with the lower corners rounded. Sometimes the 2 sides do not meet on mid-dorsum or meet only at a corner. The dorsal bar is solid mars brown, liver brown, or chocolate. The same color borders the lateral portion where the center is kaiser brown or russet. On the 3rd and 4th scale rows, this lighter central area has a very small central spot of mars brown. The saddles are thinly edged with a thread of olive-buff or cartridge buff. Below the saddles and also below the interspaces, on the 1st row of scales and extending onto the belly, is a row of prominent dark spots which are mars brown in the center and bordered with bone brown to black. The interspaces on the back are pecan brown or mikado brown. Each has 2 small spots (2nd interspace has 4), one on either side of the mid-dorsum, which are light-centered like the sides of the dark saddles. The top of the head is mikado brown, the large head plates and the postocular and preocular regions tawny-olive. On the side of the face, from the 1st to the last upper labial, is a honey yellow band outlined postocularly by a thread of chamois and another of bone brown. The iris is a beautiful tawny. The iris, face, and lower side of head are minutely flecked with mars brown. In fact, all the lighter areas of the animal attain their color from such flecking. The throat and lower side of the head are chamois, followed by an area of pale vinaceous-pink, which is succeeded by a stretch of vinaceous-pink, which gives place to onion-skin pink. Toward the tail tip the ventral surface is chamois.

Habitat: Three adjectives dominate the characterizations: mountainous, rocky, and hilly. Mountains 5, wild mountain country 1, mountain areas 1, mountainous places 2. Rocky hillsides 4, rock quarries 1, rocky bluffs 2, rocky ledges 2, rocky ridges 1, rocks 2, rock debris 1, rocky hilltops 1, rocky places 1, rocky regions 12. Elevated grounds 1, high regions 1, wooded hills 1, elevated regions 1, ledgy wooded hills 1, wooded bluffs 1, hilly regions 1, rocky hillsides 4. Woods 2, thick damp woods 1, forests 1, wooded hills 1, wooded bluffs 1, cool damp woods 1, damp woods 1, fairly thick timber 1.

Lowland habitats are: low grounds 1, wild damp meadows 1, meadows 9, wet meadows 1, low swampy places 1, swamps 2, bottomlands 1, valleys 1. This implies that the snakes may enter lowlands in summer. They are terrestrial, as the names highland moccasin and dry-land moccasin show, but they have been seen swimming in streams and ponds. It is true they have been found in cultivated places (hayfields 2, roadsides 2, open fields 1, old cellars 2, at door of residence 1, along fence rows 1), but they probably go to these places for mice and other food. Several have observed them as preferring the neighborhood of water, ponds, streams.

Their cover may be caves, cellars, slabs, stones, rocks, grass, hollow logs, banks. Ideally we picture them in earlier times at the base of the Palisades, or in recent times under the shade of loose rocks, on a hilly railroad embankment, beside a stream, or on a mountainside with rocky ledges wooded or not.

It is customary to conclude that rattlesnakes and copperheads recede from civilization and become scarce in cultivated regions, where man, his burnings, cultivation, dogs, hogs, and other agencies destroy the snake or its abodes. But the copperhead holds its own better than some surmise. See Dunn (Va., 1915), Burt (Kan., 1927), Burt and Hoyle (Gen., 1935), Welter and Carr (Ky., 1939).

Period of activity: *Early appearances*—Kansas: Apr. 14, 1923; Apr. 19, 1923 (Linsdale); Apr. 21, 1928, Apr. 30, 1926, May 7, 1926 (Gloyd); Apr., 1931, Apr. 27, 1926, May 14, 1927, May 24, 1929 (Burt). Missouri: Apr. 4; Mar. 26, 1936, Apr. 6, 1937 (Anderson); May 6 (Hurter). North Carolina: Apr. 11, 1894 (Brimley). *Fall disappearance*—Kansas: Sept., 1932, Oct. 1, 1932 (Burt); Sept. 23, 1928, Oct. (Gloyd). Missouri: Sept. 30 (Hurter); Sept. 14, 19, 21, 1937, Sept. 12, 1938 (Anderson). New Jersey: Nov., 1864 (Abbott). "Monthly catch," Raleigh, N.C., 1925—Apr., 3 snakes; May, 6; June, 11; July, 10; Aug. 10; Sept., 5; Oct., 11; Nov., 3; Dec., 2; total 61 snakes (Brimley).

Breeding: Viviparous. Males 660–1,088 mm., females 785–1,030 mm. W. Miller (Heyen, N.J., 1937) reported adult females 700–1,030 mm. *Mating*—Gloyd (Gen., 1947) gives an extended account of Joseph Ackroyd's observations on two copperheads in Virginia. The anterior two thirds of the snakes' bodies were entwined vertically and swayed, the posterior thirds being anchored.

Young—Number, 1–17. 1, 5 (Anderson); 2, 10 (Conant and Bridges, Davis and Brimley); 2, 6, 10 (Fowler); 2, 3, 6, 10 (Schmidt and Davis); 3,

10 (Necker); 4 (Hoffman); 4, 9 (Netting); 4, 6, 9, 10 (Surface); 4, 5, 6, 7, 17 (Hook); 5, 11 (Minton); 5, 10, 12 (Finneran); 6 (Ditmars, Babcock); 6, 10 (Conant); 7 (Bumpus, Lynn, Dunn); 7, 9 (Hay, Smith); 8 (Stadelmann); 8, 12 (Brimley); 9 (Ditmars, Smith); 14 (Moski). In his study of 20 broods of Pennsylvania copperheads Smith (1940) reported 3-10 young per brood. Estimates and reports of 42-50 have been made but are not considered here. Kunze quoted newspaper accounts of 60-88 young. All reports greater than 1-17 need to be carefully verified. Length, 8 to 10 inches. There are records of 8, 8.1, 8.2, 8.4, 9, 9.2, 9.7, and 10 inches, or 200-250 mm. Klauber (Gen., 1943b) gives minima of 201 mm. for a female and 180 mm. for a male. Time of birth, middle August to early October. There are records beginning Aug. 12 and 14 and ending Sept. 29, Oct. 6, and even later.

We close this topic with one of the best summaries of this form, by Smith: "1. Mating probably occurs in late April or early May. 2. Four gravid females were found in crevices and under rocks in late August. 3. Parturition, in 5 known cases, took place during the day. 4. In the last 5 specimens of one brood the duration of labor for a single fetus varied from 6 to 12 minutes, average 8. The period between extrusions was from 5 to 14 minutes, average 8. The young snakes remained within the prenatal membrane from 96 to 196 minutes, average 132. 5. Although the dates of birth for 20 litters ranged from August 23 to October 15, the majority occurred from August 28 through September 17. 6. The number of young per litter, in 19 cases, varied from 3 to 10, with 5 being the most common."

Food: Small mammals, birds, insects, toads, salamanders, but mainly rodents and insects, according to 31 authors. See especially Hook and Uhler, Cottam, and Clarke (Va., 1939).

Venom: We forgo all quotations but one under "Authorities" in order to treat this topic at length.

"After the rattlesnake, the copperhead snake is the most dreaded in the northern states" (Rafinesque, 1819). "The researches of Drs. Mitchell and Reichert show that their venom is less virulent than that of the rattlesnake, but more so than the water moccasin" (Hay, 1892).

"While the copperhead is a sullen and treacherous snake, its disposition is to remain concealed, and it will not strike unless closely pressed or trod upon" (Atkinson, 1901).

"Doctor Yarrow (13: 422-435) states that of many cases recorded in medical journals, he had found only one fatal case, the victim being a boy of six" (Branson, 1904).

"It shows a similar inoffensiveness in a state of nature. . . . I have known of 4 instances of this snake having bitten human beings . . . , all victims recovered" (Brimley, 1923).

"Copperheads only 6 hours old are in possession of a completely functional venom apparatus" (Stadelman, 1928).

"This much maligned snake will bite if trod upon, fight viciously if cornered or slide away to safety if possible" (Netting, 1923). He called *Heterodon* a better bluffer, the blue racer a better fighter.

Boyer recorded the symptoms from the bite of a 15-day-old copperhead in 1933. "Of the total of 2,376 bites reported for 1927 to 1934, 691 were from copperheads, three times as many as from water moccasin or timber rattler and 1½ times as many as from Texas diamond-back rattler" (Githens, Gen., 1935).

Pope (Gen., 1937) wrote that Kauffeld was bitten by a hibernating copperhead and that it was potent, notwithstanding a former belief to the contrary.

The old statement that poisonous snakes are immune to their own venom, Mitchell and later others found to be untrue in some cases. There may be specific and individual differences in resistance. Keegan and Andrews found a young *Ancistrodon* that succumbed to an injection of *Ancistrodon* venom.

"Experiments with *Agkistrodon mokasen mokeson* venom indicate that copperheads are more susceptible to venom of their own kind than of other venom. . . . Copperhead venom proved fatal to massasaugus, moccasin and timber rattlers, generally taking more time than with copperheads themselves, considering the amounts given and the relative sizes of the snakes. For various species of harmless snakes large doses proved fatal" (Swanson, 1946).

Field notes: Sept. 9, 1931: We received this postal card from Conewongo, N.Y.: "We think you ought to know of this incident. Some track men handling car-loads of slag to ballast the R. R. track found many copperhead snakes. They killed what they could, but *many* got away, so the big swamp here will be pretty well populated with them soon. It seems this slag came from somewhere south of here where the weather is warmer."

Authorities:

Anderson, P. (Mo., 1942)
Atkinson, D. A. (Pa., 1901)
Babcock, H. L. (N.E., 1926)
Bailey, R. M. (Ia., 1940)
Boulenger, E. G. (Gen., 1914)
Boyer, D. A. (Mo., 1941)
Branson, E. B. (Kan., 1904)
Brimley, C. S. (N.C., 1923)
Ditmars, R. L. (Gen., 1929; N.Y., 1905)
Fitch, H. S. (Kan., 1951)
Gloyd, H. K. (Kan., 1928, 1932)
Hay, O. P. (Ind., 1892)
Hook, L. (N.J., 1936)
Hurter, J. (Mo., 1911)
Keegan, H. L., and T. F. Andrews (Gen., 1942)
Kunze, R. E. (N.J., 1883)
Lynn, W. G. (Va., 1929, 1936)
Netting, M. B. (Pa., 1932)
Rafinesque, C. S. (Gen., 1819)
Reese, A. M. (W.Va., 1926)
Say, T. (Gen., 1819)
Smith, A. G. (Pa., 1940)
Smith, W. H. (O., 1882)
Stadelman, R. E. (Gen., 1928, 1929)
Surface, H. A. (Pa., 1906)
Swanson, P. L. (Gen., 1950)

1951, H. S. Fitch: At the Natural History Reservation, University of Kansas, Fitch tried a funnel trap for population density and took 158 copperheads, 145 racers, and 31 *Elaphe obsoleta.* During the same period he took 54 copperheads by hand.

Trans-Pecos copperhead (4—Gloyd and Conant 1943)

Ancistrodon contortrix pictigaster Gloyd and Conant 1943. Fig. 263; Map 64

Range: W. Texas (Reeves, Jeff Davis, Presidio, Brewster, Terrell, and Crockett Counties). *Elevation*—2,500 to 5,000 feet (Gloyd and Conant).

Size: Adults, 11–18.3 inches for the first two specimens. The Phillips and Flury specimen is 457 mm.; the Milstead specimen is 507 mm.

Distinctive characteristics: "Similar to *A. m. laticinctus* in dorsal pattern but differing in the very dark and strikingly patterned belly. Under surface dark brown, deep chestnut, or black, relieved by light, strongly-contrasting areas extending onto belly from the dorsal ground color, and by similar light areas (often in the form of an inverted "U") below each dark dorsal crossband. . . . A structural difference of possible diagnostic value is the higher number of caudals: 57 to 59 in males, 52 to 56 in females. In no other specimens of the copperhead examined to date does the number of caudals exceed 54 in males or 52 in females" (Gloyd and Conant).

Color: A snake from Independence Creek, Terrell Co., Tex., received from W. W. Milstead through the kindness of W. F. Blair. Each of the dark saddles edged with chocolate is cacao brown on mid-back, fading to vinaceous-russet toward the venter, where it forks to cross the belly as 2 bars of brick red. The light bands are vinaceous-fawn on the middorsum, light vinaceous-fawn on the sides, vinaceous-buff as they reach the belly plates, and tilleul buff or white on the venter which is flecked with fine punctae of buff-pink.

The light interval areas do not evenly unite on mid-dorsum with the counterparts of the other side. The top of the head is pecan brown. The iris and face below the postocular band is onion-skin pink; the band at top of last 3 or 4 upper labials and edge of temporals is cameo brown. The underside of head is onion-skin pink, and the first 8 ventral plates clay color. Three brick red bars cross the venter, corresponding to each dark dorsal saddle. The cephalic chocolate border of the saddle extends across the belly as the border of the foremost bar, while the rear dark margin forms the caudal margin of the rearmost one. The intermediate red bar begins as a chocolate spot on scale row 1 and covers about 2 belly plates. Its upper end is light edged front and rear, but not so prominently on its upper edge, as in U pattern of typical *pictigaster*. This typical U became prominent after shedding. This inverted light U extends into the vinaceous-russet portion of the dark saddle. The light intervals do not quite cross the venter, thus leaving a solid line of brick red down the middle.

Habitat: "A week later, or to be exact, on October 5, while staying at the

Tippit's Ranch, Mitre Peak, Davis Mountains, the writer captured a small copperhead, *Agkistrodon mokasen,* only 11 inches long, found coiled in the fork of a live oak about 4 feet above the ground. Three years ago on another visit, a mature example of this species was seen, collected by a man connected with a medicine show. He had it in a box tied to the back of his car. Exposed to the hot sun the snake had died when he reached the town of Alpine, 12 miles away. In arid regions viperine snakes are seldom encountered during the heat of the day. Copperheads are not uncommon in the Davis Mountains, which is about the western limit in the range of the species" (Engelhardt).

Flury reported it from Sanderson, Texas, and from Limpia Canyon near Ft. Davis.

Authorities:

Brown, A. E. (Tex., 1903)
Engelhardt, G. P. (Tex., 1932)
Flury, A. G. (Tex., 1949)

Gloyd, H. K., and R. Conant (Gen., 1943)
Strecker, J. K., Jr. (Tex., 1928b)

1899, R. B. McLain (Ark., 1899): What is his Crockett, Texas, record? The specimen is now in the Stanford University collection.

1903: A. E. Brown received one specimen from Pecos. Was it *A. c. pictigaster?*

1943, H. K. Gloyd and R. Conant: "Type Specimens—Holotype, Chicago Acad. Sci. 4857, adult male, Maple Canyon, Chisos Mountains, elevation 5,200 feet, Brewster County, Texas; collected by W. L. Necker. July 28, 1937. Paratypes: Chicago Acad. Sci. 7807, Oak Spring, Chisos Mountains, U. S. Nat. Mus. 103659, Pulliam Canyon, Chisos Mountains, Brewster County, Texas; Mus. Zool. Univ. Michigan 72246, Tippit's Ranch, near Mitre Peak, Cornell Univ. Mus. 913, Musquiz Canyon, north of Alpine, Jeff Davis County, Texas."

Water moccasin (67—Holbrook 1849),
Cottonmouth (45—Brimley 1895)

Ancistrodon piscivorus piscivorus (Lacépède) 1789. Fig. 264; Map 65

Other common names: Black moccasin; black snake; blunt-tail moccasin; congo; copperhead; cottonmouth water moccasin; cotton-mouthed snake; gapper; highland moccasin; lowland moccasin; mangrove rattler; moccasin; North American cottonmouth snake; North American water moccasin; North American water viper; pilot; rusty moccasin; saltwater rattler; stubtail; stump moccasin; stump(-tail) moccasin; stump-tail viper; swamp lion; Texas moccasin; trap jaw; Troost's moccasin; true horn snake; true water moccasin; viper; water mokeson; water pilot; water rattlesnake; water viper.

Range: Atlantic coastal plain from s.e. Virginia to the tip of Florida; Gulf

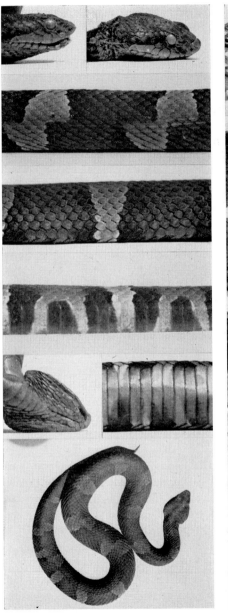 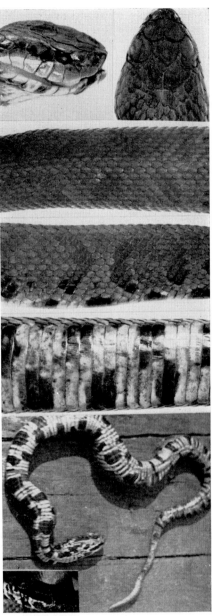

Fig. 263. *Ancistrodon c. pictigaster,* Independence Creek, Terrell Co., Tex., W. W. Milstead.

Fig. 264. *Ancistrodon piscivorus piscivorus:* 1–5, Silver Springs, Fla., E. R. Allen; 6,7, Billy Lake, Okefinokee Swamp, Ga., authors and F. Harper.

coastal plain westward to Escambia Co., Fla., and Baldwin Co., Ala.—Ala.; Fla.; Ga.; N.C.; S.C.; Va. *Elevation*—Sea level to 500 feet.

Size: Adults, 26–72 inches.

Longevity: 14 years 8 months; 5 years 5 months (Conant and Hudson, Gen., 1949); 10 years 11 months (Flower, Gen., 1925); 10 years 8 months (Perkins, Gen., 1947); 14 years 8 months (Perkins, Gen., 1950); 12 years (Stabler, Gen., 1951); 18 years 8 months (Perkins, Gen., 1954).

Distinctive characteristics: "General coloration olive, brown, or black above; belly light; crossbands with more or less distinct dark borders, the centers invaded by ground color, often giving the effect of narrow, paired, transverse bars; pattern usually obsolete in large adults; rostral and sides of snout light, usually with a distinct vertical dark line at each side of rostral; juveniles light, with brilliant patterns sharply contrasting with ground color" (Gloyd and Conant).

Color: An adult snake from Silver Springs, Fla., received from E. R. Allen, Nov. 9, 1936. The ground color of the back is light brownish olive, buffy olive, or olive-brown. On the body are 28 bands of dark olive with borders of olivaceous black (1). In the caudal portion of the body and on the tail, black predominates. The large plates on the top of the head are dark olive, becoming on the supraoculars and edge of top of head olive-brown. On the side of the head is a prominent vitta extending across the preoculars and back of the eye, which is warm sepia or bone brown and which grades through bister, sepia, and brownish olive to citrine-drab back of the angle of the mouth. This vitta is outlined with cartridge buff, and this light color appears along the lower sides as borders for the lower ends of the cross-bands. Similarly outlined, are 2 vertical stripes of bone brown or warm sepia on the sutures between rostral and 1st upper labial and extending onto the 1st 3 lower labials. On either side on the 7th and front of the 8th lower labials and on the 9th are 2 spots of citrine-drab. The rostral, mental, and upper labials are dark olive-buff, and the upper labials are crossed above by the lower cartridge buff outline of the vitta. The iris is natal brown with a narrow horizontal band of isabella color or dark olive-buff across the upper third of the eye. There is no light pupil rim. The lower side of the head and throat for about 6 plates is cartridge buff. This ends at a prominent spot of deep olive. The ventral surface is dark olive-buff to deep olive-buff blotched with citrine-drab to deep olive and with the ends and edges of ventrals occasionally outlined with cartridge buff. The underside of the tail is almost black, and this black extends forward over about ¼ of the belly and occurs forward as an occasional spot in the citrine-drab areas. This rear 4th of the venter is interspersed with dark olive-buff.— Note: Old specimens are frequently wholly black on the back.

A young snake in the green-tailed stage from a pond southwest of boys' swimming hole, Billy Lake, Okefinokee Swamp, Ga., received May 11, 1921.

The back is clove brown or medal bronze with bone brown bands. The top of the tail is courge green with some brown. There is a chestnut stripe back of the eye. The upper labials, the line ahead of the eye, nasal, rostral, and mental are apricot buff. The lower portion of the iris is deep brown or chestnut; the upper $\frac{1}{3}$ of the iris is cream colored or almost golden like the rim of the pupil. The under parts of the head are chestnut, white, or milky white, with a little purplish black. The belly is marked with purple black spots bordered with chestnut edges. The underside of the tail is javel green or calliste green.

Habitat: Marshes and lakes; ponds and streams with wooded shores; low country near water; roadside ponds; drainage ditches; coastal "banks"; keys; some Gulf coast islands; mangrove swamps.

"Abounds in swamps, sluggish waterways, old rice fields, in fact wherever marsh reeds and cane brakes grow. It hunts much on land and is fond of basking in the sun on logs and bushes above the water. Occasionally it will be found in cultivated fields and on the borders of woods not far from its natural haunts" (Rutledge). Not common in water hyacinths (Goin, Fla., 1943).

In 1878 Coues and Yarrow discussed *Ancistrodon piscivorus:* "Very numerous in woods of Bogue [N.C.] banks and on the mainland near wet and marshy places. Dr. Yarrow was informed by several individuals that both moccasins and rattlesnakes had been seen a number of times swimming from the mainland to Bogue Island." We ask, "Did Barbour and Engels' king snake, chicken snake, and water snake get there in the same way?"

In 1951 Stabler (Gen.) made an important contribution concerning a 12-year-old captive that he received when it was a yellow-tailed one-year-old. It shed 25 times in 12 years (2.1 sheddings a year). It ate 398 items in the same period or 83.2 a year. When received, it was 9 inches long. In 12 years it grew to 55 inches in length.

Breeding: Viviparous. Males 650–1,550 mm., females 635–1,225 mm. *Mating*—(See Davis and Ramsey [Tex., 1948] under *A. p. leucostoma* below.) In 1948 Lowe wrote: "For various reasons, observers have not always sexed the 'dance' participants. In those cases, where sex was *definitely* determined, the snakes were *males.*" In the same year Charles E. Shaw wrote: "At the Reptile House of the San Diego Zoo, 81 courtships and matings have been observed and recorded in the genus *Crotalus* (10 species and subspecies), . . . *Sistrurus* and *Agkistrodon* (*A. p. piscivorus*). In NONE of these was the courtship behavior pattern initiated by the dancing of the male and female, nor have male and female ever been observed to dance at any time. . . . Although we have never witnessed a male combat dance in *A. piscivorus,* we have observed courtships and matings in this species."

The period of gestation is not easily determined—earlier authors gave 4 to 6 months—because this species has been observed in captivity to mate in January, spring, summer, and fall and in nature at different periods.

Young—Number, 1–15. 1–15 (Davis and Brimley, Gen., 1944); 3–12 (Allen and Swindell); 5–10 (Wright and Bishop); 5–12 (Conant and Bridges, Gen., 1939); 7–12 (Ditmars, Gen., 1936; Safford, Fla., 1919); 8 (Stejneger, Gen., 1895); 8–15 (Necker, Ill., 1939b). Allen and Swindell recorded 31 adult snakes with embryos—with from 4 embryos in a 26-inch snake to 11 in a 44-inch one. Newspaper reporters and travelers' tales of 30–50 young in a moccasin brood must relate to false "moccasins" or to water snakes (*Natrix*). Length, 8–11 inches. One record gave 13 inches (Allen and Swindell). We have seen young from 210–270 mm. (8.4–10.8 inches). Time of birth, August and September, mostly Aug. 15 to Sept. 15.

Food: Frogs, fish, salamanders, reptiles, birds, mammals, various other vertebrates.[1] Stejneger.

Venom: We suggest that the reader consult such authorities as the following and many more in the catalogue of the Surgeon General's Library and special bibliographies on the subject: E. Loennberg (Fla., 1895), C. S. Brimley (Gen., 1905), H. Noguchi (Gen., 1909), A. H. Wright and S. C. Bishop (Ga., 1916), A. Rutledge (S.C., 1921), A. do Amaral (Gen., 1925, 1928), R. Conant (Gen., 1929), C. H. Philpott (Gen., 1929), T. S. Githens (Gen., 1935), N. O. C. Wolff and T. S. Githens (Gen., 1939), A. F. Carr, Jr. (Fla., 1940a), A. H. Alexander (Gen., 1941), E. R. Allen and E. Maier (Gen., 1941).

1948, Allen and Swindell: "Moccasin venom is of the haematoxic type, causing destruction of red blood cells and coagulation around the site of the bite. It rates third in potency, compared drop for drop, to that of the coral snake and the eastern diamond-back rattlesnake. The venom is employed medically in the treatment of haemorrhagic conditions and rheumatoid arthritis, as well as in the preparation of antivenin. Moccasins frequently bite each other while being handled. The bite shows definite effects of poisoning, causing swelling and discoloration under the skin. Following the bite, the snakes become sluggish for several days and a small percentage die. It has partial immunity to its own venom, but a large dose will cause death. The following record of moccasin bites for Florida was compiled from newspaper accounts and from records of the Bureau of Vital Statistics: Beginning in 1934 there were 8 cases of bites resulting in 3 fatalities. From that date to 1944 there were no fatalities recorded. The number of cases for each year are: 1935, 10; 1936, 16; 1937, 7; 1938, 6; 1939, 5; 1940, 3; 1941, 6; 1942, 3; 1943, 1; and 1944, 3."

In 1939 Wolff and Githens reported a 60-inch specimen yielding 3.5 cc.

---

[1] In 1955 Hamilton and Pollack found that cottonmouths ate principally reptiles (snakes and turtles), 44.4%, and amphibians (frogs and treefrogs), 44.4%.

of venom at first extraction. Five weeks later the second extraction yielded 4 cc. of liquid, or 1.094 grams of dried venom.

Field notes: We have had countless experiences with this species but have never been bitten. Many times one step more and we would have been on them. In the whole summer of 1921 we heard no report of cottonmouth bite among the 400 cypress cutters in Okefinokee Swamp. That does not indicate great aggressiveness on the part of the moccasin.

Authorities:

Allen, E. R., and D. Swindell (Fla., 1948)

Allen, E. R., and E. Maier (Gen., 1941)

Carr, A. F., Jr. (Fla., 1940a)

Conant, R. (Gen., 1929; Ill., 1933)

Coues, E., and H. C. Yarrow (N.C., 1878)

Davis, D. D. (Gen., 1936)

Ditmars, R. L. (Gen., 1930)

Gloyd, H. K., and R. Conant (Gen., 1943)

Klauber, L. M. (Gen., 1948)

Loennberg, E. (Fla., 1895)

Lowe, C. H., Jr. (Gen., 1948)

Rutledge, A. (S.C., 1921)

Shaw, C. E. (Gen., 1948)

Stejneger, L. (Gen., 1895)

Wolff, N. O. C., and T. S. Githens (Gen., 1939)

Wright, A. H., and S. C. Bishop (Ga., 1916)

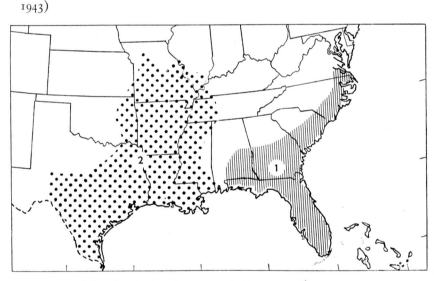

Map 65. *Ancistrodon*—1, *p. piscivorus;* 2, *p. leucostoma.*

Water moccasin (21), Cottonmouth (16)

Ancistrodon piscivorus leucostoma (Troost) 1836. Fig. 265; Map 65

Other common names: (Black) moccasin; blunt-tail moccasin; (northern) cottonmouth moccasin; stump-tail (water) moccasin; viper; western cottonmouth moccasin.

Fig. 265. *Ancistrodon p. leucostoma;*
1,6–10, Brownsville, Tex., H. C. Blanchard;
2–5, young, Livingston, Tex., J. P. Kennedy.

Range: From Rio Grande Valley (Brownsville to Devils River), n.e. through e. Oklahoma to cent. Missouri and s. Illinois, thence s. through w. Kentucky and Tennessee to Mobile Bay, Ala.—Ala.; Ark.; Ill.; Kan.; Ky.; La.; Miss.; Mo.; Okla.; Tenn.; Tex. *Elevation*—Sea level to 500 feet, some to 1,000 feet.

Size: Adults, 24–62 inches.

Longevity: 21 years (Boulenger, Gen., 1914); 14 years (Stabler, Gen., 1951).

Distinctive characteristics: "General coloration, in both adults and juveniles, dark brown or black above, and usually below; dorsal ground color usually almost as dark as markings; crossbands broad, with dusky centers, little if any invaded by ground color; rostral and sides of snout dark, with no distinct vertical dark lines at sides of rostral; juveniles dark with little contrast between markings and ground color. The displacement or reduction of the 2nd supralabial by an anterior extension of the 3rd, a character used by Baird and Girard (1853, p. 20) as diagnostic of *pugnax* from the Gulf Coast of Texas, occurs in several localities, but not with a sufficiently high frequency to be employed in characterizing this population" (Gloyd and Conant, Gen., 1943).

"They have a ground color of dark olive or dark brown and are marked with 10 to 15 dark, wide crossbands which are somewhat lighter in the center than at the edges. The bands, which have irregular edges, become a little wider along the sides. The lower jaw and upper jaw below the eye are light in contrast to the dark color on the top of the head. Young moccasins are vividly marked and look very much like copperheads. They have a ground color of reddish brown and are marked with darker brown bands which are edged with white" (Werler).

Color: Two baby snakes from 26 miles east of Livingston, Polk Co., Tex., received from J. P. Kennedy of Houston, Tex., Sept. 15, 1950. The back is marked with dark saddles and light interspaces. The light areas orange-vinaceous and 5 scales in length on middorsum, narrowing on the sides to 1½–2 scales' length and pinkish vinaceous or light russet vinaceous with a few flecks or broken-thread outline of white. The dark saddles have centers of deep brownish vinaceous outlined by a prominent border 1½–2 scales in width of vinaceous-brown or dark indian red. Sometimes in the lateral base of the dark saddle on scale rows 5 and 6 are 1–3 spots of dark vinaceous-brown. The top of the head is cameo brown. The lower labials are marked with burnt sienna, the upper ones and the throat marked with english red, white spots and stripes intermingled. Except for a buff band over the pupil, the iris is burnt sienna, as are the face and rostral. The tail is pale greenish yellow. The belly is largely black; groups of 2 or 3 ventrals are separated by deeply punctate whitish intervals. In color these snakes are startlingly like adult copperheads.

Habitat: Cypress, gum, river swamps; alluvial swamps wooded or not wooded; water courses of the south such as rivers, bayous, backwaters of small branches; hill streams in the north; "prairies" (water, south), marshy places in prairies (land, north); rice fields, bottomland pools; margins of above habitats, pools, shallow lakes, swampy places, temporary flood lands. Among, under, or on stones. In, under, or on fallen timber, in holes in banks, rocky bluffs, crayfish burrows. In short, it is very aquatic.

In 1951 Stabler (Gen.) made some important observations on a 14-year-old captive. It shed 37 times in 14 years or 2.6 times a year. The total number of food items consumed was 421 or 30.1 a year. It was 45 inches long when received and grew little in length in 14 years.

Period of activity: *First appearance*—May 11, 1929 (Force, Okla., 1930); Apr. 24 (Hurter); Feb. 26, Mar. 15, Apr. 1, Apr. 2, Apr. 4 (Corrington, Miss., 1927). "Specimens have not been found earlier than the middle of April" (Parker, Tenn., 1948). *Fall disappearance*—Sept. 5 (Hurter); Sept. 13, 1939 (Evans); Oct. 19, 1940 (Anderson, Mo., 1945). Of Travis Co., Tex., Strecker (1930) wrote, "Mr. Eanes was present at the killing of several at the mouth of Barton Creek. It was in November and when the snakes were exposed, they were too chilled to offer resistance."

Hibernation—"These snakes are usually found in this area (Stoddard, Bollinger, and Wayne Cos., Mo.) in the cypress swamps, where they are plentiful adjacent to the rocky bluffs where they hibernate through the winter. They can be collected in great numbers in the spring and fall of the year on those hillsides having southern exposure" (Evans). In Mississippi, Allen wrote: "During the colder periods of the winter they have been found in this habitat [swamps] under logs and stumps."

Breeding: Viviparous. Males 806–1,550 mm., females 671–1,200 mm. (See also Arny [La., 1949].) *Mating*—On Mar. 10, 1893, Beyer (La., 1898) cap-tured the female of a mated pair, and on Aug. 17, 160 days later, she produced 9 young. On Apr. 1, he captured two snakes, and on Aug. 25 one gave birth to 8 young after possible 157 ± days of gestation. This was 50 years ago before we knew about fall mating and various aberrations in mating. Beyer concluded 5 months to be the period of gestation. But as we understand it today, the matter is not so simple. We give an excerpt from Davis: "Mr. Perkins has repeatedly witnessed courtship in the water moccasin, *Agkistro-don piscivorus*. Under the artificial conditions of captivity matings take place at all seasons of the year. Individual pairs in captivity seem to consort together for months. Under the stimulus of artificial warmth and sunlight they frequently engage in a characteristic courtship dance, which is highly spectacular because of the extreme vigor with which it is carried on by these powerful heavy-bodied snakes. Both individuals erect the anterior half of their bodies into the air. These elevated parts of the body are then waved and lashed about erratically. Frequently the upraised parts of the pair are placed together and each snake pushes and rubs vigorously against its mate. The force with which these pushing movements are carried on is oc-casionally evidenced when one individual slips past the other. The sudden release of resistance under these circumstances may throw the other snake several feet across the cage. This extraordinary behavior may continue for hours at a time, and is usually followed by copulation. The posterior ends of the bodies are not usually twined together, although this may occasionally take place accidentally. Other snakes in the same cage do not seem to be affected by the activity of the courting pair."

In 1948 Ramsey (Tex.) entered the debate on "courtship dance" versus "combat dance": "On a recent collecting trip, the writer encountered two specimens of *Agkistrodon piscivorus leucostoma* (Troost) apparently en-gaged in a 'combat dance' similar to that described by Charles H. Lowe (*Herpetologica* 4, p. 129) and also by Charles E. Shaw, *idem*, p. 137. . . . Both specimens were collected and later examination showed that both were males. The time of the year, June 20, would seem to indicate that impulses other than the mating instinct were involved in the combat." For more on this topic see *A. p. piscivorus* above.

Young—Number, 2–15. 2, 15 (Conant); 2, 6, 7 (Hurter); 2, 12 (Mitchell); 4 (Parker); 5, 7, 9, 12 (Strecker); 6, 10 (Funkhouser); 7 (Hay, Strecker); 9 (Beyer). Never 25 or 50 as in water snakes, *Natrix* (Mitchell). Length, 6.75–10 inches. Beyer holds that Effeldt's record of 10.4 inches is a mistake. Time of birth, Aug. 15 into September. There are actual records from Aug. 17 to Sept. 19. On Sept. 6, 1950, J. P. Kennedy sent me 2 newborn young remarking that the very small female had only 3 in all.

Food: Same as that of *A. p. piscivorus*. Mitchell, Hurter, Boulenger (Gen., 1914), Allen.

Authorities:

Allen, M. J. (Miss., 1932)
Arny, S. A. (La., 1949)
Beyer, G. E. (La., 1900)
Conant, R. (Ill., 1933)
Davis, D. D. (Gen., 1936)
Evans, P. D. (Mo., 1940)
Garman, H. (Ill., 1892)

Hay, O. P. (Ind., 1892)
Hurter, J. (Mo., 1911)
Mitchell, J. D. (Tex., 1903)
Penn, G. H., Jr. (La., 1943)
Stabler, R. M. (Gen., 1951)
Strecker, J. K., Jr. (Tex., 1926c)
Troost, G. (Tenn., 1836)
Werler, J. E. (Tex., 1950)

RATTLESNAKES

Genus *CROTALUS* Linné (Figs. 266–269)

Size, medium to large, 15–60 inches, to very large 80–90 inches; body stocky except in some small species; tail usually short and stout, .040–.130 in total length; scales all keeled in rows 1–5 smooth in 21–31 rows; small scales on top of head, head plates, if large, ahead of the middle of supraoculars and in U.S. forms usually not 9 but 8 (e.g., *C. molossus*), 10, or 12 (in *C. pricei* and *C. scutulatus*); parietals, if enlarged, not in contact; subocular rows 3–4 except in some small species as *cerastes, lepidus* 2; upper labials mostly 13–16 (12–19) (except in *C. p. pricei* 8–11; *C. cerastes* 10–15; *C. lepidus* 11–13); lower labials average 14–18 (except in same snakes named above in which average is 10–13); eye in vertical of upper labials 5–10; hemipenis— strongly calyculate, lower rows becoming flounced in *C. viridis* and *C. basiliscus*. North and South America. Synonyms: *Aechmophrys; Aploaspis; Caudisona; Crotalinus; Crotalophorus; Haploaspis; Urocrotalon; Urosophis; Vipera.*

1569, Hakluyt, *Principal Navigations Voyages, Traffics and Discoveries,* IX; 450: "From hence we shaped our course to Santa Marta, where we landed, traded, and sold certaine Negroes; there two of our company killed a monstrous adder, going towards his cave with a Conie in his mouth: his body was as bigge as any man's thigh, and seven foote long: upon his tayle he had sixteene knottes, every one as bigge as a great walnut, which they say, doe shew his age; his colour was greene and yellow; they opened him, and found two conies in his belly."

1917, Vorhies (Ariz.): "Now, *all* rattlesnakes are venomous and dangerous, *deadly,*—let there be no mistake about that. Familiarity occasionally breeds contempt, even here, and some foolhardy individuals with better luck than sense, handle rattlers. Such, too, have been known to pay the penalty eventually for their foolishness. The white man had best leave the bare-handed manipulation of live rattlers to the Hopi snake priests, who are seemingly much wiser than we in the matter of remedies."

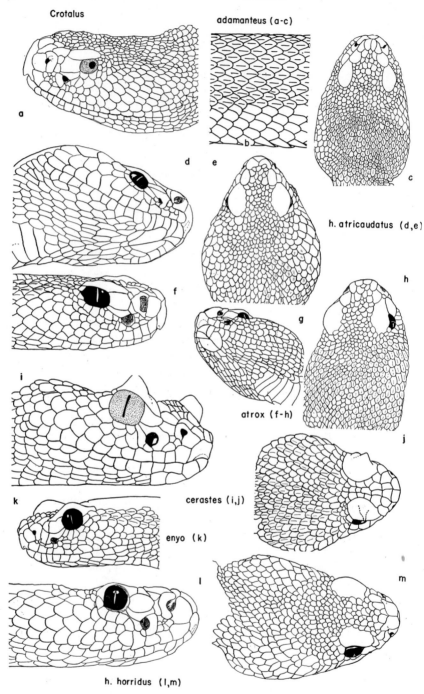

Fig. 266. Heads of six species of *Crotalus*.

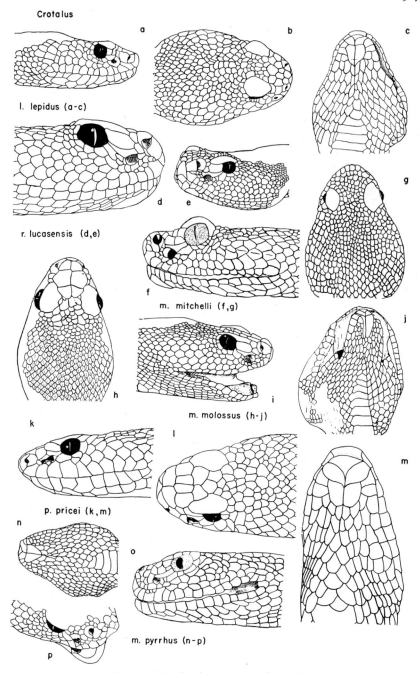

Crotalus

l. lepidus (a-c)

r. lucasensis (d,e)

m. mitchelli (f,g)

m. molossus (h-j)

p. pricei (k,m)

m. pyrrhus (n-p)

Fig. 267. Heads of six species of *Crotalus*.

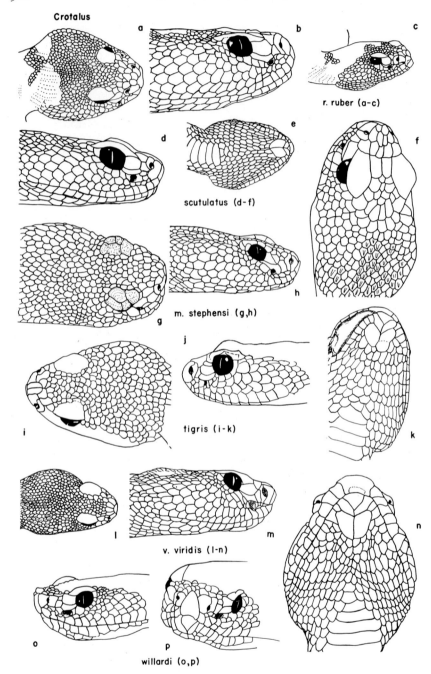

Fig. 268. Heads of six species of *Crotalus*.

Crotalus

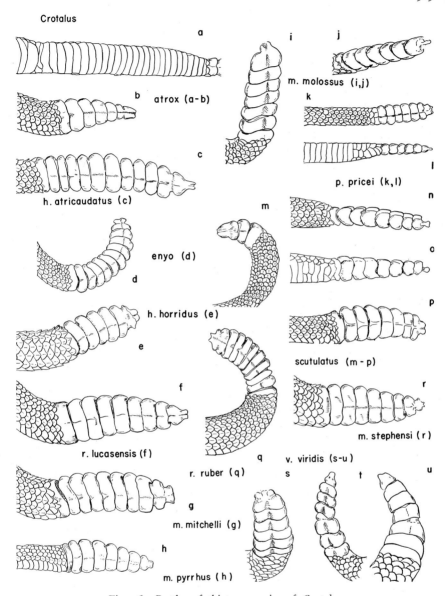

Fig. 269. Rattles of thirteen species of *Crotalus*.

KEY TO THE GENUS *CROTALUS*
(Data from Klauber [Gen., 1936; Baja Calif., 1949a])

a. Outer edges of supraoculars raised into flexible hornlike processes distinctly pointed at the tip. Dorsal scales strongly keeled and with posterior bosses. Ground color cream, straw, pink, or light-gray, with a central series of square brownish blotches, often with yellow or orange on the middorsal line.

    b. "Proximal lobe of rattle-matrix brown in adults; scale rows usually 21; ventrals in males 141 or less, and in females 144 or less."

                                              C. cerastes cerastes

  bb. Proximal lobe of rattle-matrix black in adults.

      c. Scale rows usually 23; ventrals 140–149 in males, 143–154 in females.   *C. c. laterorepens*

    cc. Scale rows usually 21, ventrals in males 132–143, in females 137–147.

                                        C. c. cercobombus[1]

aa. Outer edges of supraoculars not raised into hornlike processes.

    b. Tip of snout and canthus rostralis raised into a sharp ridge, by bending up of the outer edges of internasals and canthals.

      c. Rostral and mental usually marked vertically by a narrow light line on a red-brown ground; body pattern of 20–25 large brown or red-brown blotches separated by narrow light areas, the blotches being often without definite outlines on the sides; tail pattern terminating in longitudinal bands rather than crossbars.

                                        C. willardi willardi

    cc. No rostral and mental white line; scale rows 27 at mid-body; 25 rounded dorsal blotches well defined only middorsally (*C. w. silus* Chihuahua, Mex.).

  bb. Tip of snout and canthus rostralis not raised into a sharp ridge; no central light line on rostral and mental.

    c. Upper preocular split vertically, the anterior section higher than posterior and curved over canthus rostralis in front of supraocular; prenasal curved under postnasal; usually a pattern of widely separated crossbars.   *C. lepidus*

---

[1] On Mar. 27, 1953, Savage and Cliff (Ariz.) recorded it from Maricopa, Pima, and Pinal Cos., Ariz., and from Sonora, Mex. In the light of the recent description of *cercobombus*, this account should be treated as a composite of *cercobombus* and *laterorepens*.

d. A dark stripe passing backward from eye to angle of mouth; dorsal crossbars often not strongly differentiated from ground color; venter mottled; 13–22 brown or black blotches or crossbars on a punctate ground of gray, brown or pink: often with rudimentary or obsolescent intermediate bars; tail usually pink or reddish.

C. lepidus lepidus

dd. No dark postocular stripe; dorsal crossbars sharply contrasting with ground color; venter punctated; 14–21 dark reddish brown or black crossbars on background of green, blue-green, or blue-gray; tail usually cream or pink.   *C. l. klauberi*

cc. Upper preocular not split vertically; or if split (frequent in *mitchelli*, occasional in *triseriatus*), anterior section not conspicuously higher than posterior and not curved over canthus rostralis in front of supraocular; prenasal not curved under post; pattern not of widely separated crossbars or rings.

d. Prenasals usually separated from rostral by small scales or granules; upper preoculars often divided horizontally, vertically or both; rostral usually wider than high; pattern of dorsal blotches essentially that of punctations.

e. Head smaller; length of head in adult body length more than 24 times; original rattle-button more than 7.5 mm. wide; pattern dark gray or brown punctated blotches on gray or tan background. (Baja California.)   (*C. mitchelli mitchelli*)

ee. Head larger; length of head in adult body length less than 24 times; original rattle-button less than 7.5 mm. wide; pattern of red, gray, brown punctated blotches on cream, tan, buff, gray, pink, salmon, fawn, or brown background, often with posterior black tips on some dorsal scales between blotches. (S. California, w. Arizona, n. Baja California.)   *C. m. pyrrhus*

[Dwarfted island racer, generally gray, or ground color may be light pink; usually 23 scale rows at mid-body; higher average number of body blotches than *m. pyrrhus*. (El Muerto Island.)

C. m. muertensis]

dd. Prenasals in contact with rostral; upper preocular not divided, or if divided (a few *triseriatus*) loreal conspicuously longer than high.

e. Tail of alternating black, and light ash-gray rings, both colors being in sharp contrast with posterior body color of gray, dark gray, cream, pink, red, red-brown, or olive-brown.

f. Dark tail rings narrower than light; postocular light stripe, if present, passes backward above angle of mouth; minimum scales between supraoculars rarely more than 2; definite division line between frontal and prefrontal areas; lower half of proximal rattle light in color. Brown hexagons or diamonds on green, olive-green, or brown background; light scales bordering diamonds unicolor, following scale edges, not cutting across them.   *C. scutulatus*

ff. Dark and light tail rings of approximately equal width; postocular light stripe, if present, intersects upper labials from 1–3 scales anterior to angle of mouth; minimum scales between supraoculars 3 or more; no definite line of demarcation between frontal and prefrontal areas; proximal rattle black.   *C. atrox* group

  g. First lower labials usually divided transversely; general color pink, red, brick-red, red-brown or olive-brown; dark punctations weakly in evidence or absent from markings.

    h. Scales between chin shields usually absent; prenasals generally contact 1st upper labials; tail rings complete or broken only on middorsal line; adults exceed 3 feet.

      i. General color pink, red, brick red, or red-brown; usually no light areas within diamonds; light preocular stripe 1–2 scales wide, dull and often obscure; supraocular light crossbars usually absent. Pattern reddish, almost unicolor diamonds on a pinkish ground.   *C. ruber ruber*

      ii. General color brown, olive brown, yellow-brown; light areas usually present within diamonds; light preocular stripe 3 or more scales wide, bright and conspicuous; supraocular light crossbars usually evident. Pattern of brown or olive-brown blotches on buff ground. (Baja California.)   (*C. r. lucasensis*)

    hh. A pair of scales between chin shields usually present; generally no contact between prenasal and 1st upper labial; dark tail rings often broken laterally; size smaller; adults rarely over 3 feet. Pattern of red, circular, and ill-defined blotches on pinkish ground. (Cedros Island.)   (*C. exsul*)

  gg. First lower labials usually not divided transversely; general color cream, buff, gray, or gray-brown (sometimes pink or red in central Arizona and New Mexico); dark punctations conspicuous in markings.

    h. Upper preocular usually not in contact with postnasal, and no upper loreal present; 1st lower labials usually not divided transversely; head smaller in proportion to body. Pattern of dark-brown, punctated diamonds with lighter centers on a gray ground, with light borders of diamonds often absent laterally. (Tortuga Island in Gulf of Calif.)   (*C. tortugensis*) hh. Upper preocular usually contacts postnasal or such contact prevented by an upper loreal; head proportionately larger. Pattern of brown dorsal diamonds consisting of aggregations of punctations on a cream, buff, gray, gray-brown, or (rarely) reddish ground. *C. atrox*

ee. Tail not of alternating black and light ash-gray rings in strong contrast to the body color immediately anterior to the tail.

f. Two internasals.

g. A vertical light line on the posterior edge of prenasals and 1st upper labials. Pattern of black or dark-brown diamonds with lighter centers, surrounded by single rows of yellow scales on a dark-brown background. *C. adamanteus*

gg. No vertical light line on the posterior edge of prenasals and 1st upper labials.

h. Supraoculars pitted, sutured, or with outer edges broken. Pattern buff, gray, brown, or deep red-brown blotches on background of straw, tan, buff, brown, or gray; often with gray suffusions on sides of head and body, and with black-tipped scales scattered on dorsum particularly at blotch edges. Rock-inhabiting form. *C. m. stephensi*

hh. Supraoculars not pitted, sutured, nor with broken outer edges.

i. Distinct and evenly outlined light supraocular crossbars curving forward inwardly; scales on crown and frontal area rough, ridged, or knobby; outer edges of supraoculars raised above crown (particularly evident in life), forming a depression in the frontal area; dorsal scales sharply keeled and with prominent posterior bosses; ridged spinous process sharply evident. Dark brown blotches on fawn ground, usually with black in lateral corners of blotches at mid-body. (Baja California, Mex.) (*C. enyo*)

ii. No distinct and evenly outlined light supraocular crossbars curving forward inwardly; scales on crown and frontal area smooth and flat. General color dark with conspicuous blotches.

j. Head notably small for a rattlesnake; head length in adults contained in body length (over all) 25 times or more; proximal rattle width contained in head length less than 2 1/2 times; pattern a series of cross-rings or blotches comprising brown punctations on a pink, buff, or gray ground; size medium. Rock-inhabiting form. *C. tigris*

jj. Head larger, length contained less than 25 times in adult body length; proximal rattle width contained in head length more than 2 1/2 times.

  k. Usually a definite division between scales of frontal and the prefrontal areas; scales in anterior part of frontal area larger than those behind. Anterior body pattern not in chevron-shaped bands or not all black.

    l. Dorsal scale rows usually exceed 24; scale rows at center of tail 12 or more; ventrals rarely less than 169; 3 or more scales between bottom-center of orbit and upper labials; usually more than one loreal; if single, then higher than long. Size, large—adults almost 2 1/2 feet.

      m. Usually a single loreal; tail rings sharply contrasting in color; face oblique (see cc-dd-f.).   *C. scutulatus*

    mm. Usually 2 or more loreals; tail unicolor or with rings rather faint; tail often black; tail short—7.1% of body length (overall) in males and 5.8% in females; subcaudals rarely more than 27 in males, 23 in females; initial button over 5 mm. wide. Body color primarily olive-green or yellow-green with rarely more than 38 dark-brown blotches, often with light interior blotch on each side of the center; blotch-bordering scales unicolor; a dark-brown patch on crown in internasal-prefrontal area; face vertical, head broad between eyes.

                                      C. molossus molossus

      [A stunted form. General color grayish with smaller, lighter, higher no. of dorsal blotches, type 41; faint, olive-gray; head somewhat shorter, rattles compressed longitudinally and transversely—hence different shape than typical *m*. In *molossus*, no dark-brown patch on crown of head in internasal-prefrontal section. (Baja California.)   *C. m. estebanensis*]

    ll. Dorsal scale rows usually less than 24; scale rows at center of tail 11 or less; ventrals rarely exceed 168; 1 or 2 scales between bottom-center of orbit and upper labials; usually a single loreal, longer than high; size of snake small, adults rarely exceeding 2 1/4 feet. Dorsal pattern of 2 parallel rows of small brown blotches on a steel-gray ground; usually 2 labials in contact with pit border.

                                      C. pricei pricei

 kk. No definite division or continuous suture between scales in frontal and prefrontal areas; scales in anterior part of frontal area not conspicuously larger than those behind. Normal pattern a series of chevron-shaped crossbands sometimes broken, or with body of snake all black.

l. Dorsal scale rows usually 23; postocular dark stripe indistinct; no middorsal reddish-brown stripe evident anteriorly; sometimes snake entirely black. *C. horridus horridus*

    Black form—Head black, chevrons black, partially outlined with straw yellow tips on brownish olive. Venter thickly speckled black, undertail solid black, caudal 1/4 black.

    Yellow form—Head buffy olive, chevrons bister, outlined wholly or in part with half or entire scales of reed yellow, on buffy olive; venter seafoam green and cream-buff.

ll. Dorsal scale rows usually 25; postocular dark stripe distinct and in contrast with the ground color; a middorsal reddish brown or brown stripe evident anteriorly. *C. h. atricaudatus*

ff. More than 2 internasals, i.e., scales between nasals, in contact with rostral regardless of size or position. *C. viridis* group

  g. Light postocular stripe 1 or 1 1/2 scales wide and clearly outlined; body blotches commonly subrectangular with even edges and usually with a narrow light border.

    h. Color usually green or olive green; less often olive-brown or brown; scale rows 27 or 25; dorsal scale rows at center of tail 13 or more; adult size exceeding 34 inches. Pattern of even-edged dark-brown rectangular or subhexagonal blotches usually surrounded by a thin light line. (Of western Mississippi basin plains.) *C. viridis viridis*

    hh. Color pink, red, or red-brown; scale rows 25 or 23; dorsal scales at center of tail 12 or less; adult size rarely exceeding 24 inches. *C. v. nuntius*

  gg. Light postocular stripe 2 or more scales wide, often indefinite or absent; body blotches, if in evidence, commonly diamonds or ellipses, but if rectangles, have edges rough or serrated and often without narrow light borders.

    h. Color straw, cream, or yellow; blotches often only faintly in evidence or obsolete in adults; adult size smaller, usually under 24 inches. *C. v. decolor*

    hh. Color darker, not straw, cream or yellow; adult size larger, over 24 inches.

      i. Adult color vermilion or salmon; body blotches tend toward obsolescence in adults. *C. v. abyssus*

      ii. Adult color other than vermilion or salmon; body blotches in evidence or body black.

j. Ground color lighter, usually buff or drab; body blotches occupy less or but little more longitudinal space than interspaces; secondary series of lateral blotches little in evidence. Pattern of dark brown dorsal blotches (often with light centers) on a buff or drab ground. *C. v. lutosus*

jj. Ground color darker, usually dark-gray, olive brown, or black; dark brown or black dorsal patches (usually diamonds or hexagons) occupying considerably more longitudinal space than the interspaces; a secondary series of lateral blotches conspicuously in evidence; some mountain specimens nearly uniform black, only patches of yellow scales representing the interspaces on middorsal line.

    k. Lighter than kk; hexagonal or circular dorsal blotches; more sharply outlined head marks and lateral secondary blotches; dark tail rings uniform in width, clearly defined; last dark tail ring equals preceding dark ring; end of tail dark from birth; loreal single; scales between anterior nasal and 1st supralabial usually lacking; middorsal interspaces 2 1/2, often 3 scales wide. *C. v. oreganus*

    kk. Darker, frequently black; last dark tail ring 1 1/2–2 times width of preceding dark ring and ill defined; middorsal interspaces 2 or less scales wide; final tail ring in juveniles yellow on gray with yellow tinge.

        l. Single loreal; scales at rostral between anterior nasal and 1st supralabial usually lacking; dorsal patches diamonds, often black in adults, but with lateral border of single row of light scales which border completely the dorsal patches.

            m. Stunted form, below 700 mm. in length; insular (Coronado Islands, Baja Calif., Mex.); gravid at 528–647 mm.

                    C. v. caliginis

            mm. 1,100 mm. or more in length (mainland southern and Baja California); gravid at 600–1,100 mm. *C. v. helleri*

        ll. Two loreals; one or more scales between anterior nasal and 1st supralabial; dorsal body blotches hexagonal, round, or elliptical, without light lateral borders; *commonly black in life;* (Arizona.)

                    C. v. cerberus

Diamond rattlesnake (27—Baird and Girard 1853)
Diamond-back rattlesnake (27—Rolker 1903)

Crotalus adamanteus Beauvois 1799. Fig. 270; Map 66

Other common names: Common rattlesnake; diamond-back; diamond(-patch) rattler; eastern diamond-back (rattlesnake); eastern diamond rattlesnake; Florida diamond-back (rattlesnake); Florida rattlesnake; lozenge-spotted rattlesnake (?); rattler; rattlesnake; southeastern diamond-backed rattlesnake; southern diamond-backed rattler; southern woodland rattler, timber rattlesnake; water rattle; water rattlesnake.

Range: Lower coastal plain from Albermarle Sound, N.C. (possibly Dismal Swamp, Va.) to e. Louisiana, including peninsular Florida.—Ala.; Fla.; Ga.; La.; Miss.; N.C.; S.C. *Elevation*—Coast to 500 feet; in Florida, mainly in zone 100–500 feet.

Size: Adults, 30–90 inches.

George Van Hyning reports a 7-foot 2-inch specimen that he killed 5 miles west of Brooksville, Fla. Klauber's (Gen., 1943b) standard adult length, based on measurements of 31 males and 43 females, is 1,700 mm.

Longevity: 14 years 9 months (Perkins, Gen., 1950); 15 years (Perkins, Gen., 1948); 14 years 9 months (Perkins, Gen., 1954).

Distinctive characteristics: "Yellowish gray above, with lozenge-shaped dorsal blotches sharply defined, blackish, with centres of the body color, and separated by oblique yellow lines crossing each other in the back; on the sides in the triangular open spaces which alternate with the lozenges, there is a black spot; other indistinct markings sometimes appear on the sides; posteriorly the colors are somewhat darker, and the lozenges take the shape of crossbands, which form not very well-defined rings on the tail, but the colors there are not sharply contrasted; belly yellowish white, clouded with brown toward the sides. There is a wide dark oblique streak from below the eye to the labials, bordered in front and behind by a light one; 2 light bars from the loreal pit to labials and another in front of the nostril" (Brown, Gen., 1901). Ventrals 165–182; caudals 22–32.

Fig. 270. *Crotalus adamanteus,* Silver Springs, Fla., E. R. Allen.

Color: A snake from Cape Sable, Fla., received from S. C. Bishop, described May 6, 1936. The back is marked with black rhombs which have wood brown or verona brown centers and light borders of olive-buff or dark olive-buff. These rhombs are 14 to 16 scales wide and about 5 scales long. The ground color of the body is buffy olive, light brownish olive, or wood brown. Directly opposite the apices of the dorsal rhombs are black or mummy brown spots, located in front on the 1st to 3rd rows, in the middle on the 1st to 5th. In the central part of the body, these spots are more or less light edged like the dorsal rhombs, and a few also have the light centers. The dorsal rhombs and their opposite lateral counterparts outline quadrangles of ground color, the center of each occupied by a black or mummy brown spot about 3 scales high and about 2 scales long. Directly below this spot and on the 1st and 2nd rows of scales is another dark spot, covering about 2 scales. The tail tip is black, and just cephalad are several black bands with interspaces of buffy olive or light brownish olive. The top of the head is buffy olive, light brownish olive, or saccardo's olive marked with several irregular small black spots. There is a mummy brown or black band about 3 scales wide extending obliquely through the eye to the angle of the mouth, which is bordered on the rear by a light line of olive-buff from the rear of the supraocular to just above the angle of the mouth, this light line being about 1 scale wide. This dark band is bordered on the front by a stripe, 2 scales wide, of olive-buff, which extends from the postnasal across the prefrontal and down to the 6th to 9th upper labial. There is another such stripe across the prenasal down to the 1st upper labial and crossing the mouth onto the 1st lower labial. The rostral is outlined on either side and on its lower border by deep olive-buff. The under part of the head is white or marguerite yellow except for the mental and first 5 lower labials, which are deep olive or fuscous. The iris is mummy brown or black. On the forward part of the body, the venter is almost clear light chalcedony yellow. Toward the middle of the body, the rear edges of the plates are deep olive or fuscous, while in the caudal half of the body, these appear more or less as 2 rows of elliptical fuscous spots, one on either side of the belly.

Young. A snake from Okefinokee Swamp, Folkston, Ga., taken Aug. 12, 1922. The back is marked with olivaceous black rhombs edged with pale olive-buff. The sides are deep grayish olive, becoming toward the ends of the ventral plates, light grayish olive or smoke gray. The top of the head is iron gray with a black stripe below the eye bordered on either side by white facial stripes. Other white stripes occur on snout and underside of head. The iris is black with pale smoke gray or smoke gray. The venter is pale medici blue, but with payne's gray spots on one or both ends of the scutes.

Habitat: Because this snake occurs in the Sabalian zone or the Gulf Strip of the Austral zone, or the Low or Swampy Coastal region of the Southeast, some might wish to adopt the old common name of "water rattle" or "water rattlesnake." Several authors place them along ordinary or wild sea beaches, edges of bayous, low wet savannas, damp places, a heap of debris at the base of cypress, pine swamps, hummocks along the margins of a gum swamp. Several have recorded them on coastal islands and noted their swimming abilities, their floating seaward on mats of water hyacinth or swimming from key to key. We ourselves have known them to be in water prairies, but most records place them in dry sandy land of longleaf pine with undergrowth of grass, fern, and palmetto. They frequently live in gopher-turtle holes and other animal burrows. They enjoy the cover of logs and palmetto bushes.

Breeding: Viviparous. *Young*—Number, 7–18. Ditmars (Gen., 1907) recorded 7–12; Wright and Bishop 15; Van Hyning (Fla., 1931) 14; Conant and Bridges (Gen., 1939) 7–18; Schmidt and Davis (Gen., 1941) 9 or 10–14; and Curran (Gen., 1935) 6–12. Size, about 14 inches long.

Our knowledge of this common form is still disgracefully meager. Stejneger wrote about it almost 60 years ago, "little detailed and reliable information concerning its habits can be found in the literature."

Most writers agree with Safford "that these rattlesnakes let their little ones shift for themselves as soon as they come into the world." Doubtless this is more or less correct, yet see in "Field notes" below experience with 15 young, and note Van Hyning's (Fla., 1931) experience: *"Crotalus adamanteus* (Beauvois). On August 21, 1925, 14 young diamond-back rattlesnakes were dug out of the hole of a 'gopher,' *Gopherus polyphemus* (Daudin), 5 miles west of Gainesville, Florida. A large rattler had been seen to enter the hole, and on digging out the burrow a few hours later, the 14 young were found, although the adult was gone. These young were kept for several weeks, and would take live mice, or dead ones that were still warm, provided they were pulled along the floor of the cage. Mice which had become cold were refused."

Food: Rodents, small mammals, birds. Allen and Slatten, Carr.

Venom and bite: Mankind and all his livestock are the enemies of rattlers. In 1915 Wright and Bishop discussed this topic in relation to Okefinokee Swamp: "This largest of our poisonous snakes proves a serious economic factor to the inhabitants of Okefinokee Swamp. The Lees assert that in 1910 alone they lost 10–15 head of hogs killed by this species and other rattlers. In some seasons the rattlers and bears combined compel the Lees to go outside the swamp for new hog stock. They further contend that hogs are not wholly immune, but that the hogs will eat dead rattlers, preferring the heads."

This large and dangerous reptile has been introduced to us as formidable. It is not usually aggressive, but it is powerful and dangerous.

Githens and George found that some of our largest rattlesnakes, those with the greatest quantities of venom, are less potent than some smaller species.

Blatchley (Fla., 1931) wrote: "Although I have tramped far and wide in the country about Dunedin during the past 12 years, I have never happened upon a large living diamond rattlesnake until this spring. . . . People are bitten by rattlesnakes in some part of Florida almost every year. Three have been bitten about Dunedin since I have had my winter home here, and two of them died within a few hours."

Allen, saved from death from rattlesnake bite by blood plasma, wrote, "According to Institute records, the mortality rate from the bite of this snake is 30%."

Field Notes: Aug. 12, 1922, Ga.: Tom Chesser yesterday about 2 P.M. found a 5½ foot female diamondback rattler resting about 1½ feet from hole under a stump root. A log ended 10 inches from the exposed root over the entrance to the den. It was a gopher hole. Tom espied the snake 15 feet to 20 feet away. Tom shot the snake. Dogs stayed away and were very wild. Bill, the young dog, was not afraid. After he killed the snake, Tom saw 3 young snakes at the hole. Under end of a log was a resting place for adult. By actual measurement the female *C. adamanteus* was 5 feet 7 inches. There were 15 young ones. Seldom struck at us. They were scattered from 2 to 3 inches from the entrance to the end of tunnel. Tunnel 5–6 feet long, not more than 2½ or 3 feet broad at lower end. The young were not belligerent at all. Cannot be very old. We lifted them all out into a botany drum.

Authorities:

Allen, E. R. (Gen., 1948)
Allen, E. R., and R. Slatten (Fla., 1945)
Bartram, W. (Gen., 1791)
Beyer, G. E. (La., 1900)
Brimley, C. S. (N.C., 1941–42)
Carr, A. F., Jr. (Fla., 1940a)
Clench, W. J. (Fla., 1925)
Ditmars, R. L. (Gen., 1907, 1930)
Githens, T. S., and I. D. George (Gen., 1931)
Gloyd, H. K. (Gen., 1940)
Hallinan, T. (Fla., 1923)
Holbrook, J. E. (Gen., 1836–42)
Loennberg, E. (Fla., 1895)
Metcalf, Z. P. (Gen., 1930)
Nehrling, H. (Fla., 1905)
Robinson, R. G. (Fla., 1896)
Rolfs, P. H. (Fla., 1893)
Safford, W. E. (Fla., 1919)
Snyder, R. C. (Ala., 1945b)
Stejneger, L. (Gen., 1895)
Van Hyning, O. C. (Fla., 1931, 1933)
Williams, I. B. (Fla., 1892)
Wright, A. H., and S. C. Bishop (Ga., 1916)

1821, John Grant Forbes: "The rattlesnake and the tail part of the alligator are sometimes eaten by the traveler."

1833, Jacob Peck: "The very broad head of this serpent, often 4 inches wide, and the great number of large and long teeth make him altogether the most formidable snake in appearance, and probably he is the most fatal in North America."

1835, a reviewer in *New Eng. Mag.,* **8:** 489: "Who told Mr. [William Gilmore] Simms that this gallant and honorable and peaceable reptile ever seeks his human victim? We happen to know, that he never assails any living thing but what he needs for food. He never strikes but when struck or menaced, and never without giving fair warning. We have a very considerable respect for so generous an enemy, and do not like to hear him slandered."

1919, W. E. Safford (Fla., 1919): "Dr. Byrd . . . composed an ode in their honor, which ends with the following . . . :

> Yet all thy virtues wrest from man no lays,
> Who sings of war and love, of bird and bee,
> And e'en of rusty toad, but not of thee.
> To thee he yields but hate or fear, not praise.
> Indifferent thou to hatred, fear or wrong,
> Content in jungle drear to seek thy food
> And make thy home and launch thy royal brood
> In solitude,—I grudge thee not a song.

Western diamond rattlesnake (22—Bailey 1913), Texas rattlesnake (18—Ditmars 1903)

Crotalus atrox Baird and Girard 1853. Fig. 271; Map 66

Other common names: Adobe or "dobe" snake; Arizona diamond rattlesnake; coon tail; desert diamond-back; desert diamond rattlesnake; diamondback (rattle)snake; diamond rattlesnake; fierce rattlesnake; prairie rattler; spitting rattlesnake; Texan rattlesnake; Texas diamond-back (rattlesnake); Texas diamond rattlesnake; western diamond-back (rattlesnake).

Range: W. cent. Arkansas and s.e. Kansas to New Mexico, extreme s. Colorado to s.e. Arizona; thence to extreme tip of Nevada; s. across s.e. California and n.e. Baja California, Mex., to Zacatecas, Mex.; thence n. through Texas w. of 95° longitude to Arkansas.—U.S.A.: Ariz.; Ark.; Calif.; Colo.; Kan.; N.M.; Nev.; Okla.; Tex. Mex.: Baja Calif. (Tiburón Island also); Chihuahua; Coahuila; Durango; Hidalgo; Nuevo León; San Luis Potosí; Sonora; Tamaulipas; Zacatecas. *Elevation*—Coast to 5,000 feet. 1,000 feet (Linsdale, Nev., 1938–40); "Colorado River to lower fringes of the desert foothills" (Klauber, Calif., 1931a); 2,800–4,000 feet (Humphrey, Ariz., 1936); 5,000 feet (Gloyd, Ariz., 1937a); 2,800, 3,400, 3,700, 4,000 feet (Humphrey); 7,000 feet (Taylor, Gen., 1952). Near Tucson in 1936, Humphrey wrote: "Desert diamond-backs were found commonly at an altitude varying from 2,800 feet in the Santa Cruz Valley to an upper limit of 3,400 feet on the better grassed areas and to as high as 4,000 feet on brushy areas where grass was scanty."

Size: Adults, 30–89 inches.

Longevity: 11 years 7 months (Perkins, Gen., 1948); 10 years 8 months (Conant and Hudson, Gen., 1949); 14 years 7 months (Perkins, Gen., 1951);

6 years 8 months (Conant and Hudson); 17 years 7 months (Perkins, Gen., 1954).

Distinctive characteristics: Distinguished from *C. adamanteus* "by absence of light vertical line in front of the nostril, by the absence of sharply defined angles to the dorsal spots, and by the strongly contrasted half rings on the tail. . . . Size rather less than *adamanteus,* but form and scutellation very similar; the supraoculars are sometimes, but not always, bordered internally by a row of enlarged scales; rows of scales between supraoculars often 4 but sometimes 5 or 6" (Brown, Gen., 1901).

Color: A young snake. Forward rhombs snuff brown or light brownish olive, becoming buffy brown on rear. Each rhomb outlined with black and then white. Spaces forward smoke gray or pale smoke gray. Spaces on the rear third deep olive-buff. Alternating with the rhombs are indistinct grayish olive patches. Then on the 2nd, 3rd, and 4th rows of scales at intervals, 2 or 3 scales are blackish. These groups may come opposite rhombs or sometimes opposite the grayish olive patches. Top of head smoke gray; side of head grayish olive. A white line runs from rear of eye to angle of mouth, and an oblique white line from preocular to upper labials and along labials to angle of mouth to join first one. The space between these lines and just back of the caudal white line is grayish olive. Top of head from supraoculars forward is deep grayish olive or grayish olive. The rear half of body has quite a yellowish cast. Four black rings on tail, 3 interspaces pale gull gray or white. Pupil vertical; iris clear olive-buff above, same color in front and behind, heavily spotted with black dots. Belly is smoke gray, in rear becoming charged on the sides with colonial buff.

Abnormal coloration—Many varied colors, from gray to pink or reddish, appear in this species. For notes on cinereous to erythristic colorations, see Klauber's several papers and Gloyd (Ariz., 1937a).

Habitat: These snakes have been reported in sandy country, deserts, sheltered recesses among limestone rocks, dense cactus and thorny thickets, on plains and slopes, in scrap piles on edges of many western towns, on mesquite barrens, among boulders in foothills, in grassy and brushy areas, mesquite groves, and semidesert and arid areas. Distinctly, this is a snake of the lower levels, a truly Lower Sonoran species which, like most rattlesnakes, will die in 7–12 minutes of direct exposure to the sun.

Locomotion—Mosauer wrote: "[Caterpillar movement] is applied extensively by the big *Crotalus atrox.* The track is a wide band with longitudinal stripes, looking as if something had been dragged over the sand. No marks of the ventral scutes are visible. Where the snake has been travelling downhill or on the level, the track may be fairly straight, indicating that the rattler has slowly crept along like a gigantic caterpillar."

Period of activity: *Early appearances*—Apr. 2, 14, 25, 26, May 8, 1925 (A.H.W.); Apr. 4, 1920 (Cowles, Calif., 1920); (Strecker, 1928b); Apr.–

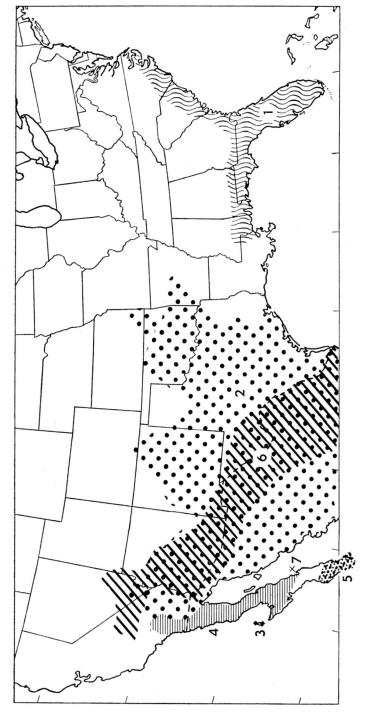

Map 66. *Crotalus*—1, *adamanteus*; 2, *atrox*; 3, *exsul*; 4, *r. ruber*; 5, *r. lucasensis*; 6, *s. scutulatus*; 7, *tortugensis*.

May 15, 1910, Apr. 11, 1912 (Van Denburgh and Slevin, Ariz., 1913); Apr. 18, 1932 (Perkins and Lentz); May 25, 1893 (Van Denburgh and Slevin, Ariz., 1897). *Fall disappearance*—Aug. 6–24, 1906 (Ruthven); Aug. 17, 1912 (Strecker); Aug. 23, Sept. 14, 1912 (Van Denburgh and Slevin); Aug. 30, 1925 (A.H.W.); Sept., Oct. 1893, 1894 (Van Denburgh, Baja Calif., 1895a); Oct. 2, 1932 (Mosauer, Calif., 1933); Oct. 28, 30, 1927 (Linsdale, Baja Calif., 1932); Nov. 4 (Sanger).

Hibernation—Many of the accounts of rattlesnakes in newspapers and magazines, and much current lore, relate to great multitudes of snakes seen around some denning area, either in the spring or fall. Concerning Texas dens, Mitchell wrote: "As cool weather approaches, rattlers drift to the bay bluff where there are fissures and holes made by water; or to some well drained ridge where holes are dug by small animals, and at first frost enter these holes and pass the winter in a torpid condition. They are neither selfish nor select in their company, in winter quarters, as will be seen by the contents of some of the dens I have dug out. . . . No. 3. On bank of Carancahua Bay, Calhoun County, contained 1 cottontail, 1 skunk, 2 coachwhips, and 7 rattlers. The rabbit had just been run into the den by a hawk; the snakes were each coiled to itself and quite stiff and were lifted out like blocks of wood." In 1936 Humphrey of Tucson reported, "A winter den of this species, which has been occupied for at least the last 4 winters, is located at an altitude of 3,700 feet."

In his "Reptiles of the south and southwest in folklore," Strecker (1926g) discussed this topic at length. So too have Mitchell and Sanger, each of Texas, and Humphrey (1936) of Arizona.

Breeding: Viviparous. *Mating*—No topic in crotalid behavior has aroused more interest among herpetologists than that of "courtship dance versus combat dance." In 1936 Perkins and Davis and in 1942 the Carrs observed ophidian dance behavior, but the first record for this species was in 1942, when Lowe recorded in detail the "courtship dance" of a supposed male and female. What puzzled him was a similar dance between two males. He wrote, "It is difficult to interpret the dance of the two males." In 1948 Lowe concluded he was mistaken in calling one observed couple a pair. "For various reasons, observers have not always sexed the 'dance' participants. . . . Thus far we observe the following facts: (1) Dancing pairs have never been seen to copulate. (2) Copulating pairs have never been observed to dance. (3) Participants, when adequately checked for sex, have always been males." At the same time Shaw reported combat dancing of two *Crotalus ruber* males from Dec. 21 to Jan. 31.

At about the time these two papers and Gloyd's Nov. 1947 paper appeared, another such dance was observed in Webb County by 3 Dallas men (Earl Cratu, Lester Godwin, Jr., and Oscar Chambers) with cameras 5 and 6–8 feet away. One snake, a 5-foot 11-inch rattler, they secured; the other escaped into a packrat's den. Read the Dallas *Morning News,* Jan. 16, 1949, for a thrilling but worth-while account headlined "Dallas Trio Witnesses Rare Spectacle: Rattlesnake Courtship or Death Battle." The evidence now points to the interpretation that the dance is territorial combat between two males.

Mating season. Customarily we have thought of the spring as the only mating season, particularly with these denning species, but our opinions have had to be changed. Spring is one of the mating seasons. Beyer received from San Antonio, Tex., 7 *Crotalus atrox,* 6 of which were adults. Mating took place between one pair May 14. But mating may also take place from January on, immediately on emergence from hibernation, and may be frequent in March and April. An example was reported by Perkins and Lentz after visiting a den in Arkansas on Apr. 18 and 19, 1932. Of part of the second day they wrote: "They seemed to be running in pairs this day. . . . Shortly after a pair was found on another mountain slope in the process of court-ship. The male was the smaller of the two. He paid no attention to us when we disturbed them. The female was lifted clear of the male and taken about 15 feet away. At her departure the male became very excited, and crawled rapidly in her direction. We moved her about several times, and each time the male would crawl towards her as fast as he could. Upon reaching her he would continue his amorous tactics. Our presence seemed to make little difference to him, for he would crawl towards us, or even between our legs, without rattling or assuming an aggressive attitude. After being disturbed the female tried to escape. Of 10 *C. atrox* caught on this and a suc-ceeding day 8 were found in pairs, 1 in association with a pair, and 1 singly."

We now know that many forms also mate in fall or at other times than in the spring. Taylor wrote: "On August 19, 1930, David M. Gorsuch of the Gambel Quail Investigation, University of Arizona, found a pair of *Crotalus atrox* copulating."

Young—As Schmidt and Davis (Gen., 1941) remarked, "Few records of number of young are available." Number, 4-25. 4, 23 (Conant and Bridges); 8 (Gloyd, Klauber); 8, 12, 18 (Mitchell); 10, 20 (Schmidt and Davis); 10, 12, 20 (Werler); 11 (Wiley); 12 (Ditmars); 16, 24 (Marr); 18 (Taylor); 46? (*Science Digest*). In conversations and correspondence, we have learned of records of 6-25 young. Marr (Gen., 1944) said: "A specimen from Pecos Co. Apr. 24, contained 24 eggs, and one from Howard Co. May 4 had 16 eggs." Size, 9-13 inches. Most writers report 12 inches or 1 foot. Klauber (Gen., 1937, IV) gave a range of 231-243 mm. for an unborn brood, but he gave an estimated average length at birth as 310 mm. (1938, V). In 1887 Garman reported: "The young are less than 10 inches in length at the time of extrusion." In 1937 Gloyd (Ariz., 1937a) reported a brood (July 31) of 8, of which 3 males measured 280, 290, 295 mm. and 5 females 293, 293, 287, 288, 301 mm. Werler (Gen., 1951) recorded that a female gave birth to 10 young 214-316 mm. long.

Food: Largely rodents, also birds. Ditmars (Gen., 1907), Ruthven, Mitchell, Boulenger (Gen., 1915), Marr, Wiley, Klauber (Calif., 1934a).

That "great lover of animals," Grace Olive Wiley, was probably the first to breed this species in captivity. Two captives were mated on Dec. 29, 1924, and 5 months and 16 days later, on June 4, 11 young were born. She wrote: "The young rattlers were fed on small bits of raw beef and liver until they were three weeks old, as no small mice were available."

Venom: Being widespread, and large, with large fangs, this is our most dangerous snake. More people have suffered from its bite than from that of any other species. Fortunately, our largest rattlesnake does not have the most potent venom, but enough people die from its bite to warrant advising outdoor people to be always on the alert. Wear good leather or canvas protection on your legs.

Contrary to some observations that crotalid snakes bitten by themselves or other crotalid snakes do not suffer harmful effects, Nichol, Douglas, and Peck (Ariz., 1933) reported cases in which *C. atrox* suffered death from bites of other *C. atrox,* died from biting itself, and died when injected with *C. atrox* venom. In 1939 Wolff and Githens (Gen., 1939) alluded to Klauber's "extraction of 3.9 cc. with 1.145 grams dry vemon from a Texas diamondback." In 1946 Swanson (Gen.) injected 21 minims of *C. atrox* venom into a 1,016-mm. *C. atrox;* 26 hours 50 minutes later it was dead.

Authorities:

Baird, S. F., and C. Girard (Gen., 1853)
Beyer, G. E. (La., 1898)
Campbell, H. (N.M., 1950)
Crimmins, M. L. (Tex., 1931)
Ditmars, R. L. (Gen., 1907, 1930)
Garman, S. (Tex., 1887)
Gloyd, H. K. (Gen., 1940, 1947; Ariz., 1937a)
Klauber, L. M. (Gen., 1938; Calif., 1929)
Lowe, C. H., Jr. (Gen., 1948; Calif., 1942)
Marr, J. C. (Gen., 1944)
Mitchell, J. D. (Tex., 1903)
Mosauer, W. (N.M., 1932; Calif., 1933)
Nichol, A. A., V. Douglas, and L. Peck (Ariz., 1933)
Ortenburger, A. I., and R. D. (Ariz., 1927)
Perkins, R. M., and M. J. R. Lentz (Ark., 1934)
Ruthven, A. G. (Ariz., 1907)
Sanger, D. B. (Tex., 1931)
Strecker, J. K., Jr. (Gen., 1926g; Tex., 1928b)
Taylor, W. P. (Ariz., 1935)
Wiley, G. O. (Gen., 1929a)

1903, J. D. Mitchell (Tex.): "The flesh of the rattlesnake is white and palatable, very much resembling the breast of quail in look and flavor. The oil makes a fine foundation for a liniment, and is used by old ranchmen on sore-backed horses; and it is claimed to be a specific for rheumatism."

1944, A. H. and A. A. Wright: Only someone who has taught systematic zoology for 40 years can appreciate how *atrocious* the term *C. cinereous* is for *C. atrox.* If repeatedly through the years one has had to correct (*Ancistrodon*)

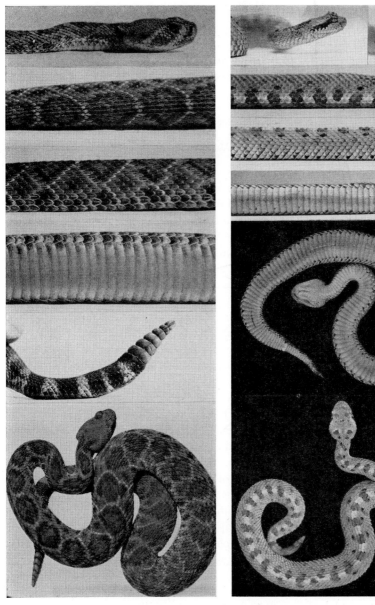

Fig. 271. *Crotalus atrox,* Waco, Tex., E. Johnson through L. T. Murray.

Fig. 272. *Crotalus cerastes cerastes,* Pasadena, Calif., R. Cowles.

piscivorous to *piscivorus,* (*Fundulus*) *diaphanous* to *diaphanus,* (*Plethodon*) *cinereous* to *cinereus,* and similar specific adjectival mistakes in Latin endings, he will rebel at *C. cinereous.* It is brought to our attention by one of our most excellent students of herpetology of the last 40 years. We can't believe any member of the classically trained family of Le Conte meant it for a specific name.

Sidewinder (57—Yarrow 1882), **Mojave Desert sidewinder**

Crotalus cerastes cerastes Hallowell 1854. Fig. 272; Map 67

Other common names: Horned rattlesnake (30—Cronise 1868); sidewinder rattlesnake.

Range: Desert areas from n.e. Los Angeles and San Bernardino Cos., Calif., northward to s. Mono Co., Calif., e. across Nevada to Washington Co., Ut., s. through Mojave Co., Ariz.—Ariz.; Calif.; Nev.; Ut. *Elevation*—500 to 6,000 feet. Desert lowlands (Gloyd, Ariz., 1937); 4,000, 4,050, 4,200, 5,300, 5,900, 6,000 feet (Linsdale); 2,100–3,300 feet (Johnson, Bryant, Miller, Calif., 1948).

Size: Adults, 17–30 inches.

Distinctive characteristics: "Proximal lobe of rattle matrix brown in adults; scale rows usually 21; ventrals in males 141 or less, and in females 144 or less. . . . Ground color fawn to light-brown. Punctations smaller and less evident. Dorsal blotches and postocular dark streak red-brown to dark-brown, sharply outlined" (Klauber, Ariz., 1944b).

Color: A young snake from Los Angeles or Pasadena, Calif., received from R. B. Cowles, July 4, 1929. Down the middle of the back are 30–32 transverse bars 4 scales wide with centers old gold or isabella color and with black or olive borders. A spot on either side of occiput is of same color or buffy olive or buffy citrine. Interspaces between dorsal spot are light—cartridge buff or pale olive-buff. Top of head and sides of body below dorsal transverse spots are vinaceous-buff or avellaneous. Stripe from eye backward a short distance is old gold with prominent black border below. Some of the scales below this border have black tips. Upper jaw from eye back is sea shell pink or shrimp pink. Iris is same color as postocular stripe with pale olive-buff area around pupil, particularly above. Belly white. Along either side of belly on ends of ventrals are black spots spaced every other scale of the 1st row or 1 in 3.

Metachrosis—Klauber and Neill remark the ability of sidewinders to display different coloration dependent on temperature.

Habitat: This snake frequents the lower Sonoran deserts of the Colorado River, occurring in open deserts with no vegetation, also in brushy deserts and in the floating sand hills. It may inhabit level tracts of loose sandy soil or, at times, rocky or sandy banks of the Colorado River. All in all, it is a dry sandy desert species.

Locomotion—Cowles described its mode of progression as follows: "The 'Side-Winder,' *Crotalus cerastes,* instead of progressing as do ordinary snakes, longitudinally, progresses laterally, leaving separate tracks, each paralleling the other, and angling in the direction in which the snake is moving. Each track is approximately the length of the snake making it, and is wavy, that is a series of 'S' shaped loops. The tracks give no sign of any part of the body moving from one mark to the other, which gives the impression that the snake jumps the 3 to 6 inch interval between the tracks. Such is not the case, however. When the snake is moving, the body is kept partially looped, and the advance seems to be through the advancing of the head and tail, while the rest of the body is rested on the intervening loop, supporting the rest of the body; the weight then seems to be shifted to the head and tail . . . and the rest of the body advanced, the whole progression being a series of graceful and continuous movements." See also Ditmars (Calif., 1923) for a description of the sidewinder's locomotion.

Period of activity: *Early appearances*—Mar. 11, Apr. 3, 6, 22, 23, 24, 28, 29, May 29, 31, June 7 (Stejneger, Calif., 1893); Apr. 1, 1920 (Cowles); Apr. 11–15, 1931, Apr. 22–26, 1932 (Klauber, Calif., 1932), May 12, 1929 (Bogert).

Breeding: Viviparous. *Mating*—Merriam (Stejneger, Calif., 1893) in his memorable account of a Death Valley expedition observed: "During the latter part of April and the early part of May these rattlesnakes were often found in pairs and were doubtless mating." Van Denburgh (Gen.) in 1922 recorded that "Mr. Slevin found a pair mating under a bush on the desert west of Barstow, San Bernardino County, California, at about 5 o'clock in the afternoon, during the last week of April, 1913." Lowe reported that on Oct. 11, 1941, a pair of sidewinders collected near Indio, Coachella Valley, Calif., were found mating in one of the snake pits of the University of California at Los Angeles.

Young—Number 7–13. Size, 161–169 mm. Time of birth, Sept.–Oct. In 1944 Klauber recorded that a female had given birth to 10 young on Oct. 15, 1939.

Food: Lizards, mice. Stejneger (Gen., 1895), Camp, Woodbury, Klauber (Calif., 1932), Cowles and Bogert (Nev., 1936).

Authorities:

Bogert, C. M. (Calif., 1930)
Camp, C. L. (Calif., 1916)
Cope, E. D. (Gen., 1900)
Cowles, R. B. (Calif., 1920)
Cronise, T. F. (Calif., 1868)
Ditmars, R. L. (Gen., 1930; Calif., 1923)
Grinnell, J., and C. L. Camp (Calif., 1917)
Hallowell, E. (Gen., 1859; Calif., 1857)

Klauber, L. M. (Gen., 1943a; Ariz., 1944b; Calif., 1932)
Linsdale, J. M. (Nev., 1938–40)
Lowe, C. H. (Calif., 1942)
Meek, S. E. (Calif., 1905)
Stejneger, L. (Gen., 1895; Calif., 1893)
Van Denburgh, J. (Gen., 1897, 1922)
Woodbury, A. M. (Ut., 1931)
Yarrow, H. C., and E. D. Cope (Ariz., 1875)

Colorado Desert sidewinder (Klauber and Perkins)

Crotalus cerastes laterorepens Klauber 1944. Fig. 273; Map 67

Range: Desert areas from cent. and e. Riverside Co., Calif., to Pinal Co., Ariz.; s. to n.w. Sonora; Mex., n.w. to n.e. Baja California, Mex., Imperial and n.e. San Diego cos., Calif.—U.S.A.: Ariz.; Calif. Mex.: Baja Calif.; Sonora. *Elevation*—500 to 2,000 feet; Colorado River to the desert foothills including isolated sandy areas in foothills at least to altitude of 1,900 feet (Klauber, Calif., 1931a); 2,200 feet (Stephens, Calif., 1918); 2,550 feet (Kauffeld).

Size: Adults, 17–31 inches.

Longevity: 11 years 8 months (Perkins, Gen., 1954).

Distinctive characteristics: "Proximal lobe of rattle-matrix black in adults; scale rows usually 23; ventrals exceed 141 in males, and 144 in females. . . . Ground color ivory to tan. Punctations, heavy and conspicuous. Dorsal blotches and post-ocular dark streak yellowish to brownish olive, indefinitely outlined" (Klauber, Ariz., 1944b).

Color: Snake from Tucson, Ariz., from S. C. Bishop, May 1, 1936. Dorsum is avellaneous, vinaceous-buff, or light vinaceous-cinnamon; scales on first 3 or 4 rows light ochraceous-salmon. Along middle row of scales are 2 or 3 scales of buckthorn brown. On 3rd row of scales below middle row is a row of olive-brown or deep olive spots with 3 or 4 scales separating each 2. On scale row 5 is another, and on row 1 is a third. In caudal half of body this 1st row of spots is diagonally connected more or less with those of row 5, making rather indistinct vertical or oblique bars on the side. There are 6 or 7 indistinct buckthorn brown crossbands on the dorsum ahead of vent, 1 of the same color on the rump and also 1 on the tail; there are 3 black ones, counting black at base of rattle. Stripe on side of head from eye to above angle of mouth is buckthorn brown or old gold. On top of head back of eye level and in middle are 2 ochraceous-tawny or buckthorn brown spots; back of these 1 spot; back of this to either side is a large spot, i.e., a pair; otherwise head has color of back or pale ochraceous-salmon. Iris same color as head with dusky specking of deep olive. Underside of head and 1st third of ventrals white; the rest pale ochraceous-buff.

Habitat: Similar to *C. c. cerastes;* possibly more varied in its haunts. It is nocturnal or crepuscular, withdrawing early into animal holes, usually long before 9 or 10 A.M.

In 1932 Mosauer and Lazier experimented with death from insolation (also experienced by our specimens in 1925). In his "Sixteen Year Census" Klauber (Gen., 1939a) gave 28 from desert foothills and 123 from the desert. He also gave as ecological conditions: cultivated field 1, rocky desert 2, brushy desert 16, sandy desert 15, barren desert 26. Total 60.

In 1944 Cowles and Bogert outlined the thermal requirements of this

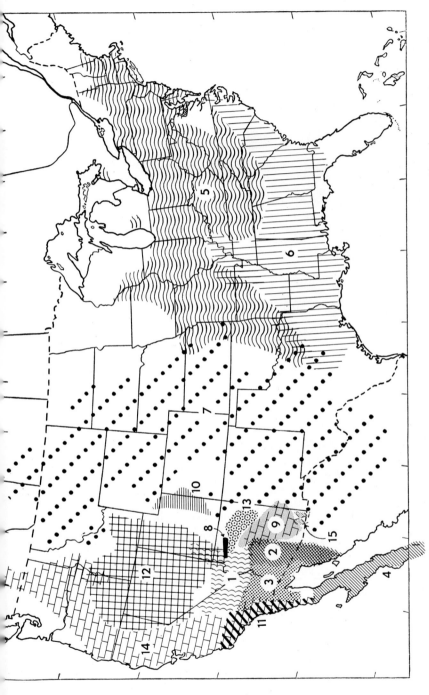

Map 67. *Crotalus*—1, *c. cerastes*; 2, *c. cercobombus*; 3, *c. laterorepens*; 4, *enyo*; 5, *h. horridus*; 6, *h. atricaudatus*; 7, *v. viridis*; 8, *v. abyssus*; 9, *v. cerberus*; 10, *v. decolor*; 11, *v. helleri*; 12, *v. lutosus*; 13, *v. nuntius*; 14, *v. oreganus*; 15, *w. willardi*.

Fig. 273. *Crotalus cerastes:* 1–5,7 *(cerco-bombus),* Tucson, Ariz., S. C. Bishop; 6 *(la-terorepens),* Colorado Desert near Tin Horn, Calif.

species. They found it more tolerant of cold than *C. atrox.* "Normally, activity is not initiated until temperatures between 17.5° and 19.5°C. are attained. . . . The body temperature was repeatedly found to vary between the limits of 31° and 32°C., with a mean of 31.4°C. The maximum tolerated temperature recorded in the cages was 34.5°C. When forced to do so, these snaked endured body temperatures as high as 37°C. . . . The critical maximum is reached at a body temperature of 41.6°C. while death has resulted from a body temperature of 42.5°C."

In 1945(a) Cowles made some observations on whether the sidewinder buries itself, "holes up," or is covered by wind-drifted sands. He inclined to the third possibility but observed one case of apparent self-submersion.

Locomotion: Long known to Arizonians as sidewinders, these snakes progress sidewise. Mosauer (Calif., 1932) contrasted the locomotion with that of *Cerastes* of the Sahara. Perkins has also described this "unique method of locomotion." Klauber (Ariz.) in 1944(b) gave a diagram "showing the consecutive positions of the snake's body in relation to the tracks."

As the result of measuring the speed of 6 forms Mosauer (Calif., 1935) found the sidewinder second fastest. He concluded that "the sidewinder does not seem to become fatigued as rapidly as the other species, a fact which agrees well with the extensive ramblings of this desert rattler."

Period of activity: *Early appearances*—Mar. 15, 17, 1912 (Hurter, Calif., 1912); Mar. 26, 29, Apr. 12, 17, 30, 1926 (Linsdale); Apr. 19, 1936, Apr. 24, 1943 (Klauber, Ariz., 1944b); Apr. 27, 1930, May 4, 1929 (Ross, Calif., 1931).

The "Sixteen Year Census" recorded *Crotalus cerastes* taken per month as: Jan., 0; Feb., 1 snake; Mar., 2; Apr., 29; May, 64; June, 23; July, 16; Sept., 10; Oct., 5; Nov., 1. Total, 151. Rank 17. Per cent, 1.17 (Klauber, Gen., 1939a). *Fall disappearance*—Aug. 20, 1930 (Gloyd, Ariz., 1937a); Sept. 12, 16, 1912 (Van Denburgh, Calif., 1912a); Sept. 25, 1938 (Klauber, 1944b); Oct. 18, 1941 (Stebbins).

Hibernation—In 1941 Cowles reported expecting to see large numbers of this snake turned up in grading operations, but he only took 3, 2 of them on Feb. 24. Not until April did they voluntarily appear. Except for these 3, tracks were not seen before April. Did they hibernate deeper than 6 to 8 feet? Cowles held this assumption tenable, but thought that possibly the disturbed snakes were reburied and continued in semihibernation to April.

Breeding: Viviparous. *Aggressive behavior*—Lowe and Norris reported an aggressive display made by 2 male sidewinders Apr. 25, 1949. The behavior follows closely the pattern that has been described for other pit vipers. At the climax of the fight each vigorously struck the other in the neck; fangs were employed. "It appears beyond reasonable doubt that such behavior is a manifestation of competition involving, as may be (1) territoriality, (2) social domination, or (3) sexual domination."

Sexual dimorphism—Differing from other rattlers, the female of this species exceeds the male in size. Klauber (Gen., 1936–40, IV) gave average length of male as 537 mm., female 556 mm. He also recorded 10 large males 602–665 mm. and 10 large females 601–767 mm. The smallest gravid female was 434 mm.

Mating—In Baja California, Linsdale recorded that "two were found March 26 lying together on the open desert." Lowe (Calif., 1942) reported observing fall mating "on a recent field trip to Red Rock Canyon, Kern County, California, on the morning of September 20, 1941. A class . . . of Dr. R. B. Cowles encountered a peculiar snake track, consisting of complicated superimposed markings in loose sand which ended in a hole. There was no indication of the identity of the snakes, but upon excavation of the hole a pair of horned rattlesnakes was found." (Time, 7:30–8:00 A.M.)

In 1944(b) Klauber (Ariz.) wrote: "I have found two mating pairs of *laterorepens*. The first was on April 21, 1935, in mesquite sand hills . . . at 9 A.M. on a clear warm day. . . . The second pair was found 8:50 P.M. May 6, 1939, on a branch road up Fargo Canyon, Little San Bernardino Mountains."

Young—Number, 5–16. Time of birth, Sept. 10–November. Size, 169–189 mm. In 1937 Klauber (Gen., 1937, IV) gave the smallest specimen measured as 192 mm. In 1937 he (Gen., 1937, IV) gave the length at birth as 200 mm. In 1944b he gave the following records of young: Nov. 4, 1937, 6 young, 176–187 mm., mean 182 mm.; female with 7 young 165–183 mm., mean 176 mm.; Nov. 28, 1942, 5 young, 172–189 mm., mean 179 mm. In nature he believes they are born from Sept. 10 to Oct. 1. On record are clutches of 6, 7, 8, 8, 11, and 16 eggs.

Food: Lizards, small mammals, insects. Van Denburgh and Slevin, Van Denburgh (Gen., 1922), Klauber (Calif., 1931a), Perkins.

Venom: Vorhies says that this form "has the reputation of being a very dangerous reptile due perhaps to agility and a vicious temperament. It is not likely that its poison is different in quality or quantity from that of other rattlers." In 1930 Hutchinson found that of 8 species reported in the order of their importance as agents in snakebite poisoning, the sidewinder occupied 7th place, with 5 bites in 1928 and 2 in 1929, while *A. mokasen* was in first place with 171 and 137. Some of these bites we might question because of looseness in the use of the term sidewinder in the Southwest. In 1931 Githens and George found *C. cerastes* intermediate in relative potency, *lepidus* most potent (0.01 MLD dried venom killed a pigeon), *ruber* less potent (0.6), and *cerastes* still less (0.12). In 1934(a) Klauber (Calif.) said: "It is not so dangerous as most people believe, the bite being much less effective than that of other species of the area, which being larger, have more venom. However, it is not to be trifled with." In 1938 Perkins declared that "this is the least dangerous of the rattlers in the county, but nevertheless is dangerously poisonous and should be avoided."

Enemies: In 1938 Cowles published an interesting article on unusual defense postures of rattlesnakes, specifically *C. atrox* and *C. cerastes* in the presence of a king snake. "This consists of the formation of a broad loop or bend in the body which is then lifted from the ground. Approximately ¼ to ⅓ of the body can be elevated from this position, and the loop is then used as a human being would use an elbow in striking a heavy blow. As the snake approaches, the rattlesnake strikes downward with such force as to render the blow a very effective defensive mechanism." He also found that the rattlesnakes began rattling at the approach of a skunk skinner and assumed the above posture as he came closer.

Field notes: Aug. 13, 1925, Tin Horn Peg's Place, Calif.: At end of plank road, camped 1 mi. beyond. Chased sidewinder trails. Started at 6:30, found our snake by 7:15. Started over desert looking for rat holes and the winder trail—a series of parallel marks (S S S) like a tractor trail. There is a curl on one end which is the tail curl. We worked in an area where the creature had coiled and rested in several places and were perplexed to know what hole he was in. In many instances the belly plate imprints show beautifully. We went out to photograph these resting coils and trails. When right near the car, we discovered what looked to be our best chance for digging one out. When we returned, about 6 ft. from the entrance to the hole I broke in. With my miner's pick, I started digging back toward the entrance hole. About 2 feet of digging brought the pick right into the snake. This burrow where the snake was, was no more than 2–3 inches below the surface. The coil from the night previous was about 1½ ft. from the entrance and the snake had drawn into the hole no more than 3 feet. He certainly is one of the most spirited rattlesnakes we have met. Some of the men at Tin Horn say that along the plank road you can find plenty of trails, but D. E. Hunt ("Peg") says that they are more numerous from Tin Horn to Holtsville where there are more rats. Has caught a lot of them at Tin Horn and has given them away to various people. He did it to make the place safer. The way to hunt them is to go out when it is cool about evening and locate trails, then go out in the morning just at daybreak and usually one finds them coiled 6 in.–1½ ft. from hole. Follow trail toward the hook as they travel that way.

Authorities:

Baird, S. F. (Tex., 1859)

Cope, E. D. (Gen., 1900; Ariz., 1866a)

Cowles, R. B. (Gen., 1938, 1941a; Calif., 1945a)

Cowles, R. B., and C. M. Bogert (Gen., 1944)

Githens, T. S., and I. D. George (Gen., 1931)

Gloyd, H. K. (Gen., 1940; Ariz., 1937a)

Grinnell, J., and C. L. Camp (Calif., 1917)

Hensley, M. M. (Ariz., 1950)

Kauffeld, C. F. (Ariz., 1943)

Klauber, L. M. (Gen., 1939a, 1943a; Ariz., 1932a, 1944b; Calif., 1931a, 1934a)

Linsdale, J. M. (Baja Calif., 1932)

Lowe, C. H., Jr., and K. S. Norris (Calif., 1950)

Meek, S. E. (Calif., 1905)

Mosauer, W. (Calif., 1932, 1933, 1935)

Mosauer, W., and E. L. Lazier (Calif., 1933)

Perkins, C. B. (Calif., 1938)

Stebbins, R. C. (Calif., 1943)

Stejneger, L. (Gen., 1895)

Van Denburgh, J. (Gen., 1897, 1922)

Van Denburgh, J., and J. R. Slevin (Ariz., 1913)

Vorhies, C. T. (Ariz., 1917)

1944(b): L. M. Klauber has described two races: *C. c. laterorepens* and *C. c. cerastes,* the first in the s. Colorado Desert and most of Arizona southward, the second in the Mojave Desert, Nevada, and Utah. This report is a distinctive contribution to the taxonomy and ecology of the sidewinders.

1944: A. H. and A. A. Wright and G. B. Upton, with a 16-inch wire loosely coiled and with twisted cloth on one end to represent the rattle, rolled it in loose flour or snow and duplicated the track, the length of each track being the length of the wire.

Sonoran sidewinder

Crotalus cerastes cercobombus Savage and Cliff

On Mar. 27, 1953, J. M. Savage and F. S. Cliff (Ariz., 1953) from the Natural History Museum of Stanford, established a new subspecies based on Stanford, Klauber, and Hensley material. The eastern half of what

Klauber considered *laterorepens* they pronounce a new form of *C. cerastes cercobombus* (buzzer tail). This occurs in Arizona in eastern Yuma, Maricopa, Pima, and Pinal Counties and southward into Sonora, Mex. We supply a diagnosis from their key (in *Nat. Hist. Misc. Chic. Acad. Sci.,* no. 119, pp. 1–7):

"1a Proximal rattle-matrix lobe black in adults.

"2a Ventrals in males 141 or less, in females 145 or less; dorsal scale rows usually 21 at midbody.   *C. c. cercobombus*

"2b Ventrals in males 142 or more, in females 146 or more; dorsal scale rows usually 23 at midbody.   *C. c. laterorepens*"

Rattlesnake (94—Wood 1634), Banded rattlesnake (98—Harlan 1827), Timber rattlesnake (71—Hay 1887)

Crotalus horridus horridus Linné 1758. Fig. 274; Map 67

Other common names: American viper; bastard rattlesnake; black rattlesnake; common (timber) rattlesnake; eastern rattlesnake; great yellow rattlesnake; mountain rattlesnake; mountain timber rattler; North American (horrid) rattlesnake; Northern banded rattlesnake (1—Gloyd 1940); northern rattlesnake; pit viper; rock rattlesnake; velvet tail; yellowish brown rattlesnake; yellow rattlesnake.

Range: N.e. United States and Ontario, Can.—from Maine to s.w. Wisconsin and s.e. Minnesota; s.w. through e. Iowa, s.e. Nebraska, e. Kansas, e. Oklahoma to n.e. Texas; thence n.e. along e. boundary of Ouachita Province and Ozark Plateau to s. Illinois and s.w. Indiana; thence s. on the w. boundary of the interior low plateau to n. Alabama and Georgia; through the Piedmont to Virginia.—U.S.A.: Conn.; D.C.; Del.; Ga.; Ia.; Ill.; Ind.; Kan.; Ky.; Mass.; Md.; Mich.; Minn.; Mo.; N.C.; Neb.; N.H.; N.J.; N.Y.; O.; Okla.; Pa.; R.I.; S.C.; Tenn.; Va.; Vt.; W. Va.; Wis. Can.: Ont. *Elevation*—500 to 5,500 feet. 1,000–5,500 feet (King, Tenn., 1939); 2,500, 3,800, 4,000 feet (Dunn, N.C., 1917); 400–1,046 feet (Norton, Me., 1929); 1,000–2,500 feet (McIntyre, N.Y., 1932); 1,500–2,400 feet (Smith, Pa., 1945); 2,750–4,000 feet (Barbour, Ky., 1950); 1,500–4,500 feet (Wood, Va., 1954).

Size: Adults, 33–74 inches. Hook's thesis (Cornell University, 1936) records a pair—a large male 1,070 mm. and a small female 835 mm. (33.4 inches).

Longevity: 13 years (Perkins, Gen., 1949); 13 years 7 months (Perkins, Gen., 1951); 15 years 7 months (Perkins, Gen., 1954).

Distinctive characteristics: "Dorsal scale rows usually 23; postocular dark stripe indistinct; no middorsal reddish brown stripe evident anteriorly; sometimes entirely black; no definite division or continuous suture between the scales of the frontal and prefrontal areas; scales in the anterior part of frontal area not conspicuously larger than those behind; normal pattern of chevron-shaped crossbands sometimes broken, or with the body all black; head larger; head length contained less than 25 times in adult body length; proximal rattle width contained in head length more than 2½ times" (Klauber, Gen., 1936).

There are two common color phases, black and yellow. Both are given in the following paragraphs.

Color: A snake from Bear Mountain Park, N.Y., caught July, 1936, and received from Claire Kelly. (Black phase.) The back is marked with 19–20 black saddles, the first 9 being incomplete chevrons. The 1st is formed by a pair of nuchal spots with a large black lateral spot just below each of them. Then follow 7 quadrate dorsal spots accompanied by similar lateral spots which may be 4 or more scales longitudinally. These are succeeded by 10 or 11 chevrons (i.e., the dorsal saddles and their corresponding lateral spots are united). These are about 4 scales long on middorsum and 1 scale long at the union with the lateral spot; the lateral spot may cover 3 scales longitudinally. These black chevrons and spots are irregularly and only partially outlined by scales tipped with straw yellow or ivory yellow. The lateral spots occur on the 1st to 5th rows of scales, becoming after the 8th or 9th spot the lateral portion of a chevron, but in every case extending onto the ventrals. On the 1st row of scales and on the ends of 2 to 4 ventrals is a row of less distinct alternating spots composed of heavy fleckings. Between the nuchal spots and between the succeeding 7 dorsal spots are areas 5 to 3 scales wide of isabella color. This color continues most of the way down the back as a middorsal band 3 scales wide between the chevrons. The interspace color below this middorsal band is brownish olive. The caudal quarter of the snake's length is almost uniform black. The head is solid black except for a thread of white extending backward on the lower edges of the upper labials from the labial adjacent to the nasal. The iris is black. The underside of the head is white somewhat flecked with black, and with the mental and lower labials black. The inner edges of the lower labials are slightly flecked with white. There are 2 pairs of black longitudinal patches on the underside of the head, the 1st on the anterior chin shields, the 2nd on the gulars. After the 7th ventral the venter becomes mustard yellow with a few black flecks on the rear edges of some of the plates. This color grades into naples yellow in mid-venter and extends thus to the vent. The whole venter except extreme forward portion is thickly speckled with black. The underside of the tail is solid black or sooty black.

A snake from Ten-Mile River Scout Camp, Camp Brooklyn, Narrowsburg, Sullivan Co., N.Y., caught August, 1937, and loaned by Lynn Bonner. (Yellow phase.) The dorsal spots are bister in the forward portion and fuscous in some of the rear chevrons. They are outlined wholly or in part with half scales or entire scales of reed yellow. There are 13 dorsal spots before chevrons are formed. The first 7 or 8 interspaces between dorsal spots bear a middorsal band of saccardo's umber about 7 scales wide. Thereafter the middorsal area has much the same color as the interval color of the sides, which is mostly buffy olive. The intervals in the 1st and 2nd scale rows are reed yellow. In this specimen there is no row of alternating spots on the 1st row of scales and ends of ventrals. The tail is black. The top of the head is buffy olive with the supraoculars saccardo's umber. The labials are deep colonial buff. The eye is clay color or tawny-olive. The underside of the head is white with a slight wash of deep colonial buff on the gulars. The venter is seafoam green with a narrow area of cream-buff down mid-venter.

Of the 37 timber rattlers that Axtell reported finding in Chemung Co., N.Y., 2 were black and 35 were yellow. Favorable habitats are scanty there, and the number of rattlers is small.

Abnormal coloration—Albinism is rare in this species. Two or 3 cases (Ditmars, Babcock, Ortenburger) have been reported. Melanism used to be regarded as a characteristic of the male only, but Netting (Pa., 1932) wrote: "Adult yellow or tan specimens are practically always females; black specimens are generally males, although black females are found occasionally." Gloyd (Gen., 1940) reported similarly. In 1935(b) Gloyd (Gen.) recorded a longitudinally striped individual.

Habitat: Probably every state in the U.S. has had at some time a Rattlesnake Mountain, Hill, Ledge, Bluff, or Point. Norton (Me., 1929) tells us that in 1925 the Maine legislature would not change the name "Rattlesnake Pond" as petitioned by some summer cottagers. Of the 28 or 29 rattlesnake states, some—but not Maine—had as many as 5–20 place names containing or consisting of the word rattlesnake.

Of more than 250 habitats on record, the first 4 named above (mountain, hill, ledge, and bluff) are the most frequent: 39 were from the mountains (31 mountains, plus mountainous regions 4, districts 2, areas 1, situations 1); hills appear 25 times (hills 19, hilly parts 1, country 1, rocky hills 1, higher hill country 1, wooded hillsides 1, wilder hill country 1); bluffs 12 times (limestone, dolomite, sandstone, and others); ledges 12 (broken, fireline rocky, timbered rocky, limestone). Several remarked that this form is not in beech-maple, white ash, or spruce-fir forests; it prefers oak lands, oak-pine woods, or oak-laurel-poplar-chestnut hills. Still one must remember exceptions, such as Barbour's virgin beech-maple-birch woodland at 3,000 feet, north slope. The form usually prefers a sunny warm southern exposure. Other natural habitats mentioned include berry patches, brambles, second-growth clearings, huckleberry, blueberry, and whortleberry areas, broken slopes, foothills, dry points of rocky ledges and ridges, wastelands, and prairies.

These snakes emerge from their dens and become active during the last of March or in April when the temperature approaches 70°F. On sunny warm slopes they linger until May and by mid-May leave their high, dry, rocky retreats and spread along the ridges into the timber and wander down to the lower lands, like foothills, the bases of precipices, and the flatlands. If need be, they swim creeks and rivers to reach good feeding grounds. In summer they may be found on river bars, river banks, bottom lands of linden, poplar, elm, etc., in meadows, open or brushy pastures, fields (open or growing hay, wheat, rye, corn, etc.), along hedgerows, in abandoned buildings, or at times near habitations, provided that rodents draw them.

Their habitats today are greatly restricted by man's activities. Settlements, the cultivation of fields, conflagrations, and man with all his improvements and livestock have much reduced them. At present many of our writers give habitats as follows: remote parts, rougher portions, unsettled mountainous districts, rough wooded hillsides, sparsely inhabited places, uninhabited areas, wildernesses, inaccessible spots seldom disturbed by man or unfrequented by man.

Where do they persist? If you wished to find a rattlesnake in Illinois, Wisconsin, Iowa, or Minnesota, you might seek the high bluffs of some of the larger rivers. If in Ontario, a Great Lakes point or a rocky ledge; if in Ohio, an island in Lake Erie; if in New Jersey, the northern mountains or, strangely enough, the wilder portions of the pine barrens or cedar or tamarack swamps with sphagnous cover. In New England each state except Maine has a few of this form—on wooded hills in Tiverton, R.I., a few mountains in Connecticut, the Blue Hills, Mt. Tom and the Berkshires in Massachusetts, an island and one or two more localities in New Hampshire, a few mountain retreats in Vermont. New York has a pocket or so along the New England border, at Lake George, in the Mohawk Valley, in two to four spots in the central part of the state, and rarely at Niagara. Today northern and mountainous Pennsylvania has more timber rattlers than any other state. Bluffs, ledges, points, mountains, islands, heavy timber are still their preferred habitats and their last resorts.

Contrast the following (Macauley, 1829, in New York) with conditions today: "They are found on Long Island and Manhattan Island; in some parts of the Highlands; around the head of Lake Champlain; at and around Lake George; at Glenville, in the county of Schenectady; at the Nose, in the county of Montgomery; along some parts of Unadilla and Susquehanna Rivers; at Lenox and Sullivan, in the county of Madison; at Manlius and Onondaga, in Onondaga County; in some parts of the county of Ontario; along Genesee and Niagara Rivers; and in many places in the Oak lands, between those rivers, and also east of the former; at several places along the Schoharie Creek; at the Helderberg, in the county of Albany; at Snake Hill, near Newberg, and in some other places. They have a predilection for oak lands."

Period of activity: *Early appearances*—Mar. 5, 1930 (Burt, Kan., 1933); Apr. 4, 26, May 18 (Hurter, Mo., 1911); Apr. 18, 1932 (Perkins and Lentz,

Ark., 1934); Apr. 29, 1938, May 1, 11, 1939 (Anderson, Mo., 1942); Apr. 23, 1928, Apr. 30, 1926, May 13, 1925 (Gloyd, Kan., 1928); Apr., 1929 (Gloyd, Kan., 1932). *Fall disappearance*—Aug. 30, 1923 (Bishop and Alexander, N.Y., 1927); Sept. 8, 13, 14, 20, 1941 (Anderson); Sept. and Oct. (Gloyd, Kan., 1932); Sept. 29, 1918 (Patch, Ont., 1919); Sept. 29, 1929 (Force, Okla., 1930); Oct. 3, 1932 (McIntyre); Oct., 1926, 1927, mid-Oct. (Gloyd, Kan., 1928); Sept. and Oct. (Gloyd, Kan., 1932).

Hibernation—There are numerous accounts of killings at the spring emergence from and fall entrance to the dens. Estimates of 50–1,000 snakes to a den have been made. Observations on dens have been recorded for a hundred years.

Breeding: Viviparous. *Mating*—In 1723 Dudley reported these snakes copulating in August. In 1827 Audubon said they mated in early spring. In 1936, in his thesis, Hook (N.J.) wrote, "It is thought that timber rattlesnakes mate in April or May before leaving the den site." He reported a mating Aug. 2, 1933. In view of the thousands killed or collected, it is a serious reflection on science that we know so little about the breeding of the common rattlesnake.

Young—Number, 3–17. 3, 7, 8, 11, 12, 13 (Breckenridge); 5 (Seiss); 5, 12, 17 (Conant and Bridges); 5, 12 (Conant); 6, 7, 12, 13 (Bishop and Alexander); 7 (Necker, Edgren); 7, 13 (Netting); 7, 14 (Lamson); 8, 9 (Brimley); 8, 9, 26 (*St. James Mag.*); 9 (Hay, Smyth); 8, 12 (Hurter, Surface); 10 (Hook); 10, 12 (Babcock); 12 (Dudley, Guthrie, Funkhouser, Ditmars); 13 (Brimley); 14 (Burt); 15 (Necker); 16 (Dunbar). In 1723 Dudley reported 12 young born in June. In 1829 Mease mentioned a female with 20–30 eggs. Some absurd estimates, such as 70 young (Carver) and another of 90, have been made. DeWitt Clinton in 1822 reported 12 young or 30 eggs with one female. Klauber (1936) recorded 5–17 in 22 egg batches or broods. Time of birth, late summer; latter part of August to October. There are definite dates Aug. 20, Sept. 18, Oct. 4.

Size, 7⅜–12 inches. In 1723 Dudley recorded finding in June a developing young 6 inches long in a female. Records of young range from 7⅜, 8, 9, 9⅜, 9⅞, 10, 11, to 12 inches. Edgren (Minn., 1948) measured 7 young— 317, 318, 319, 326, 328, 328, 334 mm., mean 322.57 mm.—just before their first molt, which may have been 1 to 2 weeks after birth. Klauber (Gen., 1936–40, IV) recorded 285 mm. as the length at birth. In 1939 Trapido (N.J.) reported on parturition in a 4-foot female as follows: 10 young were produced in 4½ hours; intervals of extrusion were from 11 minutes to less than 1 hour; the fetal membranes ruptured at or just before extrusion or 43 minutes later; young snakes shed 18 days later.

Food: Mainly small mammals, some birds. Uhler, Cottam, and Clarke (Va., 1939), Surface and McConnell (Pa., 1906), Hook (N.J., 1936), Smyth (Va., 1949), Barbour (Ky., 1950).

Venom and bite: Let a few of them live! Poisonous? Yes. Capture them by the tail or play with a recently killed rattlesnake or severed head? No! But there are few bites, fewer deaths. Know them and dispel your fear complex.

"Therefore it is simplicity in anyone that shall tell a bugbeare tale of horrible or terrible serpents that are in that land" (Francis Higginson, *New England's Plantation in 1620,* London, 1630).

"I have had an opportunity of seeing the rattlesnake, whose natural history is greatly involved in fable and mystery. Its venomous qualities have been somewhat exaggerated, and the antidotes against its poison have been much misrepresented" (De Witt Clinton, N.Y., 1822).

"The rattlesnake is now nearly as great a curiosity in the towns of America as in England" (W. Bullock, *Sketch of a Journey* . . . , London, 1827, p. xxviii).

"I remember the day when the danger of rattlesnake bites was seriously felt and urged as an objection to a removal to the West. From what I know of the notions current eastward on this subject, I have no doubt that many emigrants felt a terror of rattlesnakes hardly inferior to that they entertained respecting the savages themselves. To this day, it is currently reported by most of our friends in the Atlantic cities, and in Europe, as devoutly held an article of faith as any fact of record in the Bible, that the bite of the rattlesnake inflicts certain death. One of the last cautions I received on leaving the parental home, was to take care always to wear boots when out in the woods, and avoid all places where these reptiles were supposed to lurk. . . . My residence for many years has been in western Pennsylvania, a country infested by the reptile, and during that whole period, I never heard of a death resulting from its bite, except one" (Charles Cist in *Cincinnati Miscellany,* I [1845]: 17).

We give the above excerpts, not as sentimentalists, but realists who have photographed alive every subspecies and species of poisonous snake of the U.S. except one.

Former remedies. We hope some day a scholar with the aid of botanies, various pharmacopoeias, the Surgeon General's Library catalogue, and other sources will assemble an account of the old medical herbs called snake root, snake weed, rattlesnake master, rattlesnake piece, rattlesnake herb, etc. Some 40 or more native plants have been tried for the bite of this snake—species of *Lacinaria (Liatris), Aristolochia, Asarum, Cimicifuga, Psoralia, Polygala, Eupatorium, Eryngium, Sanicula, Actaea, Senecio, Silene, Glechoma, Thalictrum, Trillium, Solidago, Fagopyrum, Nabalus, Seriocarpus, Agave.* Usually the root was used, but the bark, leaves, or buds of white ash, the bark of the root of poplar or yellow poplar, the leaves of red willow, etc., were also applied.

We have all read about at least a few of the strange practices such as eating the heart of the offending snake, rubbing into the wound the snake's fat or liver without gall, cutting open a chicken and applying it on the wound, and applying urine cloths or tobacco juice. When we entered college, in 1900, ammonia, whiskey, and brandy were frowned on; potassium permanganate was dominant, then strychnine. In this country, many chemicals have been tried: osmic acid, chromic acid, salt, gunpowder, and chlorides of various sorts.

Snakebite treatment. We can attempt no discussion of snakebite treatment. Several workers, such as Necker (Ill., 1939b) and Davis and Brimley (Gen., 1944), have suggested the following: (a) identify your snake; (b) keep quiet; (c) apply tourniquet for 15-25 minutes, then release it; (d) sterilize bite and incise; apply suction by mouth or better by Dr. Dudley Jackson's method; (e) find a doctor or hospital; (f) inject antivenin; (g) if need be, use blood transfusions or plasma.

Authorities: In the past almost every traveler noticed the rattlesnake. Many towns offered bounties, or they organized hunts for killing it, and very few reptilian papers of the northeast omitted reference to it. Of our full bibliography of approximately 2,500 papers, we daresay a third mention this species. By actual count, there are 413 which discuss it at length; they appeared chronologically as follows: 1600-1700, 13 papers; 1701-1800, 49; 1801-1825, 46; 1826-1850, 52; 1851-1875, 35; 1876-1900, 42; 1901-1925, 67; 1926-1950, 109. These numbers represent the proportion of interest in North American herpetology for these periods—great interest from 1750 to 1850, a time of exploration and world travel; a subsidence from 1850 to 1900; great activity from 1900 to 1950.

We shall not attempt to name the host of authors from 1801 to 1954. For travelers' accounts see R. V. Medden's *Tales of the Rattlesnake.*

Canebrake rattlesnake (25—Viosca 1930),
Canebrake rattler (5)

Crotalus horridus atricaudatus Latreille 1802. Fig. 275; Map 67

Other common names: Banded rattlesnake (14); canebraker; cane rattler; chevron rattler; common rattler; common timber rattler; rattlesnake (16); rattlesnake of the bottomlands; Seminole rattler; small rattlesnake; swamp rattler; southern banded rattlesnake; timber rattlesnake; timber rattler (8); velvet-tail rattler.

Range: Coastal plain and Mississippi embayment. From Dismal Swamp, Va., s. and w. around the end of the Appalachian Mts. in Georgia and Alabama, s. to the Gulf of Mexico, but exclusive of peninsular Florida, and n. through w. Tennessee and Kentucky to s.w. Indiana and s. Illinois; thence s.w. to e. Texas.—Ala.; Ark.; Fla.; Ga.; Ill.; Ky.; La.; Miss.; Mo.;

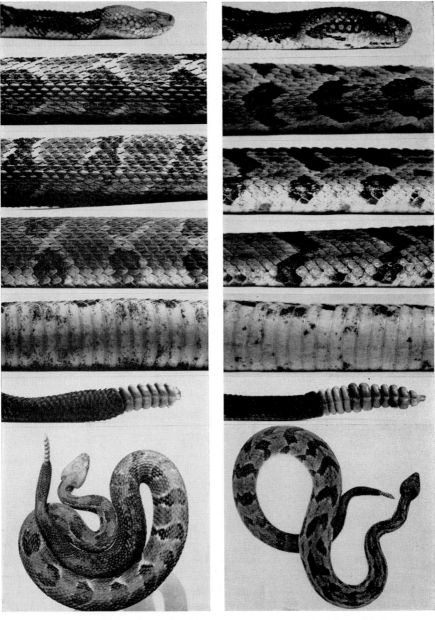

Fig. 274. *Crotalus horridus horridus,* Ramsey, N.J., L. Hook.

Fig. 275. *Crotalus h. atricaudatus:* 1–6, Key West, Fla., E. R. Allen; 7, Washington, N.C., G. Ross.

N.C.; S.C.; Tenn.; Tex.; Va. *Elevation*—Seacoast to 1,000, possibly 2,000 feet.

Size: Adults, 33–75 inches long, possibly to 84 or 96 inches. We would like to see one 108 inches. The old estimates of 32–96 inches average no higher than the 1921–1944 measurements of 33–108 inches. The largest we have seen were 2 specimens, each 4 feet 5 inches, from Jacksonville and Worthington Springs, Fla.

Distinctive characteristics: "Its dorsal scales are usually 25 instead of 23 rows. The stripe from the eye to the angle of the mouth stands out very distinctly from the ground color of the head. The black blotches of the anterior fourth of the body are divided in the middle by the bright stripe of reddish brown and on each side tend to coalesce longitudinally forming a pair of irregular black stripes. An interrupted black streak, midlateral in position, is present between and alternates with the dorsal and lateral series of blotches. The black ventralateral spots usually have distinct light centers" (Gloyd, 1935).

Color: A snake found on the pilings near the "Five Cypresses" of Billy's Lake, Okefinokee Swamp, Ga., shot by H. Lee with a bullet from a .22, and described July 5, 1921. The back is marked with black chevrons, which become bands in the rear third of the body. Down the middle of the back is a tawny stripe 3 scales wide. It may be vinaceous in part and mars brown on the dark chevrons; or hazel on the lighter part and chestnut brown over the chevron; or mars yellow on the lighter region and brussels brown on the chevron. The ground color of the body for the cephalic ⅔ is light vinaceous-fawn, pale grayish vinaceous, pale vinaceous-pink, or even flesh pink. This color is heavily dotted or flecked with grayish. In the caudal third, the body is largely deep mouse-gray or chaetura drab. Vinaceous also marks the chin scales, the upper labials, the lower labials less, and the top of the head. The side of the head back of the articulation is prominently of the same color. A stripe of dresden brown extends backward from the eye. The pupil is vertical. The iris, like the body, is light vinaceous-fawn, pale grayish vinaceous, pale vinaceous-pink, or even flesh pink marked with fine dark punctae. The rear outer portion of the iris is cream color or pale chalcedony yellow. The dorsum of the tail is practically black, as is also the venter except for some pale olive-buff on the middle of some subcaudals. The under parts of the body are white marked with the vinaceous colors of the background of the back, and flecked, particularly on the ends of the ventrals, with grayish.

A snake from Floyd's Island Prairie, Okefinokee Swamp. Ga., caught June 13, 1921, by H. H. and J. Lee. The body is drab-gray with fuscous chevrons, and with some of the dorsal scales vinaceous-tawny to salmon-orange. The upper and lower labials and side gulars are livid pink. The same color occurs more or less irregularly on the 1st row of scales in the cephalic third or half of the body. A black specimen appears rarely. See Jones, Strecker (Tex., 1908c), and Davis and Brimley.

Habitat: The cane-brake rattler distinctly is not of high uplands and, if so recorded, is found in timber uplands or wooded hills adjoining rivers or other water. Normally, it is accredited to swamp or bottomlands, cane fields and cane brakes, cedar brakes, and bayheads in flatwoods. Other habitats are pine regions and old fields with young trees and weeds, post oak country, the Big Thicket of Texas, and ridges and glades of the Dismal Swamp.

Period of activity: *First appearance*—Apr. 1, 1905 (Bailey, Tex., 1905); May, 1908 (Brimley, N.C., 1909); April, May (Strecker, Tex., 1928).

Breeding: Viviparous. *Mating*—Few notes on breeding have been devoted to this form. In 1937 Klauber (1936–40, IV) measured 8 of his large males and 8 large females of *atricaudatus,* recording males 1,200–1,600 mm., females 1,025–1,475 mm.; the largest specimen was 1,880 mm. *Young*—Probably the same as in *C. h. horridus.* In 1938 Klauber estimated 300 mm. as the average size at birth. Davis and Brimley reported "5 to 17 young, about 12 inches long," the same length given by Conant and Bridges (Gen., 1939).

Food: Toads, mice, insects, small snakes, and birds.[1] Griffith (Gen., 1831), Rutledge (Gen., 1921), Davis and Brimley.

Venom and bite: See John Lawson, 1714; G. Millegen, 1770; and John Davis, 1803, for examples of early accounts. Hall (S.C., 1727) and Audubon (Gen., 1827) report early experiments. The latter is especially good. Before 1935 much of the literature on the venom of *C. horridus* pertained to *atricaudatus.* In Hutchinson's "Study of incidence of snakebite . . ." (1929) are given 7 bites for North Carolina, 4 for South Carolina, 3 for Georgia, 1 each for Florida, Alabama, and Mississippi, 3 for Arkansas, 2 for Texas—22 in all, some of which were doubtless inflicted by *C. horridus.* See Githens and George on *C. horridus* (Gen., 1931) for the potency of the dried venom (minimum lethal dose for pigeons 0.3 mg.).

In 1942 Keegan and Andrews (Gen.) studied the old question, "Is a rattlesnake immune to its own venom or that of another snake of its own species?" Some previous writers had reported the suicide of snakes, others no effects from such venom. Keegan and Andrews used *Crotalus horridus atricaudatus,* massasaugas, and copperheads, experimenting on 31 snakes of 20 species, and reported: "The venoms apparently have the same effects as on warm-blooded animals. . . . Results of our experiments indicate specific differences in resistance to the venoms. . . . Observations of other species of *Lampropeltis,* as well as a large *Drymarchon* . . . indicate that success in overpowering and eating poisonous snakes may be due to ability to avoid bites rather than to an immunity. . . . It was found that young specimens of *Crotalus*

---

[1] Hamilton and Pollack found that its diet consisted chiefly of mammals (rodents, etc.), 73.1%.

were killed by both *Crotalus* and *Agkistrodon* venoms. . . . Reports by Mitchell (1861), Gloyd (1933), Wooster (1933), and Conant (1934) have indicated that rattlesnakes are not immune to their own venom."

Enemies: In French's *Historical Collections of Louisiana* (Part I, 1678 to 1691, p. 21) we read, "Some of our men had eaten of them and found their flesh was not amiss, and when we had killed any of them, our swine made a good meal." Rutledge (Gen., 1921) mentioned eagles, hogs, and forest fires as some of the worst enemies of this form. In 1923 Brimley (N.C.) gave an instance of an opossum eating the head of a mother snake and all her young. In 1940 Meade (La.) introduced a speckled king snake to *C. h. atricaudatus, Agkistrodon mokasen,* and *Agkistrodon piscivorus.* "The king snake and the rattlesnake seemed afraid of each other and nothing resulted from the encounter."

Authorities:

Allen, E. R. (Fla., 1949)
Audubon, J. J. (Gen., 1827)
Brimley, C. S. (N.C., 1941–42)
Davis, H. T., and C. S. Brimley (Gen., 1944)
Gloyd, H. K. (Gen., 1935, 1940)

Gowanloch, J. N. (La., 1934)
Hall, Captain (S.C., 1727)
Jones, R. W. (Miss., 1892)
Klauber, L. M. (Gen., 1936, 1936–40, III, IV)
Pope, C. H. (Gen., 1944)

Green rattlesnake (16—Mitchell 1903), **Eastern rock rattlesnake**

Crotalus lepidus lepidus (Kennicott) 1861. Fig. 276; Map 68

Other common names: Blue rattlesnake; little green rattlesnake; pink rattlesnake; rock rattlesnake; Texas rock rattlesnake (2—Conant and Bridges 1939); white rattlesnake.

Range: Davis and Chisos Mts., Tex., to Leakey, Real Co., Tex., and s. into Mexico.—U.S.A.: Tex. Mex.: Coahuila; Nuevo León; San Luis Potosí. *Elevation*—950 to 6,500 feet. 5,000, 6,000, 6,500 feet (Gloyd and Smith); 5,700, 6,000 feet (Bailey); 6,000 feet (Gloyd); 6,500–7,000 feet (Campbell, Ariz., 1934); 9,600 feet (Taylor, Gen., 1952).

Size: Adults, 15–28 inches.

Distinctive characteristics: "Distinguished from *C. l. klauberi* by a dark gray or brown stripe from the orbit to the angle of the mouth; a mottled coloration with dark crossbands only slightly distinct from the gray ground color, and usually becoming noticeably fainter toward the head; irregular intermediate blotches sometimes almost as conspicuous as the crossbands of the main series; and the relatively dark coloration of the belly" (Gloyd, Ariz., 1936b).

Color: A snake found at Devil's River Crossing, Tex., July 1, 1925. The head and background of the back are pallid neutral gray or smoke gray, crossed with bands of mouse gray, dark mouse gray, or dark olive-gray. On the sides below the dorsal crossbands are shorter bars of the same color. On the posterior half of the body these bands become drab or deep grayish olive. The 1st band on the tail is broad, the other 2 narrow and blackish. On the ground color of the back, between each 2 crossbands, are 10 to 14 indistinct pale neutral gray mottlings or irregular spots. Some of the scales of the background have pale ochraceous-buff or pale cinnamon-pink edges. Under the lens, each scale is seen to be heavily provided with fine dots. There is a vitta of pale neutral gray from the eye to the neck. There is a stripe of pale pinkish cinnamon or pale cinnamon-pink from under the eye to the angle of the mouth. The edges of the labials are pale neutral gray. The iris is pallid neutral gray with a pale grayish vinaceous cast and specked with pale neutral gray. The belly is pale cinnamon-pink or pale pinkish cinnamon mottled with pale or pallid neutral gray. Toward the tail this becomes deep grayish olive. The underside of the tail is olive-ocher or chamois. The dorsal markings are the same in a female.

Observations on coloration by Murray: "The two smaller specimens show considerable dark flecking and checkering while dark crossbands are poorly defined or absent. The largest specimen had in life well-defined black transverse dorsal bars on a pinkish-tan background. This coincides with the observations of the writer on other specimens of this species from this region. The typical banded pattern is found better developed in the larger and presumably older specimens. At all ages they usually blend well with the predominating colors of their habitat. In the Chisos Mountains there is much reddish igneous rock. Here the species of rattler is so commonly pinkish in color that it is known to the people of that region as the 'Pink Rattler.' I have seen a gray and black checkered specimen from the timbered regions of the Davis Mountains, while in limestone regions this species tends to be somewhat bleached in color."

Habitat: In 1902 Mitchell (Tex.) wrote, "Nothing is known of its habits." Bailey gave us our first insight into this animal's life in 1905. He called it the white rattlesnake and placed it in the most arid and rocky parts of west Texas in both Lower and Upper Sonoran zones. On this survey L. A. Fuertes made a careful color study of it. In 1939 Murray, a graduate of Sul Ross College, Alpine, Tex., a resident of the trans-Pecos and in his youth a guide for science trips there, wrote: "This beautiful little rattler frequents inaccessible rocky places in the higher parts of the mountains. It is never found on the flats about the mountains and but rarely in the valleys of the mountains. . . . It seems to be even more strictly nocturnal than the other rattlers of the region." From 1925 onward, Murray maintained that *lepidus* of Texas and *lepidus* of Arizona are different.

In 1942 Gloyd and Smith reported on 3 collections from the Carmen Mts., Coahuila, Mex. *C. l. lepidus* was taken in Carboneras Camp, Juárez and Diablo Canyons, at 5,000–6,500-feet elevation. They quoted from

Gregory's account of the vicinity of Carboneras Canyon: "We found our-selves in a rough country, cut with many deep, rocky, steep-walled canyons, hemmed in by wooded peaks and sheer escarpments."

In 1944 in the Big Bend, Tex., Schmidt and Smith reported "6 specimens from higher levels in the Basin and from rock slides at the west base of the peak of Mount Emory." In Coahuila, Mex., Schmidt and Owens (Tex., 1944) took two snakes near Monclova. "These specimens are topotypes of *Crotalus palmeri* Garman."

In 1949 in the Sierra Vieja range of s.w. Texas, Jameson and Flury re-ported as follows: "Four specimens were collected from the following as-sociations of the Roughland belt: catclaw-grama, 2; stream bed, 2. All were active when taken, 2 at night and 2 in the early morning. One of the catclaw-grama specimens was in a rock slide within the association."

Period of activity: *First appearance*—May 1 (Marr), May 20, 1900 (Bailey). *Fall disappearance*—Aug. 5, 1939 (Schmidt, Tex., 1944); Oct. 22, 1940 (Gloyd and Smith); other records to Nov. 11.

Breeding: Viviparous. In 1937 Klauber has reported 4 of his large males 545–648 mm. long, and 4 of his large females 445–540. *Young*—Klauber gave 197 mm. for the specimen measured; estimated size at birth 190 mm. In several publications, 4 has been given as the number in a brood, probably from the same record. Werler added that the form measures "about 7½ inches at birth." He (Gen., 1951) recorded a female giving birth to 3 young on July 21, 1950; they were 210–229 mm. long.

Food: Lizards, small frogs, mice. Falck, Gloyd and Smith, Marr.

Venom: In Githen and George's (Gen., 1931) table of fatal doses for pigeons, the venom of this species (minimum lethal dose 0.01 mg. of dried venom) seems by far the most potent, with *C. tigris* (0.04 mg.) next. In 1941 Schmidt and Davis (Gen., 1941) wrote, "They are not especially ag-gressive, and there seems to be no record of a human being being bitten by this species." In 1950 Werler supported this view: "The eastern rock rattlesnake cannot be considered a menace to humans, and apparently there is no record of anyone ever having been bitten by this snake." Seemingly one of the present writers (A.H.W.) must come out of obscurity and an-nounce that he was bitten in the thumb by one of this species, both fangs entering. (It is nevertheless a nonaggressive snake.) I was holding it by the neck when a class noise distracted me, and the snake turned on his captor. My arm swelled considerably, and my lymphatic glands were affected, but I recovered. I did not know then that it was one of the most toxic of the rattlesnakes.

Field notes: July 10, 1925, Alpine—Ft. Davis Road: In the search Bert put his hand within an inch and a half of a green rattler (*lepidus*). The snake was a gentleman. It stayed perfectly still. We photographed it in place.

Fig. 276. *Crotalus lepidus lepidus,* Chisos Mts., Tex., C. A. Miller through L. T. Murray.

Fig. 277. *Crotalus l. klauberi:* 1–4, Tucson, Ariz., C. T. Vorhies; 5, Ramsay Canyon, Huachuca Mts., Ariz.

It was in the shade of two trees and a large boulder. It was resting on a small shady ledge on the side of a small boulder.

Authorities:

Bailey, V. (Tex., 1905)
Brown, A. E. (Gen., 1901)
Campo, R. M. del (Gen., 1935)
Cope, E. D. (Gen., 1860, 1900; Ariz., 1866a)
Ditmars, R. L. (Gen., 1930)
Falck, E. G. J. (Tex., 1940)
Garman, S. (Gen., 1883; Tex., 1887)
Gloyd, H. K. (Gen., 1940; Ariz., 1936b)
Gloyd, H. K., and H. M. Smith (Gen., 1942)
Jameson, D. L., and A. G. Flury (Tex., 1949)
Kennicott, R. (Tex., 1862)

Klauber, L. M. (Gen., 1936, 1936–40, III, IV)
Marr, J. C. (Gen., 1944)
Murray, L. T. (Tex., 1939)
Noguchi, H. (Gen., 1909)
Schmidt, K. P., and T. F. Smith (Tex., 1944)
Schwartz, A., and W. A. Babis (Tex., 1949)
Smith, H. M. (Gen., 1944)
Stejneger, L. (Gen., 1895)
Strecker, J. K., Jr. (Tex., 1909b, 1915)
Werler, J. (Tex., 1950)
Yarrow, H. C. (Ariz., 1875)

Green rattlesnake (9—Ditmars 1907), Green rock rattlesnake (6—Klauber 1936)

Crotalus lepidus klauberi Gloyd 1936. Fig. 277; Map 68

Other common names: Blue rattlesnake; rock rattlesnake.

Range: From the mountains of s.e. Arizona to the Guadalupe Mts. of n.w. Culberson Co., Tex., and on the Mexican plateau in Chihuahua, Durango, Zacatecas, and Jalisco.—U.S.A.: Ariz.; N.M.; Tex. Mex.: Chihuahua; Durango; Jalisco; Zacatecas. *Elevation*—4,000 to 8,000 feet (Bailey, N.M., 1913); 6,000 feet (Gloyd, 1937a): 6,500, 7,000 feet (Campbell); 5,000 feet (Schwartz and Babis).

Size: Adults, 15–29 inches.

Distinctive characteristics: "Distinguished from *Crotalus lepidus lepidus* by the absence of a dark stripe from the orbit to the angle of the mouth; a more vivid coloration, the pattern of dark brown or black crossbands contrasting strongly with the glaucous or greenish gray ground color, and equally distinct throughout the length; the absence of dark blotches between the crossbands or their restriction to small spots on a very few scales; and the light coloration of the belly" (Gloyd, Ariz., 1936b).

Color: A snake, probably female, from Ramsey Canyon, Huachuca Mts., Arizona, 1925. Found on large rocks at the top of the first steep climb above camp. Two snakes: First, probably female. The back is deep quaker drab, becoming light quaker drab on the side. On the 2nd and 3rd rows, the scales are light vinaceous-fawn. The body is marked with crossbands of cinnamon-brown or prout's brown outlined with black, and the black margin in turn is faintly outlined with pale cendre green. These dorsal saddles have 3 or 4 short forward and rearward extensions or prongs. In this specimen, the nape spot is a transverse hourglass with 2 spots forward on the head. The tail is buffy brown on the back with 3 olive-brown crossbands. On the underside, the tail is ochraceous-tawny. The iris is shrimp pink or shell pink with numerous drab-gray spots. The belly is light vinaceous-fawn or hydrangea pink.

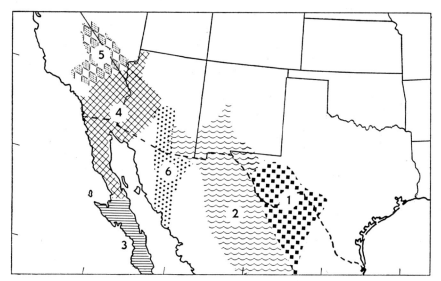

Map 68. *Crotalus*—1, *l. lepidus;* 2, *l. klauberi;* 3, *m. mitchelli;* 4, *m. pyrrhus;* 5, *m. stephensi;* 6, *tigris.*

The second snake, probably male, is very lightly colored. All along the vertebral line, there is a chrysoprase green band 3 scales wide, becoming on the forward and rear margins of the transverse bands, opaline or pale cendre green. The sides are quaker drab, the 1st, 2nd, and 3rd scale rows approaching flesh pink. The snout and a spot over either eye are light cinnamon drab or vinaceous-fawn. The hourglass spot on the nape is very prominent. The dorsum of the tail is buffy brown to onion-skin pink, and ochraceous-tawny underneath. The belly is pale salmon color. From this snake, we can see why it is called a "green" rattlesnake. About all the specimens we have seen have had the pale purplish drab or quaker drab cast; hence "blue" rattlesnake. Mr. James, of the Huachuca Mts., tells us he commonly sees green ones.

Habitat: This species was taken early crawling up a granite boulder on a hillside above Carr Canyon. They have been found under stones, rocks, pieces of bark, and in piles of rocks along the trails. They may be taken, at times, sunning themselves on flat rocks, in open areas among masses of loose stones, on slopes covered with cacti, agaves, and stunted pines, on talus slopes, and at times on shaded mountainsides.

The Flood and Wiklund (Ariz.) party of 1949 reported: "Two specimens were seen, but only one captured. Both were found under broken rock, piled around the bases of larger boulders to stop a rock slide in Morse Canyon, the Chiricahua Mountains."

Breeding: Viviparous. In 1937 Klauber (IV) gave as the range of males 593–693 mm., females 473–557 mm.; average size of males 614 mm., females 513 mm.; smallest gravid female 390 mm., largest specimen 693 mm.

Young—The data are not numerous. In 1937(a) Gloyd (Ariz.) wrote: "As nothing seems to have been published regarding the young of *Crotalus lepidus klauberi*, the inclusion of the following fragmentary notes may be justified. Several green rattlesnakes collected in the Huachuca Mountains early in July, 1928, were sent me for study by Dr. E. H. Taylor of the University of Kansas. Among these was a gravid female which died in transit and arrived in a badly decomposed condition. It was about 15 inches long and contained 2 embryos, one of which measured 160 mm. in length. The egg tooth, now probably to be regarded as a vestigial structure in ovoviviparous reptiles, was present in this individual but small and inconspicuous, scarcely projecting beyond the lower edge of the rostral plate. Mr. L. M. Klauber of San Diego, California, has permitted me to include here the measurements of a brood of 6 young in his collection. They were obtained by F. E. Walker and L. H. Cook, July 21, 1930, in Brown Cañon, Huachuca Mountains. All were found close together in a small area, and there is little doubt that they were newly born." Cook's measurements follow: total lengths range from 207–220 mm.; tail lengths are 12–16 mm.

In 1937 Klauber (IV) gave 4 in one brood born dead as 136–142 mm. long. He also gave the minimum specimen born alive as 168 mm.; estimated average size of *C. l. klauberi* at birth 195 mm., the same size given a year later (1938, V). In 1943 Kauffeld wrote: "One specimen was found on the bare surface of a huge granite boulder on Carr Peak, Huachuca Mountains, at 6,700 feet elevation, in shade, with the temperature at 90° at about 2 P.M. This was a female measuring 429 mm. which gave birth to 4 young on August 9th." In another paper (1943a) he speaks of these 4 young at length. They were irritable at birth; had sulphur yellow tails, not salmon or terra cotta; had no egg teeth and no pink underneath. "In total length they averaged 190.5 mm., measuring respectively 182, 182, 198, 200 mm. Between August 17th and 19th all shed their skins, becoming somewhat more brilliant in color. . . . The single rock rattlesnake that fed well, a male, was the longest at birth, measuring 200 mm. In 118 days this snake grew 112 mm., 56 per cent of its original length, and attained a weight of 18.5 grams. The parent snake measured 429 mm. . . . During a period of 43 days, the young snake consumed 37 grams of young and half-grown mice; previous to that, at least 20 grams of lizards were taken. The first molt took place 9 days after birth. Thereafter the skin was shed at intervals of 47, 49, and 51 days. . . . Klauber estimates the length at birth as 195 mm—5 mm. more than the average of our brood."

Food: Lizards, mice. Strasser, Campbell, Gloyd (1937a), Kauffeld.

Field notes: Aug. 1, 1925, Ramsay Canyon, Ariz.: At the top of the first steep climb, near the spring, over among the biggest rocks, we took 2 green rattlesnakes—one of which was quite greenish down the middle of the back and around the light edges of the dark crossbands. We could also see why it was sometimes called blue rattlesnake. Both had some pinkish underneath.

July 1, 1942, Carr Canyon, Huachuca Mts., below reservoir: I began to walk down the canyon, and when I reached the area of a few pools of water I spied a rock green snake escaping under a rock. Pinned it down. Then flipped it into the open and finally caught it. Immediately after bagging it, I landed in a pool of water from missing my footing. I didn't lose either the *molossus* bag or *Crotalus l. klauberi* nor injure them.

Authorities:

Brown, A. E. (Gen., 1901)
Campbell, B. (Ariz., 1934)
Campo, M. del (Gen., 1935)
Cope, E. D. (Gen., 1883–84, 1900)
Gloyd, H. K. (Gen., 1940; Ariz., 1936b, 1937a)
Hillman, H. (Calif., 1916)
Kauffeld, C. F. (Ariz., 1943, 1943a)
Klauber, L. M. (Gen., 1936, 1936–40, III, IV)
Mearns, E. A. (Tex., 1907)

Schwartz, A., and W. A. Babis, (Tex., 1949)
Stejneger, L. (Gen., 1895; Ariz., 1903)
Strasser, F. D. (Tex., 1931)
Strecker, J. K., Jr. (Tex., 1909b, 1915)
Van Denburgh, J. (Gen., 1922; Ariz., 1897; N.M., 1924b)
Van Denburgh, J., and J. R. Slevin (Ariz., 1913)
Vorhies, C. T. (Ariz., 1917)
Werler, J. E. (Tex., 1950)

1897, J. Van Denburgh (Ariz.): "One of the most noticeable features of this rattlesnake is the bright tawny coloration of the tail. The belly of the smallest specimen (320 mm.) is mottled with dark seal brown. The sides are tinted with salmon buff."

1943, C. F. Kauffeld (Ariz., 1943, 1943a): No one has spent more time and effort on the smallest species of rattlesnakes (Price's, Willard's, and green rock rattlesnakes) than Kauffeld, and anyone who goes to their haunts hears echoes of his footsteps and searches in Arizona's southern mountains. And young bloods compare their successes or failures with his results.

Bleached rattlesnake (24—Meek 1905), Southwestern speckled rattlesnake

Crotalus mitchelli pyrrhus (Cope) 1866. Fig. 278; Map 68

Other common names: Mitchell's rattlesnake (6); pale rattler; pallid rattlesnake; red rattlesnake; speckled rattlesnake; white rattlesnake.

Range: Rocky situations from Mojave Co. to Maricopa Co., Ariz., s.w. through n.w. Sonora, Mex., to 28° N. in Baja California, Mex., n. to San Bernardino Co., Calif.—U.S.A.: Ariz.; Calif.; Nev. Mex.: Baja Calif.; Sonora. *Elevation*—Coast to 4,500 feet. Coast to desert (Klauber, Gen., 1939a); foothills to desert (Perkins); 3,300, 4,500 feet (Atsatt); 4,000 feet (Grinnell); 3,200–5,150 feet (Johnson, Bryant, and Miller, Calif., 1948); 4,500–5,300 feet (Schmidt); 6,000, 8,000 feet (Meek, Calif., 1905).

Size: Adults, 25 or 26–52 inches.

Longevity: 11 years 1 month (Perkins, Gen., 1951); 11 years 9 months (Perkins, Gen., 1954).

Distinctive characteristics: "Prenasals usually separated from the rostral by small scales or granules; upper preoculars often divided, horizontally, vertically, or both; rostral usually wider than high; a pattern of dorsal blotches essentially aggregations of punctations; head larger; length of head contained in adult length less than 24 times; original rattle button, if present, less than 7.5 mm. wide. A pattern of red, gray, brown or black, punctated blotches on a cream, tan, buff, gray, pink, salmon, fawn, or brown background; often with posterior black tips on some dorsal scales" (Klauber, Gen., 1936).

Color: A snake from Vic Housholder, Phoenix, Ariz., Aug., 1938. We peeled off the shed before describing it. In the middle of the dorsum, the interspace or background color is carrot red; in the forward part, coral pink; the middorsal portion of the tail is apricot buff while the background on the sides of the tail is flesh ocher, which color is very prominent on the first 3 interspaces of the tail. The back is crossed by 35 grayish bars on the body and 5 on the tail. These bars are broader on the dorsum, where their centers are cinnamon-rufous in the rear 15 bars of the body and in the first one of the tail, whereas the centers are buckthorn brown in the forward portion. The gray margins and lateral portions of these bands are given their color by black fleckings. The tail rings are blackish plumbeous with interspaces of cinereous. All sections of the rattle are light. There are no prominent marks on top of the head, the color being a merging of the dorsal colors. The rear of the head is light grayish vinaceous very prominently flecked with gray. Ahead of the eye, it is buff-pink and gray. There is a buff-pink bar across the supraoculars and a buff-pink band beginning below the eye and extending downward to the 8th upper labial and along the upper labials to the 13th. The eye is gray flecked with black. The cephalic lower labials may be gray and white and the rear ones gray and pale pink-ish cinnamon. The underside of the head and the cephalic 3 inches of the venter are white. The rest of the venter is light ochraceous-buff with a few groups of black flecks forming gray spots on the ends of the ventrals. A few plates ahead of the vent and 6 or 8 subcaudals are solid flesh color.

Habitat: This has been called a desert species. Authors have found it be-neath brush on the desert and beneath palo verde bushes in a wash at the foot of the mountains. More have emphasized rocky country, rocky light brush areas, rocky desert foothills, and rocky chaparral areas. One author said it did not live in arid habitat conditions. Several have placed it in the lower limits of the Upper Sonoran zone. Some have called it wholly nocturnal, but we have taken it in the daytime.

Period of activity: *Early appearances*—Apr. 16, May 25, 1910 (Van Den-burgh and Slevin); Mar. 22, 1925, Feb. 28, 1926, Mar. 26, 1927, May 29, 1929 (Klauber); May 28, June 3 (Johnson, Bryant, and Miller). *Fall disap-pearance*—Oct. 6 (Johnson, Bryant, and Miller, Calif., 1948). In the "Sixteen Year Census" Klauber (Gen., 1939a) reported 1 specimen taken in Feb.; 12 in March; 39 in Apr.; 77 in May; 85 in June; 41 in July; 39 in Aug.; 21 in Sept.; 2 in Oct.; 1 in Nov.; 11 in Dec. Total 329. Rank 11. Per cent 2.54.

Breeding: Viviparous. In 1937 Klauber (1936-40, IV) reported 10 large males 1,005-1,295 mm., and 10 large females 775-1,015 mm., smallest gravid female, 786 mm. *Young*—Number 3-6. In 1936(a) Klauber (Gen.) said his smallest specimen measured 303 mm. (12 inches) and broods had 3, 4, 4, 5 young. In 1937 he (IV) gave 270 mm. for the minimum specimen meas-ured, 265 mm. the estimated average size at birth. In 1938 he (V) repeated the latter size as the body length at birth. Also in 1938 Perkins discussed the young of all rattlers under this species: "In all rattlesnakes the young are born alive, the number varying from 3 or 4 in the case of small species, to as many as 20 in large ones. Six to 12 is the usual number. At birth they are provided with fangs and poison glands, and have a button on the end of the tail. The length is 8 to 12 inches, and the markings are more or less like the adults."

Food: Small mammals, lizards, small birds. Klauber (Gen., 1936a).

Authorities:

Amaral, A. do (Gen., 1929d)
Atsatt, S. R. (Calif., 1913)
Camp, C. L. (Calif., 1916)
Cope, E. D. (Ariz., 1866a)
Garman, S. (Gen., 1883)
Gloyd, H. K. (Gen., 1940)
Grinnell, J. (Calif., 1908)
Klauber, L. M. (Gen., 1936, 1936a, 1936-40, III, IV, Calif., 1924a, 1928b, 1931a, 1932, 1934a)

Noguchi, H. (Gen., 1909)
Perkins, C. B. (Calif., 1938)
Schmidt, K. P. (Baja Calif., 1922)
Stejneger, L. (Gen., 1895)
Streets, T. H. (Baja Calif., 1877)
Van Denburgh, J. (Ariz., 1913; Baja Calif., 1894, 1896a)
Yarrow, H. C. (Ariz., 1875)
Yarrow, H. C., and H. W. Henshaw (Ariz., 1878)

Fig. 278. *Crotalus mitchelli pyrrhus:* 1,2,6–8, Phoenix, Ariz., V. Householder; 3,4, east of Phoenix, Ariz., C. L. Evans; 5,9, San Diego Zoo, Calif.

Fig. 279. *Crotalus m. stephensi,* San Diego, Calif., L. M. Klauber and C. B. Perkins through J. Rainwater.

1936(a): L. M. Klauber has given us a very much needed and thorough-going review to reduce the confusion that prevailed from 1861 to 1936 and the residence of this form in *tigris* and *confluentus* for varying periods. "This is the most variable of all the rattlesnakes in color and pattern; its bewildering variety renders any considerable accuracy or consistency of description quite impossible."

1938, C. B. Perkins: "Speckled Rattlesnake. . . . This snake is also called 'Faded,' 'Bleached,' and 'Granite' Rattlesnake. The Speckled Rattler differs from the other rattlers in having small scales between the large nose plate at the front of the head, and the plates that contain the nostrils."

1944, A. H. and A. A. Wright: In 1936(a), under *pyrrhus* material, Klauber remarked that he had "seen in excess of 400 *live* [italics ours] speci-mens." In recent years, thanks to the San Diego group of Klauber, Perkins, and others, we have a clearer working understanding of this bewildering group. In the period 1917–1925 and later, most of our live *pyrrhus* came from Evans of Phoenix, the man who probably supplied 9 out of 10 of the *Heloderma* collections received.

Panamint rattlesnake (12—Klauber 1930), **Panamint rattler**

Crotalus mitchelli stephensi Klauber 1930. Fig. 279; Map 68

Other common names: Owens Valley rattler; tiger rattlesnake (3—Van Denburgh 1897). (See also *C. m. pyrrhus* and *C. m. mitchelli.*)

Range: Desert-mountain areas of e. slopes of the Sierra Nevada from Mono Co., Calif., e. to Nye Co., Nev.; s. through s.w. Nevada s.e. to Clark Co., Nev.; thence s.w. to cent. San Bernardino Co., Calif.—Calif.; Nev. *Elevation*—3,000 to 8,000 feet. 6,000 feet (Linsdale, Nev., 1938–40); 3,000, 3,100, 4,600, 4,600, 5,000, 5,500, 6,500 feet (Stejneger, Calif., 1893); 6,200 feet (Klauber, Gen., 1936a); 6,000 feet (Cowles and Bogert); 6,000–8,000 feet (Meek); 7,000 feet (Klauber).

Size: Adults, 22–40 inches.

Distinctive characteristics: "A subspecies of *Crotalus confluentus* differing from the other subspecies except *mitchellii* in markings and coloration; in lower average internasals and scale rows; in having a rostral usually wider than high; also in high proportion of indented or sutured supraoculars. From *mitchellii* it differs in having the rostral generally in contact with the prenasal. From *C. tigris* it differs in greater number of ventrals, supra- and infralabials; in markings and color; in sutured supraoculars and in larger proportionate head size" (Klauber, Gen., 1930).

Crotalus mitchelli stephensi. "No vertical light line on the posterior edge of the prenasals and first supralabials. Supraoculars pitted, sutured or with outer edges broken. A pattern of buff, gray, brown, or deep red-brown blotches on a background of straw, tan, buff, brown or gray; often with gray suffusions on the sides of head and body, and with black-tipped scales scattered on the dorsum particularly at blotch edges" (Klauber, Gen., 1936).

Color: A snake from San Diego, Calif., received from L. M. Klauber and C. B. Perkins through Julius Rainwater, July 30, 1939. The background color of the sides is olive-gray, becoming between the saddles pinkish buff or vinaceous-buff. From the ends of these buff intervals, white or pale olive-buff scales border the dorsal saddles, the same condition obtaining with the lateral spots, but there the punctations are more prominent than on the white borders of the dorsal hexagons. Within the gray background of the sides, the keel of each scale is whitish. There are in all 48 dorsal saddles and bars counting the black ring at the base of the rattle. The first 20 are hexagonal spots except that the most cephalic is divided into a pair of spots on the neck. After the first 20, the dorsal spots have lateral extensions uniting with the lateral spots, thus forming transverse bars. These lateral spots on the forward part of the body are on the first 4 scale rows and are opposite the dorsal ones. These dorsal spots are 10 to 12 scales transversely and about 3 longitudinally with the dorsal buff interspaces of 1 to 2 scale rows. The centers of the spots are snuff brown on the forward parts, with the 12 rear spots tawny-olive. The borders of the spots and tips of some of the scales within the spots are mummy brown or clove brown, and some of the dark borders extend down on the lateral extensions, intensifying the color there to olive-brown. In the spots of the extreme rear, the tawny-olive extends down the sides to the edge of the belly. The 7 rear bars, including the black ring at the base of the rattle, are on the tail. The black ring is 5 scales wide. The 2nd and 3rd terminal rings are also more or less black. The basal segment of the rattle is black, the next one citrine-drab, the others deep olive-buff. The rostral, face, and upper and lower labials to the vertical of the eye are deep mouse gray. The top of the head forward is deep olive-gray, becoming in the rear, light drab with touches of the dorsal blotch and interval colors. The vitta, 1 to 3 scales wide, extends backward from the eye about 7 scales to about the rear of the angle of the mouth. This vitta is faintly outlined below by an indistinct thread of white, and more prominently on its upper border. Two or 3 scales back from the corner of the eye, this upper border is almost lost, and then resumed by a beautiful white, tilleul buff, or pale cinnamon-pink spot at the corner of the eye. Just above the eye is a prominent hornlike spot of the same color on the suture of the supraocular. The iris, like the face, is deep mouse gray with a narrow pupil ring of pale olive-buff which becomes broadened at the top of the pupil into an olive-buff area. The underside of the head is white, and after the first 6 to 7 inches, which are white, the venter is heavily suffused with deep olive-buff or dark olive-buff, becoming on the underside of the tail almost primrose yellow. In the forward half of the venter, each belly plate is heavily punctate with dark.

A snake from Independence, Calif., from M. Kerr, May 11, 1942. The saddle spots of the dorsum are cinnamon-brown to mummy brown with interspaces apricot buff in the cephalic portion verging through cinnamon-rufous in caudal portion to tawny-olive or honey yellow in the very rear, where the saddle spots become snuff brown. The base of the tail is black. There is a small white spot on the outer edge of each supraocular, and this plate has a broken or sutured outer edge.

Habitat: Like *C. m. pyrrhus,* this snake lives in rocky localities in desert ranges and rocky buttes. It has been called chiefly of the Upper Sonoran zones. Other places mentioned are sand dunes and sandy spots at heads of canyons and ledgy places in the piñon-juniper association.

Period of activity: *First appearance*—Mar. 30, Apr. 16, Apr. 21, Apr. 27, Apr. 29, May 1, 2, 11, 17 (Stejneger, Calif., 1893).

Breeding: Viviparous. In 1937 Klauber recorded 10 large males as 800–885 mm. long, and 10 large females 674–794 mm.; smallest gravid female 674. *Young*—In 1930, when it was described, Klauber's smallest specimen was 257 mm. In 1936(a) he recorded specimens with 6 and 8 eggs. In 1937 and 1938 he gave the estimated average size at birth as 230 mm.

Food: Kangaroo rats, pocket mice, wood rats, and lizards. Stejneger (Calif., 1893).

Field notes: May 11, 1942, at Big Pine, Calif.: The man at the Standard Station said Mark Kerr of Independence was interested in plants and rattlesnakes as an avocation. Through G. Hutchinson, Independence, we found Mr. Kerr, a very intelligent and interesting naturalist. He has a collection of plants. When asked about rattlesnakes, he at first spoke of them in general, then quietly remarked that he had a few alive. He said some men from the Cleveland Museum (Barrett *et al.*) had visited him at other times. He took us to his cages or boxes, merely covered with blankets and rugs. The snakes were cold. We truly can say it was one of the most startling surprises of our herpetologic experiences! We would survey or behold a mass, and he would say, "Which ones do you want?" He would calmly but slowly lift the specimen out of the mass. When he had one, he let it rest on his hand awhile. Into the bag it finally went. In this way we inspected several containers, but during the whole process very scrupulously "froze" so as not to disturb the rattlesnakes. They are very variable. All look to be *C. m. stephensi.* Many didn't have the prominent white spot on the superciliary; some did. He had collected them earlier from 2 dens nearby on the slopes of the Sierras. He pointed out the butte on Independence foothills where he got them. How do they all assemble in these few places? At this date the species has dispersed to the valley washes, etc. They are beautiful in color. When he handled them they were cold, as the ground was cold where we were.

Authorities:

Amaral, A. do (Gen., 1929d)

Cowles, R. B., and C. M. Bogert (Nev., 1936)

Ditmars, R. L. (Gen., 1930)

Gloyd, H. K. (Gen., 1940)

Grinnell, J., and C. L. Camp (Calif., 1917)

Klauber, L. M. (Gen., 1930, 1936, 1936a, 1936–40, III, IV; Calif., 1932)

Meek, S. E. (Calif., 1905)

Stejneger, L. (Gen., 1893; Calif., 1893)

1893, L. Stejneger (Gen.): In his famous Death Valley report, Stejneger placed his material in *C. tigris,* and the influence of his interpretation continued until Amaral's study of 1929. In 1896, Boulenger, for example, placed *C. tigris* in "Southern California, Lower California, Nevada, Colorado, Arizona, and Northern Mexico." Even Van Denburgh in 1922 regarded the specimens from "Owens Valley to the great bend of the Colorado" as *C. tigris.*

1930, L. M. Klauber: "Since the California-Nevada form hitherto considered *tigris* differs both from *Crotalus confluentus lutosus,* with which it intergrades to the north, and *Crotalus confluentus mitchellii* (as the latter must now be known) to the south, it requires a new name for which I suggest *Crotalus confluentus stephensi* subsp. nov."

1944, A. H. and A. A. Wright: A variety of talents was associated with the Death Valley expedition and report—the remarkable naturalist, Merriam; the botanist, Coville; the general, Funston; the herpetologist, Stejneger, and so on through the roster. How fitting that this form from the Panamint area should be named for a veteran naturalist who was a member of that expedition—Frank Stephens.

Black-tailed rattlesnake (26—Bailey),
Northern black-tailed rattlesnake

Crotalus molossus molossus Baird and Girard 1853. Fig. 280; Map 69

Other common names: Dog-faced rattlesnake (3—Mitchell 1903); dog-headed rattlesnake; green rattlesnake; mountain diamondback.

Range: From Grand Canyon, Ariz., s. to Mexico (Sonora, Chihuahua, Coahuila, Nuevo León); n. to cent. Texas; thence n.w. across cent. New Mexico.—U.S.A.: Ariz.; N.M.; Tex. Mex.: Chihuahua; Coahuila; Nuevo León; Sonora. *Elevation*—2,000 to 8,000 feet. 3,500–6,000 feet and above (Little, Ariz., 1940); 4,000–8,000 feet (Bailey, N.M., 1913); 4,000 feet (Murray, Tex., 1939); 4,800 feet (Murray, Tex., 1942); 4,200–4,800 feet (Humphrey); 5,200–8,000 feet (Gloyd, Ariz., 1937a); 5,000–6,200 (Gloyd and Smith, Gen., 1942); 5,500 (Stejneger, Ariz., 1903); 6,300, 6,800 (Bailey);

6,200 feet (Klauber, Gen., 1938); 6,700 feet (Kauffeld); 10,000 feet (Kingsley and Bumpus, Gen., 1885); 7,500 (Mosauer); 4,000 feet (Murray); 6,500 (Schmidt, Tex., 1944) to 7,400 (Schmidt and Smith); 3,200–3,400 (Hensley).

Size: Adults, 28–51 inches.

Distinctive characteristics: "Sulphur yellow above; tail black or dark brown; dorsal spots chestnut brown, transversely wide and irregularly lozenge shaped, usually lighter in the centres of their lateral parts; these spots are commonly prolonged down to the ventrals; belly yellowish, clouded posteriorly; a dark oblique streak behind the eye" (Brown, Gen., 1901).

"Tail often black, or with rings faintly in evidence against a dark background; vertebral process not conspicuous; tail shorter, approximately 7.1 per cent of body length (overall) in the males and 5.8 per cent in females; subcaudals rarely more than 27 in males or 23 in females; initial rattle-button (if present), over 5 mm. wide; body color primarily olive-green, or yellow-green with dark brown blotches, often with a light interior blotch on each side of the center; blotch-bordering scales unicolor; dark dorsal blotches (on the anterior half on the body) open on the sides and extending to the ventrals" (Klauber, Gen., 1936).

Color: A snake found in Fern Canyon, Tex., July 7, 1925. All the large plates on the top of the head are black with a deep dull violaceous blue reflection. The rest of top of head is between deep olive-gray and grayish olive. On the top of the head are 2 oblique lines of light seal brown or clove brown on either side. There are a few separate scales of the same. For a ways down the back is a solid band of clove brown with deep dull violaceous blue reflections. About every 7 scales a vertical bar of the same, about 2 scales wide, extends down the side. On the first 4 or 5 rows of scales this bar is citrine-drab or deep olive. Above that line it is olive-brown for 5 or 6 rows of scales; the remainder is clove brown or black with a deep dull violaceous blue reflection. For the first half of the body proper these bars are spaced 6 scales apart and contain clusters of 9–11 deep olive-buff scales. About the 10th one, the clusters break the sides of the dorsal band and are thus set on the light grayish olive or olive-gray interspaces between the vertical bars of the sides, thus forming bands of light grayish olive or olive-gray interrupted by dorsal spots of deep olive-buff and rhombs of clove brown. These interspaces each have on the 1st and 2nd rows of scales half way between the vertical bars a patch of 3 or 4 grayish olive scales. The margins of the interspaces have pale smoke gray scales. The individual scales are unicolor, either dark or light. On the dorsal band, alternating with the deep olive-buff median spots, are pairs of spots of light grayish olive or olive-gray. Forward they may consist of 2 or 3 scales. Back of the 10th median deep olive-buff spot, these alternating light grayish olive spots become more prominent, forming light centers or paired light areas in the clove brown rhombs. After about 8 prominent rhombs and bars, the caudal third of the body loses the dorsal pattern and is light grayish olive with the deep olive-buff somewhat visible. The oblique vitta from the eye may be indistinct, grayish olive margined forward with olive-buff; the upper labial border is white with light grayish olive specks; the lower labial the same. Iris above is quite prominently deep olive or olive-buff. In the rest of the eye, the buff appears as spots, as does also the black or deep olive-gray. In other words, the iris is heavily spotted with black or deep olive-gray specks on an olive-buff or deep olive-buff background, this background appearing more prominently above the pupil. The chin and first few ventrals are white. Caudally, the belly is seafoam green. In the caudal ⅔ of the body the ventrals have narrow olive-gray cephalic borders. Onto the edges for this ⅔ there extend olive-gray areas with a pallid mouse gray cast. The tail is black with the ventral half very shiny. In certain lights, it has a deep dull violaceous blue iridescence, and the underside has a pallid vinaceous-drab reflection. In the sunlight this specimen has a greenish reflection and might well be called "the green rattlesnake." We agree with Bailey and think of this one as the green rattlesnake rather than *C. lepidus.*

A snake found in Casa Blanca Canyon, Santa Rita Mts., Ariz., Aug. 6, 1925 (the common rattler of this canyon). The background on the forward half of the body is oil yellow or light yellowish olive; on the rear, tea green or light grayish olive. The rhombs are olivaceous black with purplish, violet, and greenish iridescence.

Habitat: This abundant rattlesnake of the mountains has been recorded in many diverse places. It has been found in all kinds of rocky retreats, on dry rocky ground, in rocky gulches, under canyon boulders, on rocky slopes with a few loose stones, and on ledges near trails. Several have asserted that they are absent or rare on the plains, that they belong to the mountains rather than the valley. One or two hold that they are of the foothills. They have been assigned to the Upper Sonoran and Transition zones, in chaparral-woodland, pine-fir zones, and in catclaw-cedar and catclaw-grama associations.

Period of activity: *First appearance*—Apr. 4, 1910 (Van Denburgh and Slevin); May, 1937 (Brown and Mittleman). *Fall disappearance*—July 27, 30, 1912 (Van Denburgh and Slevin); Oct., Aug., 1901 (Mosauer); Aug., 1930 (McKee and Bogert); latter part of Sept. (Quaintance); Sept., 1946 (Brown and Mittleman); Oct. (Engelhardt). "Mrs. Healy reports seeing a specimen abroad in Carr Canyon region late in November (1937) with a thin covering of snow on the ground" (Kauffeld).

Breeding: Viviparous. *Mating*—In 1936 Davis (Gen.) reported an interspecific mating. "Dr. R. T. Hatt has loaned me several photographs of a captive mating between a male *Crotalus molossus* and a female *Crotalus atrox.*" In 1939 Murray noted: "No. 6382 is a female which was killed by a tourist and left beside the trail above Boat Spring. The following day members of our party passed along this trail. No. 6383, a male, was coiled on the dead body of the female killed the day before. This must indicate that mating activities were in progress at this time, August 7."

In 1937 Klauber (IV) recorded the lengths of 37 males and 23 females. The average was 967 mm. for males and 875 mm. for females (Ariz. series). He also recorded 10 large males as 1,117–1,253 mm., 10 large females 915–1,060 mm. The smallest gravid female was 703 mm.

Young—Number, 3–7. The first record we find is Van Denburgh and Slevin's: "No. 34739, Miller Canyon, Huachuca Mts., July 27, 1912, female containing 7 young." Two of Allen's specimens from Hermosillo, Sonora, Mex., were females. "That sexual maturity had been reached is shown by the fact that both contained foetal young almost ready for birth. No. 72098 contained 5, a small amount of unabsorbed yolk with each. The hemipenes of the baby males were not yet retracted, and the egg teeth were discernible. The 3 young of No. 72099 were much larger than those of the other brood, measuring 278, 280, 297 mm. in total length, all the yolk had been absorbed, and the egg teeth were relatively much reduced. In coloration and pattern they resemble the adults except in the relatively more conspicuous tail bands."

In 1937 Klauber (IV) recorded a brood of 4 unborn snakes, minimum size 235 mm., maximum 274 mm., average 251.7 mm. He gave the length at birth as 285 mm. In 1943 Kauffeld's (Ariz.) third specimen was reported thus: "A female that gave birth to 6 young was collected in Ramsey Canyon by Mr. Jack Breed July 1937."

Food: Lizards, small rodents. MacCoy, Gloyd (Ariz., 1937a), Dodge (Ariz., 1938), Kauffeld.

Venom: In 1929(b) Do Amaral remarked, "As a matter of fact the venom of *molossus* possesses but a small amount of lipoidic substances which are responsible for the destructive action on the local tissues." In 1931 Githens and George showed this snake, though one of the larger forms, to be among the least potent, requiring 0.4 mg. of the dried venom to kill a pigeon. The same is true of the venoms of *C. adamanteus* and *C. lucasensis*. In 1933 in their tests on the immunity of rattlesnakes to their own venom, Nichol, Douglas, and Peck first used 2 black-tail rattlers 33 and 28 inches long. They were made to bite each other above the anus. The smaller died in 2 hours and 40 minutes. The larger was almost dead in 6 hours, when it was killed.

Field notes: July 7, 1925, Fern Canyon, Ft. Davis Mts., Tex.: A boy found a green rattlesnake under a boulder near the falls. How the boy's eyes bulged when I reached in to bring out the pinned snake. It was not aggressive as some rattlers are. Alas! Our snake died when exposed to 10 minutes of bright sunlight for photographs.

August 6, 1925, top of Old Baldy, Santa Rita Mts., Ariz.: Messrs. Gilman

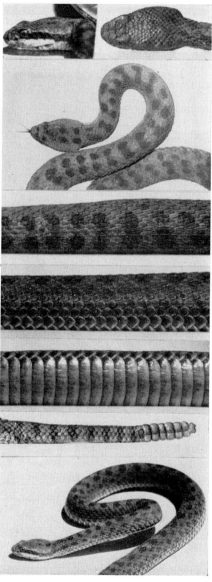

Fig. 280. *Crotalus molossus molossus:* 1–2,4–8, Alpine, Tex., L. T. Murray; 3, Fern Canyon, Ft. Davis Mts., Tex.

Fig. 281. *Crotalus pricei pricei:* 1,3–6,8, Tucson, Ariz., C. T. Vorhies; 2,7 (dead), Madera Canyon, Ariz., C. R. Dusenbery.

and Sprung gave me a fine black-tailed rattler. How to get it down the mountain? Put it in a bag and put bag in rucksack and carried it on my back. Rattlers like cover and shade. Had no trouble.

Authorities:

Allen, M. J. (Ariz., 1933)

Amaral, A. do (Gen., 1927c, 1928a, 1929b, 1929c)

Bailey, V. (Tex., 1905)

Baird, S. F., and C. Girard (Gen., 1853)

Brown, B. C., and M. B. Mittleman (Tex., 1947)

Campo, R. M. del (Gen., 1935)

Cope, E. D. (Ariz., 1866a; N.M., 1884)

Ditmars, R. L. (Gen., 1907, 1930)

Engelhardt, G. P. (Tex., 1932)

Garman, S. (Gen., 1883)

Githens, T. S., and I. D. George (Gen., 1931)

Gloyd, H. K. (Gen., 1940; Ariz., 1937a)

Hallowell, E. (Tex., 1854)

Hensley, M. M. (Ariz., 1950)

Humphrey, R. R. (Ariz., 1936)

Jameson, D. L., and A. G. Flury (Tex., 1949)

Kauffeld, C. F. (Ariz., 1943)

Klauber, L. M. (Gen., 1936, 1938, 1936–40, III, IV)

Lewis, T. H. (N.M., 1949, 1950)

Little, E. L., Jr., and J. G. Keller (N.M., 1937)

MacCoy, C. V. (Ariz., 1932)

McKee, E. D., and C. M. Bogert (Ariz., 1934)

Mosauer, W. (N.M., 1932)

Murray, L. T. (Tex., 1939)

Nichol, A. A., V. Douglas, and L. Peck (Gen., 1933)

Ortenburger, A. I. and R. D. (Ariz., 1927)

Quaintance, C. W. (Ariz., 1935)

Schmidt, K. P., and T. F. Smith (Tex., 1944)

Stejneger, L. (Gen., 1895; Ariz., 1903)

Strecker, J. K., Jr. (Tex., 1915, 1928c)

Terron, C. (Baja Calif., 1921)

Van Denburgh, J. (Gen., 1922; Ariz., 1897; N.M., 1924b)

Van Denburgh, J., and J. R. Slevin (Ariz., 1913)

1853, S. F. Baird and C. Girard: "One of the most strongly marked of all the species. . . . A remarkable character of this species is that each individual scale is of the same uniform tint to its base, and not showing 2 colours as in other species."

(1898) 1900, E. D. Cope (Gen.): "This large species is the only one within our political limits which possesses the characters of the head scales found in the Neotropical species. Among these it approaches nearest the *C. basiliscus* Cope. That species has, however, well-defined dorsal rhombs, as in *C. terrificus, C. adamanteus,* etc."

Price's rattlesnake (12—Vorhies 1917), **Arizona spotted rattlesnake** (5—Klauber 1936)

Crotalus pricei pricei Van Denburgh 1895. Fig. 281; Map 69

Other common names: Spotted rattlesnake.

Range: Mountains of s.e. Arizona, southward into Mexico in Sierra Madre

Occidental through Sonora and Chihuahua to Durango.—U.S.A.: Ariz. Mex.: Chihuahua; Durango; Sonora. *Elevation*—7,500 feet (Van Denburgh and Slevin); 8,000 feet near Old Hamburg in Pat Scott Canyon, Huachucha Mts., Ariz. (James); 7,200 feet (Gloyd, Ariz., 1937); 8,500–8,800 feet (Kauffeld, Ariz., 1943).

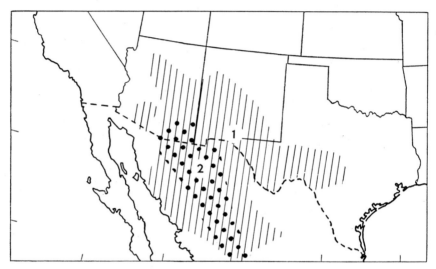

Map 69. Crotalus—1, *m. molossus; 2, p. pricei.*

Size: Adults, 13–25 inches.

Distinctive characteristics: "Small; internasal and prefrontal plates large; anterior nasal in contact with rostral; supraocular normal; 9 supralabials; 153–159 gastrosteges; 2 rows of small dorsal spots; belly dark slate" (Van Denburgh, Ariz., 1896).

"Dorsal scale rows usually less than 24; scale rows at the center of the tail 11 or less; ventrals rarely exceed 168; 1 or 2 scales between bottom-center of orbit and supralabials; usually a single loreal, longer than high; size small, adults rarely exceed 600 mm.; dorsal pattern of small brown blotches on a steel-gray ground color; usually 2 labials in contact with pit-border" (Klauber, Gen., 1936).

Color: A snake in the collection of C. T. Vorhies, Tucson, Ariz., described June 16, 1934. The background of the back and sides is olive-gray. There is a faint indication of 3 rows of dark spots on the sides, and the 1st, 2nd, and in part the 3rd rows of lateral scales have some light edging. On the back are 2 rows of deep olive spots separated by 1½ to 2 scales. Toward the tail, these become crossbands and on the tail are even more distinctly crossbands. The interspaces between these crossbands are grayish olive. The 1st 1 or

2 rattles are orange-cinnamon. The top of the head is uniform olive-gray with a suggestion of a bar between the front part of the eyes, and with 2 dark spots of deep olive on the parietal region. There is a broad band of mouse gray extending backward from the eye. There is a light vinaceous-fawn stripe from below the eye to a point beyond the angle of the mouth. The eye in its lower half is heavily mottled with deep mouse gray, and in its upper portion with dark olive-buff or even tawny-olive. The underside of the head is pale vinaceous-fawn with a little touch of vinaceous for a distance from the chin. The tip of the chin is mouse gray. The ventral plates are solid mouse gray in the forward ¾ with the rear edges white or tilleul buff, thus forming transverse bands of mouse gray.

Habitat: This "mountain sidewinder" is found in high, mountainous, dry, rocky places. Some of the habitats are: bed of a stream in a rocky canyon, on the ridge near Old Baldy, on a high ridge, on western and southern slopes, on flat horizontal stones at the edge of a rock slide. One was found in a crevice of a lichen-covered rock in an area of exposed boulders.

Kauffeld published two articles about this species in 1943. In the second paper, he included considerable pertinent data on growth: "In the first 135 days of their life the remaining 5 normal snakes increased in length, on the average, 98 mm., from the average length of 163 mm. at birth. The greatest increase was in a specimen largest at birth, from 170 mm. to 280 mm. Their weights increased to an average of 11.62 grams. At least 300 grams of lizards were consumed in that time and about 20 grams of mice. Ecdysis took place a week after birth, and thereafter 3 times at intervals of 40–44, 33–39, and 45–62 days. The last record is for only 2 snakes; the others had not yet become opaque 60 days after the third molt. The opaque period preceding ecdysis lasted 6 to 8 days. Without exception the skin was sloughed in one piece, and a new segment was added to the rattle at each molt except the first, which merely frees the button of the prebutton (Klauber, 1940). Two specimens, of this species, of a brood of 5, in the collection of the American Museum of Natural History . . . were born August 3rd, 1941, of a female collected near Safford, Cochise County, Arizona. They were preserved about one month after birth and probably had not been fed during that time. The condition of the rattle indicates that they sloughed the skin only once. They measure 200 and 202 mm., nearly 40 mm. more than the average of our brood."

From the Flood and Wiklund (Ariz., 1949) account: "Two Arizona Spotted Rattlesnakes were observed and captured. The first was found lying in the crack of a large rock on a wooded slope in Carr Canyon, and at our approach rapidly crawled under the rock which fortunately was movable. Altho it rattled fiercely, it could not be heard from more than 2 feet away. This was partly due to its small size (12 inches) and the fact that the rattles of this species are quite small. Time of capture was 10:30 A.M. and the temperature was 75 degrees. The second Spotted Rattlesnake was first observed sunning after a 2-minute drizzle which passes for rain in Arizona and was stretched on the trail which runs from Barfoot Park to Morse Canyon in the Chiricahua Mountains. Immediately, on becoming aware of us, the snake stood its ground, coiled and rattled. The sound of its large string was still weak and might easily be likened to the sound of a June bug buzzing in the leaves. These snakes were passive during capture—did not thrash about when pinned as did most of the *willardi*,—but instead lay quietly until picked up and dropped into the ever-ready collecting bag. The length of this specimen was 20 inches. Time of capture, 5:30 P.M. and the temperature 75–80 degrees. According to the trail gangs of the U.S. Forestry Service it is the most frequently seen rattler in the Chiricahua region."

Breeding: Viviparous. In 1937 Klauber (IV) recorded 10 large males as 527–619 mm., 10 large females 427–515 mm. The smallest gravid female was 301 mm. *Young*—The first intimation of size at birth is Gloyd's (Ariz., 1937a): "A small individual was coiled in a spot of sunlight on a ledge and another was startled from a bunch of grass. Since the condition of the rattle indicated that they had undergone only the first ecdysis, they were judged young of the year. One is 193 mm. and the other 206 mm. in total length." In 1937 Klauber (IV) gave 170 mm. for the minimum specimen born alive and 175 as estimated average size at birth, the same dimension being given his paper (V of 1938). In 1943 Kauffeld (Ariz.) reported on 3 adults taken in the Chiricahua Mts. "One measuring 455 mm., a gravid female, gave birth to 6 young on August 19th." In a subsequent paper, Kauffeld (Ariz., 1943a) spoke of these 6 at greater length: "These had all been born and had broken out of the membranes when they were discovered at about 10 o'clock in the morning. All were alive and active. Like the above species [*klauberi*] they were replicas of the adults in pattern, with the color less intense. These also lacked an egg tooth. They averaged 163 mm. in length, their individual lengths being 159, 160, 160, 164, 165, and 170 mm. From August 24th to August 26th all shed their skins, becoming more contrastingly colored and differing from one another in shade. Two obvious types of ground color were noted, one distinctly brown and the other decidedly gray. One specimen, the largest, was brown, 2 were quite gray; and the others were somewhat intermediate. Unlike the *klauberi* young, these were decidedly gentle, never offering to strike or otherwise displaying nervousness—a temperamental difference noted in the 'wild caught' adults of the 2 species."

Food: Lizards. Amaral, Gloyd (Ariz., 1937a), Kauffeld, Flood and Wiklund (Ariz., 1949). One of Flood and Wiklund's specimens, a 12-inch *pricei*, was found lying in a crack of a large boulder in Carr Canyon, Huachuca

Mts., Ariz., in wooded terrain. It ate, in captivity, "7/10 2 mouse hams, 7/19 1 rattling ham, 7/29 3 mouse hams, 8/8 shed skin."

Venom: In Githens and George's (Gen., 1931) study of toxicity, *C. p. pricei* was not investigated. From personal experience we know *C. lepidus* is highly toxic, and doubtless *C. p. pricei* is also. Was anyone ever bitten by one?

Authorities:

Amaral, A. do (Ariz., 1927b)
Brown, A. E. (Gen., 1901)
Campo, R. M. del (Gen., 1935)
Cope, E. D. (Gen., 1900)
Gloyd, H. K. (Gen., 1940)
Kauffeld, C. F. (Ariz., 1943, 1943a)

Klauber, L. M. (Gen., 1936, 1936–40, III, IV, 1952; N.M., 1934)
Van Denburgh, J. (Gen., 1922; Ariz., 1896, 1897)
Van Denburgh, J., and J. R. Slevin (Ariz., 1913)

1943: C. F. Kauffeld's studies are the most important contributions to our knowledge of this species.

1952: L. M. Klauber (Gen.), in his *Taxonomic Studies of Rattlesnakes of Mainland Mexico,* returns to the name *Crotalus pricei pricei* Van Denburgh, and in 1953 Schmidt's *Check List* follows his decision.

Red diamond rattlesnake (24—Grinnell and Camp 1917),
Red rattlesnake (7—Atsatt 1913)

Crotalus ruber ruber Cope 1892. Fig. 282; Map 66

Other common names: Red diamond snake; red diamond-backed rattlesnake; red rattler (8); western diamond rattlesnake (Van Denburgh 1897).

Range: Coastal s. California southward to 26°N. in Baja California, Mex.—U.S.A.: Calif. Mex.: Baja Calif. *Elevation*—Sea level to 5,000 feet. Coast to westerly fringe of the desert, but probably rare or absent from the mountains above 5,000 feet (Klauber, Calif., 1931a); from ocean to desert foothills, except on mountain tops (Perkins, Calif., 1938); 100 feet (Linsdale); 1,700, 3,500 feet (Atsatt).

Size: Adults, 24–65 inches. From the center of its range, C. B. Perkins (Calif., 1938) said he would like to see a live one 6 feet long. "Specimens slightly exceeding 6 feet in length are well authenticated" (Klauber, Calif., 1927a). Reported lengths of up to 8 feet may have been obtained from stretched skins. In 1937 Klauber (IV) gave the approximate length of a large male as 1,400 mm.

Longevity: 12 years 3 months (Perkins, Gen., 1950); 12 years 4 months (Perkins, Gen., 1954).

Distinctive characteristics: "Dark and light rings of approximately equal width; minimum scales between supraoculars 3 or more; no definite line of demarcation between the scales in the frontal and prefrontal areas; proximal rattle black; first infralabials usually divided transversely; general color pink, red, brick-red, red-brown; dark punctations weakly in evidence or absent from markings; usually no light areas present within the diamonds; light preocular stripe 1 or 2 scales wide, dull and often obscure; supraocular light crossbars usually absent. A pattern of reddish, almost unicolor, diamonds on a pinkish ground color" (Klauber, Gen., 1936).

Color: A snake from Baja California, Mex., received May 21, 1939, through Robert L. Goldfarb, to whom it was sent by B. Lasky of Los Angeles. The back is marked with 33 rhombs of russet or mikado brown, scantily outlined with pale ochraceous-buff or light buff scales. In mid-body, these light bars cross 6 scale rows transversely. For the first 4 rhombs they are indicated by a few light tips only, and the 8 caudal rhombs have no light outlines. In mid-body, a few of the scales of the rhombs, adjoining the light bars, are mars brown or warm sepia. These light middorsal bars are irregularly resumed on the lower scale rows, where they may become on the first 3 scale rows very prominently pale ochraceous-buff. The ground color between the rhombs is hazel, which on some of the scales of the first 2 rows and on the ends of the ventrals, becomes buckthorn brown or tawny-olive. On the rear half of the body, the first 2 or 3 scale rows have a wash of pale ochraceous-salmon, which with the buckthorn brown, makes them apricot buff or cinnamon-buff. The top of the head is hazel, the supraoculars, dorsal scales ahead of the eyes, and face scales cinnamon-brown. The preoculars are vinaceous-cinnamon, and there extends obliquely down from them to the labial margin just back of a vertical line from the eye a light band of pale ochraceous-salmon. The prenasal is sayal brown, and there is a touch of it in the center of the rostral. The iris is dresden brown, the pupil thinly outlined with vinaceous-cinnamon. The labials are pale smoke gray to smoke gray, as are also the mental and anterior chin shields. The throat is white, and for 6 to 8 inches the centers of the belly plates are white. In mid-body the venter becomes clear warm buff. Caudad, the venter is pinkish buff. The tail is black and white. The 5 black bars are 2½ scales wide, while the light interspaces are 4 scales wide. The 4 interspaces are white or pale drab-gray. The bar at the base of the rattle is a complete black ring.

Habitat and habits: This large red rattler is mild in disposition, non-offensive, and seldom excitable. It occurs, according to Klauber and Perkins, from coast to desert foothills, except for mountain tops. It has been assigned by various authors to chaparral-covered and rocky hillsides, boulders, and cacti and to crevices and clefts of rocks. In 1913 Atsatt held that it inhabited the Lower Sonoran zone and the lower margin of the Upper Sonoran zone. This is the form of which Prof. Ritter at La Jolla wrote an interesting account. One worker recorded it in a small bush and several times in the top of cacti. In 1939 Klauber (Gen.) recorded this species as active on the road at 6:40, 7:25, 7:55, 10:20, 11:30 P.M. and 3:25 A.M. at temperatures of

64°, 80°, 85°, and 86°F. Another tabulation reported taken from a pond, creek, or riverbank 2, from a cultivated field 2, grass 3, light brush 1, heavy brush chaparral 22, rocky boulders 5, brushy desert 6.

Period of activity: *Early appearance*—Feb. 20, 1915 (Bogert, Calif., 1930); Feb. 27, 1908 (Van Denburgh and Slevin); Mar. 13, 27, 1926, Apr. 13, 20, 1924, Apr. 27, 1927 (Klauber, Calif., 1931a); Mar. 26, 1931, Apr. 3, 1925, Apr. 11, 1927 (Linsdale); Apr. 10, 1911 (Schmidt); Apr. 13, 1924 (Klauber, Calif., 1924a). Klauber's (Gen., 1939a) "Sixteen Year Census" recorded the number of snakes caught for each month: Jan., 10; Feb., 20; Mar., 110; Apr., 273; May, 182; June, 132; July, 89; Aug., 77; Sept., 51; Oct., 44; Nov., 17; Dec., 8. Total 1,013. Rank 5. Per cent 7.82. In contrast to *C. v. helleri,* total 1,258, rank 3, per cent 9.71. In his table published in 1926(a), covering 3 years, Klauber (Calif.) recorded: Feb., 3 snakes; Mar., 2; Apr., 36; May, 33; June, 20; July, 13; Aug., 17; Sept., 10; Oct., 15; Nov., 2; or a total of 151 for the period 1923-1925. *Fall disappearance*—Aug. 23, 1908 (Atsatt); Aug. 25, 1923, Oct. 9, 1929 (Klauber, 1931a); Sept. 25, 1925 (Linsdale).

Hibernation—According to Klauber (Calif., 1927a), Faldborg, of Chula Vista, who collected in lower altitude areas between foothills and the ocean, said: " 'I have never found a snake den. . . . On the lower lands, between foothills and the ocean, these Red Rattlers are rarely found during the winter months. However, beginning in February and during the spring months until June, they are readily found in the warm sunshiny ravines, with slopes facing south, that have an abundance of cacti, sumac and brush and that are protected from the west winds.' " Thereafter they are liable to be found any place. In 1938 Perkins wrote: "The Red Rattlesnake seems to come out of hibernation earlier than the Pacific by a week or so. However, both of them, over a period of time, are taken during all months of the year."

Breeding: Viviparous. *Combat dance*—Shaw strongly indicated that the previously interpreted "courtship dance" of male and female is really a "combat dance" of two males. With captive *C. ruber* males he repeatedly observed this behavior from Dec. 21 until the writing of the paper on Jan. 31. "The persistent sparring of the raised snakes, that is, the continuous twining of necks, seems to be a sort of maneuvering for an advantageous position from which one snake may forcefully throw his opponent." The whole performance is illustrated by 8 excellent photographs, and the article is one of the most interesting of recent times. *Mating*—The first note we have is from Klauber's (Calif., 1924a) record: "A pair of *C. exsul* was found mating Apr. 13, 1924." "Apr. 20, 1924, another mating pair" (1931a).

Young—Number, 6-14. In 1937 Klauber (IV) gave 9 as a brood though Schmidt and Davis (Gen., 1941) credited Klauber with 8 in a brood. In 1943 Perkins (Gen.) reported on 4 broods of 6-14. Size, 12-13.5 inches (300-350 mm.). In 1937 Klauber (III) gave the minimum length as 299 mm.,

Fig. 282. *Crotalus ruber ruber,* San Diego Zoo, Calif.

Fig. 283. *Crotalus scutulatus scutulatus,* 1 mile south of Congress, Ariz., 3000 foot elevation, H. K. Gloyd.

maximum 316 mm.; average 307.2 mm. Time of birth Aug. 1–30 or later. Perkins (Gen., 1943) wrote: "In one of the cages in the Reptile House, a pair of *Crotalus ruber,* both captured December 1936, were observed in copulation about 7:30 A.M. on Feb. 18, 1937. Unsuccessful courting of short duration had been noticed on February 6 and also on Feb. 11. . . . On Aug. 10, 1937, 172 days later, the female gave birth to 3 young and passed 3 bad eggs. One of the young measured 340 mm. (about 13½ inches) in length. The babies began feeding on a small mouse apiece each week and now are eating good-sized rats at intervals of 2 weeks."

"Another pair of *C. ruber* was seen in copulation on March 19, 1941. . . . The male had been courting every day since March 14. . . . The young were born on August 14, 1941. Possibly there had been an earlier mating as the period was only 141 days instead of 172 days. . . . There was a total of 3 normal, 3 prematures and 7 bad eggs during that time. . . . [Later there was] another bad egg."

"Since 1941 . . . we have had several captive breedings, the most interesting ones being 2 broods of *Crotalus.* One of these was from the same parents (*C. ruber*) that bred on March 26, 1941, the female giving birth to young 141 days later. In 1942 mating occurred on March 29, and the young were born 154 days later on August 30, 1942. This year the same pair mated on March 21."

Another excerpt from Perkins (Gen., 1951a) follows: "Hybrid rattlesnakes—On 3/9/37 an adult male *Crotalus viridis helleri* was placed in a cage with a young female *C. ruber ruber.* Courting occurred in May 1941 and again in February 1942. Mating took place 2/2/42, and 9 young were born 8/11/42. (Courting was again observed in May, September, and December of 1944 and June and September of 1945, also in June of 1946, but no mating.) These hybrids were a blend of the parents as far as coloration was concerned. A pair was saved, but the young female died. The male, now grown, looks very much like a *scutulatus* but not the least like *helleri* or *ruber."*

Food: Principally small mammals; lizards, birds, other snakes. Tevis.

Venom: Being mild and more or less calm, *C. r. ruber* does not excite man. We do not believe it comes into snakebite statistics as do its relatives, *atrox, adamanteus,* and almost any other rattler, its venom being one of the least potent of rattler poisons. It is a handsome snake which has caused little grief.

Authorities:

Atsatt, S. (Calif., 1913)
Brown, A. E. (Gen., 1901)
Cope, E. D. (Gen., 1900)
Ditmars, R. L. (Gen., 1930; Calif., 1923)
Gloyd, H. K. (Gen., 1940)

Grinnell, J., and C. L. Camp (Calif., 1917)
Klauber, L. M. (Gen., 1930b, 1936, 1939a, 1949; Calif., 1924a, 1928b, 1931a, 1939)
Linsdale, J. M. (Baja Calif., 1932)
Meek, S. E. (Baja Calif., 1905)

Perkins, C. B. (Gen., 1943; Calif., 1938)

Ritter, W. E. (Calif., 1921)

Schmidt, K. P. (Baja Calif., 1922)

Shaw, C. E. (Gen., 1948)

Stejneger, L. (Gen., 1895)

Tevis, L., Jr. (Baja Calif., 1943)

Van Denburgh, J. (Gen., 1897)

Van Denburgh, J., and J. R. Slevin (Baja Calif., 1921c)

1938, C. B. Perkins: "It rattles less and hisses more than the other rattlesnakes. After a short time in captivity, it becomes so tame that it is often handled. This is a foolhardy practice by which nothing can possibly be gained to offset the inherent danger. . . . Snakes 4½ feet long are very large, and a 6-foot specimen has never been brought to the zoo. It is hard to understand why the length of snakes is so often exaggerated. A 4-foot rattler with a large head and heavy body is usually described as a 'rattlesnake 6 or 7 feet long and as big as my arm.' I would like to measure one of these while still alive, because I can't understand why I can't catch such a one!"

1949: L. M. Klauber (Calif.) concluded that *C. lucasensis* "is more like *C. atrox* than is *C. ruber.*"

Mojave diamond rattlesnake (10—Klauber 1930),
Mojave rattlesnake (4)

Crotalus scutulatus scutulatus (Kennicott) 1861. Figs. 283, 284; Map 66

Other common names: Desert diamond back (3—Klauber 1928); Mojave rattler; scutulated rattlesnake (Yarrow 1882).

Range: A diagonal band from the Mojave Desert, Calif., and extreme s.w. Utah across s.e. California, Arizona, n. Sonora, Mex., Chihuahua, Mex., s.w. New Mexico to trans-Pecos Texas, and s. to Mexico (Tamaulipas, San Luis Potosí, and Durango).—U.S.A.: Ariz.; Calif.; Nev.; N.M.; Tex.; Ut. Mex.: Baja Calif.; Chihuahua; Coahuila; Durango; San Luis Potosí; Sonora; Tamaulipas; Zacatecas. *Elevation*—2,000 to 4,500 feet. 2,000–4,000 feet (Linsdale, Nev., 1938-40); below 4,500 feet (Gloyd, Ariz., 1937a); 2,800–4,500 feet (Humphrey); 3,700–4,950 feet (Johnson, Bryant and Miller); 6,800 feet (Klauber, Gen., 1930).

Size: Adults, 25–51 inches.

Longevity: 4+ years (J. T. Wright).

Distinctive characteristics: "Tail of alternating black and light ash-gray rings, both colors being in sharp contrast with the posterior body color. . . . Dark rings narrower than light; posterior ocular stripe, if present, passes backward above the angle of the mouth; minimum scales between the supraoculars rarely more than 2; a definite division line or suture between the scales in the frontal and prefrontal areas; lower half of proximal rattle light in color. A pattern of brown hexagons or diamonds on a green, olive-green, or brown background; light scales bordering the dark diamonds are unicolor, it being characteristic of this species that the blotch edges follow the scales and do not cut them" (Klauber).

Color: A snake from Yavapai Co., Ariz., 1 mile south of Congress Junction, 3,000 feet elevation. It was collected by H. K. Gloyd, Chicago Academy of Science, No. 3471, June 3, 1937. The body is marked with 29 clear, light-edged transverse rhombs which are followed toward the tail by 8 or 9 transverse bars. The rhombs, extending 11 or 12 scales transversely and 3 to 4 scales longitudinally, usually are buffy brown in the center, outlined with clove brown, and then sharply edged with a ½- or 1-scale margin of vinaceous-buff or tilleul buff. Within the last 8 distinct rhombs are a few scales bearing center stripes and thread margins of tilleul buff or vinaceous-buff. The interspaces between these rhombs and the lateral scales from the 5th to the 11th rows are citrine-drab or buffy olive. On the 3rd to 5th scale rows and sometimes on the 1st to 5th rows is a row of small buffy brown or olive-brown spots opposite the ends of the transverse rhombs. Alternating with these spots are other small spots more or less in the same row, but located on the 1st to 3rd scale rows and just touching the ventrals. In the rear, 8 or 9 rhombs lack light margins and have united with the lateral spots, thus forming complete dorsal bars from ventral to ventral. These bars are buffy brown faintly outlined with clove brown. The interspaces between these bars are dark olive-buff or isabella color. The scales of the first 4 rows, exclusive of the lateral spots, have light margins. The 3 interspaces of the tail are pale vinaceous-fawn, becoming white toward the venter. The 3 black bars on the tail are narrower than the interspaces and do not extend across the subcaudals. The 1st segment of the rattle is reed yellow in its lower half with the other half like the other segments, deep olive-buff. The top of the head is uniform olive-brown except for the supraocular, which is clove brown behind and on its inner and front edges, but marked across the middle with a bar of citrine-drab. The dorsal color of the head extends forward to the rostral and diagonally downward on the face back to the 7th or 8th upper labial. From the front outer edge of the forward tip of the supraocular, across the preocular and down to the 7th or 8th upper labial and thence along the upper labials to the angle of the mouth, extends a clear vinaceous-buff stripe. A thread of the same crosses the outer edge of the supraocular and extends diagonally back to a point behind the angle of the mouth. These light stripes enclose a vittal band of citrine-drab. The iris is mainly citrine-drab with a part of the upper portion olive-buff. The underside of the head is white, the cephalic ventrals tilleul buff, soon becoming olive-buff. The underside of the tail is pale vinaceous-fawn to white.

Flavescence—"The coloration of a specimen found in the Lechuguilla Desert near Tinajas Altas exhibits a high degree of flavescence. The ground color was bright greenish yellow, with yellowish olive dorsal blotches" (Gloyd, Ariz., 1937a).

Jan. 28, 1934. Vorhies of Tucson took us to see Mr. and Mrs. J. T. Wright, who live on the outskirts of the city. They have two dens of rattlesnakes. In one is a peculiar rattlesnake from the Tortillita Mts., n.w. of Tucson, which at first appearance looks like a *C. m. molossus* but has no black tail. Tracing it in the keys, one would place it in the *C. d. durissus* or the *basiliscus* groups, but examination of the scales of the top of the head and the wide white interspaces of the tail shows it to be most certainly an aberrant *C. s. scutulatus* with paired stripes on the neck. In the light of the hybrid rattlesnakes *Crotalus durissus unicolor* female x *C. s. scutulatus* male recorded by Perkins (Gen., 1951) Wright's specimen may be a wild hybrid of *C. s. scutulatus.*

Habitat: One of the first notes is Cope's (Ariz., 1866a) "mountains" but another author records "on the deserts only." The name Mojave rattler suggests open deserts. It is a lowland form, "characteristic of the plains and deserts of the Lower Sonoran Zone." It seeks refuge in holes in the ground and in such animal burrows as those of the kangaroo rat and the pack rat. One often sees them beneath mesquite, creosote, and other desert shrubs. At night one finds them crossing or traveling highways. In 1936 Humphrey, one of our best Arizona authorities, reported that they were found "most commonly on the better grassed areas at elevations ranging from 2,800 to 4,500 feet"; while Johnson, Bryant, and Miller encountered them in Providence Mts., Calif., in open, gravelly, and sandy areas at altitudes from 3,700 to 4,950 feet.

Period of activity: *First appearance*—Mar. 19, 1943 (Woodbury and Hardy); May 17, 26 (Johnson, Bryant, and Miller); May, 1931 (Vorhies); May 4, 13, 1934 (A.H.W.). *Fall disappearance*—Aug. 8 (Burger, Ariz., 1949); Aug. 22, 1930 (A.H.W.).

Breeding: Viviparous. *Young*—Of its breeding we know next to nothing. Klauber (1937, IV) gave adult lengths as 1,025–1,135 mm. in 10 large males, 837–1,025 mm., in 10 large females, and he estimated the average size at birth to be 275 mm. (1938, V), while Gloyd (Ariz., 1937a) believed that "a small individual taken near Ajo, Aug. 14, 1930, may be a young of the year. It measured 250 mm. in length." In one work, Klauber is credited with giving the average brood as 8, but in 1937 (1936-40, IV) he has 2 broods, of 6 and 9, the latter from 224 to 243 mm.

Hybrid rattlesnakes—"On 8/28/46 a female *Crotalus durissus unicolor* was placed in a cage containing several rattlesnakes including a male *C. scutulatus scutulatus* from Arizona. No courting was observed. On 6/10/48, 4 young were born, 3 males and 1 female. The young had characteristics of both parents, but were more like each other in coloration than like either parent. Now (1951) the [young] female is grayer than the more yellowish males, therein favoring the mother. Courting in these hybrids was observed in early October 1950 and mating occurred on 11/9/50. On 4/28/51 the female gave birth to 5 live young, 1 dead and 1 'bad' egg. One of the young was deformed, 1 accidentally drowned, and 1 died, leaving 2. It is too early to tell much, but neither of the young resembles in coloration either of their grandparents, parents or each other. The most interesting point seems to be that the hybrids were not mules" (Perkins, Gen., 1951a).

Food: Lizards, small mammals. Vorhies, Kauffeld (Ariz., 1943), J. T. Wright, and Johnson, Bryant, and Miller.

Venom: In 1935 Cowles and Bogert experimented with a small *C. scutulatus* with but one button. It bit a small white mouse. The mouse died. "For comparison with the rattlesnakes it is unfortunate, from one standpoint, that *Crotalus scutulatus* was used . . . since its venom is among the least typical of the North American Crotalidae. It is suggested by Githens and George [Gen., 1931] that the venom of the more primitive types of rattlers (such as *C. scutulatus*) has the neurotoxic element present in greater proportion than other rattlers. This seemed to be borne out . . . [when] the mouse showed severe nervous and paralytic symptoms with little local effect from the bite by *C. scutulatus* and in direct contrast to the effects from the bite of *Trimorphodon vandenburghii*."

Field notes: Aug. 8, 1917, Castle Dome Mt., Ariz.: *Crotalus cerastes* . . . [was] beside a bush at base of some hillocks, while the Arizona diamond-back rattler (*Crotalus adamanteus scutulatus*) Munz and Ralph killed was in mesquite toward river where mosquitoes were mighty thick. They put it on top of Ford, and it revived about midnight, much to Upton's surprise. May 4, 1934: Trip west along border with Mulaiks to beyond Roma. On return caught at 8 near Mission, 10 miles west, rattlesnake which looks to be *C. a. scutulatus*. Never verified. June 9–13, 1934, Ramsay Canyon, below James' home: Mrs. Holbert below us is much interested in rattlesnakes. She goes to dens and hooks them out. She has a coat, cape, and dress of rattlesnake skins. She has known the heart to beat 57 hours after animal was decapitated. The stub will often strike if body is touched. She has observed this decapitated head to strike if a stick is waved toward it. She has never found more than 9 in a den. Often found that wild honeybees have a hole with rattlesnakes.

Authorities:

Boulenger, G. A. (Gen., 1893–96)
Brown, A. E. (Tex., 1903b)
Cope, E. D. (Gen., 1886, 1900; Ariz., 1866a)
Cowles, R. B., and C. M. Bogert (Calif., 1935)
Gloyd, H. K. (Gen., 1940; Ariz., 1937a)
Humphrey, R. R. (Ariz., 1936)
Johnson, D. H., M. D. Bryant, and A. H. Miller (Calif., 1948)
Kauffeld, C. F. (Ariz., 1943)
Kennicott, R. (Gen., 1861)
Klauber, L. M. (Gen., 1930b, 1930, 1936–40, III, IV; Calif., 1932)
Vorhies, C. T. (Ariz., 1932)
Woodbury, A. M., and R. Hardy (Ut., 1947)
Yarrow, H. C. (Ariz., 1875)

1903, A. E. Brown: "Note on *Crotalus scutulatus* Kenn. Lately the receipt of a living example from Pecos, Texas, had convinced him that they are distinct. *C. scutulatus* has the scales on the upper surface of the head larger than in most Nearctic rattlesnakes, there being but 2 scales, between the supraorbitals in front, and 3 behind. . . ."

1930, L. M. Klauber: "*Crotalus scutulatus* is a valid species distinguished from both *C. atrox* and *C. confluentus.*"

1944, A. H. and A. A. Wright: Previous to 1930, herpetologists knew little about *scutulatus*. A glance at our field notes shows we recognized it easily in 1917 in Arizona, where it is common, but our fuzzy field notes of 1934 show our uncertainty about its occurrence in Texas. Like Klauber, we wonder about the Fort Stockton and Brownsville records. Duval County records from Taylor at San Diego, Tex., may be actually from Mexico. Records of it east of the Pecos we badly need; in fact in the trans-Pecos also. Hence the hesitation in our map to touch the Rio Grande east of the Pecos River.

Tiger rattlesnake (31—Cooper 1869), Tiger rattler (2—Stejneger 1893)

Crotalus tigris Kennicott 1859. Fig. 285; Map 68

Range: Rocky foothills and mountain slopes from cent. Arizona (Maricopa and Pinal Counties) s. to Guaymas, Sonora, Mex.—U.S.A.: Ariz. Mex.: Sonora. *Elevation*—2,000 to 4,800 feet, some lower. "The tiger rattlers occurred in areas occupied by all the other species considered (*C. atrox,* 2,800–4,000 feet, *C. scutulatus,* 2,800–4,500 feet, *C. molossus,* 4,200–4,800 feet), and almost invariably in rocky districts having rough topographic relief" (Humphrey); 3,000–6,500 feet (Stejneger, Calif., 1893).

Size: Adults, 18–36 inches.

Distinctive characteristics: "No distinct and evenly outlined light supraocular crossbars curving forward inwardly; scales on the crown and frontal area smooth and flat; general color dark and with conspicuous blotches; head notably small for a rattlesnake; head length in adults contained in body length (over-all) 25 times or more; proximal rattle width contained in head length less than 2½ times; pattern a series of cross-rings or blotches comprising brown punctations on a pink, buff or gray ground" (Klauber, Gen., 1936).

Color: A snake from south of Phoenix, Ariz., from C. L. Evans, Aug. 11, 1925. On the back are 47 transverse bars of grayish olive which are dark-edged on the dorsal 4 or 5 scale rows, but elsewhere are without dark edges. These bars extend to the 1st scale row or to the ventrals. The interspaces on the back are pale grayish vinaceous, on the sides pale vinaceous-fawn, becoming on the rear of the body vinaceous-buff or tilleul buff. Obliquely

Fig. 284. *Crotalus scutulatus scutulatus,* Tortillita Mts., Ariz., photo by J. T. Wright and M. H. Frost.

Fig. 285. *Crotalus tigris:* 1–3, Phoenix, Ariz., C. L. Evans; 4–8, Tucson, Ariz., S. C. Bishop.

from the nostril to the labial border is an area of pale cinnamon-pink with few punctations. From the lower corner of the eye to the angle of the mouth there is a band of pale cinnamon-pink scales darkened with heavy punctations. To the rear of this is a pale smoke gray oblique band. The iris is pale vinaceous-fawn or pale cinnamon-pink heavily dotted. The under parts of the head are white. Each belly plate is spotted with slate violet (1) and pale vinaceous-fawn, the rear edge of the ventral being tilleul buff or vinaceous-buff. The mid-area of the belly in the middle third of the body becomes olive-buff, then deep olive-buff. The venter is dark olive-buff or pinkish buff under the tail.—The Ortenburgers declared: "The difference between the coloration of this form and that of the other rattlers of the region is very striking."

Habitat: This small, powerfully venomed, short-fanged rattlesnake is little known. Most authors place it in canyons and rocky foothills of desert mountains in sahuaro-paloverde-ocotilla associations.

In 1936 Humphrey declared: "Members of 3 of these species—*C. atrox, C. molossus,* and *C. scutulatus*—seem to occupy rather definite zones in a given locality, whereas those of *C. tigris* were observed to have a wider distribution. On the outwash slope northwest of the Santa Rita Mountains, the following altitudinal distribution was noted. Desert diamond backs were found commonly at an altitude varying from 2,800 feet in the Santa Clara Valley to an upper limit of 3,400 feet on the better grassed areas and to as high as 4,000 feet on brushy areas where grass was scanty. A winter den of this species, which has been occupied for at least the last 4 winters, is located at an altitude of 3,700 feet. Members of the species *C. scutulatus* were found most commonly on the better grassed areas at elevations ranging from 2,800 to 4,500 feet. The blacktail rattlers were found mostly in canyons at an altitude varying from about 4,200 to 4,800 feet where oaks and other trees furnished a fair amount of shade. The tiger rattlers occurred in areas occupied by all the other species considered, and almost invariably in rocky districts having rough topographical relief."

In 1948 in his account of the lizard diet of smaller species of rattlesnakes and the newborn of larger species, Vorhies (Ariz., 1948) gave as his fourth point, "A good-sized tiger rattlesnake (*Crotalus tigris*), a species that has a relatively small head and neck, cannot swallow a full-grown house mouse."

Breeding: Viviparous. *Young*—In 1937 Klauber (IV) gave the estimated average size at birth as 225 mm. (9 inches). In 1938 he gave the same for the body length at birth.

Field notes: Aug. 9, 1925; No. 631, from Chas. L. Evans, south of Phoenix: In the same box was the beautiful "tiger" which we bought from him. He pays $2 for tigers and $1 for other rattlesnakes. In the box were 2 small ones that puzzled him. They were taken at the same place as the tiger. They are young tigers. He gave me one of them. He had 2 more tigers in another box; one was at least 2½ feet, very large for a tiger. The man who collects them followed this one downward 118 feet into a mineshaft. His tigers all come from one section, old mine shafts in mountains south of Phoenix.

Authorities:

Allen, M. J. (Ariz., 1933)
Amaral, A. do (Gen., 1929d)
Baird, S. F., and R. Kennicott (Gen., 1859)
Cope, E. D. (Ariz., 1866a)
Gloyd, H. K. (Gen., 1940; Ariz., 1937a)
Humphrey, R. R. (Ariz., 1936)
Kauffeld, C. F. (Ariz., 1943)
Klauber, L. M. (Gen., 1937, IV, 1938, V; Baja Calif., 1931b)
Ortenburger, A. I. and R. D. (Ariz., 1927)
Stejneger, L. (Gen., 1895; Calif., 1893)
Van Denburgh, J., and J. R. Slevin (Ariz., 1913)

1922: J. Van Denburgh (Gen.) illustrates a real tiger rattler from Arizona but accepts Stejneger's California addition (*mitchelli*).

1931, L. M. Klauber (1931b): This is a welcome account to clear the atmosphere about a poorly understood species. From 25 specimens (15 alive) he compiled his description and diagnostic characters.

1937–38: L. M. Klauber (III, IV) added to the evidence of differences between *C. tigris* and *C. mitchelli stephensi*.

1944, A. H. and A. A. Wright: When we beheld in 1925 several unnamed, unrecognized live *C. tigris* in C. L. Evans' establishment, we were nonplussed, but guessed them to be *C. tigris*. Soon thereafter to the west we saw *C. mitchelli pyrrhus* alive. But we remember how in 1917 we at first had the transitory thought that a specimen of *C. v. abyssus* (lost in California) was possibly *C. tigris*. We therefore do not blame Stejneger, Meek, and other fine workers for mistakes in the case of this rare species. We now confidently call them different after seeing Evans' live and preserved *tigris* and seeing 125 to 150 live *C. m. stephensi* near Independence, Calif. In other words, field contact with live material gives us confidence and illuminating evidence on problematical species.

Prairie rattlesnake (68—Van Denburgh 1897), Plains rattlesnake (11—Cope 1879)

Crotalus viridis viridis (Rafinesque) 1818. Fig. 286; Map 67

Other common names: Black rattler; common rattlesnake; confluent rattlesnake (James 1823); Great Basin rattlesnake; large prairie rattlesnake; massasauga; Missouri rattlesnake; rattlesnake of the prairies; spotted rattlesnake.

Range: Great Plains from Canada (Alberta and Saskatchewan) to Mexico (n.e. Sonora, n. Chihuahua, cent. Coahuila) and w. cent. Texas; thence n. through w. Oklahoma, Kansas, Nebraska, and South Dakota to s.w. North Dakota.—U.S.A.: Ariz.; Colo.; Ida.; Kan.; Mont.; N.D.; Neb.; N.M.; Okla.;

S.D.; Tex.; Ut.; Wyo. Can.: Alta.; Sask. Mex.: Chihuahua, Coahuila, Sonora. *Elevation*—2,000 to 10,000 feet. 4,000–8,000 feet (Bailey, N.M., 1913); 4,100, 5,000 feet (Taylor, Nev., 1912); 4,050–6,000 feet (Linsdale, Nev., 1938–40); 6,500 feet (Eaton, Ariz., 1935b); 10,000 feet (Coues, Ariz., 1875).

Size: Adults, 28–60 inches.

Longevity: 2 years 2 months (Conant and Hudson, Gen., 1949); 12 years 1 month (Perkins, Gen., 1949); 15 years 1 month (Kauffeld, Gen., 1954a).

Distinctive characteristics: "More than 2 internasals, i.e., scales between nasals, and in contact with rostral, regardless of size or position; light postocular stripe 1 to 1½ scales wide and clearly outlined; body blotches commonly subrectangular, with even edges and usually with a narrow light border; color usually green or olive green; less often olive brown or brown; scale-rows 27 or 25; dorsal scale rows at the center of the tail 13 or more; adult size exceeding 850 mm. A pattern of even edged dark-brown, rectangular or subhexagonal blotches usually surrounded by a thin light line" (Klauber, Gen., 1936).

Color: A snake from Ft. Bliss, El Paso, Tex., received from Col. M. L. Crimmins, July 12–19, 1925. The background color of the back is wood brown, fawn, avellaneous, or cinnamon. Across the back are square transverse spots of snuff brown, or light brownish olive with dark edges which are in turn margined with cartridge buff or pale pinkish buff. Just below the ends of these quadrate spots is a row of light brownish olive spots on the 4th and 5th rows of scales, which are neither black nor cartridge-buff edged. The first 3 or 4 rows of scales are light vinaceous-cinnamon. On the back there are 39 spots on the body. At about the 28th or 29th, the body color becomes chamois. The upper surface of the tail is clouded chamois with 4 spots of isabella color and with 2 spots at the base of the tail which are black, blue-violet black, or bluish slate black. The top of the head is avellaneous. The supraocular area and the top of the head in front of the eye are snuff brown. The stripe on the side of the head is tawny or mikado brown. The scales near the eye are heavily speckled with black. The ocular vitta is margined behind by a pale cinnamon pink and light ochraceous-salmon border. This border is resumed on the top of the head as a transverse cartridge-buff line extending from the middle of one eye to the middle of the other. The other light border of the ocular vitta extends from the angle of the mouth to a point below the eye, where it forks, one fork going along the labial border almost to the snout, and the other fork going past the lower forward corner of the eye, and across the head just back of the internasals. The pupil is vertical. The iris is pink buff or light pinkish cinnamon. The iris above the pupil is practically without black dots, while in front of and behind the pupil, it is marked in the lower half with numerous black spots or clusters of spots. The belly is chamois with the rear edges of the plates white, and the forward edges smoke gray. The underside of the tail in its basal ¾ is chamois.

Habitat and habits: The common names (prairie and plains rattlesnake) and ecological zone names (prairie, interior, central, grassland, temperate steppe, great plains, campestrian, etc.) indicate the habitats of this form. Without classification, they are prairies (87); plains (26); Great basin; Missouri Valley; staked plains; Great plains; higher plains country; fossil fields; prairie-dog towns; badger or rodent holes; upland plains; grassy plains; badlands; rocky bluffs; breaks; dry grassland; steppe region; short grass formation; desert grassland; parklike landscape; sandy tracts; open rocky ground; higher ground; mixed prairie; flat rock hillside; rocky hillside; open prairie; sandy plains; mountains; mesquite prairies; even pastures; cultivated and wheat fields; and almost every niche except river bottoms or low lands, which they seldom prefer.

As early as 1805 Pike remarked about the communal proclivities of certain creatures of the plains. Thereafter James, Latrobe, Hinton, Maximilian zu Wied, De Smet, Palmer, and many more commented on this topic.

In 1839 Murray thought the prairie dog and burrowing owl, a discrepant couple, might live "in the bonds (not of matrimony) but of friendship," but queried whether the rattlers were welcome guests.

In 1844 Kendall held that the sociable idea was "utterly without foundation," and in 1850 Marcy said no such "friendly relations existed between them." Those who wish to pursue this topic further may read the following:

1845–46 Gregg, J. *Commerce of the Prairies*, pp. 170–171.
1866   Marcy, R. B. *Thirty Years of Army Life on the Border*, pp. 351–352.
1868   Zincke, E. B. *A Winter in the United States*, pp. 208.
1876   Trecul, M. A. *Compt. Rend.*, **83**: 603–605; or *Ann. Mag. Nat. Hist.*, 4th ser., **18**: 439–440.
1878   Williston, S. W. *Amer. Naturalist*, **12**: 203–208.
1882   Brons, H. A. *Amer. Naturalist*, **6**: 565.
1902   Mitchell, J. D. *Trans. Tex. Acad. Sci.*, **5**: 47.
1902   Chittenden, H. M. *Hist. Fur Trade*, **2**: 837–838.
1904   Branson, E. B. *Kan. Univ. Sci. Bull.*, **2**: 426.
1923   Over, W. H. *S.D. Geol. Nat. Hist. Surv. Bull.*, **12**: 30; or *Bull. Univ. S.D.*, 23d ser., no. 10.
1926   Strecker, J. K., Jr. *Pub. Texas Folk-Lore Soc.*, No. 5, 68.
1930   Medden, R. V. *Bull. Antiv. Inst. Amer.*, **2**: 109–110.

Period of activity: *First appearance*—Feb. 11, 1805 (Wheeler); Mar., 1851 (Hallowell); Apr. 20, 1935 (Gloyd, Gen., 1947); May 1, 1927 (Burt, Kan., 1933). *Fall disappearance*—Aug. 10, 1903, Sept. 18, 1908, Oct. 1, 1904, Oct. 13, 1912, Oct. 27, 1912 (Ellis and Henderson); Aug. 24, 27, Sept. 2, Sept. 23 (Marr); Aug. 28, 1932 (Burt); Sept. 3, 1890 (Stejneger, Ida., 1891). "Specimens were collected from March 29–Nov. 1, 1934" (Little and Keller).

Hibernation—In 1874 in Montana Allen "was surprised to find how late in the season they are found abroad, as we met with them quite frequently after several frosts had occurred." In 1878 Coues and Yarrow (Mont.) reported: "About half the year, in most latitudes, they hibernate in holes in the ground. . . . At Fort Randall, on the Missouri, they were stated to reappear in May with the loosening of the ground from frost." In 1923, Over (S.D.) related that "in their natural haunts they hibernate from late in October until warm days of April or May. Hibernation takes place in deserted prairie-dog burrows or in crevices in the Badlands, rocky bluffs and buttes."

Breeding: Viviparous. *Combat or courtship dance*—In 1947 Gloyd said he received a letter in which the correspondent reported 2 prairie rattlers standing up from the ground 18 or 20 inches, bobbing their heads and rubbing their necks together. It is now quite generally interpreted as a combat, not courtship performance. *Mating*—Some observations made before 1930 follow: In 1874 Allen found 2 pairs in coitu in July. Coues and Yarrow in 1878 wrote: "The pairing season of these serpents is in midsummer." In 1878 Williston declared that "when mating during May they are more vicious than at other times." Brons noted that "during the breeding season the odor of many snakes is quite distinct and perceptible at some distance. This is markedly so in the rattlesnake (*Crotalus confluentus*); its musky and foetid emanations are quickly recognized by frontiersmen." In 1933 Wood reported 2 matings, Aug. 2, 1931, and Aug. 9, 1931, in the Wind River Valley in Wyoming. In the first pair the male was 60 inches long, the female 30, with 11 well-developed embryos 8 inches long. The second pair were mating in the heat of the day. Pregnant females will mate, she finds. Rahn quoted Jackley, "It is a common experience for me to witness mating from the last days of August to about September 10th. This I have observed annually for almost 20 years."

Young—In 1923 Over recorded prairie rattlesnakes "giving birth to 8 to 17 young about 8 inches long. . . . In about 2 weeks the young cast off their old skins." Ellis and Henderson reported that on Oct. 1, 1904, 2 specimens measured 210 and 230 mm.

In 1936 Klauber (Gen., I), from a study of 2,089 specimens, gave a detailed account of the sex ratio and the birth rate. In his Platteville series, with a total of 149 females, he had 2 with 4 eggs or young in a brood; 23 with a mean of 12 eggs in a brood; 1 with 21 eggs. He believed that 9 live births per brood was the normal number. His conclusions were:

"1. The smallest fertile females in *C. c. confluentus* from Colorado are about 585 mm. long. At 640 mm. there is a sharp increase in fertility, which tends toward 100 per cent above 700 mm. These lengths are determined about 6 months prior to the birth of the initial broods.

"2. The egg-production curve of *C. c. confluentus* reaches a maximum at 750 mm., owing to the high proportion of adult females of approximately this length.

"3. Broods of *C. c. confluentus* vary from about 4 to 21. There is a definite increase in number of young with the size of the mother, the coefficient of correlation being about +0.7. The eggs average about 11 per batch.

"4. The birth rate of a rattlesnake population is about 1.65, but there is a considerable loss of juveniles between birth and hibernation, so that when the latter season arrives the juveniles number only ¼ of the population.

"5. The eggs seem to increase about 6 per cent in linear dimensions during the hibernating season.

"6. Fragmentary data from species other than *C. c. confluentus* indicate that fully adult rattlesnakes normally give birth to from 3 to 20 young, the average being 10 or 11. Smaller species, such as *triseriatus* and *lepidus*, tend to have fewer young, usually numbering 4 to 6."

In his 1937 study Klauber gave statistics on 45 broods, including some numbering 8, 10, 14, 15, 17, 11, 20, 11, 13, 9, 6, 7, and 19, with sizes from 176–325 mm. In his 1937 study (V) he gave 250 mm. as the body length at birth.

In 1940 Conant and Downs received 2 females from A. M. Jackley of South Dakota. On Sept. 7, one female 946 mm. long had 11 young, 251–290 mm.; on Sept. 10, the other had 2 dead embryos and 5 young, 237–271 mm. On June 2, 1944, Marr took a female with 14 eggs, and on Aug. 12, one with 14 embryos. In 1951 Werler (Gen.) reported 2 gravid females, one 811 mm. long with 12 embryos, the other also with 12 embryos, 233–270 mm. long except for one runt 187 mm. long.

Food: Rodents, some birds, frogs. Townsend in 1839, Williston, Brons, Taylor (Neb., 1892a), Branson, Over (S.D., 1923), Ditmars (Gen., 1930), Gloyd (Mont., 1933), Marr, Stabler (Colo., 1948), Hamilton (S.D., 1950).

Venom and bite: In 1931 Githens and George (Gen., 1931) found *Crotalus viridis viridis* quite toxic. The average fatal dose for pigeons was 0.08 mg. of dried venom, *lepidus, tigris, lutosus,* and *abyssus* being more potent.

De Smet (1841–42, pp. 113–114; in *Early Western Travels,* 1904, **27:** 178) wrote with relief: "I mention them only to give thanks to God by whose Providence we have been delivered from all such as are venomous, chiefly from the rattlesnake. Neither men nor beasts belonging to our caravan have suffered from them, though they were so numerous in places that our waggoners killed as many as 12 in one day." In 1878 Williston said, "The danger from rattlesnake's bite has been popularly over-estimated. I have observed a great many cases among the larger animals; fatal results have been the marked exception. Among horses and cattle not one case directly fatal has come within my notice." Read about the experience of President Snow of the University of Kansas in Savage's "On the bite of the rattlesnake," *Trans. Kans. Acad. Sci.,* 1877–78, **5:** 36, and read Over's "A personal experience with rattlesnake bite," *Bull. Antiv. Inst. Amer.,* 1928, **2:** 8–10.

A temperate summation of the role of this snake appeared in Chittenden's *The American Fur Trade of the Far West* (1902) as follows: "Deaths from its bites were of the greatest rarity, particularly among men." For 1927–34 Githens (Gen., 1935) reported 154 bites of *C. v. viridis* with 10 fatalities.

In this matter of snakebites, fatalities, and statistics, we must recount an interesting conversation we once had with our nextdoor neighbor, Judge F. Irvine, former dean of the Cornell Law School, a New York Public Utilities Commissioner, and earlier a Chief Justice of the Nebraska Supreme Court. As a study in evidence when in Nebraska, he wrote to postmasters and others about rattlesnake bites, and in 100 reported instances he said there was hardly one where the reports and evidence would be permitted in court. So much was the evidence dubious that he began to doubt if *C. v. viridis* was ever fatal. "Of course," he said, "I was not so foolish as to suppose they were not poisonous, but, Wright, you as a scientist, would agree with me that the evidence was faulty."

When we remember that people have died from the bites of nonpoisonous snakes, from supposed spider bites, insect "kisses" given when the victims were asleep, etc., we seriously question snakebite statistics of this sort and of all previous periods. Dread, fear, and imagination enter too strongly.

Authorities:

Allen, J. A. (Mont., 1874)
Amaral, A. do (Gen., 1929c)
Baird, S. F., and C. Girard (Gen., 1953; Okla., 1854)
Branson, E. B. (Kan., 1904)
Brons, H. A. (Kan., 1882)
Brown, A. E. (Gen., 1901)
Conant, R., and A. Downs, Jr. (Gen., 1940)
Cope, E. D. (Gen., 1900; N.M., 1884)
Coues, E., and H. C. Yarrow (Mont., 1878)
Ellis, M. M., and J. Henderson (Colo., 1913)
Gloyd, H. K. (Gen., 1947; Mont., 1933)
Hallowell, E. (Colo., 1854)
Hudson, G. E. (Neb., 1942)
Klauber, L. M. (Gen., 1930, 1936, 1936–40, III, IV; Ariz., 1932a)
Marr, J. C. (Gen., 1944)
Over, W. H. (S.D., 1923, 1928)
Rafinesque, C. S. (Gen., 1818)
Rahn, H. (Gen., 1942a)
Savage, J. (Kan., 1878)
Say, T. (Gen., 1822–23)
Stejneger, L. (Gen., 1895)
Stone, W., and J. A. G. Rehn (N.M., 1903)
Trecul, A. (Ark., 1876)
Wheeler, G. C. (N.D., 1947)
Williston, S. W. (Gen., 1878)
Wood, F. D. (Wyo., 1933)

Not even the deer or two or three of our game fishes or game birds have received the meticulous study that the versatile engineer L. M. Klauber has given to the taxonomic, ecologic, and statistical aspects of the prairie rattlesnake. His study is without peer.

1895, L. Stejneger: "I have seen no differences of such a character or stability as to render the recognition of geographical races possible or profitable."

1930 on, L. M. Klauber: Beginning with his significant paper of 1930, we have a seasoned, long-developed treatment of the *C. viridis* (*confluentus*) races.

1942: H. Rahn's "The reproductive cycle of the prairie rattler" is one of the most distinctive discussions of the whole question of reproduction.

Fig. 286. *Crotalus viridis viridis,* Carlsbad, N.M., M. Campbell.

Fig. 287. *Crotalus v. abyssus,* Grand Canyon, Ariz., E. McKee.

Grand Canyon rattlesnake (12—Klauber 1930),
Canyon bleached rattlesnake

Crotalus viridis abyssus (Klauber) 1930. Fig. 287; Map 67

Range: Grand Canyon, Ariz. *Elevation*—Mainly 5,000 feet or below.
Size: Adults, 26–40 inches.
Distinctive characteristics: "Adult color vermilion or salmon; body blotches tending towards obsolescence in adults" (Klauber, Gen., 1936).
Color: A snake from Grand Canyon, Ariz., received from E. D. McKee, Oct. 31, 1938. The background color of the mid-dorsum is vinaceous-tawny to fawn color, becoming on the first 2 or 3 lateral scale rows onion-skin pink. The back is marked with 43 indistinct transverse spots of cacao brown with slightly darker borders. In the middle length of the body, these spots are 10 scales wide and 2 to 2½ scales longitudinally; the interspaces are 2 scales long. Opposite the dorsal spots, on the 3rd to 5th scale rows, there is a lateral row of indistinct spots which are also cacao brown. Toward the tail these lateral spots unite with the dorsal spots to form transverse bars, of which there are 14. (These are part of the 43). On the tail are 6 transverse rings of cacao brown followed by one which inclines toward black and is followed in turn by a black one (the last ring). The basal segment of the rattle is black. This snake has 10 rattles; the original tip is missing. The color of the rattle is pinkish buff or light pinkish cinnamon. The top of the head is cacao brown and the upper labial region onion-skin pink. The iris is like the top of the head. There is a very faint postocular stripe; the supraocular cross mark is absent. The front lower labials are clouded or punctate. The lower side of the head is white with 2 inches of neck pale cinnamon-pink. The onion-skin pink of the lower scale rows projects onto the ends of the ventrals, but fades into a band of buff-pink across each plate except for the rear light edge, which is pale cinnamon-pink or pale pinkish buff. The ventral surface of the tail is onion-skin pink to vinaceous-tawny.
Habitat and habits: In 1934 McKee and Bogert said: "This species appears to be not uncommon, and rather widely distributed within the canyon walls. Upper and Lower Sonoran Zones." And finally in 1942 Kauffeld gave its habitat as "rock slides and floor of the Canyon; rocks mixed with chaparral."
Breeding: Viviparous. In 1936 Klauber (III) recorded: "Rattlesnake Egg Batches or Broods. *C. c. abyssus* 1 brood of 6; 1 brood of 13." In 1937 (IV) he recorded 8 large males as 777–980 mm. and 8 large females as 629–775 mm.; average size at birth 250 mm., smallest gravid female 684 mm., maximum specimen 980 mm. In 1938 he (V) gave 250 mm. as the size at birth. *Young*—We saw a small one, 271 mm. total, with tail 23 mm., just a button. It was taken at Torowcap by E. D. McKee.
Food: Small mammals, lizards. Kauffeld.
Field notes: Aug. 4, 1917, Grand Canyon, Ariz.: This was the first

abyssus we ever saw. Just as Klauber played with *tigris* and *nuntius* at first, so we did with this *abyssus,* but later in August the milk can with this specimen and most of our best material of 1917 was lost at Lemon Cove, Calif. This specimen was caught by R. C. Shannon of Rockefeller tropical disease fame. With him were Phil Munz, Ralph Wheeler, and Paul Needham.

1942: We saw specimens from the Grand Canyon in the Museum of Northeastern Arizona (kindness of E. D. McKee) and the specimen in the Grand Canyon Museum (kindness of H. C. Bryant). Some of the localities are Herman's Rest, Indian Gardens, Roaring Springs, Seep Spring's rim.

Authorities:

Ditmars, R. L. (Gen., 1930)
Dodge, N. N. (Ariz., 1938)
Grater, R. K. (Ariz., 1938)
Kauffeld, C. F. (Gen., 1942)

Klauber, L. M. (Gen., 1930)
McKee, E. D., and C. M. Bogert (Ariz., 1934)

1930: L. M. Klauber's type description of an adult male follows: "Length 905 to rattles, tail length 62, ratio of tail to total length .069. Length of head 39, times contained in body length 23.2. Width of head 32. Width across supraoculars 19.3, distance between 7.4, ratio 2.6. Head flat topped and depressed, suboval in outline, and except for the supraoculars, covered with small scales. Posteriorly these are keeled. The scale rows are 25-25-19, all except the 1st row on each side being keeled. The ventrals are 173, anal entire, caudals 25, supralabials 17-17, infralabials 15-15. The rostral is higher than wide. Four scales in contact with the rostral between the prenasals; total in contact 8, including both prenasals. Prenasal in contact with the 1st supralabial on each side. Scales along the canthus rostralis from rostral to supraocular 5-5, the posterior largest. Scales on head anterior to the supraoculars about 35. Minimum scale rows between supraoculars 6. Supraoculars rough with a slight fold in evidence on each. Nasals 2-2, loreals 1-1, upper preocular not in contact with postnasal, not divided vertically. Preoculars 2-2, sub- and postoculars 6-6. Scale rows between labials and orbit 3 + 4, 3 + 4. First infralabials undivided and in contact on median line; 4–3 in contact with genials. A single pair of genials, short and with outer edges curved. . . . Thus we have here a form which is not unlike either *lustosus* or *confluentus* in the juvenile state, but which later departs from both. In general it seems more closely related to *lutosus* in character of body markings, width of postocular stripe, scales before and between supraoculars and in tail rings. In color it more nearly resembles *confluentus,* especially the stunted red form found in the vicinity of Winslow, Arizona. The latter, however, is a darker, richer red with typical *confluentus* markings and scutellation. This may be a case of parallel development or intergradation down the Little Colorado River."

Arizona black rattlesnake, Black rattlesnake

Crotalus viridis cerberus (Coues) 1875. Fig. 288; Map 67

Other common names: Black diamond rattlesnake; brown rattlesnake; Cerberus rattlesnake (Githens 1935); mountain diamond-back.

Range: Mountains of cent. and s.e. Arizona and extreme w. New Mexico.—Ariz.; N.M. *Elevation*—2,000 to 8,000 feet. 3,500 (Little); 5,000–9,000 (Klauber, Gen., 1930); 2,000 feet (Cope); "probably occurs in Arizona only at considerable altitudes"; 7,000 8,000 feet (Van Denburgh and Slevin); 12,000 feet (Cope).

Size: Adults, 31–43 inches.

Distinctive characteristics: *"Cerberus is a subspecies characterized by its dark color and a marked subdivision of the scales of the snout. It differs from the newly delimited oreganus and helleri,* with which it was formerly merged under the name *oreganus,* in usually having paired loreals . . . , while they have single loreals. . . . Also, most specimens of *cerberus* have 1 or more scales at the rostral between the anterior nasal and the 1st supralabial, . . . while such scales are usually absent in *helleri* and *oreganus.* . . . *C. v. cerberus* has a wider terminal dark tail than *oreganus.* The dorsal body blotches are without lateral light borders, such as are generally present in *helleri"* (Klauber, Baja Calif., 1949a).

Color: A snake in the collection of C. T. Vorhies, Tucson, Ariz., described June 16, 1934. The dark spots of the back are shiny black, 9 or 10 scales wide and 4 to 5 scales long. They are separated by 33 transverse bands of baryta yellow scales, which may have keels or tips of light cadmium or cadmium yellow. The

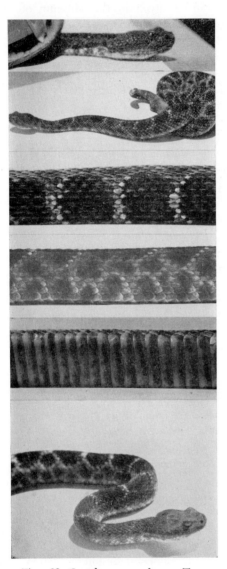

Fig. 288. *Crotalus v. cerberus*, Tucson, Ariz., C. T. Vorhies.

rear half of each belly plate is light chalcedony yellow, and the front is dark plumbeous. The background of the sides is vinaceous-slate, and there are 2 rows of spots faintly indicated on the sides, the 1st on rows 1–4, the 2nd on rows 5–7 or 8, the 2nd one alternating with the dorsal saddles. The lowest 3 rows of lateral scales are highly enameled and iridescent. The top of the head is a little darker than the ground color of the sides, being blackish from the eyes forward. There is a faint indication of light stripe from eye to angle of mouth, and very indistinct broad vitta (4 scales) of grayish olive. The face from the eye forward is drab. The iris is quaker drab with numerous flecks of mouse gray. The underside of the head is white except for the 1st 7 lower labials and symphysis, which are drab or olive-brown. There is also a touch of the same in the last 5 lower labials. The belly plates on the forward part are almost clear light chalcedony yellow.

Habitat and habits: In 1866 Cope took *Caudisona confluenta* var. *confluenta* in "San Francisco Mountains (510) No. 801 under a log on a mountain, altitude 12,000 feet. (572) No. 678, 31 inches long, had an adult *Sialia mexicana* in its stomach." Of *Caudisona lucifer* he wrote, "The numerous specimens of this species brought from Arizona by Drs. Coues and Irwin are nearly black, especially the head. 509–511, etc. San Francisco Mountains."

Van Denburgh and Slevin caught No. 34683 "at an altitude between 7,000 and 8,000 feet at the Wilderness of Rocks, on Mt. Lemon, Santa Catalina Mountains, Pima County, June 12, 1912." In 1940 Little called these "common in chaparral-woodland."

Breeding: Viviparous. About all we have discovered is Klauber's note (1949a): "I have a brood that is presumably of this subspecies, but not certainly, as there were several mothers in the cage when they were born. Of this brood of 13, the shortest is 265 mm., the longest 288 mm.; and the mean 273 mm." In 1940 in the Roosevelt Reservoir Area, Little said: "Very young rattlesnakes are light gray with dark brown blotches, but all adults observed here are black, except for narrow patterns of pink scales."

Authorities:

Cope, E. D. (Ariz., 1866a)
Coues, E. C. (Ariz., 1875)
Garman, S. (Gen., 1883)
Klauber, L. M. (Gen., 1930; Baja Calif., 1949a)
Little, E., Jr. (Ariz., 1940)

Quaintance, C. W. (Ariz., 1935)
Van Denburgh, J., and J. R. Slevin (Ariz., 1913)
Vorhies, C. F. (Ariz., 1917)
Yarrow, H. C. (Ariz., 1875)

1875, E. Coues: *Caudisona confluenta.* "*Caudisona lucifer.* . . . My numerous specimens from Arizona are nearly black, especially on the head, so decidedly different from the Oregon type as to probably warrant varietal distinction of this southern form, which may be called *C. lucifer,* var. *cerberus.*"

1913, J. Van Denburgh and J. R. Slevin: "When we reached Tucson we heard much of the black rattlesnake of the Catalinas, as this species is locally known. It was with much difficulty that we secured a specimen (No. 34683). There can be no doubt that it is specifically identical with *C. oreganus* of California. Whether it will be necessary to regard the dark Arizona snakes as a subspecies, *C. oreganus cerberus* (Coues), cannot be decided until more specimens are received."

1917: C. T. Vorhies was much interested in the black rattlesnake. He told us of leaving Tucson for a lecture with one of his very black rattlesnakes in a large container, and, to his surprise, arriving at the place of his talk with a much lighter-colored snake which showed the dorsal markings of *C. v. oreganus*.

1936, L. M. Klauber (Gen.): "The Arizona-Sonora range of *oreganus* does not conjoin the coastal range; there is an unoccupied desert gap between. Nevertheless I do not find consistent differences warranting the recognition of the Arizona form as a separate subspecies, *C. v. cerberus.*"

1949(a), L. M. Klauber: From 98 specimens he revived *C. v. cerberus* and wrote 8 pages on diagnosis, nomenclatorial and systematic problems, material, intraspecific trends, relationships, and range and locality records.

Midget faded rattlesnake (7—Klauber 1930), Yellow rattlesnake (5—Woodbury 1929)

Crotalus viridis decolor Klauber 1929. Fig. 289; Map 67

Another common name: Faded rattlesnake.
Range: The Colorado and Green River basins of e. Utah, s.w. Wyoming, and w. Colorado.—Colo.; Ut.; Wyo. *Elevation*—4,000 to 8,000 feet. 6,000 feet (Klauber).
Size: Adults, 20–30 inches.
Distinctive characteristics: "Color straw, cream or yellow; blotches often only faintly in evidence or obsolete in adults; adult size smaller, usually under 650 mm.; light postocular stripe 2 or more scales wide, often indefinite or absent . . . ; body blotches, if in evidence, commonly diamonds, ellipses, or if rectangles, with edges rough or serrated, and often without narrow light borders" (Klauber).

"General coloration pale in tone, brownish gray, cream, or straw color; pattern inconspicuous or obsolete; blotches of body subrectangular or subelliptical, 37–47 (av. 42) in number, centers usually of same tone as ground color, narrowly outlined in dark brown; 1 or 2 series of lateral spots, usually faint; tail rings same color as pattern of body, terminal ones darker, 7–11 (av. 8.5) in males, 6–10 (av. 7) in females; head markings inconspicuous" (Gloyd).

Color: We have never seen a live specimen. We give Woodbury's (Ut., 1929) coloration of the type specimen, which we have examined: "General appearance, a reddish-yellow brown. A faint or almost obsolete pattern of slightly darker brown rhombs of which there are about 40 along the dorsum difficult to trace, but mostly connecting with spots of similar color on the sides, these spots reaching the first row of scales; this pattern giving way on the tail to faint crossbands which are 10 in number. Indications of an extremely faint postocular line passing horizontally to the posterior edge of the mouth. Abdominal plates more yellow, but in most cases grading to a slightly darker yellowish brown peppered with spots of darker color at each end of the plate." Woodbury called this form *Crotalus concolor.*

Habitat and habits: In 1911 Cary (Wyo., 1917) placed it in "sandy plains" in the Colorado River drainage area; in 1915 Van Denburgh and Slevin recorded "sandy desert" for Grand Co., Ut., and in 1935 found one "on a dead branch near the ground"; and in 1942 Kauffeld gave "rocky situations."

Period of activity: *Early appearances*—Apr. 18, May 30, June 14, June, 1937 (Hardy); May 30–June 4, 1913 (Van Denburgh and Slevin). *Fall disappearance*—Sept., 1925, Oct. 5, 1937 (Hardy); Sept., 1929 (Woodbury, Ut., 1929); July 27, 1933 (Eaton).

Breeding: Viviparous. *Young*—On mating, Wood (Wyo., 1933) remarked: "Further south, in Duchesne County, Utah, during the first week in August 1928, a young prairie rattler was caught which had already passed its first moult. This may mean that fertilization occurs earlier in this region; or that there is a slight seasonal variation from year to year; or that individual cases may fluctuate over some weeks."

Food: Kauffeld gives "small mammals. Also probably lizards."

Field notes: May 11, 1947: Dr. Ann Dunham of Northampton, Mass., tells of an incident during a camping trip of a friend whose mother was asked whether she'd slept well the previous night. She said, "Yes, why?" The questioner replied, "You had your cot right where we found the pink rattlesnake last year." They had camped at Trackhyte, 49 miles from Hanksville, near or in the Blue Henry Mts., Ut.

Authorities:

Eaton, T. H., Jr. (Ariz., 1935b)
Gloyd, H. K. (Gen., 1940)
Hardy, R. (Ut., 1938)
Klauber, L. M. (Gen., 1936)

Van Denburgh, J., and J. R. Slevin (Ut., 1915)
Woodbury, A. M. (Ut., 1929, 1930, 1931)

1915, J. Van Denburgh and J. R. Slevin: *"Crotalus oreganus* Holbrook. . . . The seventh (No. 38098) seems to agree with the others in squamation, but is creamy white in color without any darker markings. This last specimen was caught out on a sandy desert south of Thompson, Grand County, May 30 to June 4, 1913."

1929, A. M. Woodbury: "The new rattlesnake herein described was taken on a zoological expedition from the University of Utah to the Henry Mts. by Prof. R. V. Chamberlain. . . .

"Scale rows 25 over middle and caudal part of anterior region, reducing in number caudad; all keeled excepting those of the 1st row; heavy dorsally but weaker on the sides. Abdominal plates 175; the tail plates numbering 25 + 2 mostly in a single series. Top of head covered by small irregular scales except for the large supraoculars; anterior nasal large, in contact with the rostral which is higher than wide (6:5); upper labials 13, separated from eye by 3-4 rows of small scales; lower labials 15; 1st pair of genials very small, the 2nd pair enlarged. . . .

"*Type locality*—King's Ranch, Garfield Co., at base of the Henry Mts. The holotype, a male, was taken in Sept. 1929, and is deposited in the Zoological Museum of the University of Utah. Cowboys say that this form, which they commonly speak of as The Yellow Rattlesnake, is not uncommon in the general region in which the type was taken."

1930, A. M. Woodbury: "The pattern markings on *C. concolor,* although faint, are distinctly different from those of *C. tigris tigris.*"

1938, R. Hardy: "The Yellow Rattlesnake *Crotalus viridis concolor* Woodbury. Reported as common at Nine Mile. Collected: Columbia, October 5, 1937; Kenilworth; in Carbon County north of Mounds; Sunnyside September 1935; Castle Gate June 1937; Soldier Canyon June 1937; 4 miles south of Price April 18, 1937, 1 mile north of Price June 14, 1937; at edge of city limits of Price May 30, 1937. At least 5 have been killed during 1937 within a quarter mile of the northern limits of Price."

In 1839 Townsend (in *Early Western Travels,* p. 186) noted a snake found in the area between Sweetwater and the Sandy River, a tributary of the Green River in Wyo.: "It is a different species from our common one at home, but is equally malignant and venomous. The horses are often startled by them and dart aside with intuitive fear when their note of warning is sounded in the path." Was this *decolor?*

Southern Pacific rattlesnake (Klauber 1949)

Crotalus viridis helleri Meek 1905. Fig. 290; Map 67

Other common names: Black diamond-back; black (diamond) rattler; gray diamond-back; mountain rattler; Pacific rattler; San Diegan rattler; timber rattler.

Range: Coastal and mountain region from n. boundary lines of Santa Barbara, Ventura, and Los Angeles Cos. (including Santa Catalina Island), Calif., s. to 29°N. in Baja California, Mex.—U.S.A.: Calif. Mex.: Baja Calif. *Elevation*—Coast to desert foothills down to an altitude of about 2,000 feet (Klauber, Calif., 1931a); ocean to foothills, 7,500 to 10,785 feet

Fig. 289. *Crotalus v. decolor,* Escalente den, Garfield Co., Utah, A. M. Woodbury.

Fig. 290. *Crotalus v. helleri,* Laguna Beach, San Diego, Calif.

(Perkins); 1,800, 2,200, 4,900, 6,000, 6,800, 7,000, 8,000 feet (Atsatt); 8,000 feet (Meek); 6,515 feet (Klauber, 1924a); 9,000 feet (Bogert).

Size: Adults, 24–55 inches.

Longevity: 16 years 10 months (Perkins, Gen., 1954). "A thing we can not help mentioning here, is the popular exaggeration as to the size of snakes. We have heard thoroly honest people tell about rattlesnakes 5 and 6 feet long and 'as big round as a man's leg.' In all our experience the largest measurement we have obtained from fresh specimens was 42 inches; in this instance the girth was just 4 inches, which is rather less than in some shorter examples we have seen. . . . But snakes look bigger to most people than they really are! Then, too, some people base their statements on the measurements of *skins*. Now a 3-foot rattler will produce a skin, when stretched and tanned, 4½ feet long! We do not doubt that 4-footers of our species do exist tho we haven't found that size yet ourselves. But we want the chance to apply the yard stick to larger ones, for our own satisfaction" (Grinnell and Grinnell).

Longevity: 13 years 10 months (Perkins, Gen., 1951); 16 years 10 months (Perkins, Gen., 1954).

Distinctive characteristics: "This subspecies usually has diamonds on the back, instead of hexagons as in *oreganus*. The dark tail ring in the adults is more than 1½ times as wide as the preceding dark ring while in *oreganus* the rings are equal. In juveniles the end of the tail in *helleri* has a wide yellow ring, gradually turning to gray or black as the snakes age; in *oreganus* the terminal crossband is dark from birth and is no wider than the rings that precede it on the tail. The button matrix is usually yellow in juvenile *helleri* and black in *oreganus*. C. v. helleri differs from *cerberus* in having a single row of light scales completely bordering the dorsal diamonds; whereas in *cerberus* the dorsal blotches laterally merge directly into the ground color. A majority of specimens of *helleri* have single loreals, while *cerberus* has two. Most *helleri* specimens have no scales between the prenasal and the 1st supralabial at the rostral; in *cerberus* such scales are generally present, at least at the rostral. The differences from the other *viridis* subspecies are similar to those cited under *oreganus*" (Klauber, Baja Calif., 1949a).

Color: Of this recently re-established form we quote the original description of 1905: "Ground color of body very dark, dark blotches on back separated by narrow yellow lines, forming a chain along back, being obscure on anterior third of body and becoming light cross streaks on posterior fifth; a light line 1 scale wide from middle of eye to 8th upper labial extending backward to angle of mouth covering the labials and a small portion of the row of scales just above them; tail a dark brown, with 3 light cross bands on anterior half; ventral surface much mottled and blotched with dark brown; on anterior half of body the white predominates, on posterior half the darker. Six rattles. . . . This species is quite different from *Crotalus atrox* B & G, which it most resembles, in being much darker, in the indistinctness of the dorsal blotches, the dark mottled ventral surface, and in having a black tail crossed with light bands; the stripes on the side of the head are quite different. Named for Mr. Edmund Heller" (Meek).

Diverse coloration—In 1934(a) Klauber (Calif.) remarked: "It varies considerably in coloration, but in this area it is usually gray or grayish brown, with a series of black or dark-brown blotches down the back. Some specimens, particularly from the mountains, are almost entirely black, and the snake is not infrequently referred to in this district as the Black Diamond Rattler."

Habitat: This form has been found in both Sonoran zones and also in the Transition zone. Groups from San Diego and Los Angeles reported it from ocean to desert in fields, brush, rocks, on trails and open stretches of sand, on canyon bottoms, and at the headwaters of rivers in the mountains. In 1939(a) in a table in his "Ecological conditions of roadsides," Klauber (Gen.) recorded: *"C. v. oreganus:* orchard or vineyard 1, cultivated fields 7, grass 22, light brush 3, heavy brush chaparral 14, trees, forest 4, rocks, boulders 2."

Period of activity: *First appearance*—Mar. 13, 1931, June 17, 1925 (Linsdale). *Fall disappearance*—Sept. 15, 1906 (Grinnells). In the "Sixteen Year Census" for *C. v. oreganus* Klauber (Gen., 1939a) gave Jan., 11 snakes; Feb., 19; March, 125; April, 223; May, 251; June, 184; July, 125; Aug., 108; Sept., 88; Oct., 81; Nov., 26; Dec., 17. Total 1,258. Rank 3. Per cent 9.71.

Breeding: Viviparous. In 1937 Klauber (IV) recorded 10 large males 1,102–1,300 mm. and 10 large females 860–1,052 mm.; smallest gravid female 596 mm.; maximum specimen measured 1,371 mm.; average size at birth 275 mm.; smallest measured 225 mm. *Young*—Number, 1–14. Size, 225–305 mm. long. In 1936 in a series of San Diego broods Klauber (I) secured 102 males and 107 females of the young of the year. Of *oreganus* (most of which were doubtless *helleri*), he recorded broods as follows: 1 of 1, 1 of 2, 8 of 3, 9 of 4, 5 of 5, 2 of 6, 3 of 7, 1 of 8, 5 of 9, 4 of 10, 3 of 11, 2 of 12, 4 of 13, 1 of 14. In 1937 he (IV) recorded of *oreganus* (doubtless mostly *helleri*): 1 brood of 7, 256–267 mm. long; 1 of 7, 260–286 mm.; 1 of 12, 225–243 mm.; 1 of 10, 231–260 mm., 1 of 13, 265–283 mm., 1 of 5, 295–305 mm. In 1949(a) he wrote that the young are normally about 275 mm., though a few may be as small as 225 mm. "The young have a light stripe across the top of the head, which is missing in the adults" (Perkins).

Hybrid rattlesnakes—See Perkins (Gen., 1951a) under account of *C. r. ruber* above for cross mating of *C. v. helleri* male with *C. r. ruber* female.

Food: Rodents, lizards, toads, insects. Grinnell and Grinnell, Grinnell, Atsatt, Ruthling, Storer and Wilson, Klauber (1934a), Von Bloecker.

Venom and bite: In 1931 Githens and George (Gen.) reported 0.1 mg. of dried venom from this form a fatal dose (MLD), the same as for *cerberus* and *enyo*. Five of 6 forms are more potent than *helleri*. Nevertheless in 1934(a) Klauber said, "It has a powerful venom and is a thoroughly dangerous snake."

"The senior author in his extended field work has encountered a great many rattlesnakes but has never been bitten and has never known anyone else in this near vicinity having been bitten. The point here made is that the chances of being bitten, even when one is by occupation particularly exposed, are extremely remote" (Grinnell and Grinnell). The following year, 1908, Grinnell said, "To the naturalist, rattlesnakes are very interesting members of our fauna, and their growing scarcity arouses regret within us, just as does the disappearance of the ground owl, road-runner and golden eagle. We wish people could be more sensible in regard to even the rattlesnake; and yet probably 99 out of 100 people would put us down as crazy for recommending that rattlesnakes, except in the thickly-settled valleys, or in the near vicinity of ranches where there are children, had better be left unharmed."

Authorities:

Atsatt, S. R. (Calif., 1913)
Bogert, C. M. (Calif., 1930)
Bryant, H. C. (Calif., 1915)
Cronise, T. F. (Calif., 1868)
Grinnell, J. (Calif., 1908)
Grinnell, J. and H. H. (Calif., 1907)
Klauber, L. M. (Gen., 1936–40, I, III, 1939a; Calif., 1924a, 1928b, 1930, 1932, 1934a; Baja Calif., 1949a)

Linsdale, J. M. (Baja Calif., 1932)
Meek, S. E. (Calif., 1905)
Perkins, C. B. (Calif., 1938)
Ruthling, P. D. R. (Calif., 1916b)
Storer, T. I., and B. M. Wilson (Calif., 1932)
Von Bloecker, J. C., Jr. (Calif., 1942)

1949(a): About the re-established form *C. v. helleri* L. M. Klauber said: "I believe I have seen well over 3,000 rattlesnakes of this subspecies alive." What a basis for judgment!

Great Basin rattlesnake (18—Klauber 1930)

Crotalus viridis lutosus Klauber 1930. Fig. 291; Map 67

Range: Great Basin from the Rockies to the Sierra Nevada: on the e. from Yellowstone Park to the Grand Canyon; thence n.w. through n. Lincoln and Nye Cos., Nev., to Mineral Co., Nev., and extreme e. California from Mono County n. through s.e. Oregon and s. Idaho.—Ariz.; Calif.; Ida.; Ore.; Ut. *Elevation*—4,000 to 9,000 feet. 4,000–7,400 feet (Taylor); 4,650 (Klauber, Gen., 1930); 4,900–6,100 (Hall); 5,400 feet (Stejneger, Calif., 1893); 6,750 feet (Ruthven); 6,500 feet (Linsdale, Nev., 1938); 7,000 (Dodge); 7,000 feet (Woodbury, Ut., 1931); 8,000 feet (Brimley, Gen., 1904); 8,000–8,900 feet (Tanner); 8,000 feet (Ditmars); 5,400 feet (Stejneger, 1891); 6,300 feet (Woodbury, 1951).

Size: Adults, 26–48 inches. Woodbury's (Ut., 1951) graph for 1940–1948 (omitting a very few young) begins at about 18 inches for 12 males, reaches a crest at 30 inches for 81 males, another crest at 32 inches for 73 males, and ends at 40 inches. The graph begins at 18 inches for 5 females, reaches a crest at 28 inches for 82 females, and ends at 37 inches.

Distinctive characteristics: "Postocular light line . . . 2 or 3 scales wide in *lutosus*, and 1 wide in *confluentus*. Likewise *lutosus* has a higher average number of scale rows between supraoculars and a greater irregularity in blotch borders than has *confluentus*. *Lutosus* is usually drab or buff in coloration; *confluentus* is gray, green, olive, brown or red-brown. From *oreganus*, *lutosus* differs primarily in color, the former being black, dark gray or dark brown; also in the character of the body blotches, which in *lutosis* tend toward narrow (measured longitudinally) hexagons well separated, while in *oreganus* the blotches are diamonds, circles, rectangles or hexagons proportionately wider along the body and with less relative separation" (Klauber, Gen., 1930).

Color: "Ground color above usually light brown or gray, but may be olive or yellowish with a central series of dark brown blotches along the back which may be circular anteriorly, but become crossbars or incomplete rings posteriorly, and are often darker around the edges. These vary in number from 34 to 46 on the body and 4 to 8 on the tail. Young specimens show 2 or 3 series of smaller, alternating, dark blotches along each side, but these often disappear in the adult. Lower surfaces usually whitish or yellow, often clouded with brown, especially on the ends of the abdominal plates. Head usually dark above with light stripe (especially in the young) running across the supraoculars, one running backward from the supraocular, but not reaching the mouth, and a third from the postnasal downward and backward along the upper labials" (Woodbury, Ut., 1931).

Habitat: This form is recorded in dry and barren regions of the Great Basin, on hills, summits, and old lake benches, and as preferring southern exposures among volcanic boulders of hillsides, rocks of butte sides, low foothills, sides of mountains and open deserts, or alfalfa fields and floors of valleys. Since the report in 1878 of the Wheeler survey "rattlesnake hills" have been so designated because of the number or prevalence of these snakes in such localities. In that year Lt. C. M. Morrison recorded a colony; and since then Richardson, Hall, and, more recently, Woodbury have made the denning of this form well known. Read Yarrow and Henshaw (1878), Hall, Richardson, and Woodbury and Hansen (Ut., 1950) for this interesting story. For the description of a den by Woodbury *et al.* (Ut., 1951), see "Hibernation" below.

Period of activity: *First appearance*—Apr. 20, 1924 (Erwin, Ida., 1925); May 8, 12, 22 (Hall); May 27, 1932 (Linsdale, Nev., 1938); May 28 (Richardson); June 7, 1944 (Evenden, Ida., 1946). "From studies of these and other data, it has been determined that the temperature of 60 degrees F. represents a close approximation to the threshold at which the snakes of the den tend to become active" (Woodbury, Ut., 1951). *Fall disappearance*—Sept. 3, 1890 (Stejneger, Ida., 1891); Oct. 5 (Yarrow and Henshaw, 1878); Oct. 23 (Woodbury, Ut., 1950). Dates of capture of specimens in the Museum of Vertebrate Zoology, Calif., range from May 11 to Sept. 9 (see Linsdale, Nev., 1938–40).

Hibernation—In 1925 Erwin recorded a spotted night snake in Ada Co., Ida., "under a rock in a den of rattlers *Crotalus oreganus* (*lutosus*), April 20, 1924." In 1929 Hall's interesting paper appeared. One pertinent paragraph is: "The den in Spring Valley is said to have been found first, in the fall, 5 years ago. As reported to us by Mr. Doyle C. Robison and Mr. W. C. Kirkland, they, late one evening when caring for sheep nearby, heard what sounded like bees swarming. Investigation revealed large numbers of rattlesnakes collected into balls about the edge of the, then smaller, hole or entrance to the den. In fall and more especially in spring, since that time, several persons have more or less regularly visited the den and killed the rattlers by shooting. On May 22, 1929, Mr. Lloyd Robison, County Game Warden, told us that a day or two earlier several people with shotguns killed 139 rattlers at the den. A lesser number had been killed on several other days. The piles of empty gun shells and the large number of dead rattlers, in various stages of decay, which we saw in and about the margin of the den bore out these statements. As reported to us the snakes began emerging about 10 days or 2 weeks previous to our visit on May 22. When I again visited the den on June 12 no live or freshly killed snakes were found."

According to Woodbury (Ut., 1951), the den which he and his associates visited for 10 years "consists of a large number of loose cobblestones just below the shoreline of ancient Lake Bonneville where former springs had washed the loose material from among the rocks and left underground channels into which the snakes descend for hibernation. It is located on an easterly facing slope at the foot of the Stansbury Mountains bearing a heavy stand of sagebrush that is replaced about a mile down the slope by the salt-tolerant shadscale. This forms a belt below the sagebrush, and in turn yields to greasewood in the bottom of the valley. About a mile above the den, the sagebrush intermingles with the junipers and pinyon pines which extend upwards into the mountains. Such a den was discovered on April 9, 1940. Snakes captured on repeated trips to the den during intervening years have been marked by tattooing a number on each snake to provide individual identification. . . . In procuring these records, 151 fruitful trips were made to the den between Apr. 12, 1940 and November 12, 1949, in addition to many trips on which no snakes were found.

"From the den have come records of the Great Basin rattlesnake, western striped racer, mormon blue racer, Great Basin gopher snake, desert spotted night snake, thimble snake, and the long-nosed snake. A total of 930 rattle-snakes, 632 striped racers, 127 blue racers, 36 gopher snakes, 2 spotted night snakes, 2 thimble snakes, and 1 long-nosed snake have been recorded and all but the last 2 tattooed. There have been in addition 1,080 recaptures of rattlesnakes, 443 striped racers, 28 blue racers, 4 gopher snakes and no recaptures of the thimble, spotted night or long-nosed snakes. This makes a total of 2,010 rattlesnake records and 1,075 striped racer records, with a grand total from the den of 3,285 of all snake records from 1940 to 1944 inclusive." The threshold of emergence was at 60°F.

Breeding: Viviparous. Males 650–1,211 mm., females 555–1,072 mm. *Sexual dimorphism*—In 1937 Klauber (IV) measured 96 males and 48 females, the males averaging 875 mm., the females 784 mm. Of 10 large specimens of each sex, he recorded 1,075–1,211 mm. for males and 879–1,072 mm. for females. Woodbury and Julian (Ut., 1951) found that the sexes are about equal in numbers for the first 3 years. Thereafter, at sexual maturity, the preponderance of males increased with the years. Why do the females drop out faster? According to Glissmeyer (Ut., 1951) the females may become gravid at 3 or 4 years of age, beginning at 22.2 to 27.3 inches.

Mating—According to Taylor, "two specimens captured in Humboldt County on August 7, 1909, at an altitude of 4,300 feet were thought to be a mating pair." In 1931 Woodbury (Ut.) wrote, "Klauber reports that they mate in the spring and the young are born alive in the fall, a specimen of this species giving birth to young on Sept. 3, 1925. A female taken in August, 1929, in Zion Canyon, contained 6 large eggs, 4 in the right and 2 in the left oviduct." In 1940 Linsdale wrote, "Females captured July 6 and 10 contained large eggs." In 1951 observing 12.5–66.7 per cent gravidity (average 49%), Glissmeyer (Ut.) inclined to accept the biennial cycle for females.

Young—Number, 3–13. Size, 242–270 mm. Time of birth, September–October. In the spring of 1929 the smallest that Hall observed was 11.25 inches long. In 1930 Klauber gave his smallest specimen as 270 mm. In 1936 he (III) recorded egg batches or broods of *lutosus* as follows: 1 with 3; 1 with 5; 2 with 6; 2 with 9; 2 with 11; 1 with 12; 3 with 13; total, 12 batches or broods averaging 8. In 1937 his (IV) minimum specimen was 242 mm. and the estimated average size at birth 265 mm. In 1938 he (V) gave body length at birth as 265 mm. In 1942 Kauffeld gave the brood as 3–13. In 1950 Woodbury and Hansen recorded from a snake den in the Tintic Mts., Ut., 6 females having 11, 7, 6, 7, 6, and 8 eggs. In 1951 Glissmeyer (Ut.) gave the range of eggs as 2–9, average 5.5.

Food: Small mammals, lizards, other vertebrates. Richardson, Ruthven and Gaige, Woodbury (1928, 1931), Hall, Pack, Linsdale (1938–40), Kauffeld.

Venom and bite: In 1946 Gloyd and Bevan (Gen.) recorded an instance where two *C. v. lutosus* bit each other. One died the same night, but the other finally recovered after a bad time.

In 1951 in Woodbury's symposium (Ut.) Sanders concluded his account of intraspecific poisoning as follows: "After considering these data, it seems probable that the amount of venom required to kill adult snakes is greater than the amount the average snake of this subspecies produces. Of 32 snakes milked in one day, a volume of 3.8 ml. of venom was obtained. This is an average of 0.118 ml. of venom per snake. If 200 gms. is taken as the average weight of an adult snake, and a known lethal dose of 0.04 ml. per gms. body weight is considered necessary to kill, it becomes apparent that the average snake does not have sufficient venom to kill a snake of comparable size. However, it is entirely possible that an old adult of 400 gms. could inject sufficient quantity of venom into a smaller snake to kill it."

Field notes: (We give only notes for 1942.) May 26, Salt Lake City, Ut.: Went at 1 P.M. with Woodbury to one of his prize dens. This one is on the Lake Bonneville shore line near Grantsville. In two large piles of round stones are 3 depressed areas where the snakes principally emerge. Two areas are in one pile, and the other area is in a somewhat smaller pile. There are many more such piles of boulders in a wash nearby, but these 2 areas are of the old Bonneville bench and probably older than the wash masses of boulders. In this area a while ago, he took *Diadophis r. regalis.* There are plenty of *C. t. taeniatus, C. c. mormon, P. c. deserticola, Heterodon* and lots of *C. v. lutosus.* We found alive 3 marked ones and 3 new ones alive not marked and 1 marked dead one with a rock on it. Looks as if someone has been here—one of the difficulties of a naturalist.

Authorities:

Amaral, A. do (Gen., 1929c)
Brown, A. E. (Gen., 1901)
Cope, E. D. (Gen., 1860, 1900; Mont., 1872; Nev., 1884; Ore., 1884)
Ditmars, R. L. (Ut., 1905)
Dodge, N. N. (Ariz., 1931)
Eaton, T. H., Jr. (Ariz., 1935, 1935b)
Gloyd, H. K. (Gen., 1940)
Hall, E. R. (Nev., 1929)
Kauffeld, C. F. (Gen., 1942)
Klauber, L. M. (Gen., 1930, 1936, 1936–40, III, IV; Ariz., 1935b; Baja Calif., 1949a)
Linsdale, J. M. (Nev., 1938, 1938–1940)
Pack, H. J. (Ut., 1930)
Richardson, C. H. (Nev., 1915)
Ruthven, A. G. (Ut., 1932)
Ruthven, A. G., and H. T. Gaige (Nev., 1915)
Stejneger, L. (Gen., 1895; Ida., 1891)
Storm, R. M., and R. A. Pimental (Ore., 1949)
Tanner, V. M. (Ut., 1930)
Tanner, W. W. (Ut., 1940)
Taylor, W. P. (Nev., 1912)
Van Denburgh, J., and J. R. Slevin (Nev., 1921a)
Woodbury, A. M. (Ut., 1928, 1931, 1950, 1951)
Yarrow, H. C., and H. W. Henshaw (Ariz., 1878)

(1898) 1900, E. D. Cope: *Crotalus confluentus lecontei.* "This is the *C. confluentus* of the Great Basin."

1930, L. M. Klauber: *C. v. lutosus.* This is one of the landmark papers of the southwest.

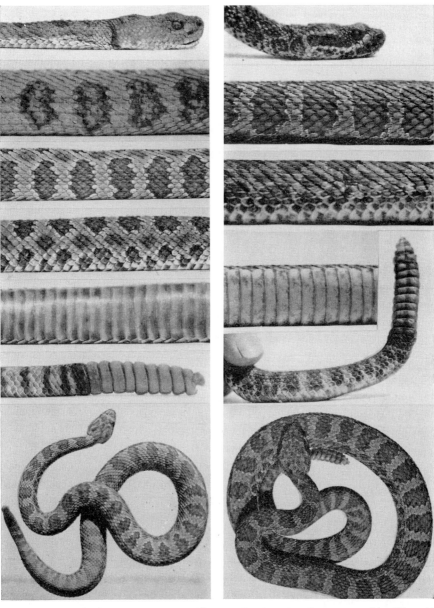

Fig. 291. *Crotalus v. lutosus,* Grantsville den, Salt Lake City, Utah, A. M. Woodbury and A. H. Wright.

Fig. 292. *Crotalus v. nuntius,* Wupatki Nat. Monument, Ariz., P., B., and D. Jones.

1949(a): Klauber compared *lutosus, oreganus,* and *helleri* and their ranges.

1951, A. M. Woodbury *et al.:* "Symposium: A snake den in Tooele County, Utah." This is a compendium of data we cannot review in our limited space.

Arizona prairie rattlesnake (8—Klauber 1935)

Crotalus viridis nuntius Klauber 1935. Fig. 292; Map 67

Another common name: Prairie rattlesnake.

Range: N.e. Arizona. *Elevation*—4,500 to 7,000 feet. 4,800–5,200 feet (Klauber, Ariz., 1935).

Size: Adults, 16–30 inches.

Distinctive characteristics: "Color pink, red or red brown*; scale rows 25 or 23; dorsal scales at the center of tail 12 or less; adults rarely exceeding 650 mm. *Specimens from the plateau south of the Grand Canyon, Arizona, are usually greenish or grayish but should be referred to this subspecies" (Klauber, Gen., 1936).

Color: A snake from Wupatki National Monument, Ariz., received from Paul, Ben, and Dave Jones and described July, 1939. The general background of the dorsum is grayish olive, with that on the neck buffy olive. The 1 to 2 scale rows between the dark saddles are light brownish olive. On the body, there are 44 quadrate dorsal saddles slightly emarginate front and rear, with 6 more on the tail. These saddle spots are olive-brown or brownish olive in their centers and outlined with mummy brown or black, outside of which is a broken thread of olive-buff or marguerite yellow. These spots usually cover 10 scales transversely and 2½ longitudinally. After the 29th, the dorsal spots unite with the lateral spots to form transverse bands. These bands are not outlined with the light thread. On the 3rd to 5th scale rows and opposite the dorsal saddles is a row of spots colored like the dorsal ones, and on the 5th to 7th rows is a less distinct series. Many of the scales below the lateral spots have lower margins of olive-buff, and this is particularly true of the lower and rear margins of the 1st row of scales. The basal segment of the rattle is black, the rest being olive-buff. The vitta on the side of the head is mummy brown. The top of the head is buffy olive outlined by a narrow band of deep olive-buff, which extends from the upper rear edge of the eye, along the upper margin of the vitta, turning down back of the angle of the mouth and returning along the lower margin of the vitta to the vertical back of the eye, whence it passes obliquely upward across the loreal. From the angle of the mouth to the loreal, this light band is primrose yellow or olive-buff. On the supraocular is an obscure bar of deep olive-buff. The mental, forward part of anterior chin shields, first 5 lower labials, first 4 upper labials, all of the face ahead of the labial pit, rostral, and top of head forward of the supraocular bars are fuscous-black or chaetura drab. From the 4th upper labial backward for 4 or 5 plates is a labial light line or edge of olive-buff. Most of the underside of the head is white or pale olive-buff, and this color breaks through the dark of lower and upper labials to make 2 or 3 light bars to the prominent light stripe on the side of the head. The iris is, like the vitta, mummy brown. The venter is white in the forward part, then pale olive-buff or olive-buff in mid-body, with the ends of the ventrals clouded. The black ring at the base of the rattle is about 4 scales wide and extends across 4 or 5 ventrals.

Habitat and habits: There is almost nothing on the ecology, habits, or habitat of this little Colorado River subspecies. In 1942 Kauffeld placed it on "high prairies covered with scattered low brush and grass."

Breeding: Viviparous. In 1936 Klauber (1936–40, I) wrote: "From certain rattle studies I would estimate this increase at not less than 120 mm. per snake, so that we may presume the smallest females to have a length of about 700 mm. at the time of their first broods. This refers only to the Platteville series of *C. c. confluentus* as found in east-central Colorado. In the Dakotas and Montana they will be about 100 mm. longer, and near Winslow, Arizona, where they have differentiated into the stunted subspecies *C. c. nuntius,* they will be about 250 mm. shorter than the Colorado specimens." In 1937 Klauber (IV) recorded a brood of 7 killed before birth; 135 mm. was the minimum, 146 mm. the maximum. His ten large adult males were 658–732 mm.; his ten large females were 521–558 mm.; 180 mm. was average size at birth; 395 mm. the smallest gravid female; he estimated 650 mm. as the approximate size of the large adult male. Elsewhere in his data (1936, III) we find 1 brood or egg batch of 3, 1 of 4, 2 of 5, 1 of 7, and 1 of 10—6 broods in all, with an average of 6 per snake. He states that stunted subspecies like *C. c. nuntius* have fewer young than large species. In 1942 Kauffeld recorded 3–10 young.

Food: Small mammals, lizards. Kauffeld.

Venom and bite: Here we consider the well-known handling of snakes by Indians during ceremonial dances often without serious effects, and some explanations for the Indians' apparent immunity, including the use of antidotes, the defanging or milking of snakes, and other theories.

Indian snake dances—The earliest references to the Hopi snake dance we have chanced upon are those of Marcy (1866) and Schoolcraft. The year 1884 marked the publication of Bourke's *The Snake Dance of the Moquis of Arizona,* which more than any other study focused attention on the Hopi ceremonial. An old student of Agassiz, Fewkes, pioneered (1889–1907) in this study with some 15 or more published papers. Later, Dorsey and Voth

(1902–1905) gave detailed accounts of these dances. We recommend to your attention Klauber's "A herpetological review of the Hopi snake dance," *Bull. Zool. Soc. San Diego,* no. 9 (1932), which is an excellent annotated bibliography of 114 titles, in which the earliest reference is for 1881. Although Klauber makes no claim for completeness, he covers the most significant literature of the Hopi snake dance, especially the snake hunts, snake washings, snake dance, snake myth, and snake antidote. We readily believe that 50 or more secondary titles—including anonymous accounts but excluding newspaper ones—had appeared by this time, but Klauber knew of these even better than we.

In 1933 Bogert's description "Notes on the snake dance of the Hopi Indians" (Ariz.) appeared. One of the dances he visited was the following: "At the Shongopovi Dance, with 15 Antelope Priests and 16 Snake Priests participating, a total of 23 snakes were counted as they were received from the *kisi* by the dancers. Of this number, 10 were prairie rattlers, *Crotalus confluentus confluentus,* of 2 phases. One rattler was the phase which Klauber (1932: pls. 1–3) terms the 'large green,' while the other 9 were 'intermediate olive greens.' At the dance at Hotevilla on August 25, 8 Antelope Priests and 14 Snake Priests participated and 30 serpents were used. This time, however, out of 12 rattlers, 9 were the 'large green' phase of *C. c. confluentus* while only 3 were of the 'intermediate olive greens.' None of the 'small red' phase seen by Klauber in the 1931 Mishongnovi Dance were observed in either 1932 dance observed by the writer, although it might be remarked that these phases are easily distinguishable. Other snakes used in the Hotevilla Dance were 16 *P. c. rutilus* and 1 *C. t. taeniatus.*"

Antidote—A pint of the antidote so frequently mentioned as in use among the Indians was secured by Coleman (Gen., 1928). An excerpt from his account follows: "Much has been written of the fearlessness of the Hopi Indians of Arizona in handling rattlesnakes, and of their freedom from fatalities when bitten either during their snake dances or at other times. I was present at two of the snake dances last August and asked many questions of educated and intelligent Indians. The following statements were made to me by them: (1) Neither the fangs nor the poison glands of the snakes used in the dances are removed. (2) The Indians are occasionally bitten during the dance. One Indian Priest was bitten in the face last August at Walpi. They are occasionally bitten at other times. (3) There appears to be no natural immunity among Indians to rattlesnake venom. (4) An antidote is prepared by boiling the leaves and stems of some plant the nature of which is kept secret. This secret is known to only one person in the tribe and when his death becomes imminent is handed down to another. One Indian said the plant is boiled in water 10 minutes, another said half an hour, and a third reported 2 or 3 hours. Many of the Indians are said to have this remedy constantly on hand, and it is said to be effective for 2 or 3 months after being prepared. The usual procedures are adopted in cases of rattlesnake bite, that is, the application of a tourniquet when possible, and lancing of the wound. After this the wound is moistened with the antidote which is also taken internally. . . . Coleman experimented on a few guinea pigs and concluded "that the 'antidote' at least 2 months after its preparation, does not protect guinea pigs against small amounts of rattle-snake venom."

Several writers have referred to Yarrow, but we quote from a work that most herpetologists have overlooked, his "Poisonous reptiles" in *Reference Handbook of Medical Science* (1888, VI: 172): "The writer while sojourning among the Moqui Indians of Arizona, at the time of their celebrated 'snake dance,' was shown the so-called antidote which they employ in case a dancer is bitten; it is a pale, dirty-green fluid, without odor, and slightly bitter in taste, but its composition could not be ascertained, only 2 individuals in the tribe knowing how to prepare it. This preparation is used, mixed with saliva and the charcoal of piñon nuts, to smear the bodies of those Indians who are to participate in the dance, and after it is finished copious draughts of it are swallowed which produce prompt emesis. In case one is bitten, which happens occasionally, the wound is immediately sucked, some of the anti-dote rubbed into the wound, and a large quantity swallowed. During the last 10 years, in which period 5 dances have occurred, but one individual has perished from snake-bite; and this is more surprising when the fact is made known that the salient feature of the dance consists in the dancer holding one or two rattlesnakes in the mouth. The writer saw two individuals bitten, both by harmless snakes. Unfortunately for science, no opportunity was afforded to test the permanganate solution, which had been prepared and was on hand for use should occasion offer."

Defanging snakes—In 1886 Mindeleff wrote (*Science,* 1886, p. 12): "At [Yarrow's] request a large rattlesnake, selected by himself, was held up for his examination by one of the Indians, and, upon prying its mouth open, he found the fangs intact and of large size. I may add, that at the conclusion of the 1883 snake-dance, 2 rattlesnakes were captured, and sent to the na-tional museum. They were examined soon after their arrival by Dr. S. Weir Mitchell of Philadelphia, who found them in perfect order: their fangs had not been disturbed, and the poison-sacks were intact and full of venom." In 1891 Powell confirmed this (*7th Annual Report of U.S. Bureau Ethnol.,* 1891, p. xxix): "Dr. Yarrow visited (1885) the Moki pueblos in Arizona. . . . From his knowledge of the reptilian fauna of the country he was able to identify the species of serpents used in the dance and from personal ex-amination satisfied himself that the fangs had not been extracted from the poisonous reptiles." In 1922 Curtis in *The North American Indian* (XII,

136) thought the snakes were defanged. Lummis in 1924 (*Sunset Magazine,* **52**: 32) asserted that the rattlers are not defanged.

Bogert (Ariz., 1933) disagreed with Lummis. With a small telescope, he and his party observed where the priests released the snakes, and they recovered a bull snake and a "medium green" rattlesnake. He wrote: "In the sanctum of a gully not far from the shrine, a stop was made to examine the rattlesnake in case anything were to happen which might not later allow us the opportunity to do so. From Klauber's observations, and from the accounts of most ethnologists (except Curtis, 1922: 136) I fully expected to find the venom apparatus intact. Therefore, it was something of a surprise, upon prying the snake's mouth open with a pencil, to find the fangs entirely lacking and obviously removed. With the object of learning something regarding the condition of the venom glands, pressure was applied with the thumb and finger to the proper region, but no venom, at least none recognizable as such, was forced out into the mouth. Of course, with the fangs removed, it would be difficult to observe and identify a discharge of venom. . . . While evidence in this one case is conclusive, there are the following possibilities: 1) Such complete defanging is a recent change in the ritual. 2) Such defanging is practiced at Shongopovi only. (Presentations of the snake dance as given at each of 5 Hopi villages are known to be different in minor particulars.) 3) Only the rattlers used by the neophytes are defanged. 4) If such skillful defanging is practiced at one village, some other protective measure, such as plugging the hollow fangs, or 'milking' the snakes of their venom as suggested by Klauber, while only a dubious possibility, may be used in other villages. Examination of one additional rattler used in a snake dance held at a village other than Shongopovi would furnish a basis for answering most of the questions raised by these possibilities. The rattler from Shongopovi is now in the collection of the University of California at Los Angeles."

Oliver has also published recently on possible defanging in present-day rituals.

Milking snakes—In 1925 Lawrence wrote (*Living Age,* Apr. 4, 1925, **325**: 55): "Therefore, during the 9 days of the kiva, when the snakes are bathed and lustrated, perhaps they strike their poison away into some inanimate object. And surely they are soothed and calmed with such things as the priests after centuries of experiences know."

In 1932 Klauber (Ariz.) concluded "that, if any explanation of the Indians' apparent immunity from serious accidents be necessary, beyond the known docility of snakes in captivity, it is to be found in the evacuation of the venom glands before the ceremony. The final word on this will not be spoken until some herpetologist has had an opportunity to examine carefully several of the rattlesnakes used in the rite, sometime between the ceremonial washing in the kiva at noon on the day of the dance, and the ultimate dispersal of these messengers to the gods at the foot of the cliffs after the ceremony."

In 1942 Stirling (Gen.) stated: "Owing to knowledge of the habits of the rattlesnakes, previous manipulation and confinement of the snakes, skill in handling, and teamwork in the dance, the Hopi dancers are not frequently bitten. However, occasional bites do occur but apparently never with serious results. The principal reason for this is probably that during previous handling the poison glands of the snakes have been emptied or the venom considerably reduced in quantity."

Other theories of protection—These were discussed at length by Klauber (Gen., 1932a) under such topics as audience, priest, or snake hypnotism; antidotal measures; body smears; snakes blinded, paralyzed, tamed, teased of their venom, or starved; priestly immunity, health, purification, fearlessness. Anyone who ever saw Mrs. Olive Wiley in her Minneapolis–St. Paul days knows what fearless handling can do. On this matter it is apropos to mention Dr. Yarrow's belief as reported by Powell in the account quoted under "Defanging" above. "He thinks, however, that the reptiles are somewhat tamed by handling during the 4 days that they are kept in the estufas and possibly are made to eject the greater part of the venom contained in the sacs at the roots of the teeth, by being teased and forced to strike at different objects held near them. He does not think that a vegetable decoction in which they are washed has a stupefying effect, as has been supposed by some."

Authorities:

Bogert, C. M. (Ariz., 1933)
Dodge, N. N. (Ariz., 1938)
Kauffeld, C. F. (Gen., 1942)

Klauber, L. M. (Gen., 1936–40, III, IV;
Ariz., 1932, 1935b)
Stejneger, L. (Ariz., 1860)

Pacific rattlesnake (68—Van Denburgh 1897), Black rattlesnake (5—Grinnell and Camp 1917)

Crotalus viridis oreganus Holbrook 1840. Fig. 293; Map 67

Other common names: Arizona diamond rattlesnake; black diamond rattlesnake; black snake; California rattlesnake; confluent rattlesnake; diamond-back rattlesnake; Great Basin rattlesnake; Hallowell's rattlesnake(?); Missouri rattlesnake; Oregon rattlesnake; Pacific rattler (19); rattlesnake (Ross 1849); southern rattlesnake; western black rattlesnake; western rattler.

Range: From the n. boundary lines of Santa Barbara, Ventura, and Los Angeles Cos., Calif., n. through California to s.w. Oregon, thence n.e.

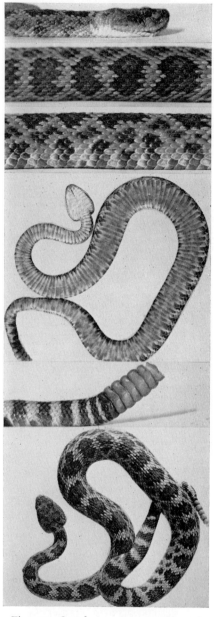

Fig. 293. *Crotalus v. oreganus,* Yosemite National Park, Calif., C. A. Harwell.

through Oregon, extreme w. Idaho and e. Washington to s.cent. British Columbia, Can.—U.S.A.: Calif.; Ida.; N.M.; Ore.; Wash. Can.: B.C. *Elevation*—500 to 12,000 feet. 600, 5,200, 5,400, 5,600 feet (Grinnell, Dixon, and Linsdale, Calif., 1930); 3,000 feet (Martin); 3,500 (Little, Ariz., 1940); 5,000 feet (Klauber, Calif., 1933); 7,500 feet (Storer and Wilson); 8,100 feet (Grinnell and Storer); 8,600 feet (Stejneger); 10,875 feet (Ewan, Calif., 1932); 1,200 feet (Cope, Calif., 1868); below 3,000 feet (Ferguson, Ore., 1954).

Size: Adults, 24–60 inches. We doubt if miners of California today meet the 6-foot "huge rattlesnakes" which Charles Dickens' *All the Year Round* mentioned (July 13, 1861), nor do they behold William Seton's "smallest rattlesnake . . . the *Crotalus oreganus* . . . whose length does not exceed 15 inches" (*Catholic World* 55: 696). Unscientific rattlesnake literature is very entertaining.

Longevity: 16–20 years, according to Fitch's (Calif., 1949) observations for a 9-year span.

Distinctive characteristics: "This subspecies is characterized in most areas by a generally lighter color than *helleri* or *cerberus;* and by hexagonal or circular blotches compared with the diamonds prevalent farther south. It has more sharply outlined head marks and lateral secondary blotches. The dark tail rings are of uniform width and are clearly defined, whereas in the other 2 subspecies the last dark ring is about twice as wide as the others and is ill-defined. In *oreganus,* especially the juveniles, the terminal tail ring is usually darker than those that precede it, and the matrix of the rattle button is generally black; in *helleri* and most specimens of *cerberus* the terminal tail ring in the juveniles is yellow and so is the button. The rattles are of smaller average dimensions in *oreganus* than in *helleri*. From *viridis viridis* and *nuntius, oreganus* differs in having a wider postocular light stripe and fewer tail rings. It is not vermilion or orange in color like *abyssus,* and has less widely separated body blotches than *lutosus*. It is larger and darker than *decolor"* (Klauber, Baja Calif., 1949a).

Color: A snake from near Big Creek, Calif. (near Huntington Lake), received July 10, 1939, from Kern. The back is marked with 41 rhombs and bars, counting the one at the base of the rattle; of these, 5 are on the tail. In addition, there is a broken spot on the nape. There are about 25 good rhombs, but thereafter the dorsal rhombs unite with the lateral series of spots to form transverse bands, of which there are 9 on the body and 5 on the tail. The rhombs extend 9 to 10 scales transversely and 3 to 4 longitudinally. In this distinct dorsal series, the central scales are light brownish olive and the edging scales clove brown. The rhomb at the base of the rattle is entirely black, and the basal ring of the rattle entirely dark, with the rest deep olive-buff. In the forward portion of the body, the space between these dark rhombs is deep olive-buff for 7 to 8 scales transversely, with a few scales of the same color partially and irregularly bordering the forward edges of the rhombs. Toward the tail these interspaces become dark olive-buff, and the light rings on the venter of the tail are cream-buff. The background color of the sides is light mouse gray or light drab, within which directly opposite the olive-buff interval is a dusky indistinct dark area of mouse gray. These dusky areas alternate with the dorsal rhombs. The top of the head is drab-gray with a light transverse bar of smoke gray across the supraocular. The light postocular stripe is very indistinct, and the dark vitta from the eye toward the mouth is hair brown. From the labial pit to the upper border of the upper labials is a dark area like the posterior vitta of the eye. The iris is olive-buff in the upper portion, smoke gray in the lower, with a pupil ring of olive-buff. On the lowest 4 or 5 lateral rows of scales is a series of vertical spots 1 to 1½ scales longitudinally. These are neither dark nor light-edged like the dorsal rhombs, but are deep grayish olive or grayish olive; this color usually extends as a block onto the ventrals. Sometimes there are intermediate blocks of grayish olive on the belly between the extension spots. The belly is mottled with about 2 irregular rows of this color. The ground color of the underside of the head is white or cartridge buff, becoming caudad on the belly cream-buff to colonial buff.

Habitat: The Pacific rattlesnake usually has been taken in rocky situations near rivers, on bluffs and cliffs above lakes, in interior valleys and slopes, in sagebrush country, in chaparral, or in oak and pine forests. In general, it is found below the 3,000-foot belt of the elevated coniferous forests and below the mountain tops, although it has been recorded as high as 10,000 to

12,000 feet. Many have thought of this form as of the foothills of the Sierras, occasionally straying into the lower valleys.

Period of activity: *Early appearances*—Mar. 1, 3, Apr. 12, 22, May 15 (Fitch and Twining); Mar. 21, 26, Apr. 8, 9, 11, 14, 16, 21, 22, 24, 26, 27, May 2, 3, 5, 8, 10, 11, etc. (Fitch, Calif., 1949); May 6, 1928 (Klauber, Calif., 1932); May 12, 1934 (Fitch, Ore., 1936). "It is apparent that the adult snakes reach a peak of their abundance in April, and that their numbers dwindle rapidly in May and June, while the young snakes do not reach maximum numbers until May, and then dwindle more gradually through the dry season" (Fitch, Calif., 1949). Males reach the maximum of abundance earlier in spring than females; they reach another peak in August and September. Females reach the maximum in early May. *Fall disappearance*—Aug. 4, 12, 14 (Stejneger); Sept. 29, 1915 (Grinnell and Storer); Sept., Oct., Nov. (Fitch and Twining); Oct., Nov. (Fitch, Calif., 1949).

Hibernation—"In the winter, rattlesnakes 'den up,' that is, go into dormancy in holes in the ground and sometimes in crevices in rocks. In certain places, ground squirrel burrows are used" (Grinnell and Storer, Calif., 1924). In 1930 Martin reported that from his yearly den hunts in May in Okanogan Co., Wash., he averaged 100 rattlers. From 4 days' hunt in 1929, he secured 140 rattlers; from 7 days in 1930, 201. "They were captured over an area of perhaps one half mile of broken granite rock hillside."

In 1949 Fitch related that "on warm days in early spring an occasional rattlesnake is encountered before general emergence from hibernation has occurred. During the first period of mild weather, when daytime temperatures are consistently above 70°F., there is a general emergence from hibernation. At this time the snakes are most often found in compact resting coils at the edge of rock outcrops, or in grass under dead brush. . . . Ordinarily in this region no rattlesnakes are to be seen during the winter months from sometime in October until perhaps mid-March or even in April."

Breeding: Viviparous. *Combat dance*—In 1934 Bromley described an hour's combat between 2 males; their striking each other had no ill effects. One escaped, one was killed by Bromley. *Mating*—"For a period of weeks after emergence a large proportion of the adults are likely to be found in pairs. More than ⅓ of those taken in the spring of 1938, for example, were paired, indicating that mating either extends over a long time or occurs frequently. Sometimes the members of a pair were found coiled near together. On many other occasions actual courtship was seen, the male moving over the female in animated, jerky movements. Pairs were usually in well concealed situations, such as burrow entrances or rock crevices, or under the edges of brush or logs. They were sensitive to disturbance and quick to separate. In 1938 pairs were found over a 54-day period, in 1939 over a 36-day period, and in 1940 over a 54-day period. Judging from these records the duration of the breeding season is about 8 weeks" (Fitch, Gen., 1949).

In 1937, from his Pateros, Wash., series of 127 males and 83 females, Klauber (Gen., IV) gave a minimum size of 550 mm., the average length of males 691 mm., of females 599 mm. In 1949(b) his "longest specimen of the series . . . was a female measuring 1,320 mm.; a male of proportionate size would be about 1,550 mm."

Young—Number 1-16. Time of birth, Aug., Sept., and Oct. Size, 251-300 mm., average 270 mm. (Fitch, Calif., 1949). In 1936 Klauber (Gen., III, see *C. v. helleri*) reported broods or batches of 1-14 young or eggs. The smallest that Martin found in his spring den hunts of several years was 9 inches. In 1932 in British Columbia, Logier reported a female 284 mm. long. In 1949 Klauber's "shortest specimen measured was 221 mm., but specimens under 250 mm. are unusual. It is believed that in most areas the young average about 270 mm. at birth."

In Fitch's (Calif., 1949) detailed study, "weight at birth may average less than 20 grams." In 1949 he gave the size of batches of ovarian eggs for 34 females: 6 with 7 eggs each, 6 with 9; 6 with 11; 3 with 5; 3 with 8; 3 with 14; 1 with 4; 1 with 6; 1 with 10; 1 with 15; 1 with 16; 1 with 19; and 1 with 25: "Litters probably averaged somewhat smaller than the 9.9 average of eggs per female." For his growth studies he began with 251 mm.

Food: Small rodents, lizards, toads, birds. Grinnell and Storer, Logier, Storer and Wilson, Fitch and Twining, Fitch (Calif., 1949).

Venom and bite: For the period from 1927 to 1934, Githens reported 134 bites of *C. v. oreganus* (*oreganus + helleri*) with 9 deaths. "Abundant as this rattlesnake is in many parts of the foothills, it does not appear to be offensive. I have almost trodden on it a score of times" (Townsend). "Very few persons are actually bitten, and of those who are bitten but a small percentage succumb, as in most cases prompt application of proper treatment counteracts the effect of the poison" (Grinnell and Storer). In his snake hunts Martin has had his dog with him. "This dog has been struck 7 or 8 times over a period of a few years, but has always fully recovered apparently) after short periods of vomiting and resultant temporary stiffness or paralysis." Logier held that "it is not an aggressive species, and cases of bite in British Columbia are extremely rare." Conant gave two instances of a moccasin killing two Pacific rattlesnakes, showing the latter susceptible to moccasin venom.

Authorities:

Amaral, A. do (Gen., 1929b)

Blum, H. F., and C. R. Spealman (Calif., 1933)

Bromley, R. I. (Calif., 1934)

Conant, R. (Gen., 1934)

Ditmars, R. L. (Gen., 1930)

Fitch, H. S. (Calif., 1949; Ore., 1936)

Fitch, H. S., and H. Twining (Calif., 1946)

Githens, T. S. (Gen., 1935)

Gloyd, H. K. (Gen., 1940)

Grinnell, J., and T. I. Storer (Calif., 1924)

Holbrook, J. E. (Gen., 1836-42)

Kingsley, J. S., and H. C. Bumpus
    (Gen., 1885)
Klauber, L. M. (Gen., 1930; Baja Calif.,
    1949a)
Logier, E. B. S. (B.C., 1932)
Martin, P. J. (Wash., 1930)
Stejneger, L. (Calif., 1893)

Storer, T. I., and B. M. Wilson (Calif.,
    1932)
Svihla, A. and R. (Wash., 1933)
Swift, L. W. (Calif., 1933)
Townsend, C. H. (Calif., 1888)
Van Denburgh, J. (Ore., 1898)

1946, H. S. Fitch and H. Twining: This is a fine study of the feeding habits of the Pacific rattlesnake, but it was superseded by Fitch's paper of 1949 (Calif.), the best study of the subspecies.

Willard's rattlesnake (10—Van Denburgh 1922), Ridge-nosed rattlesnake (3—Klauber 1936)

Crotalus willardi willardi Meek 1905. Figs. 294, 295; Map 67

Another common name: Willard's rattler.

Range: Santa Rita and Huachuca Mts. of s.e. Arizona. *Elevation*—6,000 to 9,000 feet. 6,800–7,500 feet (Kauffeld); 7,000 feet (Swarth); 7,500 feet (Vorhies); 6,500–9,000 feet (Hallowell, Calif., 1856).

Size: Adults, 15–24 inches.

Distinctive characteristics: "Tip of snout and canthus rostralis raised into a sharp ridge, by bending up of the outer edges of internasals and canthals; rostral and mental usually marked vertically by a narrow light line on a red-brown ground. Body pattern of large, brown or red-brown blotches separated by narrow light areas, the blotches being often without definite outlines on the sides; tail pattern terminating in longitudinal band rather than crossbars" (Klauber, Gen., 1936).

Color: A snake in the possession of C. T. Vorhies, University of Arizona, Tucson, described June 16, 1934. The back is crossed by 18 white or pale olive-gray crossbars bordered on either side by blackish mouse gray. The spaces between these light bars are mouse gray. The light bars cross about 10 to 12 scales, are 1 scale wide, and are separated by about 8 scales. The dorsum of the tail is uniform mouse gray. The background of the sides is olive-gray, and on the sides are 3 rows of alternating round spots of blackish mouse gray. The spot opposite the end of each light crossbar is larger. The lowest row is on the 1st and 2nd scale rows, the next is on the 3rd and 4th, while the upper row of spots is on the 6th, 7th, and 8th. A white stripe extends from the rostral plate to the angle of the mouth, and another through the rostral and symphysis of the lower jaw. The 1st stripe from the rostral to the angle of the mouth expands as a white area on the lateral gular scales and sends one oblique extension to the lower labial margin, from which it extends forward as white on the middle chin to the front of the anterior chin shields. There is a thin olive-buff line from the eye backward onto the temporal region. This serves as the upper border of the black or fuscous band which extends from the rostral through the eye to behind the angle of the jaw. The lower jaw has a broad band of black, broken by the oblique light bar, and then continuing as a black band to the angle of the mouth. The eye is at present covered with an unshed scale. The belly is white with mottlings of olive-gray or deep mouse gray.

Habitat: This high-mountain species Willard took in the Transition zone, above Hamburg in the Huachuca Mts., at about 7,000 feet. Slevin found it at Hamburg in Ramsey Canyon, in a pile of rocks by the side of the trail.

In 1943 a valuable contribution to our scanty knowledge of this form came in Kauffeld's "Field Notes": "Two fine specimens of this species were secured in Ramsey Canyon, Huachuca Mountains at about 6,800 feet. The day had begun overcast with clouds from storms of the night before still obscuring the sun, but at 11 A.M. the temperature was about 75° and there was strong sunlight, which had not yet heated the ground sufficiently to prevent activity of snakes. The larger of the 2 specimens, a male measuring 600 mm., was found basking on a rock in a stony glade, completely surrounded by dense forests, at a point below the site of the old Hamburg Mine between the trail and the nearby stream. The

Fig. 294. *Crotalus willardi,* Tucson, Ariz., C. T. Vorhies.

snake rattled briefly as I approached and disappeared rapidly under a rock. On turning the rock, a second specimen, a 460 mm. female, was found partly covered by the snake that had just entered the retreat. Although both resented capture fiercely, they ceased rattling immediately on being placed in a bag, and thereafter were exceptionally quiet. Many more rocks were turned but no other snakes were found. So little has been recorded regarding the habitat of *Crotalus willardi* that 9 plants associated in this spot were collected at random . . . : New Mexican locust (*Robinia neomexicana*), buckthorn (*Rhamnus crocea ilicifolia*), big-tooth maple (*Acer grandidentata*), ash (*Fraxinus velutina glabra*), Arizona white oak (*Quercus arizonica*), timber pine (*Pinus flex- ilis*), Douglas fir (*Pseudotsuga taxifolia*), white fir (*Abies concolor*), and red cedar (*Juniperis scopularum*). All these grew within a radius of 20 feet and indicate the moist, heavily wooded nature of the *Crotalus willardi* habitat niche. This is in contrast to *Crotalus lepidus klauberi* which usually chooses dry, bare prominences of canyon walls, with exposed and exfoliating rocks, supporting little growth other than cacti and agavis, but adjoining the forest areas. Although both may occur in the same general locality, *Crotalus willardi* is an alpine forest snake. Such a restricting factor would in part account for the highly localized distribution of the species in south- eastern Arizona. . . . *C. willardi* may eventually be found in the Chiricahua Mountains. . . . A further specimen has come into my possession, collected by Mrs. Healy during June 1942, at the head of Carr Canyon [Huachuca Mts.] at 7,500 feet elevation. This snake is an adult male, exceptionally stout and light in coloration."

We quote from a manuscript account (Flood and Wiklund, Gen., 1949a) of one of the most successful herpetological forays we know of: "We had a stroke of tremendous luck with this species, capturing 6 in Carr Canyon, the Huachuca Mountains. All were caught in a large, open rocky area about 250 feet above a stream in the canyon floor in the late afternoons of 2 suc- cessive days. Temperatures at the times of capture (3–6 P.M.) were between 85 and 90 degrees Fahrenheit. Many of the rocks had concave surfaces suit- able for holding water, and clumps of small pines and oaks were scattered about the slope offering shade. All of the specimens attempted to glide away, some without bothering to rattle. The behavior of these snakes during capture, and the general appearance of their habitat reminded me very strongly of collecting the northern copperhead in Connecticut. Instead of the expected lunge or strike, they tried to turn and deliberately bite. When pinned, they thrashed about wildly, unlike the reported behavior of most of the larger rattlesnakes. However they became quiet when dropped into the collecting bag and did not rattle thereafter. The measurements of the 6 specimens are 20½; 19; 18½; 11¼; 9¼; 8¼ inches."

Period of activity: *First appearance*—May 28, 1912 (Vorhies, Ariz., 1917).

Breeding: Viviparous. In 1937 Klauber (IV) recorded 7 large males as 508–579 mm., 7 large females 448–565 mm.; the average size of these males was 535 mm., of females 499 mm. The smallest gravid female was 481 mm. Klauber estimated the approximate size of a large male as 560 mm.; the maximum specimen he measured 588 mm. *Young*—Number 3–6. In 1937 Klauber (IV) gave 165 mm. as the estimated size at birth, and 216 mm. as

Fig. 295. *Crotalus willardi*, Carr Canyon, Huachuca Mts., Ariz., Mrs. J. H. Healy through C. F. Kauffeld.

Fig. 296. *Crotalus enyo*, San Diego Zoo, Calif.

the minimum size measured. In 1938 (V) he had given 165 mm. as size at birth. In 1949(b) (Gen.) he remarked that "3 recently born young, 189 to 193 mm. (about 7½ inches) long, indicate the approximate size at birth"; also that "a specimen of *w. willardi* 481 mm. (19 in.) long contained 6 eggs."

Food: Mice, lizards, small snakes. Van Denburgh, Kauffeld, Vorhies, Flood and Wiklund (Gen., 1949a).

Field notes: Our field notes are for June 9, 15, and 20, 1934, and June 30, 1942, but we substitute some written in 1949 by two students, Walter A. Flood, Jr., and Erik Wiklund.

"June 12: To Huachucas and to top of Carr Peak. Camped.

"June 13: Down trail to bottom of Carr. At 10:30 saw a small *pricei* in crack of rock, caught him; continued hunt on this hill yielded nothing more. Ate lunch, waited for drizzle to let up. Walking along trail about 200 yards from stream, saw and captured small *willardi*. Investigation of slide above trail yielded 4 more, 3 of larger size. All were alongside rocks in sun. Most did not rattle, but noise of progress through leaves drew attention.

"June 14: Too hot, 110$^+$. Down to Carr, worked slope high all around canyon. Got nothing. Worked Ramsey trail over divide. Worked Willard area—nothing. Worked *pricei* area, got one alligator lizard. At 5 o'clock worked slide below *willardi* area—one small willard's. At 5:30 broke camp, went down to Nicksville. Drove at night to Bisbee."

Authorities:

Curran, C. H. (Gen., 1935)
Hartman, F. A. (Ariz., 1911)
Kauffeld, C. F. (Ariz., 1943)
Klauber, L. M. (Gen., 1936, 1936–40, III, IV, 1949b)
Meek, S. E. (Calif., 1905)
Swarth, H. S. (Ariz., 1921)
Van Denburgh, J. (Gen., 1922)
Vorhies, C. T. (Ariz., 1948)

1935, C. H. Curran: "It seems remarkable that any rattlesnake should have escaped the eagle eye of scientists for so long as *willardi* did. . . . It is extremely unlikely that there will be any new species added to the known rattlesnake fauna of the United States, although, as so often happens, a statement such as this may be the forerunner of such a discovery. It seems probable that the future will give us merely additional races of the known species."

1949: L. M. Klauber (Gen., 1949b) reviewed the known material and established 3 forms (*willardi willardi,* Arizona; *w. silus,* Sonora and Chihuahua; and *w. meridionalis,* Durango and Zacatecas). *Silus* has no rostral or mental vertical white line as the others do; *w. willardi* has 25 scale rows, 150 ventrals or more; while *meridionalis* has more than 25 scale rows and fewer than 150 ventrals.

1950, A. H. and A. A. Wright: On our hurried trips of 1 to 3 days to various parts of U.S.A., we have had fine luck in capturing alive almost

Fig. 297. *Crotalus mitchelli mitchelli,* San Diego Zoo, Calif.

Fig. 298. *Crotalus r. lucasensis,* San Diego Zoo, Calif.

every amphibian and reptile in the country, but never a *willardi* greeted us when we went to Ramsey Canyon (Hamburg mine) twice, Carr Canyon twice, White Horse Canyon, Temporal Gulch, Mt. Baldy (summit), and other likely places. We have seen and photographed Vorhies' and Kauffeld's live specimens. In Carr Canyon we even helped to escort Mrs. Healy to the mail box or express box with Kauffeld's third specimen of 1943, but never did we capture *willardi* ourselves. Such is collecting. Kauffeld probably did not know we envied him such a prize possession, and if he did he heaped coals of fire on our heads, for he promptly shipped it to our laboratory in our absence to have photographs made for us. And one of those photographs our secretary made the sole decoration on our office door. Yet that did not bring us luck.

GROUND RATTLESNAKES, PIGMY RATTLESNAKES, MASSASAUGAS

Genus *SISTRURUS* Garman (Fig. 260)

Size medium, 14–40 inches; 9 large head plates; upper labials 9–14, lower 9–15; eye in vertical of upper labials 4–6; scales keeled in 21–25 rows; ("anteriorly sometimes 27 . . . posteriorly 17, rarely 16"—Gloyd); ventrals 122–128; caudals 20–39; rattle small; hemipenis finely flounced; confined to North America. Synonyms: *Caudisona, Crotalinus, Crotalophorus, Crotalus, Vipera.*

KEY TO THE GENUS *SISTRURUS*

a. Head without distinct markings, uniform gray or stippled with brown; canthus rostralis not distinct; rostral low, tapering to a point between internasals; blotches on body conspicuously longer than wide. (Southern portion of Mexican Plateau.) *Sistrurus ravus*

aa. Head with distinct markings or nearly all black; canthus rostralis high, truncate above; body blotches not conspicuously longer than wide, usually widened transversely.

b. Prefrontals not contacting loreal proper (lower loreal, if 2 be present), the preocular contacting the postnasal; white stripe from posterior nasal or pit passes below eye to angle of mouth; a dark spot often present on parietal suture; tail short and stocky, tail length/total length average .09–.108; rattle medium in size, relatively sturdy in appearance; tail bands few, average 5–8; middorsal interval less than dorsal spot; no middorsal stripe.

c. General coloration light grays intermingled with pinks; light outlines of spots and stripes of pink and buffy tints; higher number of dorsal blotches: ♂ 28–46, ♀ 30–50; higher number of ventrals: ♂ 140–154, ♀ 143–160; venter sparsely blotched or immaculate. (W. Missouri and s.e. Nebraska to s.e. Arizona and extreme n. Mexico.) Size, 21–36 inches. *Sistrurus c. tergeminus*

cc. General coloration dark grays to black, light outlines of spots and stripes white or of somewhat yellowish or ochraceous tints; fewer dorsal blotches: ♂ 21–40, ♀ 24–47; fewer ventrals: ♂ 129–147, ♀ 136–151; venter heavily blotched or nearly all black. (N.w. New York and n.w. Pennsylvania through Ontario to n.e. Kansas and s.e. Nebraska.) Size, 20–40 inches. *Sistrurus catenatus catenatus*

bb. Prefrontals broadly contacting loreal, preocular separated from postnasal by loreal; white stripe below center of eye to angle of mouth; parietal suture unspotted; tail slender and attenuate, tail length/total length average .101–.123; rattle small, slender, tapering to fine point and relatively inconspicuous; tail bands more numerous, average 8–10; middorsal interval equal to or greater than middorsal spot; median dorsal stripe of reddish brown usually present, if only on neck.

c. Dorsal background dark grays heavily stippled with black (i.e., purplish gray tints); scale rows 25; median series of blotches 27–45; 3 lateral rows of spots; belly has heavy clear-cut black spots and white intervals on forward half, and larger black flecked spots and intervals on caudal half. (S.e. states from s. South Carolina to Pearl River [Miss.–La.].) Size, 14–20 inches. *Sistrurus m. barbouri*

cc. Dorsal background light grays or browns (i.e., purplish gray tints) with black stippling sparse; scale rows 21 or 23; 1 or 2 lateral rows of spots; venter pale brownish vinaceous or pale grayish vinaceous with black spots less distinct and more diffuse.

d. Scale rows at mid-body 23; middorsal blotches 25–36 (♂ s average 30, ♀ s 33), usually about oval with regular shape and edges, and about equal longitudinally to the interspaces; 2 series of lateral spots, midlateral ones opposite middorsal blotches, relatively round, edges indistinct, other series on lower scale rows and ends of ventrals; ventral spots merge into stippling at their edges; chin region cinnamon-brown. (North Carolina to n. Alabama.) Size, 15–24 inches. *Sistrurus miliarius miliarius*

dd. Scale rows at mid-body 21; middorsal blotches 23–42 (usually about 30), wider than long, irregular in shape, frequently with extending corners or divided into 2 spots, and much narrower longitudinally than the interspaces; 1 or 2 series of lateral spots, midlateral opposite dorsal and higher than wide; venter heavily checked, flecked, and stippled black or fuscous; chin region yellow, flecked with brown. (E. Texas to s.e. Missouri, s.e. Tennessee, n. Mississippi, Louisiana.) Size, 16–25 inches.

Sistrurus m. streckeri

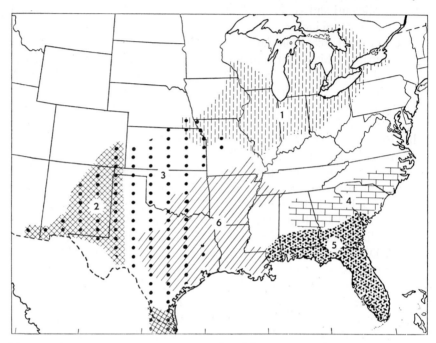

Map 70. *Sistrurus*—1, *c. catenatus*; 2, *c. edwardsi*; 3, *c. tergeminus*; 4, *m. miliarius*; 5, *m. barbouri*; 6, *m. streckeri*.

Massasauga (107—Bradford 1846), Prairie rattlesnake (34—Bradford 1846), Eastern massasauga (4)

Sistrurus catenatus catenatus (Rafinesque) 1818. Figs. 299, 300; Map 70

Other common names: Black massasauga; black rattlesnake; black snapper (6); dwarf prairie rattlesnake; gray rattlesnake; great adder; ground rattlesnake; Kirtland's rattlesnake; little black rattlesnake (Barton 1805); massasauga rattlesnake; massasauger; pigmy rattlesnake; prairie (rattlesnake) massasauga; rattlesnake; sauger; small prairie rattlesnake; snapper; swamp rattler (9); swamp rattlesnake (9); triple-spotted rattlesnake.

Range: A swamp form from Georgian Bay, Bay, Ontario, Can., w. across s. peninsula of Michigan and s. Wisconsin; southwestward to s.e. Nebraska and n.e. Kansas; e. across n. Missouri, most of Illinois, Indiana, and Ohio; with pockets in w. Pennsylvania and s. border of Lake Ontario.—U.S.A.: Ia.; Ill.; Ind.; Kan.; Mich.; Minn.; Mo.; Neb.; N.Y.; O.; Okla.(?); Pa.; Wis.

Can.: Ont. *Elevation*—Most records are below 1,000 feet, possibly to 2,000 feet.

Size: Adults, 20–40 inches. Klauber's (Gen., 1943b) standard adult length for 177 males and 170 females is 700 mm.

Longevity: 14 years (Perkins, Gen., 1948); 4 years 6 months (Conant and Hudson, Gen., 1949); 14 years (Perkins, Gen., 1954).

Distinctive characteristics: "General coloration dark, sometimes entirely black; belly all black or heavily blotched; dorsal blotches of body exclusive of tail 21–40 (av. 32); ventrals 129–151 (males 129–150, av. 137; females 136–151, av. 142)" (Gloyd).

Color: Four snakes (3 gravid females and 1 half-grown snake) from Bergen swamp, N.Y., received May 20, 1939; caught by H. Trapido, Mc-Cauley, Jr., and a party of 8. The half-grown snake: The background between the dorsal spots is light olive gray or pale smoke gray, becoming on the sides, between the 2 upper lateral rows, olive-gray or light grayish olive.

A large female: The background of the back is grayish olive. There are 29 dorsal spots of clove brown outlined with a thread of deep olive-buff, plus 5 clove-brown dorsal bars on the tail. There are 3 rows of lateral spots of dark olive or fuscous, which, under the lens, show the individual scales to be olive-brown heavily flecked with fuscous, and the interscale color to be fuscous. In mid-body, the lateral spots of the 2nd series are outlined with a thread of ochraceous-tawny. On the 1st row of scales and partly on the 2nd, the tips of the scales are white-edged. Occasionally this white extends along the rear edges of the ventrals. The 5 bars on the tail cross 3 to 3½ scales longitudinally, the bar at the base of the rattle being a complete ring of fuscous black. The spaces between these bars cover 1½ scales longitudinally and are grayish olive except that a little dark olive appears on the underside of the terminal interspace. The dark markings on the head, like the middorsal spots, are clove brown except the vitta back of the eye, and the white-enclosed dark area below it, which are olive-brown. There extends from the eye across the rear of the supraocular and on the rear of the frontal, a clove-brown bar which stops short of meeting its fellow on the meson. From the middle of each bar there extends backward, on top of the head and neck, a clove-brown longitudinal band 3 to 3½ scales wide and at least 1 or 1½ inches long. The space between these bands is, like the ground color, grayish olive, and surrounds a clove-brown spot on the suture between the parietals. In front of the supraocular-frontal bar is a prominent bar of grayish olive, ahead of which, on the internasals and prefrontals, is a prominent transverse bar of clove brown. Except for the prenasal, the facial plates and the rostral are grayish olive. The prenasal is buffy brown, and the area below the nasal pit is clove brown, which color continues across the labial border onto the ventral surface of the head between the pair of median white lines there and the white stripes which begin in the middle of the lower labial border and extend backward onto the neck just back of the angle of the mouth. Just back of the angle of the mouth this last white stripe is joined by an oblique white stripe which begins under the eye and 1 scale back of the nasal pit. This oblique nasal-pit stripe and the lower labial stripe enclose the dark area of olive-brown, mentioned above. The prominent vitta back of the eye is beautifully outlined below by the nasal-pit white stripe, but there is no such outlining of the upper margin, a mere thread appearing there. The rostral and facial stripes are of ground color. The iris is olive-brown with a patch of deep olive-buff above the pupil. The venter is largely fuscous or black with considerable white on the cephalic 3 or 4 inches.

Abnormal coloration—Holbrook described *Crotalophorus kirtlandi* of Ohio and Michigan, a black rattlesnake "not unfrequently found in cranberry marshes." Many later observed this color phase, one of the more recent accounts being by Conant in Ohio.

Intergeneric hybrid rattlesnake? In 1942 Bailey (Ia.) recorded a hybrid between *Crotalus h. horridus* x *Sistrurus catenatus catenatus*. It is an odd specimen. Is it hybrid (Bailey), a queer *Sistrurus c. catenatus* (Gloyd), or what (Klauber)? It has many of the characters of each species and is a startling problem for the authorities.

Habitat: When we summarize almost 100 accounts of habitat, we find *swampy* situations, localities, country, ground, land, and meadows in the lead with 24 citations. Marshes are mentioned 6 times, meadows 10, including low, wet, inundated, swampy, damp, and bottom-land. Grassy fields, pastures, bottomland, landings, hummocks, and piles command 13 mentions. One author says the form is not found in open prairies, but prairies, usually designated as wet, low, or damp, have 5 or 6 notices. When the form occurs in marshes, swamps, meadows, or sphagnum bogs, it prefers elevated hummocks, tufts of grass, weeds, and small brush. Several records specify lake borders and streams, rivers, or fields bordering wet localities. Another mentions an "outwash plain." This snake is seldom taken in elevated dry ground except in summer. It has been taken in prairie country in unusual places, such as in a limestone outcrop, under rocks in a prairie ledge, in a potato field, in a wheat field, and in a stone quarry.

In Indiana, Evermann and Clark wrote: "We have heard, however, of numerous examples being killed in marshy meadows northwest, west and south of the lake. In those regions there are numerous and considerable meadows of the wild grass or sedge, *Carex stricta,* which are cut in the early fall by farmers and others for hay or for use in the ice-houses, and other purposes. It is then that this venomous snake is met with most frequently."

Atkinson and Netting in Pennsylvania are probably right in feeling that the snappers "desert the swamps and go into the surrounding fields in the summer." "This statement is supported by the testimony of the farmers near Pymatuning Swamp. They agreed in stating that they found the snakes quite generally along fence rows and under planks about the edges of their fields during the summer months, but that in the spring they found the Massasaugas in the swamp itself.

Whiffen (in Ditmars, Gen., 1929) described it as inhabiting Cicero Swamp, New York. "The Massasauga seems to like the neighborhood of swamps, though it shuns the actually wet places. In the harvest season it is usually found either in the hay-fields or oat-lots, or it may be seen out on the moss among the bushes, or under the evergreen trees. However, it may occur almost anywhere." For many years, W. A. Dence, at Syracuse University, has had swamp rattlers from Cicero Swamp for laboratory mascots. For *Sistrurus* in the Detroit area, read Roberts and Quarters.

Period of activity: Specimens have been collected in every month from April to November (Conant). *Early appearances*—May 3, 18 (Roberts and Quarters); Apr. 7, May 30 (Walker, Gen., 1931); Apr. 10 (Selous); May 30 (Gloyd, Kan., 1928); Apr. 25, 26, May 4, 5, 8, 11, 13, 14, 17, 23 (Atkinson and Natting); May 8 (Burt and Hoyle, Gen., 1935); Apr. 15, May 15, 20 (Evermann and Clark); May 15 (Hurter); May 26–27 (Loomis, Ia., 1948). *Fall disappearance*—Sept. 2 (Cope, Okla., 1894); Sept. 16, 1910 (Thompson and Thompson, Mich., 1912); Sept., 1928 (Pope, Wis., 1928); Aug. 24, 1871 (Pope, Wis., 1928); Aug. 24, Sept. 7 (Swanson); Aug. 29, 1928 (Minton); Sept. 11 (Selous); Sept. 2 (Atkinson and Netting); Sept. 2 (Atkinson, Pa., 1901); Oct. 1 (Anderson, Mo., 1942); Sept. 3 (Evermann and Clark); Sept. 6 (Peters, Ill., 1942).

Hibernation—Concerning the Bergen Swamp, where we began some of our botanical studies, we have the following from Gebhard in 1853 (N.Y.): "Their habitat is a white cedar swamp in said town, containing an area of about 1,000 acres. During the summer season, they leave the swamp, and go into the adjoining fields of grain, where they remain until fall, when they return to the swamp and hibernate. They have not been observed at any other locality in this State."

Breeding: Viviparous. *Mating*—We have no evidence except the inconclusive, incomplete matings (May 7) of which Guthrie (Ia., 1927) wrote.

Young—Number, 5-14. 5 (Wright, Reddick); 5, 6 (Hay); 5, 6, 8 (Swanson); 5, 9 (Atkinson and Netting); 5, 8, 11 (Pope); 6 (Selous, Triplehorn); 7 (Ramsey, Conant); 7, 9 (Hurter); 8 (Netting); 9 (Roberts and Quarters); 9, 13 (Necker); 12 (Guthrie, Minton); 14 (Wright). Time of birth, late July–Sept. 2. Late July, August (Atkinson and Netting); Aug. 2 (Triplehorn); Aug. 6 (Reddick); Aug. 6, 30 (Pope); Aug. 7 (Selous); Aug. 13 (Ramsey); Aug. 17, 31, Sept. 1 (Wright); Aug. 19, 30 (Tobiasz); Aug. 22, Sept. 2 (Hurter); Sept. 1 (Gordon). Size at birth, 5.44 (136 mm.)

to 10 (250 mm.) inches. 5.44, 9.76 (Gloyd); 6, 7.5 (Hay); 6.34, 7.4 (Tobiasz); 7.87, 8, 8.62 (Surface); 8 (Pope, Netting); 8, 8.62 (Swanson); 8, 8.75, 9, 9.25 inches (Conant). The young male 11½ inches long taken in May by Roberts and Quarters must have been a hatchling of 1941.

For development of the snake see the Garmans, (Gen., 1886–88) "The rattle of the rattlesnake." Hurter said: "The end of the tail in newly born is whitish yellow. . . . They were ejected in a thin yellowish covering or egg shell, which broke immediately. The first thing the young ones did was to open their mouths as if trying their fangs." One of the best detailed studies of the young came from Wright, who had 6 females 551–671 mm. long. They had 6 complements of young averaging from 204–250 mm. or ranging from 190–264 mm. on Aug. 17, 20, 30, 31, Sept. 1, and Sept. (indefinite). Three females had litters of 8, 14, and 10, and no undeveloped embryos, one had 12 and 1 undeveloped, one 5 and 3 undeveloped, and one 8 and 11 undeveloped.

Food: Rodents, frogs, toads, birds, insects, crayfish, fish. Hoy, Gastman, Selous, Taylor (Neb., 1892), Surface, Evermann and Clark, Atkinson and Netting, Swanson, Wright.

Venom and bite: According to Hoy, the bite "is not fatal, but causes great swelling and irritation." In 1936 Lyon and Bishop (Gen., 1936) published "The bite of the prairie rattlesnake. . . ." In 1946 Swanson (Gen.) wrote, "There is the possibility that *Sistrurus catenatus catenatus* is immune to venom of its own kind. Of the other species used, none seems immune to venom of its own kind."

Authorities:

Atkinson, D. A., and M. G. Netting (Pa., 1927)
Conant, R. (O., 1938a)
Creaser, C. W. (Mich., 1928)
Evans, P. D., and H. K. Gloyd (Mo., 1948)
Evermann, B. W., and H. W. Clark (Ind., 1920)
Gastman, E. A. (Ind., 1884)
Gloyd, H. K. (Gen., 1940)
Hay, O. P. (Ind., 1887)
Hoy, P. R. (Wis., 1883)
Hurter, J. (Mo., 1911)
Minton, S., Jr. (Ind., 1944)
Moesel, J. (N.Y., 1918)
Pope, C. H. (Ill., 1944)
Roberts, A. R., and J. Quarters (Mich., 1947)
Schmidt, K. P. (Gen., 1938)
Selous, P. (Gen., 1895)
Smith, W. H. (O., 1882)
Surface, H. A. (Pa., 1906)
Swanson, P. L. (Pa., 1930)
Tobiasz, E. C. (Gen., 1941)
Wright, B. A. (Ill., 1941)

1938: K. P. Schmidt wrote that Atkinson and Netting had interpreted the eastward peninsular range of the Massasauga: "The great range of the massasauga on the plains has an extension through Indiana and Ohio to western New York and Pennsylvania, fitting almost exactly into our hypo-

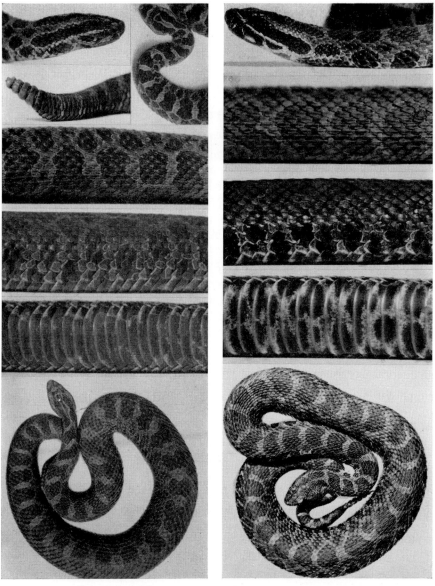

Fig. 299. *Sistrurus catenatus catenatus,* Bergen Swamp, N.Y.: 1,2,4–7, R. T. Clausen; 3, J. D. and H. Hood, photo by S. C. Bishop.

Fig. 300. *Sistrurus catenatus catenatus,* Riley Co., Kansas, B. C. Marshall.

thetical steppe peninsula. It is fairly evident that its populations were de-clining before the advent of man, and that this decline may be associated with the change of habitat conditions which has overtaken the subspecies."

Edward's massasauga (15—Mitchell 1903), Western massasauga (10), Massasauga (16—Garman 1887)

Sistrurus catenatus tergeminus (Say) 1823. Fig. 301; Map 70

Other common names: Ground rattlesnake; Gulf coast massasauga (*con-sors*); large ground rattlesnake; pigmy rattlesnake; prairie rattlesnake; Say's false rattlesnake; Sonora ground rattlesnake (Yarrow 1882); Texas mas-sasauga (*consors*); three-spotted shield rattler; triple-spotted rattlesnake.

Range: From s. Missouri and s.e. Nebraska southwestward to s.e. Arizona; thence e. to the Gulf coast of Texas and probably Tamaulipas, Mex.; north-ward through cent. Texas and Oklahoma to Missouri.—U.S.A.: Ariz.; Colo.; Kan.; Neb.; N.M.; Okla.; Tex. Mex.: Tamaulipas. *Elevation*—Sea level to 5,000 feet. 2,800–5,000 feet (Bailey, N.M., 1913).

Size: Adults, 14–36 inches. Klauber's (Gen., 1943b) standard adult length for 43 males and 63 females is 680 mm.

Distinctive characteristics: "*Crotalus tergeminus,* S. *Body* dusky cinereous, a triple series of deep brown spots; beneath with a double series of black spots. *Body* pale cinereous brown, a triple series of fuscous spots, dorsal series consisting of about 42 large, transversely oblong-oval spots, each widely emarginate before, and obsoletely edged with whitish; lateral series, spots transversely oval, opposite to those of the back; between the dorsal and lateral series, is a series of obsolete, fuliginous spots alternating with those of the 2 other series; *head* above with 9 plates on the anterior part, on which are a band and about 3 spots, 2 undulated vittae terminating in and confluent with the first spot of the neck, a black vitta passes through the eye, and terminates on the neck each side; *beneath* white a double irregular series of black spots, more confused towards the tail; *tail* above with 5 or 6 fuscous fasciae, beneath white irrorate with black points, 6 terminal plates bifid" (Say).

Color: A snake found 2 miles east of Vaughan, N.M., in a clump of bear grass, Aug. 29, 1925. Down the middle of the back is a series of drab or buffy olive transverse spots which are more or less emarginate in front and behind. This is particularly true in the cephalic part of the body. These spots are outlined with black and then with cartridge buff or pale cinnamon-pink. Along the lower side, opposite the dorsal spots, is a series of smaller spots of the same color as the dorsal spots. Between the dorsal series and the lateral one and alternating with the dorsal is a series in which the spots are indistinct and light grayish olive. The first 4 or 5 scale rows are pale vinaceous-pink with deep olive centers. The tail at the base of the rattle is court gray or pale olive-gray. The top of the head is marked with a pair of long spots colored like the dorsal saddles and bordered in the same way. These two spots are narrow on the large dorsal head plates, widen on the temporal region, and narrow again on the nape. The snout is also dark, bordered behind by a thin line of cartridge buff. This line extends from supraocular to supraocular and then backward as a dorsal border to the eye vitta, this border being less distinct than the lower one. There is a prominent vitta of brownish olive or prout's brown outlined above and below with black followed by a line of cartridge buff. The lower border forms a prominent light line extending from the angle of the jaw below the eye to a point close to the nostril. The eye is drab gray, vinaceous-buff, or cream-buff, clearest above, but heavily specked in front of and behind the pupil. The underside of the head is cartridge buff heavily marked, particularly in mental and gular regions, with chestnut-brown. The entire under parts are flesh pink or pale flesh color, spotted with deep grayish olive or light grayish olive.

Habitat: This form is usually accredited to low lands, moist spots near rivers and small streams, moist sandy regions, meadows, and swamp lands. Like its eastern relative, it migrates in summer into drier spots such as wheat, grain, potato, hay, and other fields. It has also been credited to canyon country. Primarily it is a prairie form but may be found in quite diverse spots. Our favorite places to find them were to be bear-grass clumps in the panhandle of Texas.

Period of activity: *First appearances*—Apr. 23, 30, June 2 (Burt); May 30, June 9 (Gloyd, Kan., 1928). *Fall disappearance*—Sept. 11 (Gloyd); Oct. 1, 23, Sept. 28 (Burt).

Breeding: Viviparous. Males 281–820 mm. *Young*—Number, probably as in *S. c. catenatus*. Time of birth, "Produces a small number of living young in late summer" (Hudson and Davis, Neb., 1941). Size, 8.5–9.6 inches. "Young at birth measure 8½ inches" (Garman, Tex., 1887). In 1940 Gloyd (Gen.) reported: "Only 3 new born young, all males, have been available for measurement. The lengths of the 3 are 219, 239 and 241 mm."

Food: Rodents. Taylor, Gloyd (1928).

Venom: Little information has appeared. In 1904 Branson (Neb., 1904) wrote: "Its poison is no less virulent than that of the larger snake (*confluentus*). I have known personally of several persons being bitten and the results were always serious. In one case, the victim, a child of 5 years, died." In 1913 Ellis and Henderson (Colo.) warned: "It is to be remembered that although they are small, they are dangerous."

Field notes: July 3, 1942: Twenty miles southwest of Rodeo on the Douglas road (Route 80), we picked up dead on the road *Sistrurus c. tergeminus*.

There was little or no bear grass nearby. The roadside was a grassy meadow. On July 9 we showed it to Jacot and Vorhies. They had never seen it in Arizona.

In view of our find, we give three excerpts of correspondence received later from the same region of Cochise Co., "I suppose the snake you found near Chiricahua was what we call the side winder" (Frank Krentz, letter, Jan. 15, 1946, Douglas, Ariz.).

Rucker Canyon region: "I have seen small ground rattlesnakes which cowboys call 'sidewinders.' In fact I killed one several years ago, and she had with her 5 babies, the only newborn snakes I have ever seen. They were perfectly formed, still reddish in color, and about as big as a good sized earthworm" (Charles L. Rak, letter, Jan. 21, 1946, Douglas, Ariz.).

"Our sidewinder is a very small rattlesnake not often found over 18 inches long and has very small rattles" (Henry A. Smith letter, March 15, 1946, Bisbee, Ariz.).

Authorities:

Baird, S. F., and C. Girard (Gen., 1853)
Brown, A. E. (Gen., 1901)
Burt, C. E. (Kan., 1933)
Burt, C. E. and M. D. (Kan., 1929)
Burt, C. E. and W. L. Hoyle (Gen., 1935)
Campo, R. M. del (Gen., 1935)
Coues, E., and H. C. Yarrow (Mont., 1878)
Cragin, F. W. (Kan., 1881, 1885)

Garman, S. (Tex., 1887, 1892)
Gloyd, H. K. (Gen., 1940; Kan., 1928)
Hudson, G. E. (Neb., 1942)
Maslin, T. P. (Colo., 1950)
Mitchell, J. D. (Tex., 1903)
Say, T. (in James) (Gen., 1822–23)
Stejneger, L. (Gen., 1895, 1940)
Strecker, J. K., Jr. (Tex., 1910, 1915)
Taylor, W. E. (Neb., 1892b)
Terron, C. C. (Baja Calif., 1921)
Wied, M. zu (Gen., 1865)

1902: J. D. Mitchell described in detail *Sistrurus c. consors.*

Edward's massasauga

Sistrurus catenatus edwardsi Gloyd 1955. Map 70

We note that Woodin's and Bogert's recent captures prompted Gloyd in "A review of the massasaugas" (*Bull. Chicago Acad. Sci.,* **10,** no. 6: 83–78) to revive the old name of *Sistrurus catenatus edwardsi* (Baird and Girard) for the form of s.e. Arizona, New Mexico, trans-Pecos Texas, and the lower Rio Grande Valley. It is paler than *S. c. tergeminus,* with a nearly white venter, 23 mid-body rows of scales instead of 25, and a lower number of ventrals and dorsal blotches. This is the form we captured in Arizona in 1942 (see "Field Notes" under *tergeminus* above). Therefore the *S. c. tergeminus* account includes Gloyd's recent *S. c. edwardsi.*

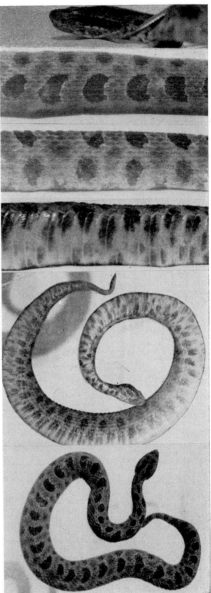

Fig. 301. *Sistrurus c. tergeminus,* Vaughn, N.M.

Fig. 302. *Sistrurus miliarius miliarius,* "Bughouse Laboratory," Washington, N.C., G. Ross.

Ground rattlesnake (28—Pope 1792), Pigmy rattlesnake (10—Ditmars 1910), Eastern pigmy rattlesnake

Sistrurus miliarius miliarius (Linné) 1766. Fig. 302; Map 70

Other common names: Bastard rattlesnake; Carolina ground rattlesnake; Carolina pigmy rattlesnake; Catesby's small snake; dwarf rattlesnake; grey rattlesnake; ground rattler (7—Garman 1887); hog-nosed rattler; little rattlesnake; miliar(y) rattlesnake; North American smaller rattlesnake; oakleaf rattler; pigmy ground rattlesnake; small rattlesnake; southeastern ground rattlesnake; southern ground rattlesnake; southern pigmy rattlesnake; spotted rattler; spotted rattlesnake.

Range: Cent. Alabama, cent. Georgia, South Carolina, and s. North Carolina.—Ala.; Ga.; N.C.; S.C. *Elevation*—Coast to at least 2,500 feet.

Size: Adults, 15–24 inches. Klauber's (Gen., 1943b) standard adult length for 36 males and 20 females is 450 mm.

Longevity: "Regarding life span in captivity, our records are not helpful. . . . A few specimens lived 12 months without taking food of any kind. Of 10 individuals, the average length of life in captivity was 8 months with a maximum period of 20 months" (Chamberlain).

Distinctive characteristics: "Scale rows at midbody usually 23; dorsal spots oval or subcircular, edges more or less regular; lateral spots usually round, not much if any higher than wide; pigmentation of ventral surface posteriorly more restricted to indistinct blotches occupying 2 adjacent scutes" (Gloyd).

Color: A snake from Washington Field Museum, Washington, N.C., Sept. 17, 1937. The back beginning with the nuchal spot is marked with 29 spots on the body. These dorsal spots are black, chestnut-brown, or carob brown and are 7 to 8 scales wide and 1½ to 2½ scales longitudinally. Beginning at the rear end of the parietal is a prominent middorsal longitudinal band, 3 to 4 scales wide, of ferruginous, vinaceous-rufous, or vinaceous-tawny. This continues across interspaces between the dorsal spots as a band 1½ to 2½ scales wide. The remainder of the background of the dorsum is light grayish olive, smoke gray, or pale mouse gray. There is 1 distinct row of lateral spots located on the 2nd to 5th or 6th scale rows and opposite the ends of the dorsal spots, with an interval of 1 to 2 scales. These spots are black or of the browns of the middorsal spots and usually are 3 scales deep and 2 scales long. Alternating with the median dorsal spots and the lower lateral row is an indistinct series of spots located on the 5th to 8th rows and often extending up to the ferruginous middorsal band. These spots are dark grayish olive and deep grayish olive. There is a semblance of a row of black spots on the 1st or 1st and 2nd scale rows or on the 1st and the ends of abdominal scutes. These alternate with the prominent lateral series described above. There are 2 prominent black or chestnut-brown bowing longitudinal bands on the dorsum of the neck which extend onto the parietals and to the rear half of the supraoculars. Across the front half of the supraoculars and across the head is an indistinct band of ecru-drab or light cinnamon-drab. The same color is on the rostral, and there are washes of it on the cinnamon-brown face. (In young specimens, the ferruginous median neckband extends along the middle of the head with a transverse band of the same from supraocular to supraocular; the face, rostral, and canthus rostralis are of the same color.) Below the dark longitudinal band, from the eye backward, there is a light grayish olive area with a black or chestnut-brown vitta extending to the rear angle of the mouth, crossing in width 1 temporal scale and half of the supraocular. From below the eye to the angle of the mouth this vitta has a white labial border. The iris is cinnamon-drab or cinnamon brown below and apricot buff or pinkish cinnamon in the upper half. The underside of the head, mental, 3rd and 4th lower labials, and anterior chin shields are so dotted with brown as to appear cinnamon-brown. The rest of the underside of the head is dotted with mars brown or black and white. There are 2 oblique bands of white across the middle lower labials, i.e., the 5th and 8th. The belly is pale grayish vinaceous or pale vinaceous-fawn. Down the belly are 2 irregular rows of black spots usually occupying sutures of 2 adjoining scutes. In the rear half in the middle of the belly is an army brown or natal brown band which becomes more prominent rearward.

Habitat: In 1803 Barton (Gen., 1807) described this form as "inhabiting marshy grounds" and said it is "seldom more than a foot in length, and is deemed extremely venomous." In 1842 Holbrook wrote, "It is found in dry places, among leaves and frequently in high grass, in search of small field mice on which it feeds." In 1929 Corrington's (S.C.) one specimen came "from the sand hills."

We believe that in spite of the common name "oak-leaf rattler" they frequent drier parts of low swampy grounds, as Allen indicates for *S. m. barbouri*. It is true this species does also occur in sandy areas, as stated by Conant and Bridges (Gen., 1939). Davis and Brimley (Gen., 1944) also observed this fact: "It is common in its preferred habitat about sandy ridges and in pine forests." In 1940 Jopson (S.C.) said they were "occasionally found on the sand roads in the summer time." In any case, it is both a coastal and a piedmont form.

Period of activity: In South Carolina, particularly in the Charleston area, Chamberlain obtained 55 specimens. "Over 65 per cent of the specimens were taken during the months of July, August and September. The earliest seasonal record is January 9 (snake found under old stump but active) and the latest November 21. The entire series shows the following distribution by months: January 1, February 2, March 0, April 1, May 2, June 2, July 9, August 12, September 15, October 6, November 1, December 0, month not recorded 4. From this it appears that some individuals may be active at almost any time during the year except in the coldest weather."

Breeding: Viviparous. This subject is usually dismissed with the comment, "Ovoviviparous." Few records exist. *Young*—Number 5–18. In 1907 Ditmars (Gen.) held that 7–9 was the number, though this may have included *barbouri* as well. Conant and Bridges (Gen., 1939) gave 5–17 young of 6½ inches hatchling size, and Davis and Brimley accepted this number and size. Schmidt and Davis (Gen., 1941) gave 8–18. In 1940 according to Gloyd, measurements were "available on two new born young: a male 173 mm., and a female 148 mm. in total length." Chamberlain remarked, "The smallest individuals measure 175, 185 mm. and about 6½ inches, and since their rattles each consist of one button only, may be newly born or young of the year. In specimens of this size the distal 7 or 8 mm. of the tails are sulphur yellow." It was a small specimen that bit Chamberlain Aug. 10, 1926. He suffered few bad effects. Nearly 6 weeks later, Sept. 19, the snake measured 175 mm. Hamilton and Pollack found a mated pair on Sept. 18, 1951.

Food: Small mammals, lizards, insects, small birds, frogs.[1] Griffeth, Holbrook, Stejneger, Chamberlain, Brimley, Brimley and Davis.

Venom: In 1893 Stejneger wrote: "While thus the bite of these small snakes may be attended with comparatively little danger, a person bitten would act very foolishly were he to neglect to pay proper attention to the wound and to apply as soon as possible proper remedies, as otherwise he might pay dearly enough for his carelessness." In 1942 Brimley wrote: "On account of its small size, we have but few records of it, and the only biological item derived from them is that it occasionally bites 'bird dogs' in the fall. While too small to be really dangerous, the bite of this snake will give the victim quite an unpleasant time for several days."

Authorities:

Brimley, C. S. (N.C., 1941–42)
Brimley, C. S., and H. T. Davis (Gen., 1944)
Chamberlain, E. B. (S.C., 1935)
Gloyd, H. K. (Gen., 1940)
Griffith, E. (Gen., 1831)
Holbrook, J. E. (Gen., 1836–42)
Stejneger, L. (Gen., 1893)

1878, E. Coues and H. C. Yarrow (N.C.): *"Caudisona miliaria* Linn. Spotted Rattler. Ground Rattlesnake. A few individuals of this species are said to have been seen on Bogue banks, none, however, observed or secured by the writers, but they are quite common on Shackleford banks, a few miles from Fort Macon. It has also been taken on the mainland. It is a fact worthy of remark, that while on Bogue banks, rattlesnakes and moccasins are extremely abundant, this is the only venomous species found on the neighboring island of Shackleford."

---

[1] Hamilton and Pollack (Ga., 1956) found that this species ate reptiles (lizards and snakes), 50%; centipedes, 33%; and mammals (mice), 17%.

Florida ground rattlesnake (4), Southeastern ground rattlesnake (4), Pigmy rattlesnake (6—Wachtel)

Sistrurus miliarius barbouri Gloyd 1935. Fig. 303; Map 70

Other common names: Barbour's pigmy rattlesnake; dusky pigmy rattlesnake; ground rattlesnake (4); hog-nosed rattler; pigmy ground rattlesnake; pigmy rattler (3); small rattlesnake.

Range: From s.e. South Carolina to Pearl River, Miss.; thence e. through Alabama and Florida—Ala.; Fla.; Ga.; Miss.; S.C. *Elevation*—Practically all records are below 500 feet.

Size: Adults, 14–30 inches. Klauber's (Gen., 1943b) standard adult length for 103 males and 80 females is 535 mm.

Distinctive characteristics: "Dorsal coloration dark gray to black; ventral surface white, heavily blotched with dark brown or black; head markings obscure; lateral spots in 3 series" (Gloyd, Gen., 1935c).

Color: A snake from Silver Springs, Fla., received from E. R. Allen, Apr. 13, 1936. The back is marked with 42 black saddle spots, 7 of which are on the tail. In the cephalic ⅔ of the body these are edged with white on front and rear, but only slightly so on the sides. The white edges become very indistinct in the rear third of the body, and the spots themselves become less distinct. These spots are 7 to 8 scales wide and 2½ or 3 scales long. Three rows of alternating spots mark the sides, the lowest being on the 1st 4 rows of scales and extending slightly onto the ventral plates. The most distinct row, the middle one, is either on the 1st to 5th scale rows, or on the 2nd to 7th rows of scales, and the spots are opposite the ends of the dorsal saddles. The topmost, and most indistinct row, has spots which may be 5 scales wide, alternating with the dorsal spots. In the rear of the body, these spots of the opposite sides may come within 1 scale or less of meeting. The general ground color down to the midlateral rows of spots is hair brown or mouse gray, which is heavily stippled with black, as are also the white intervals between the spots of the lowest lateral row. Extending forward and marking the suture between the parietals with ground color touched with vinaceous-rufous, there is a middorsal neck stripe 10 scales long and 2 to 4 scales wide of carnelian red or vinaceous-russet. The same color occurs in the intervals between the black dorsal saddles, being there 1 to 2 scales wide and 1 to 2 scales long. On the rear of the body, this interval color may be hay's russet or may be almost obscured by ground color. The terminal half of the tail may be hazel or ochraceous-tawny above and ochraceous-tawny below. The top of the head and neck are marked with a pair of irregular long black bands ending forward in a black spot on the supraocular. The top of the head and face forward of the eyes is a flat dull black as are also the upper labials, except for the row of white spots extending from the eye backward toward the angle of the mouth. These white spots form the lower border of the black vitta, 3 scales wide, which passes backward from the eye over 10 to 11 scale rows. The iris is black with a longitudinal band bowing around the top of the pupil of pale chalcedony yellow, becoming cream, and above that a border of hay's russet. The chin is almost pure black with a few white touches. The forward part of the underside of the head is free of white except for the center of the chin shields. The lower labials are black, but beginning below the eye, some of them have white spots, and from the same level backward, the underside of the head has more white. The striking ventral pattern is formed of sharply outlined black spots and clear white intervals on the forward third or half of the body. Caudad, the black spots become larger, their margins less sharply defined, and the white interspaces speckled with black.

Habitat: This little ground rattlesnake has been taken in edges of bayous, in dry ground, on cutover pine lands, in river drift, in the drier sections of swamps, in dense thickets, and in moist or rocky situations.

The most extended account occurs in Carr's volume. "All types of flat-woods; nearly any kind of terrain where lakes and marshes are frequent. Abundance—Fairly common; locally numerous. Habits—Usually found near water. When the Everglades are flooded, pigmy rattlers may often be seen in small trees, and lying coiled on cabbage palm leaves 8 or 10 feet high. I have taken several under logs on the shore of Lake Yale, Lake County."

Period of activity: *First appearance*—Feb. 5, 1911, and Feb. 26, 1919 (Blatchley); Feb., 1937 (W. T. Neill). *Fall disappearance*—Sept., 1913 (Wright and Bishop); Nov. 7, 1948 (Babis, Fla., 1949); Oct. 23, 1948 (Catlin, Fla., 1950).

Breeding: Viviparous. Males 300–700 mm., females 300–658 mm. *Young*—Number, 5–9. In 1935 Chamberlain reported his smallest individuals from South Carolina were from 175 to 185 mm. Doubtless most of his material was *S. m. miliarius.* Ditmars' "7–9 young" no doubt pertained largely to Florida specimens. In 1939 Conant and Bridges (Gen.) gave the hatchling size as about 7 inches. In 1915 Wright and Bishop wrote: "Like the other poisonous Crotalids this species is ovoviviparous, but the number of the young is few, usually from 5 to 9 being the range. One 14-inch specimen (No. 6,243) taken between July 15–November 1, 1912, has 8 medium-sized embryos, the caudal one being the smallest. Another, the largest specimen (19 inches long), taken September, 1913, has 9 embryos." The most definite evidence is from Gloyd (Gen., 1940). "New born young in a brood of 8 from Silver Springs, Marion County, Florida, (MZUM 79248) ranged from 157 to 173 mm. in total length."

Food: Frogs, field mice, insects, lizards, spiders. Wright and Bishop, Blatchley.

Venom: From the time of Williams in 1827, much has been written about the poison of this little ground rattler of Florida. We give only excerpts from an article by Allen (*Proc. Florida Acad. Sciences,* **2** [1938]: 70–76):

Fig. 303. *Sistrurus m. barbouri:* 1–5, Silver Springs, Fla., E. R. Allen; 6,7, Eureka, Marion Co., Fla., C. C. Tyler.

Fig. 304. *Sistrurus m. streckeri,* New Orleans, La., P. Viosca, Jr.

"Sistrurus miliarius barbouri. This specimen weighed 3 ounces, was injected with 25 milligrams of venom (cottonmouth) and died in 10 hours.

"Snake Bites in Florida Recorded by Florida Reptile Institute[:] Pigmy Rattlesnake 1935, 10 Bites, 0 Deaths; 1936, 13 Bites, 0 Deaths; 1937, 5 Bites, 0 Deaths.

"On one collecting trip in the Everglades, Bill Piper, my assistant, was bitten by a Pigmy Rattlesnake. . . . In spite of the treatment, however, there was a severe pain and swelling for about 24 hours.

"Effect of Pigmy Rattlesnake (*Sistrurus miliarius barbouri*) venom on the Coral Snake (*Micrurus fulvius fulvius*). We have a concrete pit 6 feet square and 5 feet deep in which we keep coral snakes and pigmy rattlesnakes. On Sept. 15, 1937, David Boyer, an employee at the Florida Reptile Institute, put a new coral snake into the pit. Almost immediately a small Pigmy Rattlesnake bit the coral snake on the back, 2 inches back of the head. . . . Twenty-four hours later the coral snake was dead and it is evident that death was caused from the venom of the Pigmy Rattlesnake."

Enemies: In 1948 Babis (Fla., 1949) found 2 ground rattlers in the digestive tract of a 6-foot indigo snake, just west of Royal Palm State Park, Fla.

Authorities:

Allen, E. R., and E. Maier (Gen., 1941)	Loennberg, E. (Fla., 1895)
Blatchley, W. S. (Fla., 1932)	Safford, W. E. (Fla., 1919)
Carr, A. F., Jr. (Fla., 1940a)	Say, T. (Gen., 1819)
Gloyd, H. K. (Gen., 1935, 1935c, 1940)	Wright, A. H., and S. C. Bishop (Ga.,
Kauffman, F. E. (Fla., 1928)	1916)

1837, J. L. Williams, *The Territory of Florida:* "The Ground Rattlesnake is about 12 inches long. It is frequently seen coiled in a circle, flat like a piece of ferreting; in this situation it lies on a fence rail, or log, and has been seized by children as a plaything. Its bite often produces a lingering illness, though not frequently mortal."

Pigmy rattlesnake (11—Strecker 1915), **Ground rattlesnake**
(11—Smith 1879), **Western pigmy rattlesnake** (4)

Sistrurus miliarius streckeri Gloyd 1935. Fig. 304; Map 70

Other common names: Southern pigmy rattlesnake; Strecker's pigmy rattlesnake; western ground rattlesnake (3).

Range: E. and cent. Texas through s.e. Oklahoma to s. Missouri; southeastward through w. Tennessee to n.w. Alabama; s. to Louisiana.—Ala.; Ark.; La.; Miss.; Okla.; Tenn.; Tex. *Elevation*—Sea level to 1,500 feet, possibly to 2,000 feet.

Size: Adults, 16–25 inches. Klauber's (Gen., 1943b) standard adult length for 55 males and 49 females is 520 mm.

Distinctive characteristics: "The smaller number of anterior scale rows

23-21-17, will separate most specimens of this subspecies from *miliarius* and *barbouri* each of which normally has 25-23-17. The pattern is distinct and very irregular; the blotches of the middorsal series are conspicuously wider than long; there are but 1 or 2 series of spots on the sides, those of the mid-lateral series are usually higher than wide; the dark pigment of the ventral surface is diffuse, and the ventral blotches are usually not wider than 1 scute. The average number of ventrals is lowest in this form" (Gloyd, Gen., 1935c).

Color: A snake from New Orleans, La., received from P. Viosca, Jr., June 16, 1936. The background of the sides and dorsum is ecru-drab, except for the 3 middorsal rows of scales, which are cinnamon or sayal brown. Between the 2 long dark dorsal spots of the head and neck, this middorsal interspace becomes tawny-olive or snuff brown. Toward the tail, it becomes cinnamon-buff or even pinkish cinnamon. The transverse dorsal spots, 29–30 on body + 5 on tail, are 1 to 1½ scales long and 7 scales wide and have centers of snuff brown bordered by warm sepia or fuscous. This darker edge is outlined by a thread of pale pinkish buff or pale olive-buff. Back of the head, the first 5 or 6 transverse spots have a tendency to be split into 2, thus forming pairs. The dorsal interspaces are 2 to 3 scales long. The dorsal spots of the tail, with the exception of the 1st 2, make complete bars from sub-caudal to subcaudal. On the caudal half of the body, there are indistinct clouded areas alternating with the dorsal saddles and the spots of the mid-lateral row. These areas are not distinct enough to be called spots. On the side, on the 2nd to 5th rows of scales, is a series of warm sepia spots about 1 scale long. The spots of this midlateral series are directly opposite the dorsal saddles. Below this lateral series and alternating with it, is a row on the 1st or 1st and 2nd rows of scales, the spots extending very slightly onto the ends of the ventrals. On the ends of the ventrals is another series of similar-sized spots which more or less alternate with the lowest lateral row. Beginning at the rear corner of the eyes are 2 longitudinal marks that travel across the outer edges of the parietals, curving outward on the broad portion of the head and then approximating on the neck. This pair of warm sepia spots is at least an inch in length. The interspace of the top of the head has much of the cinnamon or sayal brown of the dorsal interspaces. Above each nostril and extending onto the internasal is a pair of warm sepia spots, and across the front of the supraoculars and the frontal is a transverse bar of the same. A white or vinaceous-pink oblique postocular stripe crosses the upper labials and serves as a lower border for the warm sepia or fuscous band which extends to the neck from the lower half of the eye. A prominent white bar extends from the labial border along the suture line between the 4th and 5th lower labials onto a gular. There is a similar one between the 6th and 7th. These are connected on the gulars and have an extension backward to the angle of the mouth, which joins the oblique postocular light stripe. The mental plate is primrose yellow or colonial buff. The 1st, 2nd, 3rd, and part of the 4th lower labials are heavily spotted with fuscous or warm sepia and some marguerite yellow. The 1st and 2nd pairs of chin shields have considerable white down the center. The upper part of the iris is pale olive-buff, the lower part hazel flecked with fuscous. The ground color of the ventral surfaces is pale brownish vinaceous, heavily checked, flecked, and stippled with black or fuscous. On the tail, the ground color becomes light pinkish cinnamon, and down the middle in the rear half is a streak of mikado brown. On the throat and underside of the head, the ground color is white.

Habitat: In 1900 Beyer (La.) said: "Preferring dry localities for its habitat, this snake is absent from the swampy and marshy sections. In the pine regions and hummocks it is fairly common, living among leaves and other rubbish, and thereby escaping notice." In 1903 Mitchell said: "They are found everywhere in Texas. Their general color is adapted to their surroundings, thus, those that live in open prairie in the grass, or that live on sandy land, are much lighter in appearance than those that live on black ground or in dense brush, or under houses." In the same year Hurter (Mo.) found it in the "debris of an old shanty on the slope of a hill." One of Strecker's 1908 records is "under an old newspaper," while much later, in 1924, he found it in "timberland districts."

Breeding: Viviparous. *Young*—Number, 6–14. In 1887 Garman observed: "A young one, how long at birth not known, with only a button, measures 6½ inches. The average size of full grown is rather less than 17 inches." In 1898 Beyer told of a female which on Aug. 12 gave birth to 6 young. "They were born during the night, and I found each one of them curled up in the manner of the old one in different places in the cage. The newcomers were the exact counterpart of their mother in color and markings, the ground color, however, much lighter, and the head being much more obtuse. Their length was 5½ inches by a trifle less than ¼ of an inch." In 1940 Gloyd recorded "young 151–178 mm. in length."

In 1903 Mitchell said, "I have dissected a good many females, but have never found one that had either young or eggs." Stejneger quotes Putnam (*American Naturalist,* 2[1868]: 134) as saying that he had once "dissected a specimen having 14 eggs, all with embryo 2 inches in length in the oviduct." In 1911 Hurter reported: "From one he had taken 7 embryos, August 19th, each about 165 mm. long. . . . It is ovoviviparous."

Food: Mice, insects. Mitchell, Viosca (La., 1926).

Venom: In 1903, Mitchell wrote: "They are much dreaded by the country people, not so much on account of their poison (I never knew of any person bitten by a ground rattlesnake but what suffered more from the remedies administered than from the poison of the snake) as from their quietness, their habit of living around homes and outhouses, and their sudden attack. I have found in their stomachs mice and crickets. They are nocturnal, but move about on cloudy and rainy days." In 1911 Hurter said: "So small is the rattle of this species that its whirring can only be heard a few feet away. . . . Their bite . . . is not regarded as at all dangerous, the effects having been compared to the sting of a hornet." In 1926, however, Viosca (La.) wrote: "Upon attempting a similar experiment with a pigmy rattlesnake (*Sistrurus miliarius*) 8 days old, Prof. Beyer suffered serious consequences, the resulting inflammation not disappearing until after 3 days." Viosca concluded that "the venom glands of pit vipers are completely functional 8 days after birth, but it seems doubtful that they secrete venom until some time after the first day."

Authorities:

Beyer, G. E. (La., 1898)   Hurter, J. (Mo., 1911)
Garman, S. (Tex., 1887)   Mitchell, J. D. (Tex., 1903)
Gloyd, H. K. (Gen., 1935c, 1940)   Strecker, J. K., Jr. (Tex., 1915)

1935(c): H. K. Gloyd named this subspecies after the late Dr. John K. Strecker of Baylor University, Waco, Tex., whose papers on amphibians and reptiles of Texas and Arkansas have filled in many gaps in the knowledge of these groups.

Glossary

Abdomen: lower surface of body between neck and anus.

Anal plate: scale lying just in front of anus, single or paired, "anal entire" or "anal divided"; when divided, division is oblique.

Angle of mouth: meeting point of upper jaw (maxilla) and lower jaw (mandible).

Anus: posterior opening of digestive tract marking division between body and tail.

Anterior chin shields: the pair toward the snout.

Anterior frontal, anterior vertical: a plate between prefrontals in some *Contia tenuis* or *Charina* species.

Anterior nasal: anterior of two plates surrounding the nostril.

Anterior ocular: preocular.

Anterior orbital: preocular.

Anterior parietal: first large scale posterior to ocular in blind snakes.

Anterior temporal: *see* Temporals.

Apical scale pits: depressions (commonly 2) faintly evident on posterior end of scale.

Azygous plate: usually elongate, unpaired scale medially located on anterior portion of top of head (between internasals); sometimes used, as by Stull (1940), for odd, usually single scales occurring among otherwise typical head plates.

Body: head to anus.

Button: terminal rattle (*see* Rattle).

Canthals: scales of edge of crown between internasals and supraoculars.

Canthus rostralis: outer edge of crown where it turns downward on face, extending from rostral to supraoculars.

Carinae: keels.

Carinate: with a keel.

Caudals: *see* Subcaudals.

Cephalic plates or scutella: head plates.

Chin shields: paired, elongate scales on underside of head between lower labials; usually two pairs (anterior and posterior), rarely three or four pairs or with intergeneials (*see* Geneials).

Compressed: flattened laterally.

Crown shields: head plates.

Denticulate: with teeth or serrations.

Depressed: flattened vertically.

Dermal: relating to skin.

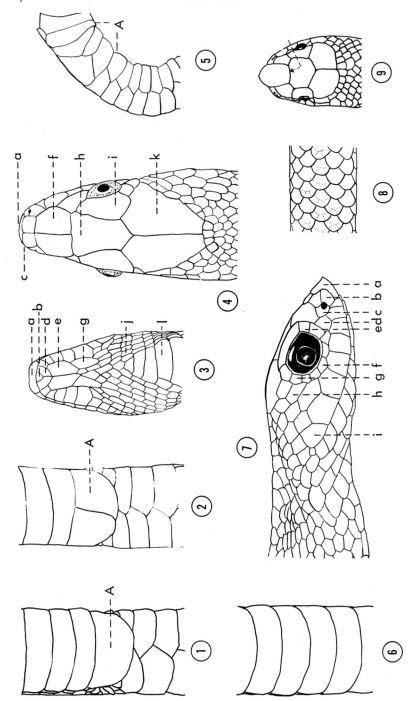

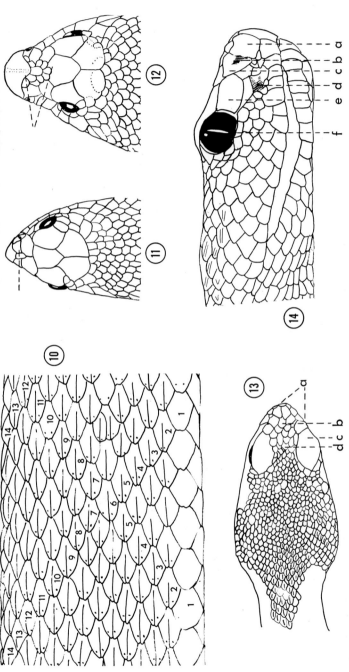

Fig. 305. Species used to illustrate glossary terms: 1, *Drymarchon corais erebennus*—anal single; 2, *Salvadora hexalepis hexalepis*—anal divided; 3 and 4, *Elaphe obsoleta* and *Elaphe triaspis intermedia*—(a) rostral, (b) mental, (c) internasal, (d) first lower labial, (e) anterior chin shields, (f) prefrontal, (g) posterior chin shields, (h) frontal, (i) supraocular, (j) gulars, (k) parietal, (l) ventral; 5, *Heterodon nasicus nasicus*—anal double; 6, *Coluber flagellum flagellum*—wide ventrals; 7, *Heterodon platyrhinos platyrhinos*—(a) rostral, (b) prenasal, (c) postnasal, (d) loreal, (e) preocular,

(f) subocular, (g) postocular, (h) temporal, (i) upper labials; 8, *Leptotyphlops humilis humilis*—uniform dorsal and ventral scales; 9, *Ficimia olivacea streckeri*—broad contact of rostral and frontal; 10, *Natrix taxispilota*—scale rows 14, keeled and pitted; 11, *Heterodon platyrhinos platyrhinos*—azygous plate; 12, *Heterodon simus*—supplementary azygous scales; 13, *Crotalus viridis viridis*—(a) canthals, (b) prefrontal area, (c) supraocular, (d) frontal area; 14, *Crotalus atrox*—(a) prenasal, (b) nostril, (c) postnasal, (d) pit, (e) precular, (f) vertical pupil.

Dorsal: relating to back.

Dorsal scales: scales of upper surface of the body; dorsal scale formulas include lateral scales.

Ecdysis: act of shedding or casting the outer coat or integument.

Epiglottis: cartilaginous vertical flag at the glottis (in *Pituophis*).

Eye shield: ocular of blind snake.

Facial pit: pit between eye and nostril in pit vipers.

Fang: enlarged tooth for prehension, usually with lengthwise groove on its anterior edge or a canal opening near tip.

Frontal: median unpaired plate on top of the head between the eyes. In blind snakes, the second plate in the median dorsal line on top of the head behind the rostral.

Fronto-nasal: second of 3 pairs of plates between rostral and frontal in *Charina* (rubber boas). In blind snakes it may be an upper nasal or large plate posterior to rostral, sometimes meeting its fellow on middorsal line.

Gastrostege: *see* Ventrals.

Geneial, genial: chin shield.

Glottis: opening of wind pipe.

Gulars: scales below the jaw between lower labials, chin shields, and ventrals.

Head plates, head shields: large scales on top of the head.

Hemipenes: two evertible intromittent organs of the male.

Infralabials, inferior labials: *see* Labials.

Intercanthals: *see* Prefrontals.

Intergeneial: scale located between the chin shields. In *Crotalus exsul*.

Internasal: plate or plates (2) on top of the head between the plates which surround the nostrils.

Interoccipital: in a blind snake, the fourth plate in the median dorsal line on top of the head behind the rostral, i.e., a scale between occipitals.

Interorbital, intersupraocular: scales on top of the head of a rattlesnake between the plates surmounting the eyes.

Interparietal: either interoccipital or the third plate in dorsal line behind the rostral in blind snakes, i.e., a scale between parietals.

Juxtaposed: placed side by side without overlapping.

Keel: (1) median longitudinal ridge on a scale; (2) angle at the side of the venter when ventrals turn up on the sides as in *Elaphe* or *Chionactis*.

Labial pits: pits on infralabials or supralabials in some boas, but not present in our forms.

Labials: plates bordering the mouth opening exclusive of the median one of each jaw. Upper labials or supralabials extend from the rostral to the angle of the mouth. Lower labials, infralabials, or inferior labials extend from the mental to the angle of the mouth (*see* Nasolabial *and* Oculolabial).

Lachrymal pit: pit.

Loreal, loral: a scale on the side of the head between the nostril and the eye but not usually touching either structure.

Lower labial: *see* Labials.

Lower nasal: plate below the nostril of a blind snake.

Lower ocular: subocular.

Mandible: lower jaw.

Maxilla: upper jaw.

Median gular: a scale located between the chin shields or on the median ventral line between the chin shields and the first ventrals.

Mental: median plate at the tip of the lower jaw or symphysial.

Middorsal scales: dorsal scales located on the median line above.

Museum abbreviations:

AMNH—American Museum of Natural History, New York City.

ANSP—Academy of Natural Sciences, Philadelphia, Pennsylvania.

Baylor—Baylor University Museum, Waco, Texas.

BMNH—British Museum (Natural History), London, England.

CA—Chicago Academy of Sciences, Chicago, Illinois.

CAS—California Academy of Sciences, San Francisco.

CM—Carnegie Museum, Pittsburgh, Pennsylvania.

Cornell—Cornell University Museum, Ithaca, New York.

FMNH—Field Museum of Natural History, Chicago, Illinois.

FSM—Florida State Museum, Gainesville.

KSC—Kansas State College, Manhattan.

KU—University of Kansas, Lawrence.

LMK—L. M. Klauber, San Diego, California.

MCZ—Museum of Comparative Zoology, Harvard University, Cambridge, Massachusetts.

MVZ—Museum of Vertebrate Zoology, University of California, Berkeley.

MZUM—Museum of Zoology, University of Michigan, Ann Arbor.

ROMZ—Royal Ontario Museum of Zoology.

SDS—San Diego Society of Natural History, San Diego, California.

Stanford—Museum of Zoology, Stanford University, California.

UOMZ—Museum of Zoology, University of Oklahoma, Norman.

USNM—United States National Museum, Washington, D.C.

Nasal: a plate containing or adjacent to a nostril. When a pair of scales, prenasal and postnasal, or, in blind snakes, upper and lower.

Nasal pit: *see* Pit.

Nasolabial: nasal or inferior nasal of blind snakes; same as supralabial no. 1.

Occipitals: parietals or, in blind snakes, the second plate behind that covering the eye entering the angle between the third and fourth plates of the median rows.

Ocular: one of the scales forming the margin of the eye. Supra-, pre-, post-, and subocular, a scale above, in front of, behind, or below the eye.

Oculolabial: a subocular united to a supralabial.

Orbital: ocular.

Oviparous: laying eggs.

Ovoviviparous: producing eggs hatched before exclusion from body.

Parietals: a pair of large plates (occasionally single as in *Charina*) on top of the head behind the frontal. In blind snakes, a plate behind that covering the eye and entering the angle between the second and fourth of the median dorsal rows.

Pit: "A deep depression on side of head below and back of nostril . . . ; this is the external opening of a sensory organ, probably auditory in function. Where the pit-border scales are mentioned, those constituting the internal rim or lip are meant, rather than those completely external to the pit" (Klauber, Gen., 1936, p. 222).

Postgeneials: normally a posterior pair of chin shields.

Postnasal: *see* Nasal.

Post-occipital, post-parietal: a variable term for the first body scales back of the occipitals or parietals.

Postoculars: *see* Oculars.

Postrostral: azygous.

Post-temporals, posterior temporals: *see* Temporals.

Prefrontals: a pair of plates just ahead of the frontal. In blind snakes, the first middorsal plate behind the rostral.

Pregeneial: *see* Anterior chin shields.

Prenasal: *see* Nasal.

Preocular: *see* Ocular.

Rattle: terminal appendage on the tail of rattlesnakes. "The proximal rattle is that next the tail and is one most recently added to the string. The button (or rattle-button) is the first permanent rattle acquired by a young snake, the rattle present at birth (the prebutton) being invariably lost with the first exuviation. The button remains as the posterior terminus of the rattle-string until lost by breakage; it is usually present in juveniles or young adults, but rarely in older specimens" (Klauber, Gen., 1936, p. 224).

Rictus: gape of the mouth.

Rostral: a median plate on the tip of the snout bordering the mouth opening above.

Scaleboss: a knobby prominence on the posterior part of a scale evident on the middorsal row in some rattlesnakes, as *C. cerastes*.

Scale rows: "The lines of dorsal scales, counted obliquely. . . . The number may vary from one end of the body to the other, but the maximum number is always meant (unless otherwise stated), and this is determined by counting the rows somewhat anterior to the middle of the body, or by making several such counts. Scale rows, or scale formula, 19-21-17, means 19 rows at anterior end of body, a maximum of 21 rows, near the middle, and a minimum of 17 rows, at the posterior end. By a 'higher' formula is meant one showing a greater number of scale rows. Thus 23-19 is a higher formula than 21-17, and the latter is higher than 19-21-17. A 'lower formula' than the last would be such a one as 19-17 or 17-19-15" (Blanchard, Gen., 1925, p. 56).

Sclerotic ring: a complete ring of ocular scales, with subocular scales present.

Scutellum: little scale.

Scutellation: arrangement of scales.

Sex: "Sex is definitely determined by dissection of under side of tail behind anus. A slit an inch or less in length will reveal, in the male, a hollow spiny organ lying ventral to the scent gland; in the female, only the scent gland will be found here. Sex is often also determined by the shape of the base of the tail, which is wide in the male, narrow and more quickly tapering in the female" (Blanchard, Gen., 1925, p. 56).

Sheath: a membrane about the base of a fang.

Shed: a molt, a castoff skin.

Slough: *see* Shed.

Spurs: vestigial limbs of boas laterad of anus.

Subcaudals: enlarged plates on the underside of the tail.

Submental: plate back of the mental. Rare.

Suboculars: *see* Oculars.

Suborbitals: suboculars.

Superciliaries: supraoculars.

Supralabials: *see* Labials.

Supraoculars: *see* Oculars.

Suture: meeting edge of 2 plates or scales.

Tail: part of a snake posterior to anus.

Temporals: *Anterior*—one, two, or occasionally more longitudinally elongated scales arranged one above another behind the postoculars and between the parietals and upper labials; i.e., the first vertical row. *Posterior*—one, two, three, or more longitudinally elongated scales lying one above another behind the anterior temporals, i.e., the second vertical row.

Tubercles: male characters such as chin tubercles, supraanal tubercles, and knobby dorsal scale tubercles.

Urosteges: caudals (*see* Subcaudals).

Ventrals: large scales or plates on the lower surface of the body from the head to the anal plate.

Vertical: frontal.

Viviparous: bearing living young; having eggs hatching within the body. Many writers prefer this term to *ovoviviparous* because of intermediate conditions.

Important North American

References

These selected general works are the principal tools of our herpetologists. The complete bibliography will appear in Volume III. The citations quoted throughout this work after the names of individual authors refer to the comprehensive bibliography of Volume III. They do not refer to the present list, which is an entirely independent list of ready references.

HANDBOOKS, FIELD GUIDES, CATALOGUES, KEYS

Baird, S. F., and C. Girard. Catalogue of North American Reptiles in the Museum of the Smithsonian Institution. Pt. I, Serpents. *Smithson. Misc. Colls.,* 2 (1853).

Baird, S. F., and C. Girard. *Reptiles of the Boundary.* In: W. H. Emory. *Report of the United States and Mexican Survey Made under the Direction of the Secretary of the Interior.* 34th Cong., 1st sess., Sen. Ex. Doc., vol. 30 (1859).

Baird, S. F., E. Hallowell, and A. L. Heermann. In: U.S. War Department. *Reports of Explorations and Surveys to Ascertain the Most Practicable Route for a Railroad from the Mississippi River to the Pacific Ocean . . .* 1856–1859. 33d Cong., 2d sess., Sen. Ex. Doc. no. 78, vol. 10 (1859).

Barbour, T. *Reptiles and Amphibians.* Boston and New York, 1926. Pp. 1–125.

Berridge, W. S. *Marvels of Reptile Life.* London, 1926.

Blanchard, F. N. A key to the snakes of the United States and Canada and Lower California. *Papers Mich. Acad. Sci. Arts Letters,* **4,** pt. 2 (1925). Other eds: 1939, 1941.

Boulenger, E. G. *Amphibia and Reptilia.* In: *Regan's Natural History.* London, 1936. Pp. 297–392.

Boulenger, E. G. *Reptiles and Batrachians.* London and New York, 1914.

Boulenger, G. A. *Catalogue of the Snakes in the British Museum (Natural History).* 3 vols. London, 1893–96.

Brown, A. E. A review of the genera and species of American snakes north of Mexico. *Proc. Acad. Nat. Sci. Phila.,* 53 (1901): 10–110.

Calmette, A. *Venoms, Venomous Animals and Antivenous Serum-Therapeutics.* London, 1908.

Catesby, M. *The Natural History of Carolina, Florida and the Bahama Islands.* London, 1731–43.

Conant, R. *Reptiles and Amphibians of the Northeastern States.* 2d ed. [Philadelphia], 1952. 1st ed., 1917.

Conant, R., and W. Bridges. *What Snake Is That? A Field Guide to the Snakes of the United States East of the Rocky Mountains.* New York and London, 1939.

Cope, E. D. Catalogue of the Colubridae in the Museum of the Academy of Natural Sciences of Philadelphia. *Proc. Acad. Nat. Sci. Phila.,* **12** (1861): 74–79, 241–266, 553–566.

Cope, E. D. Catalogue of the venomous serpents in the Museum of the Academy of Natural Sciences in Philadelphia. *Proc. Acad. Nat. Sci. Phila.,* **11** (1860): 332–347.

Cope, E. D. The crocodilians, lizards and snakes of N.A. *U.S. Nat. Mus. Rept., 1898* (1900), 153–1270.

Curran, C. H., and C. Kauffeld. *Snakes and Their Ways.* New York, 1937.

Daudin, F. M. *Histoire naturelle, générale et particulière des reptiles.* 8 vols. Paris, 1801–03.

DeKay, J. E. *Zoology of New York, or the New York Fauna.* Reptiles and Amphibia. Pt. 3: 59–72; pt. 4: plates 19–22. In: *Natural History of New York.* Albany, 1842.

Ditmars, R. L. *A Field Book of North American Snakes.* Garden City, N.Y., 1939.

Ditmars, R. L. *The Reptile Book.* New York, 1907. See also 1936 edition.

Driver, E. C. *Name That Animal . . . Amphibians and Reptiles.* Northampton, Mass., 1942. Pp. 293–413.

Duméril, A. M. C. *Catalogue méthodique de la collection des reptiles de Muséum d'Histoire Naturelle de Paris.* 2 parts. Paris, 1851.

Duméril, A. M. C., and G. Bibron. *Erpétologie générale, ou histoire naturelle complète des reptiles.* 9 vols. in 10 and atlas, Paris, 1834–44.

Duméril, A., F. Bocourt, and F. Mocquard. Études sur la reptiles et les batrachians. In: France. *Mission scientifique au Mexique.* Recherches zoologique, pt. 3. Paris, 1870–1909.

Dunn, E. R. A tentative key and arrangement of the American genera of Colubridae. *Bull. Antiv. Inst. Amer.,* **2** (1928): 18–24.

Gadow, H. F. Amphibia and Reptilia. In *Cambridge Natural History.* Vol. VIII. London, 1901.

Garman, S. North American Reptilia. Part I, Ophidia. . . . *Mem. Mus. Comp. Zool.* Cambridge, Mass., 1883. 185 pp. 9 pls.

Girard, C. Herpetology. Vol. XX and atlas of *U.S. Exploring Expedition during the Years 1838–1842 under the Command of Charles Wilkes.* Philadelphia, 1858.

Gloyd, H. K. The rattlesnakes, genera Sistrurus and Crotalus. . . . *Chicago Acad. Sci. Spec. Pub.,* no. 4 (1940).

Gray, J. E. *Catalogue of the Specimens of Snakes in the Collection of the British Museum.* London, 1849.

Gray, J. E. *Zoological Miscellany.* London, 1831–45.

Günther, A. *Catalogue of Colubrine Snakes in the Collection of the British Museum.* London, 1858.

Günther, A. C. L. G. *Reptilia and Batrachia.* In: F. D. Godman and O. Salvin, eds. *Biologia Centrali-Americana: Zoology.* London, 1885–1902.

Hamilton, W. J., and J. A. Pollack. The food of some crotalid snakes from Fort Benning, Georgia. *Nat. Hist. Misc. Chicago Acad. Sci.,* no. 140 (1955).

Harlan, R. *American Herpetology.* Philadelphia, 1827. Pp. 1–63.

Harlan, R. Genera of North American Reptilia and a synopsis of the species. *Jour. Acad. Nat. Sci. Phila.,* 1st ser., **5**, pt. 2 (1827): 345–372.

Harlan, R. *Medical and Physical Researches.* Philadelphia, 1835.

Holbrook, J. E. *North American Herpetology.* Philadelphia, 1832–36. 3 vols. There is a scarce 4th volume.

Holbrook, J. E. *North American Herpetology.* 5 vols. Philadelphia, 1836–42.

Hopley, C. C. *Snakes; Curiosities and Wonders of Serpent Life.* London, 1882.

Hudson, W. H. *The Book of a Naturalist.* New York, 1919. Chs. ii, xiv–xvii.

Jan, G., and F. Sordelli. *Iconographie générales des Ophidiens.* 3 vols. Milan, 1860–82. I, livr. pl. 1–17 (Dec. 1860–Oct. 1866): 1–9; II, livr. pl. 18–34 (Oct. 1866–Mar. 1870): 1–9; III, livr. pl. 35–50 (Mar. 1870–Nov. 1881): 1–20; livr. pl. 51 (1882).

Jordan, D. S. *Manual of the Vertebrates of the Northern U.S.* Chicago, 1876. pp. 172–184. Later editions to 1929.

Klauber, L. M. Studies of reptile life in the arid Southwest. *Bull. Zool. Soc. San Diego,* no. 15 (1939): 1–23.

Linnaeus, C. *Systema naturae per regna tria naturae, secundum classes, ordines, genera, species cum characteribus, differentiis, synonymis locis.* 10 ed., Stockholm, 1758. 12 ed.; Stockholm, 1766.

Lydekker, R., J. T. Cunningham, G. A. Boulenger, and J. Arthur Thomson. *Reptiles, Amphibians, Fishes and Lower Chordata.* London, 1912. Pp. 1–156.

Morgan, A. H. *Field Book of Animals in Winter.* New York, 1939.

Neill, W. T. Ranges and taxonomic allocations of amphibians and reptiles in the southeastern United States. *Pubs. Research Station Ross Allen's Rept. Inst.,* **1** (1954): 75–96.

Noguchi, H. Snake venoms. Carnegie Inst. Wash. Pub., no. 111 (1909).

Oliver, J. A. *The Natural History of North American Amphibians and Reptiles.* New York, 1955.

Palmer, E. L. *Field Book of Natural History.* New York, 1949.

Perkins, C. B. A key to the snakes of the United States. *Bull. Zool. Soc. San Diego,* no. 16 (1940): 1–63. 2d ed., 1949.

Phisalix, M. *Animaux venimeux et venins.* Paris, 1922. 2 vols.

Pickwell, G. *Amphibians and Reptiles of the Pacific States.* Stanford, Calif., 1947.

Pope, C. H. *The Reptile World.* New York, 1955.

Pope, C. H. *Snakes Alive and How They Live.* New York, 1937.

Pope, C. H. *Snakes of the Northeastern United States.* New York Zool. Soc. (1946), 1–52.

Pratt, H. S. *A Manual of Land and Fresh Water Vertebrate Animals of the U.S.* Philadelphia, 1923. Pp. 144–187.

Pycraft, W. P. *The Story of Reptile Life.* London, 1905.

Schlegel, H. *Essai sur la physionomie serpens.* Leiden, 1837. 2 vols. and atlas. Edinburgh and London, 1844.

Schmidt, K. P., and D. D. Davis. *Field Book of Snakes.* New York, 1941.

Shaw, G. *General Zoology.* London, 1802. III, pt. 2: 1–579.

Slevin, J. R. *A Handbook of Reptiles and Amphibians of the Pacific States.* San Francisco, 1934. Spec. pub. of Calif. Acad. Sci.

Sonnini, C. S., and P. A. Latreille. *Histoire naturelle des reptiles.* 4 vols. Paris, 1801–02.

Stebbins, R. C. *Amphibians and Reptiles of Western North America.* New York, Toronto, and London, 1954.

Stejneger, L. The poisonous snakes of N.A. *U.S. Nat. Mus. Rept. 1893,* pt. 2 (1895): 337–487.

Storer, D. H. In: Massachusetts Zoological and Botanical Survey. *Reports on Fishes, Reptiles and Birds of Massachusetts.* Boston, 1839. Pp. 20–206, 221–235.

Van Denburgh, J. The reptiles of the Pacific Coast and Great Basin. *Occ. Papers Calif. Acad. Sci.,* **5** (1897): 1–236.

Van Denburgh, J. The reptiles of western North America. *Occ. Papers Calif. Acad. Sci.,* **2** (1922): 617–1028.

Zweifel, R. G., and K. S. Norris. Contributions to the herpetology of Sonora, Mexico. *Amer. Midl. Naturalist,* 54 (1955): 230–249.

CHECK LISTS

Brown, B. C. *An Annotated Check List of the Reptiles and Amphibians of Texas.* (Baylor Univ. Studies.) Waco, 1950.

Cope, E. D. North American Batrachia and Reptilia. *Bull. U.S. Nat. Mus.,* no. 1 (1875): 22–23, 33–44.

Davis, N. S., Jr., and F. L. Rice. Descriptive catalogue of North American Batrachia and Reptilia east of the Mississippi River. *Bull. Ill. State Lab. Nat. Hist.* no. 5 (1883): 27–44.

Garman, S. The North American reptiles and batrachians: A list of the species occurring north of the Isthmus of Tehuantepec. *Bull. Essex Inst.,* **16** (1884): 3–46; snakes, 20–36.

Klauber, L. M. A key to the rattlesnakes. *Trans. San Diego Soc. Nat. Hist.,* **8** (1936): 185–276.

Logier, E. B. S., and G. C. Toner. Check-list of the amphibians and reptiles of Canada. *Contr. Roy. Ont. Mus. Zool. and Paleont.,* no. 41 (1955).

Mills, R. C. A check list of the reptiles and amphibians of Canada. *Herpetologica,* **4** (1948): second suppl.

Schmidt, K. P. *A Check List of North American Reptiles.* 6th ed. Chicago, 1953.

Smith, H. M., and E. H. Taylor. An annotated checklist and key to the snakes of Mexico. *Bull. U.S. Nat. Mus.,* no. 187 (1945): 1–239.

Stejneger, L., and T. Barbour. *A Check List of North American Amphibians and Reptiles.* Cambridge, Mass., 1917. Later eds.: 2d, 1923; 3d, 1933; 4th, 1939; 5th, 1943.

Wright, A. H. Scientific and popular writers on American snakes (1517–1944). *Herpetologica*, **5** (1949): first suppl.

Wright, A. H. and A. A. List of the snakes of the United States and Canada by states and provinces. *Amer. Midl. Naturalist*, **48** (1952): 574–603.

Yarrow, H. C. Check list of North American Reptilia and Batrachia. *Bull. U.S. Nat. Mus.*, no. 24 (1882–83).

Index

[Numbers in boldface give the pages of species accounts. Scientific names are abbreviated and not italicized. Most common names ending in *adder, snake,* etc. (except those applied to genera) are indexed under those terms. The letter *f* indicates that other references by the same author occur in the same species account.]

Aaron, S. F., 29
Abastor, 18, 21, 24, 30, 74, 75, 82-86, 87, 270, 276, 669
  erythrogrammus, 22, 75, **82-86**
Abbott, C. C., 107, 307, 308, 367, 697f, 912
Abies concolor, 1036
Ablabes, 156, 159, 330
Abnormal coloration, *see* Color
Acacia greggi, 429
Acer grandidentata, 1036
Acer saccharum, 6
Acker, G., 181, 501
Ackroyd, J., 912
Acontias, 901
Adams, C. C., 170
Adams, L., 185
Adder, 306, 368, 588, 593, 834; black, 306; black water, 511; blowing, 297, 306, 312; checquered, 306, 364, 368; common spreading, 306; copper, 910; corals, 890; deaf, 1, 306; death, 903; flat-head, 306; great, 1042; highland, 368; hissing, 306; hog-nosed, 306, 312; North American, 306; prairie water, 490; puff, 311; puffing, 1, 297, 306, 312; red, 910; rock, 306; sand, 306; shovel-nose spreading, 312; speckled, 388; speckled chain, 604; spotted, 1, 262, 306, 364, 368, 697; spotted spreading, 306; spotted water, 511; spreading, 115, 297, 312; three-striped, 834; water, 500, 511, 526; western hognosed, 297; yellow-bellied, 138
Aechmophrys, 925
Agassiz, L., 825, 1025
Agave, 454, 961
Agkishodon, 901
Agkistrodon, 901
  laticinctus, 910
  mokasen, 907, 914, 966
  piscivorus, 966
  p. leucostoma, 924

Akers, W. W., 567
Alcorn, G. D., 143f
Alexander, A. H., 920
Alexander, W. P., 186f, 233, 371f, 558, 701f, 717f, 815, 826, 838, 841, 960
Allard, H. A., 106f
Allen, A. A., 187f, 233, 513, 718f, 745, 825f, 837f
Allen, A. R., 60
Allen, E. G., 188
Allen, E. R., 10, 29, 84, 146f, 177, 229, 236, 246f, 252, 254, 276, 313, 376f, 386f, 419f, 432, 474f, 477, 481, 495, 522f, 538f, 548, 616, 621, 629f, 662, 664f, 693f, 698, 733f, 831, 900, 905f, 918f, 940, 963f, 1053, 1055f
Allen, G. M., 560, 716, 844
Allen, J. A., 136, 300, 607, 1003f
Allen, M. J., 141, 191, 226, 250f, 289, 294, 308, 314, 325, 351, 354, 358, 389, 445, 473, 482f, 501f, 516f, 529, 554, 713, 721, 731, 829, 834, 905, 923f, 1001, 1053
Allen, R., 480, 486
Allen's Helicops, 420
Alves, Mrs. R. B., 460, 797, 887
Amaral, A. B. do, 29, 202, 206, 566f, 889, 920, 975, 980, 983f, 989, 1001, 1006, 1022, 1033
Ameiurus, 560
American cobra, 890
Amphiardis inornatus, 4, 288, **295-296**
Amphiuma, 28, 286, 422
Ancistrodon, 18, 25, 560, 901-925
  c. contortrix, 4, 900, **903-907**, 908
  c. laticinctus, 902, 904, **907-910**, 915
  c. mokeson, 33, 901, 904, **910-915**, 954
  c. pictigaster, 902, 904, **915-916**
  piscivorus, 19, 516, 901, 902, 903, **916-921**, 948
  p. leucostoma, 903, **921-925**
Anderson, O. I., 319, 329

Anderson, P., 111, 141, 181f, 294, 308, 348, 365f, 390, 492f, 554, 706f, 830, 856, 912f, 923, 960, 1045
Anderson, R., 823
Andrews, T. F., 914, 965
Anguis, 51, 330, 551
Ankistrodon, 901
Anota, 4
Anthony, A. W., 162, 164
Aplosaspis, 925
Appearance, 10; *see also* "Period of activity" *in each species account*
Aristolochia, 961
Arizona, 21, 24, 25, 68, 69, 86-104, 585
  e. elegans, 87, 88, **89-91,** 96, 98, 101, 103, 283, 329
  e. blanchardi, 88, 89, **92-93,** 96, 98, 101, 103, 104
  e. candida, 89, **93-95,** 96, 98, 101, 103
  e. eburnata, 3, 88, 89, 90, 92, 95, **96-98,** 101
  e. expolita, 92, 96, 98, 101, 103
  e. noctivaga, 88, 89, 90, 92, **98-100,** 101, 103
  e. occidentalis, 3, 88, 89, 90, 92, 96, 98, **100-103**
  e. pacata, 2
  e. philipi, 29, 88, 89, 92, 96, 101, 102, **103-104,** 656
Arnold, L. W., 46, 118, 398, 401, 579, 688f
Arny, S. A., 925
Artemisia, 600
Artemisia tridentata, 8
Arthur, C., 217
Artran, A. P., 96, 194, 196
Asarum, 961
Aspic, 544
Atkinson, D. A., 107, 189, 233f, 291, 371, 499, 509, 514, 717, 841f, 913, 1044f
Atomarchus, 755
Atriplex, 440
  canescens, 257
  torreyi, 383
Atsatt, S. R., 62, 64, 163, 382f, 404, 409, 450, 581f, 588, 596, 633, 637, 638f, 658, 660, 974, 989, 991, 993, 1015f
Audubon, J. J., 960, 965f
Auffenberg, W., 113f, 149, 150f, 421, 423
Authorities, 31; *see also each species account*
Axtell, H. H., 145, 186, 234, 372, 374, 514, 558f, 560, 699f, 717f, 813f, 826, 836f, 855f
Axtell, R., 813, 858
Axtell, R. W., 281, 343f

Babbitt, L. H., 149, 229, 423, 629, 699, 716
Babcock, H. L., 135, 188, 371, 514, 558, 701f, 826, 841, 913f, 968

Babis, W. A., 202, 970f, 1056f
Bailey, J. R., 155
Bailey, L. H., 242
Bailey, R. M., 18, 106, 111, 348, 349, 611f, 701f, 702, 826, 838, 914
Bailey, V. O., 31, 41, 58, 110, 192, 197, 204, 257f, 283, 297, 302f, 326, 390, 397, 401, 439, 446, 453, 458, 487, 516f, 553f, 560, 593, 600, 642f, 646, 653, 706, 725, 741, 795, 799, 854, 882, 941, 965, 966f, 980f, 1002, 1048
Baird, S. F., 39, 44, 105, 124f, 142f, 155, 156, 159, 163, 171f, 176, 184, 191, 192, 214, 218, 240f, 286, 288, 290, 360f, 372, 382, 391, 396f, 423, 456f, 505f, 515, 630, 633f, 644, 646f, 648, 669, 678, 696, 722, 728f, 735, 741, 772f, 795, 803f, 806f, 810, 830, 842, 858, 898, 922, 936, 941, 946, 980f, 1001, 1006, 1050
Baker, F. C., 492f
Ballard, J. J., 314
Ballou, W. H., 145
Barbour, R. W., 29, 106f, 110, 133f, 185f, 234, 553, 714, 835f, 956f
Barbour, T., 4, 179, 229, 238, 253, 269f, 311, 349, 376f, 413f, 423, 459, 511, 518, 521f, 544, 547f, 566f, 616f, 919
Barry, L. T., 322, 456
Bartlett, W. E., 308, 310
Barton, A. J., 371, 388, 502, 626, 908f
Barton, B. S., 1042, 1053
Bartram, W., 243f, 436, 555, 609, 616f, 940
Bascanion, 425
  f. frenatus, 446
  f. piceus, 446
  testaceum, 438
Bascanium, 425
Bassler, H., 273
Bateman, G. C., 227, 245, 376, 509, 528f, 612
Bean, G. T., 430, 431
Beattie, S. H., 567, 568
Beauvois, A. M. P. J. P. de, 901, 936, 939
Beck, D. E., 50, 403, 799
Behre, E. H., 893
Belkin, J., 718
Bell, J., 536
Bell, L. N., 149
Bellophis, 330
  zonatus, 411
Bentley, G. H., 319
Berberis trifoliata, 654
Berridge, W. S., 1070
Bevan, W. A., 1021
Beyer, G. E., 114, 251, 307, 314, 351, 356, 433, 492f, 501, 505, 515f, 830, 842, 905f, 924f, 940, 945f, 946, 1060
Bibron, G., 249, 472, 1071

Bicknell, E. P., 188
Binney, W. G., 731, 833, 847
Bishop, C. A., 1049
Bishop, M. B., 521f
Bishop, S. C., 106, 115, 133f, 157, 160, 178f,
    186f, 227, 233, 251, 274f, 355, 371, 375f,
    529, 546f, 555, 558, 700f, 710, 717f, 721,
    815, 826, 833f, 838f, 870, 900, 920f, 939f,
    952, 960, 999, 1047, 1056f
Black, J. D., 192
Black-headed snake, 722-755; Arizona, 752;
    Blanchard's, 750; California, 737; desert,
    738; Eisen's, 737; Florida, 733; Great
    Plains, 746; Gunther's, 725; Huachuca,
    752; Kennicott's, 746; Mexican, 725;
    northern slender, 742; slender, 740;
    southern Appalachian, 732; southeastern,
    728; southern slender, 740; Texas, 725;
    746; 748; Utah, 750; Wilcox's, 752
Black Pituophis, 612
Black snake, 133, 230; Alleghany, 230; Amer-
    ican, 133; common, 133, 138; dotted, 388;
    Dunn's, 145; eastern, 133; Florida, 145;
    Fox's, 138, 142; Louisiana, 136; Mexican,
    204; mountain, 230; pilot, 230; red-
    bellied, 477; rusty, 230; scaly, 230; slick,
    133; spotted, 136; swamp, 664; true, 133;
    white-throated, 133; yellow-bellied, 13,
    138, 142; yellow-spotted, 388
Black snapper, 1042
Blainville, H. M. de, 53, 379, 382, 407, 413,
    588, 851f
Blair, A. P., 791, 799
Blair, W. F., 92, 345, 769, 915
Blanchard, F. C., 836, 842
Blanchard, F. N., 11, 21, 31, 91, 98, 100, 103,
    104, 107, 109f, 111, 137, 143, 161, 163f,
    166f, 170f, 172f, 176, 180f, 186f, 191,
    194f, 197, 242, 274, 292, 294f, 296, 348f,
    351, 354, 356f, 364f, 368, 371f, 376, 380,
    383f, 384f, 391f, 398f, 422, 474, 482f,
    485, 501f, 513, 525f, 541, 558f, 602f,
    613f, 615, 629, 679f, 718f, 727f, 733f,
    737f, 741f, 747, 749, 750, 752, 795, 836,
    842, 876f, 882f
Blanchard, H. C., 87, 154, 239, 280, 301, 395,
    449, 462, 463, 465, 489, 557, 604, 641,
    771, 922
Blaney, Valeria, 290
Blarina, 30
Blatchley, W. S., 109f, 141, 145, 148, 178f,
    187f, 234, 266, 506, 555, 721, 825f, 830,
    842, 893, 940, 1056f
Blevins, J. L., 624
Blind snake, 2, 36-50, 105; brown, 44; Cali-
    fornia, 44, 46; New Mexican, 41; Tanner's,
    50; Texas, 39; Utah, 50

Blouin, A., 701
Blower, 306
Bluffer, 297
Blum, H. F., 1033
Blumenbach, J. F., 113, 355
Boa, 2, 52-66, 296; California, 62, 64; desert,
    1, 64-66; desert rosy, 64; Great Basin rub-
    ber, 53, 58; many-scaled, 62; Pacific rub-
    ber, 53; rosy, 60-66; rubber, 53-60, 64
Bocourt, M. F., 166, 852
Boettger, O., 258
Bogert, C. M., 57, 96f, 104, 118, 123f, 145,
    147f, 166f, 195, 202, 205f, 316, 323f,
    406, 429, 435, 438, 440f, 450, 568f, 573,
    575, 579f, 582f, 596f, 637, 639f, 644, 647,
    651, 653f, 658f, 663, 678, 684f, 790,
    870f, 889, 949f, 955, 977f, 982, 985, 991,
    997, 1008, 1015f, 1019, 1026f, 1050
Boidae, 2, 32, 33, 35, 52-66
Boie, F., 51, 885
Bonner, L., 957
Borell, A. E., 42, 58f, 217f, 498
Bosc, L. A. G., 354
Boulenger, E. G., 308, 612, 911, 914, 922,
    924, 946
Boulenger, G. A., 33, 35, 36, 228, 245, 285f,
    406, 502, 555, 573, 676f, 727, 735, 841,
    997
Bourke, J. G., 1025
Boyer, D., 1058
Boyer, D. A., 140f, 233, 391, 493, 501, 714,
    841f, 914
Boyer, R. H., 783f
Boyle, C. C., 382
Brachyorrhos, 104
Bradford, W. J. A., 1042
Bradleia, 669
Bradley, J. C., 165, 274
Bradt, G. McC., 593
Brady, M. K., 133, 229f, 235f, 378, 555
Bragg, A. N., 181f, 823
Bragg, L. M., 274
Branson, E. B., 111, 141, 181, 234, 348f, 361f,
    492, 607f, 707, 746, 747, 823, 842, 858,
    884, 913f, 1003f, 1049
Brattstrom, B. H., 49, 442, 583
Breckenridge, W. J., 707, 718f, 822f, 837f,
    858, 960
Breder, C. M., Jr., 840f
Breder, R. B., 841
Breed, J., 983
Breeding, 10-26; see also each species account
Brennan, G. A., 840
Brennan, L. A., 181, 361, 435
Bridges, W. A., 91, 136, 233, 268, 289, 348,
    375f, 436, 492, 505, 508f, 529, 537, 611,

Bridges, W. A. (*cont.*)
616, 665, 674, 679, 733, 826, 830, 834, 893, 903, 912, 920, 939, 960, 965f, 1053f, 1056
Brimley, C. S., 85, 86, 106f, 113f, 135f, 178f, 226f, 232f, 243f, 274, 289, 291, 308f, 314, 349f, 353f, 366f, 371, 374f, 422f, 435, 479f, 509, 513f, 528f, 554, 611, 627, 630, 665, 669, 695, 701, 713, 716f, 731f, 819, 825f, 835f, 892f, 905f, 912f, 916f, 940, 960f, 965f, 1018, 1053f
Brimley, H. H., 31, 422
Bromley, R. I., 1032f
Brons, H. A., 141, 446f, 605, 823, 1003f
Brooking, W. J., 456, 509, 799
Brooks, W. S., 229
Brown, A. E., 91, 118, 158, 197, 229, 240f, 255f, 296, 302, 325, 337f, 347f, 360, 362, 380, 386, 397f, 448, 465, 479f, 506, 507, 573, 606, 619, 628, 642f, 648, 666, 674, 692, 694f, 735, 738, 746f, 749, 774, 778, 784, 795, 804f, 809, 815, 832, 842f, 849, 852f, 858, 860, 865, 916, 942, 973, 981, 989, 997f, 1006, 1022, 1050
Brown, A. M., 815
Brown, B. C., 154f, 285, 505f, 750, 982f
Brown, E. E., 26, 29, 513f
Brown, H., 571, 573
Brown, J. R., 186
Brown, K. H., 171
Brown, S. H., 171, 494
Brown, Mrs. S. H., 171, 173, 299, 495
Brown snake, 288, 292, 526, 696-722; central, 712; DeKay's, 704, 712; Florida, 707; gentle, 1, 157; grey-bellied, 712; Kennicott's, 292; little, 288, 697, 704, 712, 714, 740, 834; Mexican, 703; Pacific, 157; red-bellied, 714; small, 697, 712; small-eyed, 288; smooth, 290; spotted, 697, 704; Storer's, 714; Texas, 704; Virginia, 294; Wrights', 712
Bryant, H. C., 144f, 787, 1009, 1018
Bryant, M. D., 66, 216, 217, 439, 448, 453f, 500, 600f, 639, 653f, 948, 974, 994f
Bulbilis dactyloides, 6
Bull snake, 585-626; Arizona, 593, 600; Bellona, 588; black, 613; blue, 200, 204; Churchill's, 588; common, 604, 609; desert, 600; eastern, 593, 609; elegant, 89; Florida, 616; Great Basin, 604; Louisiana, 620; Mexican, 604; North American, 604; Oregon, 588; Pacific, 588, 596; plain, 604; prairie, 593, 604; Say's, 604; southern, 600, 615; spotted, 604, 620; western, 588, 593, 600, 604; yellow, 604

Bullock, W., 961
Bumpus, H. C., 308f, 913, 981, 1034
Burger, L. W., 555
Burger, W. L., 277f, 325, 654, 741f, 746, 907, 996
Burhans, W. H., 572
Burnett, W. L., 362
Burt, C. E., 41, 42f, 63, 91, 93, 137, 140f, 181f, 234, 289, 300, 349, 361, 390, 393f, 411, 435, 448, 488f, 501, 513, 607f, 624, 635, 674, 687f, 706, 741, 746, 747, 749, 778, 821, 829f, 855f, 882f, 913, 959f, 1003, 1045, 1049f
Burt, M. D., 63, 300, 777, 838f, 1050
Butler, A. W., 186, 508, 714, 816, 842f

Cagle, F. R., 138, 502, 547
Cain, B. C., 59
Calamaria, 104, 156, 159, 286
    elapsoidea, 354
Call, R. W., 883
Callisaurus, 4, 130
Callopeltis, 209
Callopisma, 82, 270
Calmette, A., 29, 1070
Calopisma, 82, 270
Camin, J. H., 535
Camp, C. L., 64, 116, 121, 125f, 126, 143, 157, 165, 323, 382f, 402, 450, 591, 637, 691, 737, 788f, 949, 975, 980, 989, 993
Camp, H. H., 201
Camp, R. D., 241, 466, 706
Campbell, B., 325, 567f, 635f, 769, 871, 966, 972f, 973
Campbell, G. R., 630
Campbell, H., 30, 946
Campbell, M., 1007
Campo, R. M. del, 970, 973
Candy-stick, 890
Carex stricta, 1044
Carl, G. C., 158
Carlson, A. J., 852
Carnegiae gigantea, 6
Carpenter, A. J., 852
Carphophiops, 104
Carphophis, 4, 5, 7, 18, 21, 24, 26, 72, 73, 104-111, 116, 156, 730
    a. amoenus, 13, 104, **105-107**
    a. helenae, 73, 104, 105, **109-110**
    a. vermis, 73, 104, 105, **110-111**
Carr, A. F., Jr., 84, 115, 147f, 178f, 201f, 226, 229, 235f, 244f, 251, 254f, 273, 274f, 289, 311, 314, 354f, 378, 385, 421f, 435f, 476f, 480, 517, 521f, 536f, 541, 543f, 546f, 553f, 618, 665f, 694f,

Carr, A. F., Jr. (cont.)
709f, 721, 735, 833f, 892, 896, 920f, 940, 1056, 1058
Carr, K. D., 251, 393, 841, 912
Carr, T., 710f
Carson, H. L., 202
Carson, R. D., 341
Carver, J., 534, 960
Cary, M., 453f, 561, 795, 1013
Castanopsis chrysophylla, 6
Casuarina equisetifolia, 248
Catesby, M., 227, 372, 433, 527, 824, 834f, 1052
Catlin, W. P., 1056
Catodon, 37
Caudisona, 925, 1040
  confluenta, 1011
  lucifer, 1011
  l. cerberus, 1011
Caulwell, W. H., 609, 614
Cazier, H. H., 60
Ceanothus cuneatus, 170
Celtis pallida, 429
Celuta, 104, 286
Cemophora, 7, 21, 22, 68, 69, 70, 111-115
  coccinea, 20, 112, 113-115, 355
Cenchris, 901
Centophilus rogera, 388
Centophilus umbrosus, 388
Cephalanthus occidentalis, 485
Ceratophylum emersum, 473
Cercocarpus, 402
Chain snake, 368, 388; black, 391; common, 372; Kennicott's, 345; Say's, 345
Chamberlain, E. B., 505, 517, 667, 1052f, 1056
Chamberlain, R. V., 1014
Chambers, O., 944
Chapel, W. C., 130, 754, 764, 797, 800, 802
Charina, 7, 18, 25, 33, 52-60
  b. bottae, 33, 52, 53-56, 57
  b. umbratica, 53, 54, 56-57
  b. utahensis, 53, 54, 58-60, 61
Chaser, 1; black, 133, 142; blue, 138
Chenoweth, W. L., 611, 906f
Chesser, T., 940
Chicken snake, 1, 133, 364, 368, 388, 608; banded, 243; Barbour and Engel's, 269; black, 230; blotched, 249; Deckert's, 235; Everglades, 245; four-lined, 243; gray, 249; Gulf hammock, 253; N.A., 243; red, 224; red-headed, 249; southern, 249; spotted, 249; striped, 243; striped house, 243; West Florida, 253; yellow, 243; see also Rat snake
Chilomeniscus, 7, 18, 72, 73, 116-120, 130, 637

cinctus, 3, 73, 116-120, 579
punctatissimus, 2, 116, 117
stramineus, 2, 116, 117
s. esterensis, 2, 116, 117
Chilopoma, 755
Chilopoma, red-spotted, 762
Chionactis, 7, 21, 25, 76, 77, 118, 119, 120-130, 669, 815, 840
  o. occipitalis, 77, 119, 121-124, 126
  o. annulata, 121, 122, 124-127
  o. klauberi, 121, 122, 126, 127, 128
  o. talpina, 121, 122, 128-129
  palarostris, 120, 122, 126, 129
  p. organica, 120, 122, 129-130
Chittenden, H. M., 1003
Chlorosoma, 551
Chrysemys, 85
Chrysothamnus, 602
Chunkhead, 306, 903, 910
Churchill, S., 588
Churchilla, 585
Cimicifuga, 961
Cist, C., 961
Clanton, W., 238, 365, 502
Clark, D. R., 512
Clark, H., 309
Clark, H. L., 480, 484f, 816, 829f, 837
Clark, H. W., 141, 266, 308, 513f, 713f, 1044
Clark, J. H., 515
Clark, P. J., 343
Clarke, R. F., 348
Clarke, T. E., 29, 107, 188, 310, 371, 514, 559, 826, 841, 912, 960
Classification, 3-5
Clausen, H. J., 699, 700f, 815, 840
Clausen, R. T., 175, 1047
Clay, W. M., 473, 476f, 486, 493, 507, 511f, 515f, 527f, 531f, 541
Clayton, J., 133, 224, 226, 272
Cleaves, H. H., 839
Clements, F. E., 6
Clemmys marmorata, 411
Clench, W. J., 940
Cliff, F. S., 955
Clinton, D. W., 960f
Clonophis, 467
Cnemidophorus, 345, 550, 871
  sexlineatus, 731
Cockerell, T. D. A., 674, 798, 858
Cohen, E., 133f, 293, 718f
Cohen, N. W., 102, 322f
Coleman, G. E., 1026f
Coleonyx brevis, 770
Coleonyx variegatus, 583
Color, 9, 10; see also each species account
Coluber, 18, 21, 24, 25, 35, 72, 73, 78, 79, 82, 104, 113, 130, 159, 200, 209, 213,

Coluber (*cont.*)
  270, 286, 296, 423, 425, 467, 551, 565, 585, 697, 755, 901
  allegheniensis, 251
  chlorosoma, 261
  coccineus, 115, 355
  confinis, 234, 251
  constrictor, 7, 20, 22, **133-136**, 435, 550
  c. anthicus, 78, 134, 138, **136-138**
  c. flaviventris, 7, 79, 134, **138-142**, 143, 181, 233, 365
  c. foxi, 134, **142**
  c. haasti, **149**
  c. mormon, 73, 78, 135, **142-145**, 329, 852, 1022
  c. paludicola, **149**
  c. priapus, 133, 135, **145-149**
  c. stejnegerianus, 73, 78, 135, **149-151**
  doliatus, 115, 354, 355
  flagellum, 435, 1064, 1065
  f. flavigularis, 329, 438
  f. frenatus, 438, 441, 446
  f. piceus, 446
  f. testaceus, 447
  guttatus, 227
  g. rosacea, 227, 229
  g. sellatus, 229
  infernalis, 853
  lateralis, 451, 452
  lindheimeri, 251
  obsoletus, 79, 131, 133-136, 143, 148, 214, 234, 251
  piceus, 446
  rosaceus, 229
  schotti, 466
  spiloides, 234, 251
  subocularis, 256
  taeniatus, 441, 1022, 1026
  t. girardi, 459, 461, 649
  t. ornatus, 459
  t. schotti, 461
  zonatus, 406, 411
Coluber: Baird's, 214; black, 230, 240; Davis Mt., 255; Emory's, 218; four-banded, 243; four-lined, 243; gray, 249; Lindheimer's, 240; red, 224; red-headed, 249, 262; smooth-scaled, 89, 100; spotted, 224
Colubridae, 2, 32, 33, 35, 67-884
Combat dance, 11
Common names, 12; *see also each species account*
Compsosoma, 200
Compton, L. V., 849
Comstock, A., 883
Comstock, J. H., 883
Conant, I. H., 542, 544
Conant, R., 9, 26, 91, 106, 110, 135f, 136,
148, 155, 186f, 224, 233f, 240, 253, 262f, 266f, 274f, 289f, 309, 347f, 364, 367f, 371f, 372, 375f, 384, 388f, 393f, 416, 436, 462, 465f, 474f, 480, 482f, 492, 495f, 498f, 499, 505, 508f, 509, 529f, 537, 558, 609f, 620, 636, 642, 650f, 665, 674, 679, 695, 699, 701f, 715f, 733, 810, 816f, 824f, 828f, 834, 840f, 893, 903f, 907f, 911f, 920, 922f, 939, 941f, 942, 960, 965f, 1002f, 1034, 1043f, 1053f, 1054, 1056
Condit, J. M., 370
Congo, 916
Congo eel, 26
Coniophanes, 7, 18, 21, 67, 74, 75
  fissidens, 19, 153
  imperialis, 75, **153-155**
Contia, 7, 18, 25, 78, 79, 120, 156-159, 160, 651, 669
  episcopa, 674
  isozona, 674
  mitis, 159
  tenuis, 79, **157-159**, 160
  torquata, 674, 676
Cook, C. W., 544
Cook, F. A., 348, 351
Cook, L., Jr., 123
Cook, L. H., 103, 581f, 972
Cook, S. F., Jr., 18
Coontail, 941
Cooper, J. G., 10, 12, 13, 56, 143f, 150, 163, 382f, 399, 440, 593, 595, 608, 651, 778, 782, 825, 833, 845, 859f, 998
Cope, E. D., 4, 18, 19, 20, 41, 44, 53, 55f, 60, 64, 82, 84f, 111, 115, 116, 118, 120, 124, 136f, 138, 150f, 153f, 172, 184, 207f, 218, 226, 227f, 233, 242, 245, 273, 283f, 296, 297, 316, 354, 355f, 360, 362, 364f, 366, 371f, 385, 391, 397, 400, 421f, 429, 439, 442, 451f, 474, 480, 492, 501, 514, 516f, 525, 535f, 541f, 555, 573, 627f, 651f, 660, 663, 664, 674, 677, 678f, 686f, 706, 722, 727, 735, 746, 748, 750, 764f, 770, 772, 778f, 799, 801, 812, 814f, 816, 825, 829f, 833f, 842f, 845, 847f, 861, 865, 866, 869f, 872, 876, 879, 885, 889, 898, 949, 970, 973, 975, 985, 993, 996f, 1001, 1010f, 1022, 1030, 1045
Cope, J. B., 351
Copper-bell, 910
Copper belly, 477, 522, 910; Mississippi Valley, 481; northern, 484; yellow-bellied, 481
Copperhead, 1, 30, 91, 202, 262, 901-925; broad-banded, 907; narrow-banded, 903; N. A., 710; northern, 903; southeastern,

Copperhead *(cont.)*
    903; southern, 903; Texas, 907; Trans-
    Pecos, 915
Corais, 204
Coral snake, 2, 26, 30, 91, 115, 351, 360,
    885-900; Arizona, 885-886; Barbour's,
    894; common, 890; eastern, 890; false,
    113; Florida, 890; harlequin, 8, 890, 894;
    N. A., 890; Sonoran, 886; South Florida,
    894; Texas, 897; western, 886
Coronella, 159, 330, 627
    coccinea, 354
    doliata, 354
Corrington, J. D., 106f, 114f, 133, 176f, 190,
    226f, 233, 251, 274, 289f, 324, 435f,
    473, 479f, 528, 665f, 713, 716f, 728, 892,
    906f, 923, 1053
Coryphodon, 425
Cottam, C. C., 29, 107, 188, 310, 371, 514,
    559, 841, 913, 960
Cottam, W. P., 144f
Cottonmouth, 30, 916, 921
Couch, D. M., 782
Coues, E., 141, 184, 224, 244, 285, 300, 308,
    362, 414, 593, 605, 630, 799, 810, 821f,
    828, 844, 852, 854f, 919f, 1002f, 1010f,
    1050
Couper, J. H., 202
Courtship, 11, 18; *see also each species account*
Coville, F. V., 980
Covillea tridentata, 8
Cowan, I, McT., 809
Cowles, R. B., 96f, 123f, 125f, 202, 204f, 206,
    302f, 319, 435, 441f, 582f, 595, 602f,
    871, 874f, 942, 947f, 950f, 952f, 955,
    977f, 997
Cowsucker, 133, 368, 372
Cragin, T. W., 184, 218, 262, 644, 674, 686,
    746, 842, 881, 883, 1050
Craig, C. L., 237
Crandall, L. S., 700
Cratu, E., 944
Crawford, R. F., 745
Creaser, C. W., 841, 1046
Cribo, 204
Criddle, S., 561f, 718f, 719, 821
Crimmins, M. L., 102, 103, 199, 258, 457f,
    680f, 876, 946, 1002
Cronise, T. F., 44, 55, 165, 171, 382, 439,
    593, 633, 948, 1018
Cross timbers, 6
Crotalidae, 2, 18, 33, 34, 901-1061
Crotalinus, 925, 1040
Crotalophorus, 925, 1040
    kirtlandi, 1044
Crotalus, 9, 25, 35, 329, 414, 905, 910, 925-
    1040

adamanteus, 25, 926, 933, **936-941,** 983,
    985
a. scutulatus, 997
atrox, 3, 11, 25, 29, 33, 905, 926, 929, 932,
    933, **941-948,** 952, 954, 983, 994, 998,
    1000, 1016, 1065
basiliscus, 925, 985, 996
c. cerastes, 25, 390, 582, 925, 926, 930,
    948-949, 951, 955, 997
c. cercobombus, 930, 951, 952, **955-956**
c. laterorepens, 3, 10, **950-956**
cinereous, 946
c. confluentus, 258, 977, 998, 1004, 1009,
    1022, 1025, 1026
c. lecontei, 1024
c. lutosus, 980
c. mitchelli, 980
c. stephensi, 977, 980
durissus, 996
d. unicolor, 18, 996
enyo, 2, 926, 929, 933, 951, 1037
exsul, 2, 932, 943, 991
h. horridus, 18, 25, 27, 926, 929, 935, 961,
    956-962, 965, 1044
h. atricaudatus, 389, 926, 929, 935, 951,
    962-966
lecontei, 1022, *see also* v. viridis
l. lepidus, 337, 925, 927, 930, 931, 954,
    966-970, 971, 986, 1005
l. klauberi, 931, **970-973,** 986, 988, 1036
lucasensis, 926, 927, 983, 994
m. mitchelli, 2, 927, 929, 931, 971, 977,
    986, 1001, 1039
m. muertensis, 2, 931
m. pyrrhus, 927, 929, 931, 971, **974-977,**
    986, 1001
m. stephensi, 928, 929, 933, 971, **977-980,**
    986, 1000
m. molossus, 925, 927, 929, 934, 973, **980-**
    985, 996, 1000
m. estabensis, 2, 934
oregonus, 25, 1012, 1013
o. cerberus, 1012
palmeri, 968
p. pricei, 25, 890, 925, 927, 929, 934,
    985-989, 1038
ruber ruber, 3, 11, 18, 928, 929, 932, 943,
    954, **989-994,** 1017
r. lucasensis, 2, 932, 943, 1039
s. scutulatus, 18, 33, 925, 928, 932, 934,
    943, **994-998,** 1000
terrificus, 985
tigris, 928, 933, 968, 971, 977, 980, 986,
    998-1001, 1005, 1014
tortugensis, 2, 932, 943
triseriatus, 1005
t. pricei, 985

Crotalus (*cont.*)
  v. viridis, 19, 925, 928, 935, 951, **1001-1006,** 1031, 1065
  v. abyssus, 935, 951, 1001, 1005, **1008-1009,** 1031
  v. caliginis, 2, 936
  v. cerberus, 936, 951, **1010-1012,** 1030f
  v. concolor, 1013, 1014
  v. decolor, 935, 951, **1012-1014,** 1031
  v. helleri, 3, 18, 936, 951, 993, 1010, **1014-1018,** 1024, 1030, 1031, 1033
  v. lutosus, 50, 602, 936, 951, 1005, 1009, **1018-1024,** 1031
  v. nuntius, 935, 951, **1024-1029,** 1031
  v. oreganus, 18, 390, 936, 951, 1010, 1012, 1017, 1024, **1029-1034**
  w. willardi, 25, 890, 928, 930, 951, **1034-1040**
  w. meridionalis, 1038
  w. silus, 1038
Crotaphytus baileyi, 397
Crowell, M. F., 309
Culbertson, A. E., 787f
Culpepper, F., 367
Cunningham, J. D., 774
Cunningham, J. T., 1072
Cupressus macrocarpa, 6
Curran, C. H., 939, 1038
Curtis, E. S., 1027
Curtis, L., 285, 358, 502, 505f
Cyclophis, 551
Cyclops, 472

Dabney, T. G., 277
Dall, W. H., 886
Dalquest, W. W., 590
Darling, D., 170, 343, 899
Dasylirion, 454
Daudin, F. M., 609, 612f, 613, 910, 939, 1071
Davis, A. W., 506
Davis, D., 141, 264, 300, 348, 362, 448, 830, 856, 1049
Davis, D. D., 11, 118, 233, 264, 268, 277, 289, 291, 308, 342, 348, 353, 371, 479, 492, 499, 502, 505, 582, 592, 611, 665, 674, 812, 813, 817, 826, 834, 893, 912, 919, 924f, 944f, 982, 991, 1054
Davis, H. T., 893, 912, 920, 965f, 968, 1053f
Davis, J., 787, 965
Davis, L. I., and wife, 152, 155, 209, 282
Davis, N. S., Jr., 312, 714, 830, 842
Davis, W. B., 561f, 919
Davis, W. T., 31, 307, 375, 612, 962
Deckert, R. F., 114, 147, 178, 201, 226, 237, 244, 274, 289, 314, 353, 479, 833, 896
DeKay, J. E., 136, 189, 230, 306, 376, 506, 555, 560, 826

Dellinger, S. C., 192
Dence, W. A., 1045
Deniston, R. H., 303
De Smet, P. J., 1003f
Desmognathus f. fuscus, 495
Deuel, J., 874
Dexter, R. W., 558
Diadophis, 7, 18, 21, 22, 24, 25, 30, 70, 73, 78, 79, 106, 159-200, 730
  a. amabilis, 160, 161, **163-166**
  a. anthonyi, 2, 162, 164
  a. modestus, 161, 164, **166-167,** 170
  a. occidentalis, 73, 162, 164, **169-171**
  a. pulchellus, 73, 79, 162, 164, 169, **171-172**
  a. similis, 3, 162, 164, **172-175,** 196
  a. vandenburghi, 73, 161, 164, 169, **175-176,** 177
  dugesi, 162
  p. punctatus, 163, 171, **176-179,** 197, 627
  p. arnyi, 24, 163, **179-182,** 184, 198
  p. docilis, 162, 171, 179, 180, **182-185,** 198
  p. edwardsi, 21, 79, 162, 179, **185-189,** 291
  p. stictogenys, 163, 179, 180, **189-192,** 198
  r. regalis, 7, 20, 30, 70, 78, 161, 164, 170, 179, **192-194,** 197, 198
  r. arizonae, 194, 196
  r. blanchardi, 161, 164, 179, 194, **196-200**
  r. laetus, 26, 161, **194-196**
Diamond-back, 936
Dicamptodon ensatus, 30
Dice, L. R., 128, 150, 181, 765
Dickens, C., 1030
Dickson, J. G., 115
Dills, L. E., 305, 617, 620, 621
Dipsadomorphinae, 321
Dipsas, 415
Dipsosaurus, 130
Distinctive characteristics, 9; *see also each species account*
Ditmars, R. L., 31, 39, 53, 85, 107, 115, 118, 135, 163, 165, 166, 175, 178, 188f, 192, 194, 201, 206, 214, 226f, 235, 244f, 249, 255, 279, 282, 310, 324, 337, 345, 351, 354, 360, 371, 375f, 379, 386, 400, 415f, 436, 456, 461, 472, 479, 502, 504, 535, 559, 611, 620, 719, 737, 748, 766, 770, 779, 810, 826, 828, 830, 832f, 840, 855, 872, 876, 884, 893, 894, 913f, 920f, 939f, 941, 1018f, 1033, 1052f, 1056
Dixon, J., 143f, 157, 158f, 382, 450f, 588f, 603, 772f, 778, 782, 849, 1030
Dodge, N. N., 329, 402f, 456, 595, 603, 659f, 684f, 983, 1009, 1018f, 1029
Dolley, J. S., 907
Donaldson, I., 797, 850
Dorsey, G. A., 1025
Douglas, V., 946, 985

Dowling, H. G., 209, 213, 214, 218, 224, 235, 245, 253, 264, 663-669
Downs, A., Jr., 135f, 233, 268f, 274f, 385, 476f, 488, 490, 509, 537, 611, 636, 1005f
Dromicus, 153, 627
Dromicus, Yarrow's, 627
Drowne, F. P., 842f
Drude, O., 848
Dryinus, 565
Drymarchon, 7, 18, 24, 26, 70, 71, 200-206, 651, 965
  corais couperi, 22, 71, **200-203**
  c. erebennus, 71, 200, 201, **204-206**, 1064, 1065
Drymobius, 7, 18, 24, 76, 77, 206-209, 425, 426, 651
  m. margaritiferus, 77, 205, **207-209**
Dudley, P., 960
Duellman, W. E., 498f, 508f, 555, 826
Duméril, A. H. A., 249
Duméril, A. M. C., 249, 472, 893
Dunbar, W. S., 960
Duncan, P. M., 890
Dundee, H. A., 41, 44, 181f, 270, 328f, 372, 547, 551, 717
Dunham, A. L., 1013
Dunn, E. R., 105, 133, 137, 145f, 186, 230, 249, 326, 349, 368, 372, 416f, 480, 486, 499, 508f, 609f, 627, 700, 714f, 837, 883f, 893, 894, 912f, 956
Dury, C., 308
Dury, R., 109, 349, 366, 394
Dusenbery, C. R., 984
Dymond, J. R., 558, 718

Eames, E. A., and wife, 557
Earth snake: Arizona, 678; Big Bend, 679; Grand Canyon, 683; Great Plains, 672; South Texas, 676; striped, 688; western, 686
East, C. S., 188
Eaton, T. H., Jr., 453, 600, 836, 1002, 1013, 1022
Ecdysis, 26, 27
Echinochloa, 48
Eckel, E. C., 307, 480, 719, 842f
Eddy, B., 360, 363
Edgren, R. A., Jr., 304, 309, 960
Edwards, L., 1050
Eggleston, L. A., 718
Eggs, 21-24; see also each species account
Eisen, G. A., 409
Elaphe, 9, 21, 24, 25, 68, 72, 73, 80, 81, 82, 92, 130, 137, 209, 210-270, 651
  bairdi, 211, 213, **214-218**, 235
  chlorosoma, 258, 261

emoryi, 20, 210, **218-222**, 242, 347
e. intermontana, 73, 210, **222-224**
guttata, 211, **224-227**, 229, 236
g. emoryi, 218, 222, 224
g. rosacea, 211, **227-230**
laeta, 181
lindheimeri, 218
mutabilis, 262
o. obsoleta, 212, 214, 215, **230-234**, 235, 241, 242, 251, 262, 365, 914, 1064, 1065
o. bairdi, 213, **214-219**
o. confinis, 236, 242, 255
o. deckerti, 212, 213, 229, **235-238**
o. lemniscatus, 270
o. lindheimeri, 184, 213, 214, 235, **240-243**
o. parallela, 212, 213, 235, 236, **269-270**
o. quadrivittata, 212, 213, 215, 229, 235, 238, **243-245**, 270
o. rossalleni, 212, 213, 235, 236, 238, **245-249**
o. spiloides, 81, 212, 213, 235, 242, **249-253**, 347
o. williamsi, 81, 212, 213, 235, 236, **253-255**
quadrivittata, 229, 237, 244, 269, 347
q. deckerti, 230, 236, 237
q. parallela, 269, 550
rosacea, 230
rosaliae, 2, 211
sclerotica, see E. *subocularis*
subocularis, 80, 82, 210, 217, **255-258**, 340, 345, 656
t. intermedia, 211, **258-262**, 1064, 1065
vulpina, 210, **262-266**
v. gloydi, 22, 210, **266-269**
Elaphis, 209, 585
Elapidae, 2, 18, 33, 34, 35, 885-900
Elaps, 113, 886
  corallinus, 19
  euryxanthus, 889
  fulvius, 354
Eldridge, D. M., 403
Elegant Virginia, 1
Eleutherodactylus, 770
Elevation, 7; see also "Range" in each species account
Ellis, M. M., 141, 181f, 187, 300, 307, 360f, 448, 456, 513, 558, 560f, 606f, 674, 687, 747, 798f, 801, 821f, 829, 855f, 1003f, 1049
Ellis, R. H., 411
Emory, W. H., 218
Endsley, J. R., 189f
Enemies, 29-31
Engelhardt, G. P., 31, 133, 307f, 699, 717, 837, 916, 982, 985
Engels, W. L., 269f, 412-415, 547f, 919

English equivalents of Latin names, 3
Entechinus, 551, 560
Epiglottophis, 585
Eriocaulon, 422
Erwin, R. P., 318f, 687f, 1019f
Eryngium, 961
Erythrolamprus, 153
Eteirodipsas, 415, 866
Etheridge, R. E., 274, 505f
Eumeces brevirostris, 770
Eupatorium, 961
Eurycea bislineata, 495
Eurypholis, 551
Eutaenia (Eutainia), 755, 815
  angustirostris, 764
  atrata, 778
  cyrtopsis, 766
  c. ocellata, 770
  elegans, 772, 853
  e. marciana, 770
  eques, 766, 767
  infernalis, 774, 853
  leptocephala, 815
  macrostemma, 800
  megalops, 800
  multimaculata, 764
  parietalis, 853
  proxima, 772, 774, 800
  radix, 822
  rufipunctatus, 764
  saurita, 766, 826
  sirtalis, 815
  trilineata, 865
Evans, C. L., 381, 635, 678, 976f, 998f
Evans, H. E., 233, 268f, 307, 514, 558, 717,
  826, 836, 842
Evans, P. D., 297f, 672f, 923f, 1046
Evenden, F. G., Jr., 602, 1019
Evermann, B. W., 141, 266, 304, 308, 513f,
  558, 602, 713f, 825, 829f, 837f, 841f,
  1044f
Ewan, J., 1030

Fagopyrum, 961
Fairchild, D. H., 259f
Fairie, J., 828
Falck, E. G. J., 986f
Faldborg, L. P., 991
Fannin, J., 806
Farancia, 7, 9, 18, 21, 24, 25, 26, 30, 74,
  75, 82, 270-279, 669
  a. abacura, 20, 272-276
  a. reinwardti, 28, 75, 272, 276-279, 280
Faris, G. A., 783f
Favry, F. C., 205
Feagen, L. W., 283, 287

Fenneman, N. M., 14, 15, 41, 128, 464, 783,
  852
Fenner, J. H., 729
Ferguson, D. E., 58, 143, 797, 846, 1030
Fewkes, J. W., 1025
Fichter, G. S., 841
Ficimia, 7, 18, 279
  cana, 74, 75, 303
  o. streckeri, 75, 279-282, 1064, 1065
Field notes, 31; see also each species account
Finneran, L. C., 700, 820, 913
First and last, 834
Fisher, E. M., 590f, 848f
Fisher, G. C., 558
Fitch, C., Sr., 793
Fitch, H. S., 4, 55f, 137f, 141f, 157f, 169f,
  213, 323, 383, 435, 453f, 524, 590f, 620f,
  624, 637, 772f, 777f, 781, 784, 786f,
  790f, 806f, 844, 848f, 851f, 858, 860f,
  863, 864f, 914, 1030f
Fitzinger, L. J. F. J., 36, 200, 206, 209, 330,
  415, 551, 755
Flat-head, 306
Flat-nosed snake, 312, 649; Arizona, 651;
  banded, 646, 651; Brown's, 571; Gra-
  ham's, 646, 651
Flood, W. A., Jr., 100, 396f, 575, 582, 972,
  987f, 1036f
Flower, S. S., 9, 272, 416, 511, 609, 918
Flury, A. G., 49f, 197f, 217, 224, 237, 341,
  345, 607, 640, 643f, 655, 768f, 806, 876,
  915f, 968f, 985
Food, 26-29; see also each species account
Forbes, J. G., 940
Force, E. R., 42f, 111, 114f, 140f, 181f, 250,
  289f, 295, 308, 348, 365, 390f, 435f, 488,
  492, 495, 502, 507, 555, 674, 707, 741,
  743f, 856f, 882f, 923, 960
Forster, J. R., 482, 531
Fouquette, M. J., 93, 826, 830
Fouts, C. L., 430, 431
Fowler, H. W., 133f, 178f, 292, 308, 367,
  514, 701, 825, 840
Fowler, J. A., 106, 107, 115, 188, 227, 233,
  371, 375, 718
Fox, C., 142, 262
Fox, Wade, Jr., 774f, 777f, 794f, 806, 844f,
  861f, 865, 867
Fox, Wade, Sr., 114
Frampton, Mrs., 237, 896
Franklin, D., 801
Franklin, M. D., 546f
Fraxinus v. glabra, 1036
Freeman, B., 41, 181, 300, 448f, 607, 799
French, B. F., 966
Friddle, S. B., 105, 233, 290f, 368, 375f, 376,
  557, 825f

Frierson, L. S., Jr., 137, 307, 907
Frost, M. H., 999
Fry, F. E. J., 558, 718
Fry, G., 345
Fry, N. P., 86, 246, 271, 352, 353, 387, 432f, 695
Fuertes, L. A., 967
Fugler, C. M., 624, 625f
Fundulus:
   chrysotis, 710
   diaphanus, 948
Funkhouser, W. D., 111, 136, 188, 264, 266, 308, 365f, 393f, 486, 611, 719, 840f, 924, 960
Funston, F., 980

Gadow, H., 56, 136, 208, 258, 856
Gage, S. H., 822
Gaige, H. T., 141, 143f, 208f, 602f, 798f, 1021f
Gaines, A., 227, 354
Garman, H., 110, 141, 242, 308, 364, 393, 509, 714, 715f, 830, 840f, 882f, 925
Garman, S., 133, 141, 158, 182, 184, 240f, 245, 295f, 362, 419, 422, 555, 639, 642, 707, 735, 741, 746, 804, 945f, 968, 970, 975, 985, 1015, 1040, 1048, 1049f, 1052, 1061
Garni, L., 488
Garnier, J. H., 506, 509
Garter snake, 755-866, 890; Arizona, 799; black, 775, 806; black-spotted, 810; Boyd's, 772, 806; broad, 834; brown, 766; brown-spotted, 762; Butler's, 816; California, 772, 788, 844, 846; California, red-barred, 851; Candy-stick, 897; Cascade, 846; checker-board, 766; Churchill's, 834; coastal California, 794; collared, 766; common, 810, 834, 954; Cooper's, 806; Cope's, 778; corn, 897; Couch's, 766, 782-784; desert, 803; dusky, 834; dwarf, 879; eastern, 834; eastern Butler's, 814; Edward's plateau spotted, 772; elegant, 772; embellished, 844; Emory's, 799; Fairie's, 828; giant, 782, 784-788; grass, 834; gray, 795; Great Basin, 795; green, 795; green-bellied, 766; green-spotted, 834; green-striped, 854; Hammond's, 788; Hay's, 810; Hayden's, 820; Hoy's, 810; Klamath, 778; little, 824; long-headed, 762; long-nosed, 762; Long's, 828; Marcy's, 803, 804; Mexican, 799; Mexican highland, 762; middle California, 775; moccasin, 782; mountain, 772; narrow-headed, 806; New York dwarf, 814; Nisqually, 858; N. A., 834; north-eastern, 834; northern, 834, 854; northern California coast, 774; northwestern, 778, 844, 846, 858; ocellated, 766, 772; one-striped, 844, 851; ordinary, 834; ordinary spotted, 834; Oregon, 790; Oregon gray, 700; ornate, 854; Ostensacken's, 832; Pacific, 788, 844, 846, 851, 854; Pacific coast, 775, 806; Pacific red-barred, 844, 846; Pacific red-sided, 844; parietal, 854; Pickering's, 844, 858; plain, 834; plains, 810, 820; prairie, 810, 820; Puget, 806; Puget Sound, 806; Racine, 810; red, 854; red-backed, 854; red-barred, 854; red-bellied, 714; red-sided, 854; red-spotted, 762, 844, 854; red-striped, 806, 828; Reuss, 766; Rocky Mountain, 854; Sacken's, 832; Say's, 810, 828, 854; Sierra Nevada, 782; single-striped, 772, 775, 851; slender, 824, 828; slim, 824; slow, 835; Sonoran, 804; South San Francisco peninsula, 861; Southern California, 788; spotted, 762, 766, 803, 828; striped, 834; swamp, 834; swift, 824; transition, 810; Twining's, 820; Vancouver, 865; wandering, 795; Washington, 778, 858; water, 824, 834; western, 775, 795, 806, 810, 851, 854; western dwarf, 816; western spotted, 762; white-bellied, 766; yellow-headed, 824
Gastman, E. A., 1045
Gebhard, J., Jr., 1045
George, I. D., 939f, 954f, 965, 968, 983f, 1005, 1017
Gerrhonotus:
   l. infernalis, 772
   multicarinatus, 853
Gessing, W., Jr., 349, 366, 394
Gibbs, R. M., 719
Gill, T. N., 31
Gilpin, J. B., 558
Gilman, H. G., 983
Girard, C. F., 39f, 105, 142f, 156f, 163, 171f, 176, 184, 191, 192, 218, 240f, 242, 262, 286, 288, 290, 360f, 372, 382, 391, 396f, 423, 456f, 505f, 515, 630, 633, 637, 644, 669, 678, 697, 722, 728f, 735, 772f, 795, 803f, 806f, 809, 810, 830, 858, 897f, 922, 936, 941, 946, 980, 985, 1006, 1050
Githen's, T. S., 920, 939f, 946, 954f, 965, 968, 1005, 1010, 1017, 1033f
Glaphyrophis, 153
Glauconia, 37, 44
   dissecta, 44
Glechoma, 961
Glissmeyer, H. R., 1021

Glossy snake, 96-104; Arizona, 98; California, 100; desert, 96; Kansas, 92; Painted Desert, 103; Texas, 89; western, 100; western Mohave, 93

Glover, T., 133

Gloyd, H. K., 11, 29, 100, 111, 118, 138f, 181, 214, 232f, 290, 294f, 303f, 341, 348f, 390f, 399, 403, 438, 441f, 445, 446, 462f, 465f, 488f, 492f, 501f, 513f, 554f, 561, 575, 593f, 607f, 654, 673, 706f, 716f, 821f, 829f, 856f, 882f, 889, 904, 907f, 911f, 915f, 921f, 940f, 946, 956f, 966f, 972, 980, 983f, 986f, 992f, 997, 1001, 1003f, 1012f, 1021, 1033, 1043f, 1046, 1049f, 1052f, 1058f

Glyphodonts, 67

Godwin, L., Jr., 944

Goff, C. C., 474, 477

Goin, C. J., Jr., 84f, 86, 149, 178, 274, 292, 314, 385, 421, 541f, 664f

Goldfarb, R., 95, 122

Goldstein, R. C., 274f

Good, H. G., 249f, 271, 290, 307, 729f, 736

Goode, G. B., 85, 525

Goodman, J. D., 305, 319

Gopher snake, 200-206, 585-626; Arizona, 593; black, 204; blue, 200, 204; California, 624; coast, 588; coastal, 596; Couper's, 200; desert, 600; Great Basin, 600; Mexican, 204; Pacific, 588, 596; sagebrush, 600; San Diegan, 596; Santa Cruz Island, 604; slender, 89; smooth-scaled, 89; Sonora, 100, 593; spotted, 604; Utah, 600; western, 588, 604; white, 609; yellow, 588, 604

Gopherus polyphemus, 939

Gordon, K. L., 57, 157f, 160, 170, 411, 584, 603, 807f, 841f

Gorsuch, D. M., 945

Gottsch, W. H., 623, 704

Gowanloch, J. N., 966

Graf, W., 841

Graham, J. D., 490, 646f

Graham's Salvadora, 646, 651

Grant, C., 45, 349, 855

Graptemys barbouri, 388

Grass snake, 712, 832; brown, 697, 704, 712; green, 551; northern, 555; smooth, 555, 560; Storer's, 714; striped, 834

Grater, R. K., 684, 1009

Gray, I. E., 114, 133, 178, 351

Gray, J. E., 52, 53, 56, 67, 82, 270, 279, 901

Gregg, J., 1003

Green snake, 551-565; American smooth, 555; common, 555; keel-scaled, 551; keeled, 551; little, 551; northern, 555; rough, 551; rough-coated, 551; rough-keeled,

551; rough-scaled, 551; smooth, 555; smooth-coated, 555; smooth-scaled, 555; southern, 551; summer, 551

Griffith, E., 965, 1054

Grimshawe, F. M., 274f

Grinnell, H. W., 63f, 167, 384, 440f, 442, 599, 663, 790, 1016f

Grinnell, J., 31, 54f, 63f, 116, 125, 143f, 157f, 165, 167, 172, 320f, 382f, 402, 405f, 409f, 440f, 442, 450f, 588, 593, 599, 663, 691, 737, 772f, 778, 788f, 798, 849, 874, 949, 974f, 980, 989, 993, 1016f, 1030f

Griscom, L., 371

Grizzell, R. A., Jr., 106, 187, 291

Grobman, A. B., 557f, 560f

Ground rattlesnake, 1040-1061; Carolina, 1052; Florida, 1055; large, 1048; pigmy, 1052, 1055; Sonora, 1048; southeastern, 1052; 1055; southern, 1052; western, 1058

Ground snake, 105, 106, 111, 286-296, 349, 669-692, 697, 707, 712; Arizona, 116; banded, 121; bicolor, 121, 672; black-banded, 672, 686; Blanchard's, 679; Carolina, 1052; DeKay's, 704; desert, 121; eastern, 105, 290; Gloyd's western, 683; Grand Canyon, 683; Great Plains, 672; Hallowell's, 121; Klauber's, 128; large, 1; Mohave, 121; Mosauer's, 668, 670; Pacific, 157; pinkish, 686; prairie, 672; red and black, 116; red-bellied, 714; ringed, 121, 686; St. George, 683; Sonora striped, 672; South Texas, 676; southern, 288; speckled, 207; spotted, 290; striped, 49, 672, 686, 688; Taylor's, 676; Texas, 672, 686, 688; tricolor, 121, 124, 128; two-banded, 128; vermilion, 686; vermilion-lined, 688; vermilion-striped, 688; western, 292, 679; yellow, 672

Guidry, E. V., 19, 41, 249f, 289, 309, 348, 474, 483, 502, 517, 830

Gunther, A. C. L. G., 159, 261, 725f, 735, 741

Gustafson, J. A., 548f, 550

Guthrie, J. E., 111, 141, 182, 264f, 289f, 295, 300, 308, 365, 491f, 496, 564, 707, 718, 812, 856f, 960, 1045

Gyalopion, 7, 18, 74, 75, 279, 282
canum, **282-286**, 890

Gyalopium, 282

Habitat, 10; see also each species account

Habits, 10; see also "Habitat" in each species account

Hadsall, L. F., 160, 381, 783f

Hahn, W. L., 109f, 140, 187, 295, 308, 718

Haines, T. P., 417

Hakluyt, R., 925
Haldea, 4, 7, 18, 25, 30, 79, 80, 106, 286-296
    striatula, 22, 79, **288-290**, 295
    v. valeriae, 287, 288, **290-292**
    v. elegans, 287, 288, **292-295**
Hall, Capt., 965f
Hall, C. W., 261, 568
Hall, E. R., 1018f
Hall, H. M., 409
Hallinan, T., 148, 201, 940
Hallowell, E., 121f, 141, 153, 349, 362, 368,
    393, 438, 450, 453, 486, 490, 500f, 593f,
    624, 719, 746, 774, 844, 849, 879, 881f,
    948f, 985, 1003f, 1034
Halter, E. R., 893
Haltom, W. L., 86, 109, 115, 192, 203, 249f,
    354, 394, 502, 529, 732, 834
Hamilton, H. R., 190, 557
Hamilton, W. J., Jr., 29, 190, 511, 534, 617f,
    719, 841, 882, 905f, 920, 966, 1005,
    1054
Hammar, A. G., 525
Hammond, W. A., 788
Hankinson, T. L., 31, 140f, 498, 811, 821
Hanley, G. H., 55f, 103
Hansen, R. M., 456, 602, 1019f
Haploaspis, 925
Hardy, R., 58f, 193, 318f, 321f, 362, 455,
    602f, 635f, 750, 806, 996f, 1013
Harlan, R., 345, 555, 826, 893, 956
Harlequin snake, 409, 890, 897, 910; Elaps,
    890; Florida, 890; Sonora, 886; tawny,
    897; Texas, 897
Harper, F., 28, 133, 178, 308, 374, 479, 528,
    619, 917
Harris, G. D., 525
Harrison, M. B., 838f
Harshberger, J. W., 128, 445, 613, 623, 690,
    765, 852, 905
Hart, J. L., 806f, 856
Harter, P., 327f, 397, 493f, 606, 641, 650,
    672f, 802, 829
Hartweg, N. E., 208f, 486, 651, 804
Harvey, G. W., 567f
Harwell, A., 782
Harwell, C. A., 408f, 1030
Harwood, P. D., 701f
Hassler, W. G., 814f
Hatt, R. T., 172, 982
Hauck, W. J., 527
Hawken, J. L., 145, 159, 165f, 384, 591f
Hay, O. P., 31, 110f, 141, 189, 251, 266,
    289, 295, 309f, 365, 391f, 474, 492,
    499, 500, 504f, 555, 701, 707f, 714,
    820f, 826, 828f, 841f, 854f, 884, 913f,
    924f, 960, 1045f
Hay, W. P., 133, 290

Hayden, F. V., 820
Hazel head, 910
Hazeltine, K. S., 28, 163
Healey, Mrs. J. H., 655f, 890, 982, 1035f,
    1040
Hebard, M., 833
Hebard, W. B., 797f, 806f, 849, 860f, 865
Hecht, B. M., 21f, 268f
Hecht, M., 21f, 283
Heermann, A. L., 1070
Hegener, R., 444, 820, 857
Heilprin, A., 547
Heinze, A. A., 140f, 181f, 233, 391, 493,
    501, 714, 841f
Heiser, J. M., Jr., 277, 898
Helicops, 82, 270, 419
    alleni, 422
Heller, E., 1016
Heloderma, 977
Hemphill, C., 57, 171, 173, 494
Henderson, J., 141, 181f, 299f, 360f, 448,
    456, 513, 560f, 606f, 674, 686, 744,
    798f, 801, 821f, 855f, 1003f, 1049
Henshaw, H. W., 774, 790, 849, 975, 1019f,
    1022
Hensley, M. M., 99, 325, 400, 430f, 433,
    573f, 579f, 583, 637, 654, 769, 889,
    955, 981, 985
Herald, E. S., 171
Herms, W. B., 123
Herpetodryas, 207, 330, 425, 551
Herrara, A. L., 336, 407
Herring, W. C., 186, 190
Herriman, J. A., 342
Hersey, A. L., 42f
Heterodon, 18, 21, 24, 25, 33, 35, 81, 82,
    113, 115, 283, 296-314, 914, 1032
    n. nasicus, 7, 81, **297-300**, 304, 365, 1064,
        1065
    n. gloydi, 298, **304**
    n. kennerlyi, 296, 298, **302-304**
    niger, 392, 393
    p. platyrhinos, 4, 18, 20, 22, 26, 81, 296,
        298, 300, **306-310**, 311, 314, 392, 1064,
        1065
    p. browni, 296, 298, **310-312**
    simus, 7, 18, 33, 81, 297, 304, 309, **312-314**,
        617, 1065
Hewlett, R. I., 887f, 912
Heyen, A. B., 187, 912
Heyrend, F. L., 456
Hibbard, C. W., 44, 114f, 186, 326f, 329,
    349, 611
Hibernation, 10; see also "Period of activity"
    in each species account
Hierophis, 132
Higgins, H., 506, 685, 911

Higginson, F., 961
Highton, R., 695f
Higley, W. K., 266, 307, 607, 714, 842f
Hikel, R., 342
Hillman, H., 973
Hilton, E. P., 678
Hindman, J., 881
Hinds, R. B., 865
Hinton, J. H., 1003
Hofen, R., 50
Hog-nosed snake, 296-314; black, 306; blow-
    ing, 302; Brown's, 310; common, 306;
    common western, 297; eastern, 306;
    Florida, 310; Gloyd's, 304; Kennerly's,
    302; North American, 306; prairie, 297;
    southern, 312; southwestern, 302; Texas,
    297; western, 297, 302
Holbrook, J. E., 115, 178f, 189, 200f, 227,
    234, 243f, 271f, 314, 349f, 354, 375f,
    388, 480, 500, 504, 529, 544, 555, 585,
    610f, 697, 702, 826, 890, 893, 916, 940,
    1033, 1044, 1053f
Holbrookia, 871
  texana, 4
Hollibough, G. O., 559
Homalocranion, 722
Homalocranium, 669, 722, 735
Homalopsis, 82, 153, 270
Homalosoma, 156, 159, 669
Hook, L., 231, 909, 911f, 914, 956, 960f,
    963
Hook-nosed snake, 280-286
Hopi snake dance, 1025
Hopley, C. C., 1072
Horn snake, 1, 82, 270-279, 368, 608; bastard,
    372; eastern, 272; red-bellied, 272, 276;
    red-lined, 82; true, 916; western, 276
Horn-tail, 276
Horton, B. J., 612
House snake, 349, 360, 368; scarlet, 355;
    striped, 243
Householder, V. H., 443f, 574, 689, 974f
Howell, A. B., 687
Howorth, J. C., 691
Hoy, P. R., 1046
Hoyle, W. L., 93, 181f, 289, 361, 501, 607,
    674, 687f, 743, 747, 830, 882, 912, 1045,
    1050
Hubbellia marianifera, 388
Hudson, G. E., 93, 111, 141, 181f, 264f, 300f,
    347, 362, 448, 492, 564, 747, 830, 856,
    1005f, 1049f
Hudson, R. G., 9, 135, 224, 240, 249, 364,
    368f, 384, 388, 416, 477, 508f, 609,
    642, 715, 810, 823, 824, 828, 907, 918,
    1002, 1043
Hughes, E., 140, 508

Humphrey, R. R., 941, 944, 980, 985, 994,
    996f, 1000f
Hunt, D. E., 955
Hurter, J., Sr., 111, 140f, 181f, 232f, 242, 251,
    277, 289f, 294, 307f, 348f, 365f, 385,
    390, 397, 473f, 482f, 488, 492, 501f,
    511, 514, 525, 540f, 554, 563, 629,
    664f, 713f, 717, 811f, 829f, 837f, 880f,
    893, 899, 912f, 923f, 952, 959f, 1045,
    1060f
Hutchinson, E. G., 108f
Hutchinson, G., 979
Hutchinson, R. H., 29, 954, 965
Hydrophidae, 32, 33
Hydrophis, 51
Hydrops, 82, 153, 170
Hydrus, 51
Hyla:
  septentrionalis, 230
  squirella, 230, 238
Hypopachus cuneus, 727, 830
Hypsiglena, 7, 21, 24, 27, 80, 283, 314-330,
    696
  t. torquata, 316
  t. chlorophaea, 325, 329
  t. deserticola, 315, 317, **318-319**
  t. klauberi, 315, 317, **320-321**
  t. loreala, 315, 316, **321-322**
  t. nuchulata, 315, **322-324**
  t. ochrorhyncha, 3, 20, 79, 315, 317, 319,
    324-326, 874
  t. slevini, 2, 315f, 324
  t. texana, 315, 317, **326-330**
  t. tortugensis, 2, 315, 317
  t. venusta, 315, 316, 325, 329
  venusta, 2

Ilex opaca, 8
Indigo snake, 200-206
Inger, R. F., 343
Irvine, F., 1006
Irwin, B. J. D., 1011
Ischnognathe, 697
Ischnognathus, 467, 697, 879
Isoptera, 49

Jackley, A. M., 1004f
Jackson, A., 112
Jackson, D., 29, 962
Jacobs, D. I., 821
Jacot, E., 1050
James, E., 142, 1001f
James, H. C., 261f, 861, 997, 1050
Jameson, D. L., 49f, 197f, 217, 224, 257f, 303,
    337, 341f, 600, 607, 640, 643f, 655,
    768f, 806, 876f, 968f, 985
Jan, G., 35, 194f, 197, 428, 733f

Jenkins, O. P., 304
Jennison, G., 611f
Jewett, S., Jr., 457, 841, 850
Jewkes, F. W., 59
Johnson, D. H., 66, 318f, 325, 439, 453f, 639, 653f, 948, 974f, 994f
Johnson, D. W., 41
Johnson, J., 595
Johnson, M. L., 409f, 798, 845, 849, 860f, 864f
Johnson, R. M., 233, 251
Jones, A. D., 293
Jones, D., 1023f
Jones, J., 200
Jones, J. K., Jr., 141, 365f, 718, 747
Jones, J. M., 187, 557, 837, 841
Jones, L., 128, 150
Jones, P. B., 1023f
Jones, R. W., 965f
Jopson, H., 709f
Jopson, H. G. M., 263, 350, 668f, 710, 854
Jordan, D. S., 31, 109, 294, 345, 411, 605
Jordanella, 710
Judd, W. W., 701f
Julian, G., 1021
Juniperus scopularum, 1036

Kapp, K., 417f
Kauffeld, C. F., 7, 9, 29, 133, 201, 224, 240f, 273, 283f, 287, 292, 347, 353, 366f, 372, 379, 395, 402, 535, 593, 606f, 609, 655f, 914, 952f, 972f, 981f, 985f, 997, 1001f, 1009, 1021f, 1025f, 1034f
Keegan, H. L., 56, 202, 263, 266, 914, 965
Keller, J. G., 233f, 438, 461, 595, 985, 1003
Kellogg, R., 31
Kelly, C., 957
Kelly, H. A., 506
Kendall, G. W., 1003
Kennedy, J. P., 620f, 922f
Kennerly, C. B. R., 302
Kennicott, C., 496
Kennicott, R., 86, 89f, 109f, 179, 292f, 302f, 345, 358f, 362, 415f, 496f, 518, 672f, 747, 762f, 775, 782f, 788f, 799, 810, 820f, 828, 832f, 889, 966f, 994f, 998f
Kern, C. W., 143, 581, 597, 660, 1031
Kerr, M., 979
Kerr, R., 176, 312f
Kezer, J., 292
Kilby, J. D., 709f
Kilpatrick, J. W., 300, 308f
King, E. D., Jr., 615
King, F. W., 105f, 107, 133, 185f, 230, 290, 306f, 366f, 372, 393f, 440, 513f, 553, 597, 697, 714f, 731, 835, 956

King, S., 151, 204f, 219, 301, 357f, 462, 604
King, W. A., Jr., 462
King snake, 30, 330-415; Arizona, 398, 409; Arizona coral, 400; Arkansas, 360; banded, 360, 379, 400; Bank's, 413; black, 372, 391; black and white, 382; Blainville's, 379; Blair's, 243; Blanchard's red, 366; blotched, 245; Boyle, 382; boundary, 396; Brook's, 376; brown, 345, 349; California, 379, 382, 404, 409; California coral, 409; California striped, 379; Catalina Island, 373; Chipola River, 386; Coast-Range coral, 404; common, 372; coral, 1, 351, 404, 409; Davis Mt., 337; desert, 398; eastern, 372; Eisen's, 409; Evan's, 345; Florida, 384; Fresno, 379; Holbrook, 388; house, 224, 351; Kansas, 345; Kennicott's, 345; Mexican, 396; mountain, 409; northern scarlet, 366; Okracoke, 413; Pacific, 382; painted, 360; prairie, 345; prairie painted, 360; red, 351, 360; Ridgway's, 391; ring, 358; ringed, 358, 360, 409; salt-and-pepper, 388; Santa Catalina, 373; Say's, 388; scarlet, 351; Sierra coral, 409; Sonora, 396; Sonoran, 396, 409; South Florida, 376; southern, 388; speckled, 388; splendid, 91, 396; spotted, 388; striped, 379; Virginia red, 366; western coral, 409; yellow, 376; yellow-bellied, 376; yellow-speckled, 388; yellow-spotted, 388; Yuma, 398
Kingsley, J. S., 84, 245, 981, 1034
Kinney, K., 442
Kinosternon, 85
  bauri palmarum, 897
Kirkland, W. C., 1020
Kirn, A. J. B., 22, 64f, 90, 183f, 359f, 448, 516f, 564, 643, 674, 741, 743f, 749, 754, 802, 804
Kirtland, J. P., 364, 496
Klauber, L. M., 4, 10, 21, 37f, 41f, 45f, 46f, 49f, 53f, 56f, 58f, 60f, 64f, 88f, 92f, 93f, 96f, 104, 115, 118, 120, 124f, 128, 129, 143f, 172f, 243, 319, 320, 325, 332, 336, 343, 380f, 383, 398f, 404f, 409f, 439f, 443f, 449f, 457, 516, 570f, 574f, 576f, 587f, 593, 595, 597f, 600f, 604, 606f, 625, 633f, 638f, 653f, 660f, 688f, 736f, 739f, 774, 775, 778f, 788f, 797, 804, 826, 841, 851f, 867, 871f, 873f, 877f, 911, 913, 930, 937, 941f, 948f, 950f, 952f, 960, 965f, 968f, 972f, 977f, 980f, 989f, 994f, 998f, 1001f, 1008f, 1010f, 1013f, 1014f, 1018f, 1024f, 1030f, 1043f, 1048f, 1052, 1055, 1058
Klein, T. A., Jr., 488, 492, 502, 830

Klots, A. B., 108, 186, 190, 307, 369, 556, 720, 796
Knepton, J. C., Jr., 375f
Knobloch, I. W., 261, 751
Knowlton, G. F., 798
Knox, C., 318f
Koller, A. C., 399
Koster, W. J., 23, 328f, 369, 879
Kranzthor, G. M., 218
Kuntz, R. E., 328f
Kunze, R. E., 914

Lacépède, B. G., 368, 916
Lacertilia, 4
Lachner, E. A., 825, 838
Lagler, K. F., 26, 29, 514, 841
Lampropeltis, 5, 18, 21, 24, 25, 35, 70, 71, 330-415, 650, 965
　agalma, 335, 413
　alterna, 71, 330, 331, 337-342
　blairi, 330, 331, 338, 343-345, 624
　boyli, 380
　c. calligaster, 21, 71, 330, 331, 334, 345-349, 350, 696
　c. rhombomaculatus, 21, 331, 334, 349-351, 696
　catalinensis, 2, 332, 373
　d. doliata, 4, 5, 9, 18, 71, 115, 330, 336, 338, 351-355, 367
　d. amaura, 336, 338, 355-358
　d. annulata, 18, 338, 345, 358-360
　d. elapsoides, 368
　d. gentilis, 337, 338, 360-362
　d. syspila, 7, 233, 337, 338, 364-366
　d. temporalis, 337, 338, 366-368
　d. triangulum, 336, 338, 368-372
　elapsoides, 5, 355, 368
　e. virginiana, 367
　g. getulus, 18, 20, 21, 330, 331, 333, 351, 372-376, 378, 397, 550
　g. boyli, 333, 373, 381-384, 411, 413
　g. brooksi, 334, 373, 376-378, 897
　g. californiae, 3, 331, 332, 373, 379-382, 390, 413
　g. californiae (boyli), 28, 33, 373, 382-384, 413, 853
　g. conjuncta, 2, 333, 373, 413
　g. floridana, 334, 373, 376, 378, 384-386
　g. goini, 334, 373, 386-388
　g. holbrooki, 334, 373, 388-391, 398
　g. niger, 332, 373, 391-394
　g. nitida, 2, 332, 373, 413
　g. splendida, 22, 332, 373, 396-398
　g. stictoceps, 269, 331, 373, 413-415, 550
　g. yumensis, 3, 49, 71, 333, 373, 397, 398-400, 690
　herrerae, 336, 413
　leonis, 878

multicinctus, 336, 406, 411
multifasciata, 335
　p. pyromelana, 71, 330, 335, 338, 400-404
　p. infralabialis, 403, 404
　p. knoblochi, 403, 404
　p. woodini, 403, 404
　t. triangulum, 20, 368
　t. annulata, 259
　t. elapsoides, 368
　t. syspila, 365
　t. temporalis, 368
　z. zonata, 27, 335, 338, 404-408, 412
　z. agalma, 2, 338, 407, 413
　z. herrerae, 411-413
　z. multicincta, 334, 335, 338, 409-413
　z. multifasciata, 335, 407, 408, 411
　z. parvirubra, 407, 408
　z. pulchra, 407, 408
Lamprosoma, 120, 669
Lamson, G., 106, 371, 718
Lane, H. H., 41
Langebartel, D. A., 46, 111, 181f, 856
Langlois, T. H., 189, 558f, 718f, 826
La Rivers, I., 686f, 795
Larrea divaricata, 257
Lasky, W. R., 95, 122, 657f, 990
Latham, R. C., 133, 178, 186, 308f, 837
Laticauda, 51
Latreille, P. A., 296, 306, 355, 962
Latrobe, C. J., 1003
Laufe, L. E., 649, 651, 704
Laurenti, J. N., 467
Lawrence, D. H., 1028
Lawson, J., 965
Lazier, E. L., 950, 955
Leach, E. R., 55
Leaf-nosed snake, 569-585; Brown's, 571; cloudy, 576; desert, 580; Maricopa, 574; Pima, 571
Learn, Mrs. W. O., 87, 91, 395, 397, 449, 463, 466, 501, 641, 642, 900, 909
Leary, M., 460
Leather(y) snake, 506; brown banded, 504; Graham's, 490
LeBuff, C. R., Jr., 202f, 559
Le Conte, J. L., 150, 731
Lee, D., 375
Lee, H. H., 374, 528, 832, 964
Lee, J., 135, 964
Leffingwell, D. J., 59f, 143f, 796, 861
Leimadophis, 627
Leiolopisma laterale, 772
Lentz, M. J. R., 435, 905f, 944f, 959
Leonard, A. B., 93
Leptodeira, 19, 21, 27, 67, 80, 81, 415-419
　annulata polysticta, 417
　a. septentrionalis, 7, 19, 329, 415-418, 812
Leptodira, 326, 415

Leptophis, 207, 425, 551, 755
Leptotyphlopidae, 2, 32, 33, 35, 36-50
Leptotyphlops, 7, 21, 24, 33, 35, 36-50
  albifrons, 37
  bressoni, 37
  d. dulcis, 33, 37, 38, **39-41**
  d. dissecta, 37, 38, 39, **41-44**
  d. myopicus, 37, 38
  h. humilis, 3, 33, 39, 43, **44-46,** 690, 888,
    1064, 1065
  h. cahuilae, 3, 39, **46-49,** 690, 691
  h. dugesi, 46
  h. segregus, 38, 39, **49-50**
  h. slevini, 2, 38, 39
  h. utahensis, 37, 38, 39, **50**
  myopicus, 37
LeRay, W. J., 509
Lett, W. P., 719
Lewis, T. H., 54, 102, 133, 244, 256f, 318f,
  395f, 454f, 595, 636, 643, **656, 682f, 985**
Liatris, 961
Lichanura, 7, 18, 19, 25, 53, 55, 60, 61-66
  r. roseofusca, 3, **62-64,** 66
  r. gracia, 3, 52, **64-66**
  trivirgata, 2, 19, 60
Lieberman, S. K., 206
Lindheimer, F., 240
Lindsay, H. L., Jr., 93
Lindsay, R. V., 233
Lindsley, J. H., **717, 826, 837**
Lined snake, 879-884
Liner, E. A., 141f
Linnaeus, C., 130, 133, 224, 288, 312, 351,
  354f, 372, 511, 525, 529, 824, 834,
  903, 925, 956
Linsdale, J. M., 45f, 54, 58, 64, 97f, 118f,
  141, 143f, 157f, 181, 361, 382f, 404f,
  411, 439f, 445, 450f, 456, 573, 579,
  588, 591f, 596f, 600f, 633, 637, 653,
  658f, 686f, 706, 772f, 778, 790f, 795f,
  829, 849, 851, 855f, 872, 912, 941f,
  952f, 977, 1002f, 1017f, 1018f, 1030
Liodytes, 7, 18, 25, 30, 74, 75, 419-423
  a. alleni, 75, **419-422**
  a. lineapiatus, 419, **423**
Liopeltis, 551
  vernalis, 560
Liophis, 159, 425, 627
List, J. C., Jr., 191, 517, 837, 840f
Litchfield, P. L., 185
Lithodytes latrans, 770
Little, E. L., Jr., 325, 398, 436f, 439, 453,
  458f, 593f, 633, 637, 725, 795, 886f,
  980, 985, 994, 1002f, 1006, 1017, 1018f,
  1030
Littleford, R. A., 233f, 701f
Livezey, R. L., 158, 505, 905f
Livingston, B. E., 6, 8

Lloyd, W., 390
Lobelia boykinii, 669
Lockington, W. N., 404f, 412
Lockwood, S., 611f
Lodia, 156
  tenuis, 158, 159
Loding, H. P., 82, 178, 189f, 201f, 261, 271f,
  289, 294, 305f, 351, 436, 501f, 515f,
  519, 613f, 630, 732
Loennberg, A. J. E., 114, 145f, 178f, 227,
  245, 274, 354, 384f, 476, 521f, 537,
  547, 618f, 666, 695, 709, 721, 734
Logier, E. B. S., 58f, 136, 144f, 233, 269,
  307f, 534, 603, 719, 806f, 817f, 836f,
  848, 864f, 1033f
Long, S., 828
Longevity, 9; *see also each species account*
Long-nosed snake, 630-634; desert, 638; east-
  ern, 642; N. A., 297; western, 633
Loomis, R. B., 141, 270, 365f, 547f, 608,
  718, 747, 882, 1045
Lord, J. K., 145, 603, 849
Love, C. L., 904
Loveridge, A., 558, 560, 893
Lowe, C. H., Jr., 11, 442, 889, 921, 924,
  944f, 949, 953f
Lowe, R. L., 136, 185f, 514, 826, 841
Lowery, G. H., 626
Lucas, G. H. W., 558
Lueth, F. X., 812
Lummis, C. F., 1028
Lutz, F. E., 579
Lycodon, 866
Lydekker, R., 1072
Lynn, W. G., 107, 292, 913f
Lyon, M. W., Jr., 1049
Lyre snake, 869-879; Arizona, 869; California,
  872; Sonoran, 869; Texas, 876; Vanden-
  burgh's, 872; Wilkinson's, 876
Lysoptychus lateralis, 727

McAtee, W. L., 308f
Macauley, J., 511, 714, 826, 841, 959
McCallion, J., 495, 804
McCauley, R. H., Jr., 84f, 106f, 115, 133,
  178, 188, 292, 366f, 375, 381, 509, 631,
  718, 835f, 1043
McClellan, G. B., 605
McClellan, W. H., 292
McClintock, H., 41, 49f, 180, 185, 218, 257,
  285, 360, 397, 448, 459, 488f, 607f, 643,
  650, 727
McConnell, W. R., 960
McConkey, E. H., 477
MacCoy, C. V., 595, 769, 983f
McKee, E. D., 31, 596, 658, 684f, 982f, 1007f
McLain, R. B., 506, 541, 801, 806, 916
McLees, F., 612

Maier, E., 907, 920f, 1058
Malnate, E., 627f
Mann, W. M., 141, 347f, 828
Mansueti, R., 233f
Manville, R. H., 714, 835
Marcy, R. B., 1003, 1025
Marnock, G. W., 466, 770
Marr, J. C., 91, 93, 141f, 300, 328f, 362, 448f, 465f, 488f, 494f, 607, 644, 741, 806, 821f, 823, 829f, 945f, 968f, 1003f
Marshall, B. C., 40, 183, 293, 320, 356f, 363f, 475, 481f, 538, 743, 827, 881, 1047f
Martin, J. S., 875
Martin, P. J., 1030f
Martof, B., 841f
Maslin, T. P., 181f, 450, 453, 456, 644, 858, 882, 888
Massasauga, 1040-1061; black, 1042; eastern, 1042; Edward's, 1048, 1050; Gulf Coast, 1048; prairie, 1042; rattlesnake, 1042; Texas, 1048; western, 1048
Massasauger, 1042
Masticophis, 18, 21, 24, 25, 76, 77, 207, 423-466, 651
    anthonyi, 2, 424, 427
    aurigulus, 2, 424, 426
    barbouri, 2, 424, 426
    b. bilineatus, 77, 423, 424, 425, **428-429**, 432
    b. lineolatus, 424, 426, **430-433**, 436-438
    f. flagellum, 20, 77, 217, 423, 426, 427, **433-436**, 446
    f. cingulum, **442**
    f. flavigularis, 438, 448, 450
    f. lineatulus, 427, 434, **436-438**
    f. piceus (frenatus), 3, 77, 424, 427, 434, 438, **439-442**, 578
    f. piceus (piceus), 423, 424, 425, 426, 429, 434, 438, **442-446**, 578
    f. ruddocki, **442**
    f. testaceus, 22, 345, 427, 428, 434, 438, **446-450**, 656
    lateralis, 3, 424, 426, **450-452**
    l. euryxanthus, **453**
    semilineatus, see b. bilineatus above
    t. taeniatus, 217, 424, 425, 426, **453-456**, 465, 466
    t. girardi, 463, 466
    t. ornatus, 424, 425, **456-461**
    t. ruthveni, 77, 424, 425, 426, **461-464**
    t. schotti, 424, 425, 426, **464-466**
Mattlin, R. H., 268f, 530f, 534, 841
May, H., 42, 811
Mayer, A. G., 841
Mayr, E., 382
Meacham, F. B., 41, 250
Mead, A. R., 169

Meade, G., 28, 138, 276f, 353f, 358, 389f, 474, 502f, 525f, 841, 966
Mearns, E. A., 837, 973
Mease, J., 960
Mecham, J. S., 49f, 180, 184f, 197, 218, 257, 285, 337, 340f, 360, 397, 448, 459, 488f, 607f, 643, 650, 726
Medden, R. V., 581, 962, 1003
Medsger, O. P., 309, 372
Meek, S. E., 31, 118, 124, 382, 404, 599, 651, 949, 955, 974, 980, 993, 1014f, 1016f
Mehrtens, J. M., 608
Meng, H., 717
Mercer, P., 691
Merrem, B., 185
Merriam, C. H., 599, 833, 980
Mertens, R., 262
Mertensia foliata, 563
Metachrosis, see Color
Metcalf, Z. P., 178, 201, 266, 906f, 940
Mexican border species, 7
Meyenberg, E., 197, 217, 257f, 340f
Michaels, J. S., 187
Microps, 879
Microtus, 133
Micruroides, 7, 27, 30, 885-886
    euryxanthus, 727, **886-890**
Micrurus, 7, 25, 33, 35, 885, 886, 890-900
    euryxanthus, 889
    f. fulvius, 191, **890-895**
    f. barbouri, 886, 890, 891, **894-897**, 1058
    f. tenere, 890, 891, **897-899**
    tristis, 897
Milk snake, 30; Arizona, 400; banded, 382; Blanchard's, 366; Boyle's, 382; California, 379, 382; cape, 355, 366; coastal plain, 366; common, 368; desert, 398; East Shore, 366; eastern, 351; Louisiana, 355; Lower Misissipp Valley, 355; Mexican, 358; red, 355, 364, 366, 409; ringed, 358; Sonoran, 396; southern, 360; Virginia red, 366; western, 360, 382
Millegen, G., 965
Miller, A. H., 66, 318f, 325, 439, 453f, 600f, 639, 654, 948, 974f, 994f
Miller, C. A., 969
Miller, G. S., Jr., 31, 351
Miller, L., 125
Miller, T. J., 219, 256f, 594
Miller, W. DeW., 31, 135, 187f, 233, 292, 371f, 513, 700, 838, 912
Mills, R. C., 1073
Milstead, W. W., 41, 49f, 180, 185, 218, 257, 285, 337, 340f, 345, 360, 397, 448, 459, 488f, 607f, 643, 650, 726, 772, 915f
Mindeleff, C., 1027

Minton, S. A., Jr., 114f, 136, 188f, 233f, 295, 309f, 348, 393f, 498f, 502, 509, 513, 563, 608, 701, 718, 730f, 799, 826, 837, 899, 913, 1045f

Mitchell, J. D., 289f, 388, 516, 525, 899, 906, 908f, 924f, 944f, 966f, 1003, 1048f, 1060f

Mitchell, S. W., 31, 913f, 1027

Miter snake, 672, 686, 740, 746; banded, 672, 686; Wagner's, 733

Mittleman, M. B., 115, 354, 502, 600f, 656, 713, 803f, 805f, 982

Moccasin, 515, 526, 535, 790, 828, 916; bay, 515; black, 372, 916, 921; blunt-tailed, 1, 916, 921; copper-bellied, 477; copper-belly, 522; copperhead, 907, 910; cotton-mouth, 916; cottonmouth water, 916; dia-mond, 500; diamond-back, 500; dry-land, 903, 907; false, 500, 544; highland, 903, 907, 910; house, 368; lowland, 916; mountain, 306; mud, 511; northern cot-tonmouth, 921; N.A. water, 916; orange-bellied, 477; rusty, 916; salt-water, 515, 518; spread-head, 306; striped, 490, 504; stump, 916; stump-tail, 916, 921; Texas, 916; Troost's, 916; true water, 916; upland, 910; water, 486, 511, 525, 526, 915, 916, 921; western cottonmouth, 921

Mocquard, F., 118, 442, 452, 456, 688, 1071

Moesel, J., 1046

Mole catcher, 1, 224, 349

Moody, C. S., 29

Moore, C. B., 84

Moore, J. E., 300

Moore, J. P., 611f

Morgan, C. L., 29

Morrison, C. M., 1019

Morse, A. P., 608

Morse, M., 110, 141, 291, 307f, 498, 532f, 841f

Mosauer, W., 47f, 64, 118, 126, 224, 406, 442, 593, 606f, 688, 769, 942f, 946, 950f, 955, 981f, 985

Moski, H., 913

Mouse snake, 1, 89, 220, 224, 805; spotted, 220; striped, 649

Mozley, A. E., 138, 179, 230, 360, 388, 446, 842

Mud snake, 82, 272, 276, 419-423; Allen's, 419; Carolina, 667; eastern, 272; red-bellied, 663-668; South Florida, 666; western, 276

Mulaik, D. D., 150f, 279f, 360, 462, 675f, 977

Mulaik, S., 150f, 217f, 281f, 360, 416f, 674f, 682f, 685, 997

Mulford, I. L., 16, 17, 41, 783, 809, 865

Munro, D. F., 141f, 300, 856f

Munz, P. A., 997, 1009

Murphy, R. C., 133, 308f, 837

Murray, C. A., 1003

Murray, E., 216

Murray, K. F., 2

Murray, L. T., 217, 337f, 346, 400, 447f, 459f, 600, 727, 947, 967, 969f, 980f

Museum abbreviations, 1067

Myers, G. S., 114, 217f, 349, 391, 716f, 801

Myrica cerifera, 248

Nabalus, 961

Names, 1-5; *see also each species account*

Nash, C. W., 826, 842

Natrix, 18, 25, 30, 74, 81, 82, 159, 209, 286, 296, 330, 425, 467, 551, 755, 829, 901, 920

angustirostris, 765

bisectus, 511

clarki, 7, 467, 544

compressicauda, 355, 467, 472, 517, 521, 853

c. bivittata, 521

c. compsolaema, 472

c. obscura, 472, 521

c. taeniata, 472, 543

c. usta, 472, 518, 520

c. walkeri, 472, 521

cyclopion, 81, 467 469, **472-474,** 524, 528

c. floridana, 467, 469, **474-477**

erythrogaster, 470, 473, **477-480,** 482, 483, 496, 498, 524, 531, 540

e. flavigaster, 470, 477, **482-484**

e. neglecta, 470, 477, 478, **484-486**

e. transversa, 81, 469, 470, 473, 478, **486-490,** 493, 494, 496

fasciata, 470, 480, 483, 487, 525, 544

f. confluens, 470

f. pleuralis, 539

grahami, 76, 77, 422, 467, 468, **490-498,** 505

harteri, 469, **493-496,** 512, 766

kirtlandi, 26, 74, 76, 77, 467, 468, 491, **496-499**

rhombifera, 81, 467, 468, 469, 472, 473, 482, 483, 494, **500-504,** 524, 540, 547

rigida, 76, 77, 467, 468, 491, **504-506**

septemvittata, 26, 76, 77, 467, 468, 491, **506-509**

s. sipedon, 20, 26, 27, 28, 467, 470, 471, 483, 490, 496, **511-514,** 700, 811

s. clarki, 471, 491, **515-518,** 541

s. compressicauda, 471, 491, 517, **518-522,** 541

s. confluens, 512, **522-525,** 527, 540

Natrix (*cont.*)
s. engelsi, 470, 512, **547-551**
s. fasciata, 470, 512, 516, 518, **525-529,** 536, 539
s. insularum, 471, 512, **529-535**
s. pictiventris, 468, 471, 512, 517, 518, 527, **535-537**
s. pleuralis, 471, 512, 527, 537, **537-541**
s. taeniata, 269, 491, **541-544**
s. transversa, 473
taxispilota, 81, 467, 469, 472, 474, 500, 502, **544-547,** 1065
transversa, 483
valida, 2, 472
v. celaeno, 472
Necker, W. L., 185f, 561f, 913, 916, 920, 960, 1045
Needham, J. G., 274
Needham, P., 1009
Nehrling, H., 354f, 940
Neill, W. T., Jr., 10, 18, 106, 114f, 148, 178f, 201f, 226f, 229, 236, 243f, 247, 251, 269f, 274f, 309, 314, 378, 384f, 422, 476, 479f, 508f, 528f, 540f, 546f, 611f, 618f, 630, 710, 713f, 731, 892f, 906f, 907
Nelson, D. J., 362
Nelson, G., 271, 412f
Neoseps reynoldsi, 734
Nerodia, 467, 755
fasciata, 539
Netting, M. G., 228f, 233f, 238, 308, 376, 627f, 630, 816, 913f, 958f, 1044f
New, J. G., 610f
Newcome, W. A., 806
Newcomer, E. J., 687
Newton, L. F., 307
Nichitami, S., 59
Nichol, A. A., 946, 985
Nichols, J. T., 308f, 514
Night snake, 314-330
desert spotted, 318
Great Basin spotted, 318
San Diegan spotted, 320
Sierra Nevada spotted, 322
Sonoran spotted, 324
spotted, 324
Texas spotted, 326
Utah spotted, 321
Noble, G. K., 205, 207, 371f, 521f, 544, 700f, 815, 840
Noguchi, H., 29, 417, 893, 970, 975, 1072
Norris, K. S., 953f, 1073
N.A. cottonmouth, 916
Norton, A. H., 956f
Notestein, F. N., 842f
Number, 2-3

Oak leaf, 372
Obrecht, B., 178, 629f, 893, 907
Oliver, J. A., 29, 118, 208, 258, 316, 323f, 325f, 429, 438, 442, 568f, 573f, 639f, 656, 804, 871f, 889, 1028
Opheodrys, 21, 24, 25, 30, 33, 72, 73, 551, 560
aestivus, 33, 550, **551-555,** 556, 560
vernalis, 7, 20, 552, **555-560**
v. blanchardi, 552, **560-564,** 821
Ophibolus:
calligaster, 696
coccineus, 354
doliatus, 414
getulus, 397
g. boyli, 380
g. niger, 392
g. sayi, 392, 398, 414
splendidus, 391, 398
triangulus, 414
Ophidia, 4
Ophisaurus ventralis, 414, 613
Opisthoglyphs, 67
Opuntia, 8
Orontium, 669
Ortenberger, A. I., 39, 41, 60, 100, 136, 137f, 181, 300, 308, 428f, 435f, 442f, 448f, 456f, 461f, 464f, 512, 572f, 596, 607, 674f, 692, 740, 799, 946, 985, 1000
Ortenberger, R. D., 100, 428f, 442, 445, 572f, 596, 946, 985, 1000
Osborn, H., 506
Osceola, 1, 330
clerica, 355
coccinea, 355
doliata, 355
elapsoidea, 355
parallela, 355
syspila, 355
Osten-Sacken, Baron C. R., 832
Over, W. H., 141, 181, 266, 300, 564, 608f, 823, 856f, 883, 1003f
Owens, D. W., 257, 465f, 727, 968
Owens, J. C., 877
Owens, V., 135, 181, 233, 858
Oxybelis, 27, 67, 74, 75, 261, 565
acuminatus, 19, 75, 566
aeneus auratus, **565-569**
microphthalmus, 568, 569
Oxyrhina, 296

Pack, H. J., 58, 143f, 319, 455f, 603, 659f, 686, 751, 798f, 858, 1021f
Palmer, E. L., 1072
Palmer, J., 1003
Palmer, K., 199
Pantherophis, 209

Parker, M. V., 110, 191f, 226, 251, 271, 392f, 474, 482f, 524, 541, 714, 923f
Parker, U. R., 273
Parriott, D. W., 225
Patch-nosed snake, 644-663; Big Bend, 654; chaparral, 660; desert, 651; eastern, 646, 649; Graham's, 646; Mohave, 658; mountain, 646; Pacific, 660; plateau, 646; Rio Grande, 649; Texas, 649; western, 651, 658, 660
Paxman, A., 50
Peck, J., 940
Peck, L., 946, 985
Pelamis, 2, 7, 19, 25, 33, 35, 51
Pelamydrus, 51
Pelias, 296, 901
Penn, G. H., Jr., 473
Perez, F., 208
Period of activity, 10; see also each species account
Perkins, C. B., 4, 9, 11, 18, 25, 44f, 49, 56, 62f, 98, 103, 126, 143f, 147, 151, 167, 172, 175, 201f, 206, 230, 243f, 249, 301, 320, 355, 358, 376, 381f, 404f, 408f, 439f, 445, 446, 449f, 451, 516, 583, 596f, 609f, 631, 633f, 638f, 654, 663, 691, 738, 739, 742, 771, 772, 788f, 852, 872f, 904, 908, 911, 918, 924, 937, 941f, 974f, 989f, 996f, 1002, 1015f, 1043
Perkins, C. M., 96, 194, 435
Perkins, R. M., 11, 347, 422, 880f, 905f, 944f, 959
Peromyscus, 617
Perry, A., 514
Peters, J. A., 1045
Peters, J. L., 411
Peterson, A. E., 289, 554, 684
Pflueger, A., 230
Phamnovis, 755
Phibolus, 330
Phillips, E. S., 824f
Philpott, C. H., 920
Phimothyra, 644
Phisalix-Picot, M., 29
Phrynosoma, 4, 29, 321
    coronatum, 853
Phyllorhynchus, 7, 21, 24, 48, 68, 69, 569-585, 651
    b. browni, 20, 569, 570, 571-574, 575, 577, 582
    b. lucidus, 569, 570, 574-576, 582
    b. fortitus, 569, 570, 580
    decurtatus, 2, 569, 570, 575, 576, 579, 580, 581
    d. arenicola, 2, 569
    d. norrisi, 569
    d. nubilus, 118, 569, 570, 572, 576-580

d. perkinsi, 319, 569, 570, 572, 580-585, 637
Piatt, J., 110, 233
Pickens, A. L., 716
Pickering, C., 858
Pickwell, G. B., 56, 103, 165, 319, 1072
Pierce, J., 368
Pigmy rattlesnake, 1040-1061; Barbour's, 1055; Carolina, 1052; dusky, 1055; eastern, 1052; southeastern, 1055; southern, 1052, 1058; Strecker's, 1058; western, 1058
Pilot, 306, 368, 910
Pilot snake, 230, 263, 604, 609; Baird's, 214; black, 230; checked, 240; Davis Mt., 255; Emory's, 218; gray, 240, 249; Lindheimer's, 240; mountain, 230; rattlesnake, 907, 910; spotted, 249; Texas, 240; water, 544; western, 220
Pilsbry, H. A., 261f
Pimental, R. A., 319, 799
Pine snake, 1, 585-626; black, 612; common, 609; eastern, 609; Florida, 616; Loding's, 613, 616; Louisiana, 620; New Jersey, 609; N.A., 609; northern, 609; Pacific, 588; Ruthven's, 613, 616, 620; Say's, 604; southern, 616; western, 588, 604
Pinkus, L. F., 883
Pinus:
    edulis, 8
    flexilis, 1036
    palustris, 6, 623
    strobus, 8
Pirnie, M. D., 139, 142
Pittman, A., 366
Pituophis, 9, 18, 21, 24, 25, 33, 68, 69, 86, 585-626, 656
    c. catenifer, 27, 588-593, 618, 619, 624, 853
    c. affinis, 329, 587, 589, 590, 593-596, 603
    c. annectens, 3, 10, 18, 21, 592, 596-600
    c. bimaris, 2, 588, 589
    c. coronalis, 2, 588, 589
    c. deserticola, 2, 329, 587, 589, 592, 596, 600-604, 626, 1022
    c. fuliginatus, 2, 588-589, 590
    c. heermanni, 626
    c. insulanus, 2, 588, 589
    c. pumilus, 588, 589, 590, 604
    c. rutilus, 596
    c. sayi, 233, 585, 587, 589, 604-609
    c. stejnegeri, 600, 605, 625, 626
    c. vertebralis, 2, 587, 625
    deppei, 5, 586, 607, 624
    m. melanoleucus, 11, 586, 587, 589, 609-613, 615, 616
    m. lodingi, 585, 586, 589, 613-616, 618
    m. mugitus, 585, 586, 589, 616-619

Pituophis (cont.)
  m. ruthveni, 585, 586, 589, 615, 616, 620-
    626
  sayi, 365
Pityophis, 209, 585
Plethodon c. cinereus, 106, 948
Polemonium, 459
Pollack, T. A., 617f, 905f, 920, 965, 1054
Polygala, 961
Polygonum, 422
Pomerat, C. M., 588
Pope, C. H., 29, 227, 258, 290, 337, 371,
    508f, 562, 676, 707, 714f, 811f, 830,
    838f, 914, 966, 1045f
Pope, T. E. B., 140, 141, 308, 558, 560f, 1045
Poplar leaf, 903, 910
Porter, J. P., 231f
Porter, T. C., 833, 848
Potamophis, 288, 628
  striatulus, 286
Powell, J. W., 1027f
Praeger, W. E., 142
Preble, E. A., 855
Presnall, C. C., 193, 319
Price, W. W., 595
Problematic species, 5-6
Proctor, J. B., 308
Prosopis juliflora, 6, 257
Prymnomiodon, 755
Psammophis, 425
Pseudemys, 85
Pseudobranchus, 422, 710
Pseudoelaps, 330
Pseudoeryx, 53
Pseudotsuga taxifolia, 1036
Psoralia, 961
Putnam, F. W., 558, 826, 841f

Quaintance, C. W., 196, 769, 983f, 1011
Quarterman, L., 375
Quarters, J., 1045f
Queen snake: brown, 506; Graham's, 490;
    green, 504; rigid, 504
Quercus arizonica, 1036
Quercus densiflora, 8
Quillin, E. S., 41, 90, 217, 341, 466, 516f,
    706, 771, 898
Quillin, R. D., 41, 90, 217, 341, 459f, 466,
    515f, 519, 706, 749, 771

Racer, 30, 130-152, 184, 230, 249, 262;
    American, 133; Arizona, 428; banded,
    450; Barbour's, 894; black, 133, 138,
    230, 434, 442, 446; blue, 136, 138, 142,
    179, 182, 230; brown, 136; California,
    450; California striped, 450; central
    Texas, 456; common black, 133; Eagle

Pass, 464; eastern, 133; Emory's, 218;
    Florida black, 145; fox, 262; Fox's blue,
    133, 138; Girard's, 456; Great Basin
    striped, 453; green, 133, 138, 142, 446,
    464; green-spotted, 207; half-striped, 428;
    horse, 133; Mormon blue, 142; moun-
    tain, 453, 456; Nevada striped, 453; New
    Mexican, 436; olive, 138; ornate, 456;
    pink, 446; pink-bellied, 442; plains blue,
    138; prairie, 446; red, 224, 241, 439, 442,
    446, 660; Rio Grande queen, 149; Ruth-
    ven's, 461; San Francisco, 453; San Joa-
    quin, 442; scarlet, 224; Schott's, 91, 464;
    Scott's, 464; Sonoran, 428; southern
    Texas, 149; spotted, 224; Stejneger's,
    149; striped, 450, 453, 456, 464; Ta-
    maulipas, 461; variegated, 136; western,
    138; western blue, 142; western striped,
    453; western yellow-bellied, 142; white,
    446; white oak, 136; white-throated, 133,
    230; yellow-bellied, 138, 142
Rafinesque, C. S., 913f, 1001f
Rahn, H., 417, 718, 856, 1004f
Rainbow snake, 82-86
Rainwater, J., 976f
Rak, C. L., 1050
Ramsey, E. E., 141, 509, 841, 1045
Ramsey, L. W., 882f, 919, 924
Rana:
  boyli, 793
  b. sierrae, 411
  catesbeiana, 495
  clamitans, 495
  grylio, 710
  pipiens, 418
  pretiosa, 158, 860
  sphenocephala, 28, 710
  sylvatica, 495
  tarahumarae, 568
Raney, E. C., 29, 507f
Range, 6; see also each species account
Rat snake, 1, 30, 204, 209-270; Allen's, 245;
    Baird's, 214; black, 230; blotched, 249;
    brown, 218; Davis Mt., 255; Deckert's,
    235; eastern Texas, 240; Emory's, 218;
    Everglades, 245; four-banded, 235, 243;
    four-lined, 243; gray, 245; Great Bend,
    214; green, 258; Gulf hammock, 253;
    intermountain, 222; Key West, 227;
    Lindheimer's, 240; Matecumbe, 235;
    Mexican, 204; Mexican green, 258; North
    Carolina Banks, 269; oak, 253; orange,
    245; pink, 227; prairie, 229; red, 222,
    227; rosy, 227; South Florida, 235;
    southeastern, 249; Texas, 220; Trans-
    Pecos, 255; Utah spotted, 202; yellow,
    243

Rattlesnake (*or* Rattler), 925-1061; adobe, 941; Arizona, 1010; Arizona black, 1010; Arizona diamond, 1029; Arizona prairie, 1024; Arizona spotted, 985; banded, 956, 962; bastard, 306, 1052; black, 1001, 1010, 1014, 1029, 1042; black diamond, 1010, 1014, 1029; black-tailed, 980; bleached, 974; blue, 966, 970; bottomland, 962; brown, 1010; California, 1029; cane, 962; canebrake, 962; Canyon bleached, 1008; cereberus, 1010; chevron, 962; common, 936, 962, 1001; confluent, 1001, 1029; desert diamond, 941, 994; diamond, 936, 941; diamond-back, 936, 941, 1029; diamond-patch, 936; dobe, 941; dog-faced, 980; dog-headed, 980; dumb, 910; dwarf, 1052; dwarf prairie, 1042; eastern, 956; eastern diamond, 936; eastern diamond-back, 936; eastern rock, 966; faded, 1012; false, 1048; fierce, 941; Florida, 936; Florida diamond-back, 936; Grand Canyon, 1008; gray, 1042, 1052; gray diamond-back, 1014; Great Basin, 1001, 1018, 1029; great yellow, 956; green, 966, 970, 980; green rock, 970; ground, 1042; Hallowell's, 1029; hardwood, 262, 266; hognosed, 306, 1052, 1055; horned, 948; horrid, 956; Kennicott's, 966; Kirtland's, 1042; large prairie, 1001; little, 1052; little black, 1042; little green, 966; lozenge-shaped, 936; mangrove, 916; massasauga, 1042; midget faded, 1012; military, 1052; Missouri, 1001, 1029; Mitchell's, 974; Mohave, 974, 994; Mohave diamond, 994; mountain, 956, 1014; mountain diamond-back, 980, 1010; mountain timber, 956; N.A. banded, 956; N.A. horrid, 956; N.A. smaller, 1052; northern, 956; northern banded, 956; northern black-tailed, 980; oak leaf, 372, 1052; Oregon, 1029; Owens Valley, 977; Pacific, 1014, 1029; pale, 974; pallid, 974; Panamint, 977; pigmy, 1, 30, 1040-1061; pink, 966; plains, 1001; prairie, 1, 941, 1001, 1024, 1042, 1048; Price's, 985; red, 974, 989; red diamond, 989; red diamond-back, 989; ridge-nosed, 1034; rock, 956, 966, 970; saltwater, 916; San Diegan, 1014; Say's, 1048; Say's false, 1048; scutulated, 994; Seminole, 962; side-winder, 948; small, 962, 1052, 1055; small prairie, 1042; southeastern diamond-back, 936; southern, 1029, 1058; southern banded, 962; southern diamond-back, 936; southern Pacific, 1014; southern woodland, 936; southwestern speckled, 974; speckled, 974; spitting, 941; spotted, 985, 1001, 1052; swamp, 962, 1042; Texas, 941; Texas diamond, 941; Texas diamond-back, 941; Texas rock, 966; three-spotted shield, 1048; tiger, 977, 998; timber, 936, 962, 1014; triple-spotted, 1042, 1048; velvet-tail, 962; water, 544, 916, 936; western, 1029; western black, 1029; western diamond, 941; western diamond-back, 941; white, 966, 974; Willard's, 1034; yellow, 1012; yellowish brown, 956

Rattlesnake pilot, 372, 384, 907, 910
Rattlesnake's mate, 910
Rausch, R. L., 812
Rea, P. M., 615f
Red eye, 907
Red oak, 903
Reddick, G., 509, 820, 1045
Reese, A. M., 914
Regina, 25, 76, 467, 468
    grahami, 468
    kirtlandi, 468
    rigida, 468
    septemvittata, 468
Rehn, J. A. G., 1006
Reichert, E. T., 913
Reimer, W. J., 776, 795
Reinwardt, C. G. G., 276
Rena, 37; California, 44; Texas, 39
Reuss, A., 766, 769
Reynolds, F. A., 98, 103, 274f, 521
Rhadinaea, 7, 18, 78, 79, 153, 627-631
    flavilata, 79, **627-630**
Rhamnus c. ilicifolia, 1036
Rhinechis, 585
Rhineura, 4, 734
Rhinocheilus, 7, 18, 24, 25, 68, 69, 630-644
    l. lecontei, 3, 578, 631, **633-637**, 637-640, 696
    l. antoni, 632, 633, 634
    l. clarus, 578, 632-635, **638-640**
    l. tessellatus, 632, 634, **642-644,** 656
Rhinochilus, 630
Rhinostoma, 113, 120
Rhoads, S. N., 251, 307, 366, 472f, 511, 541, 835, 842, 906f, 907
Ribbon snake, 755-866; Arizona, 799; eastern, 824; Fairie's, 828; Florida, 832; Long's, 828; N.A., 824; Ostensacken's, 832; plains, 828; Say's, 828; southeastern, 832; southern, 832; spotted, 795, 824; western, 828
Rice, F. L., 312, 714, 830, 842
Richardson, C. H., Jr., 126, 602f, 798f, 1018f
Richmond, N. D., 84f, 292, 505, 547, 816

Ridgway, R., 9, 278
Riemer, W. J., 452f, 862
Riley, W. A., 400
Ring(ed) snake, 360, 415; Arizona, 400; Mohave, 121; Sonora, 1, 116, 686
Ring-neck(ed) snake, 159-200; Arizona, 179; Arny's, 179; beautiful, 171; Big Bend, 196; California, 163, 171; coral-bellied, 171; eastern, 176, 179, 185; Los Angeles, 166; Mississippi, 189; Mississippi Valley, 189; northeastern, 185; northern, 185; northwestern, 169; Ozark, 179; Pacific, 163; prairie, 179; regal, 192; San Bernardino, 166; San Diegan, 172; Santa Barbara, 175; Sierran, 171; Sonoma, 169; Sonoran, 179, 192, 194; Southern California, 172; southeastern, 176; southern, 176; southwestern, 192, 194; spotted, 163, 179; Texas, 182; Trans-Pecos, 196; Van Denbergh's, 166, 175; western, 163, 166, 169, 171, 172, 179
Risley, P. L., 856
Ritter, W. C., 698
Ritter, W. E., 990
Roberts, A. R., 1045f, 1046
Robertson, H. C., 506
Robinia neomexicana, 1036
Robinson, R. G., 148, 200, 940
Robison, D. C., 1020
Rodeck, H. G., 300, 747, 797
Rodgers, T. L., 158, 786
Rodman, G. B., Jr., 875
Roecker, R. M., 29, 266, 268f, 507f, 514, 711f, 836, 842
Rolfs, P. H., 940
Rolker, A. W., 936
Rose, F. L., 476
Ross, A., 1029
Ross, G., 963, 1051
Ross, R. C., 54f, 952
Rossel bastard, 306
Ruick, J. D., Jr., 898f
Rundle, W., 401, 604
Runner: black, 133; blue, 133; prairie, 446; race, 446; white oak, 243
Ruthling, P. D. R., 596f, 635, 637, 851, 1017f
Rutledge, A. H., 905f, 907, 919f, 965f
Ruthven, A. G., 3, 44f, 54, 58f, 100, 143f, 171, 189, 204f, 269, 283f, 285, 300, 442f, 462, 493, 499, 509, 560, 593f, 600f, 654, 718f, 765, 774, 781, 790, 795f, 806, 815, 817f, 821, 830, 833-835, 838f, 845, 848f, 852, 856f, 860, 888f, 944f, 1018f

Sacken, C. R. Osten, see Osten-Sacken
Sackett, T. T., 148

Safford, W. E., 148, 202, 247, 311, 476, 535, 554, 833f, 920, 940
Salicornia perennis, 543
Salix marginata, 669
Salvadora, 21, 24, 74, 75, 184, **644-663**
  g. grahamiae, 645, **646-649,** 656
  g. lineata, 7, 645, 646, **649-651,** 656
  h. hexalepis, 3, 75, 645, 646, **651-654,** 655, 656, 1064, 1065
  h. deserticola, 645, 646, 650, **654-658**
  h. klauberi, 3, 645, 646
  h. mojavensis, 646, **658-660**
  h. virgultea, 3, 645, 646, **660-663**
  lineata, 656
  pulcherrima, 644
Salvadora, Graham's, 646
Salyer, J. C., II, 26, 514, 841
Sand hog, 82
Sanders, E., 102
Sanders, J. J., 898
Sanders, R. J., 1021
Sanger, D. B., 944f
Sanicula, 961
Sargent, C. S., 809, 825, 848, 852
Sass, H. R., 613
Sauger, 1042
Savage, J. M., 611, 955, 1005f
Say, T., 105f, 179, 234, 314, 345, 446f, 826, 828f, 854f, 893, 910f, 1006, 1048f
Scaphiopus, 184
Sceloporus, 321
  consobrinus, 342
  couchi, 727
  olivaceus, 345
  torquata poinsetti, 342
  variabilis marmoratus, 345
Schenck, J., 841
Schlegel, H., 276, 354f
Schmidt, K. P., 2, 4, 29, 44, 49f, 118f, 142, 174, 193f, 197f, 218, 233f, 245, 253, 264, 266, 285f, 289, 296, 300, 342, 353, 371, 375, 398, 442, 446, 460, 465f, 479, 492, 499, 502, 505, 525, 529, 560f, 573, 579, 582, 592, 596, 630, 647f, 651, 654f, 674, 682, 742, 812, 814f, 817f, 826, 834, 885f, 889, 893, 894, 896f, 899, 912, 945, 968f, 974f, 981f, 989, 991f, 1046, 1054
Schonberger, C. F., 701f, 799, 860
Schoolcraft, H. R., 1025
Schott, A. C. V., 464
Schroder, R. C., 608
Schuck, N., 199
Schulz, E., 706
Schuster, R., 699
Schwardt, H. H., 192, 540f, 829f, 906f
Schwartz, A., 547, 732, 970f

Schwenkmeyer, R. C., 49, 452f
Scolecophis, 669, 722
Scotophis, 209
Scrophularia, 564
Scytale, 296, 901
Scytalum, 296, 901
Sea snake, 51
Seiss, C. F., 837f, 960
Seminatrix, 7, 25, 30, 78, 79, 663-668
  pygaea, **664-666**, 667
  p. cyclas, 663, **666-667**
  p. paludis, 663, **667-668**
Senecio, 961
Serenoa serrulata, 8
Seriocarpus, 961
Serpentes, families, 32
Serven, J. E., 678, 680
Seton, E. T., 31, 561f, 856, 858
Seton, W., 1030
Seymour, S. E., 674
Shanklin, S. M., 448
Shannon, F. A., 144, 155, 281, 448, 462, 465,
  804, 830
Shannon, R. C., 1009
Sharp, S. S., 713
Shaw, C. E., 11, 126, 433, 739, 908, 924,
  991, 994
Shaw, G., 314, 376, 433, 826, 919f
Shelford, V. E., 56, 128, 150, 865
Sherman, F., Jr., 31
Shields, F. B., 701f, 898
Shilladay, G. L., 387f
Shovel-nosed ground snake, 120-130; Colorado
  desert, 124; Mohave desert, 121; northern,
  128; Organ-Pipe, 129; Sonora, 129; south-
  central Arizona, 128
Shreve, F., 6, 8, 49, 150, 445, 464, 690
Shufeldt, R. W., 31, 142, 351, 555
Siagonodon, 37
Sibon, 415, 696
Sidewinder, 1, 948; Colorado Desert, 950;
  Mohave Desert, 948; Sonoran, 955
Siebert, H. C., 557, 811
Sigmodon ochrognathus, 217
Silene, 961
Simms, W. G., 940
Simotes, 113
Simpson, S. E. R., 841
Sinclair, R. M., 291f, 294f, 618f
Siren, 422, 669
Sirman, G. F., 239, 311f, 894f
Sirman, Q., 311, 505, 896
Sistrurus, 25, 901, 919, 1040-1061
  c. catenatus, 18, 825, 902, 1041, **1042-1048**
  c. consors, 1050
  c. edwardsi, **1050**

c. tergeminus, 890, 1041, 1042, **1048-1050**
m. miliarius, 7, 33, 902, 1041, 1042, **1052-1054**
m. barbouri, 902, 1041, 1042, **1055-1058**
m. streckeri, 33, 1042, **1058-1061**
ravus, 1040
Size, 7; *see also each species account*
Slack, K. V., 233
Slater, J. R., 157f, 455, 522, 806f, 857, 859f,
  864f
Slatten, R., 229, 940
Sleepy John, 230
Slevin, J. R., 2, 44, 48, 55, 97f, 118, 125,
  129f, 144f, 157f, 171, 196, 325, 399f,
  402f, 440f, 455, 514, 583, 595f, 602, 604,
  626, 634f, 639, 648, 653f, 659f, 687f,
  690f, 727, 751f, 755, 765, 769, 772f,
  778, 783f, 786f, 790f, 795f, 801, 806,
  808f, 845, 848, 852, 863, 871, 944, 954f,
  973, 982f, 986f, 991f, 1001, 1010f, 1013,
  1035, 1073
Small, H. B., 717
Small, J. K., 187, 554
Smart, E. W., 144, 318f, 455f, 602, 635
Smith, A. G., 109f, 110, 133, 230, 290, 368,
  497, 506, 511, 557f, 697, 810f, 815,
  820f, 835, 913f, 956
Smith, H. A., 125, 726f, 1050
Smith, H. H., 261
Smith, H. I., 849
Smith, H. M., 4, 5, 40f, 42f, 46, 93, 115,
  128, 142, 155, 181f, 197f, 201f, 206f,
  218, 257, 260f, 265, 273f, 277f, 281,
  282f, 300, 303f, 337f, 354, 360f, 366,
  380, 429, 436f, 445, 446f, 462, 465, 501f,
  624, 639f, 648, 649f, 656, 663, 704, 726f,
  735f, 741f, 743f, 747, 749, 752f, 765,
  800f, 804, 810f, 823, 828f, 866, 871, 876f,
  966f, 980
Smith, M. A., 51
Smith, P. W., 191, 277f, 393, 492, 517, 713,
  907
Smith, T. F., 44, 49f, 193, 196f, 200, 218,
  257, 285f, 460, 682, 968f, 980f, 985
Smith, W. H., 109f, 142, 262, 308, 611, 699,
  837f, 903, 913f, 1046
Smyth, T., 960
Snake: adobe, 941; Allen's, 419; Allen's helicops, 420; American corais, 200; annulated, 1, 415; Arizona, 1, 89, 428; Arizona long-headed, 565; Arizona vine,
  565; ash, 136; banded, 124, 506, 525;
  banded burrowing, 1, 116-120; barber-
  pole, 897; bead, 224, 890, 897; beech,
  224; beech-leaf, 910; belle, 642; black,
  230, 240, 249, 434, 916, 1029; black and

Snake (*cont.*)

red, 185; black and white, 609; black-banded, 153-155; black-striped, 153; Blaney's, 290; blind, 36-50, 105; blow, 297, 306, 593, 599; blowing, 306; blue, 525; blue-spotted, 834; Brazos, 493; broad, 834; brown, 292, 349, 525, 834; brown-headed, 627; brown sand, 740; brown sedge, 224; buckwheat-nose, 306; bush, 415; calico, 306, 364, 366; carpet, 609; Catesby's small, 1052; cat-eyed, 415; central twig, 109; chain, 368; chaser, 1; checquered, 272, 368; Clark's, 515; cloudy leafnosed, 576; collared, 185; common spreading, 306; common streaked, 834; copper, 714, 910; copper-bellied, 477; Cora Kennicott's, 496; corn, 30, 224-227, 262, 355, 360, 364; corral, 409; cotton-mouthed, 916; Couch's, 486; Couper's, 200; cricket, 105; crowned, 728; cyclops, 472; dart, 272; deaf, 910; DeKay's, 677, 704, 707; desert, 124, 128; desert burrowing, 121; dog-nosed, 279; eastern fox, 226; eastern gray, 290; eastern spotted, 218; eastern twig, 105; egg, 388; elegant, 292; Emory's, 218; faded, 89, 100; fasciated, 525; fish, 1, 782; flat-nosed, 312; Florida crowned, 733; Florida red-bellied, 721; fodder, 185; fox, 21, 22, 23, 224; garden, 834; Garman's, 295; garter, 351; Georgia, 200; glossy, 1, 89; goose, 616; Graham's, 490, 646, 649; Graham's Arizona, 651; gray, 290, 292; Great Basin blow, 600; green bush, 551; green spotted, 834; green summer, 551; green tree, 551; guinea, 388; harmless, 2; Harter's, 493; haynose, 306; Hay's, 707; Helen Teunison's, 109; Helen's, 109; hissing, 306; hog-nosed, 306, 910; Holbrook's, 388, 504; hook-nosed, 280-286; hoop, 1, 82, 133, 272, 276, 834; horned, 272, 609, 613; horse, 116; huckleberry, 551; humble sheep, 44; imperial, 153; indigo snake, 200-206; Irwin's, 324; Kennicott's, 89; king snake, 185, 368, 642, 886, 890; Kirn's dark-headed, 748; Kirtland's, 496; Kirtland's red, 496; large-headed striped, 795; Le Conte's, 91, 633, 642-644; leopard-spotted, 368; Lindheimer's, 240; lined, 879; little black-and-red, 185; little brown, 288, 697, 704, 712, 714, 740, 834; little green, 834; little grey, 712; little red, 105, 496; little red-bellied, 714; little striped, 288; live oak, 249; magnolia, 551; master, 372; Mexican indigo, 204; miliar(y), 1052; milk, 1, 105, 113, 345, 360; mole, 349,

391; moon, 506; mouse, 1, 89, 220, 224, 805; nocturnal tree, 415; N.A. copperhead, 910; N.A. corn, 224; N.A. cottonmouth, 916; N.A. moccasin, 526; N.A. red-bellied, 272; N.A. rhomb-marked, 500; N.A. striped, 834; Ontario fox, 266; Osceola, 351; pale, 506; Palo Pinto, 493; pencil, 121; pike-head tree, 565-569; pike-headed, 565; pilot, 1, 133, 240, 609, 903; pine, 1, 224, 262, 372, 551; poplar leaf, 1; prairie fox, 264; pug-nosed, 282; purple-tailed, 157; rainbow, 82-86, 272; red, 109, 113, 224, 306, 351, 355, 368, 903, 910; red bead, 891; red-bellied, 272, 721, 740; red-bellied DeKay's, 714; redhead, 890; red-lined, 82; ring, 176, 409, 886; rock, 697; rubber: Great Basin, 53, 58; Pacific, 53; Southern California, 56; sachem, 368; salt marsh water, 515; sand, 82, 89, 740, 746; saurite, 824; scalenosed, 633; scarlet, 224, 351, 355, 360; Schlegel's, 207; sea, 51; sedge, 224; sharpnosed, 633; sharp-tailed, 156-160; sheepnosed, 44; short-mouthed, 1, 814, 816; short-tailed, 692-696; silver, 53; sirtal, 835; slender dark-headed, 740; small-headed striped, 806; South Texas hooknosed, 279; spoonbill, 297; spot-necked, 714; spotted, 224; spotted gray, 249; spread-head, 297, 306, 312; spring, 560; stiff, 504; stinging, 272, 276; Storer's, 714; straw, 116; streaked, 511, 835; Strecker's hook-nosed, 279; striped, 504, 515, 810, 816; summer, 1, 560; swift, 824; swift streaked, 824; swift striped, 828; Tantilla, 728; Taylor's, 676; Texas rock (Hypsiglena t. texana), 326; thimble, 192; thunder, 1, 105, 272, 276, 351, 355, 360, 372, 391, 897, 907, 910; thunder-and-lightning, 364, 368, 372, 890, 897; timber, 53, 262; tree, 551; tropical indigo, 204; tropical vine, 565; twig, 105-110; two-headed, 53, 58, 62; Utah blow, 600; Valeria Blaney's, 290; Valeria's, 290; vine, 1, 551; Virginia red, 366; Virginia's, 290, 292, 294; Wagner's crowned, 733; wampum, 276, 372, 526; water, 30; western faded, 100; western fox, 262, western smooth, 560; western twig, 110; white oak, 1, 249, 903, 910; Wilkinson's, 876; willow, 506; wolf, 249; wood, 53; yellow, 834; yellow-bellied, 506; yellow-lipped, 627-631; Xantus, 324

Snapper, 1042

Snyder, R. C., 115, 131, 227, 250f, 289, 307, 731, 940

Solberg, A. N., 274f